Course   MUS100

South Dakota State University

Music

http://create.mheducation.com

ISBN-10: 1308264992   ISBN-13: 9781308264998

Contents

Credits

Preface

McGraw-Hill is revolutionizing the Music Appreciation course by introducing its first adaptive learning experience with Roger Kamien's *Music: An Appreciation.* Using this market-leading instrument that brings great music to the course in more ways than ever before, students are now transformed into active participants in the Music Appreciation space. The result is active listening, active reading, and active learning.

Experience Active Listening with LearnSmart

How many students *think* they know what they know but struggle on the first exam? *LearnSmart,* McGraw-Hill's adaptive learning system, identifies students' metacognitive abilities and limitations, identifying what they know—and, more importantly, what they don't know. Using Bloom's Taxonomy and a highly sophisticated "smart" algorithm, LearnSmart creates a customized study plan, unique to every student's demonstrated needs, where they can practice active listening skills. With virtually no administrative overhead, instructors using LearnSmart are reporting an increase in student performance by one letter grade or more.

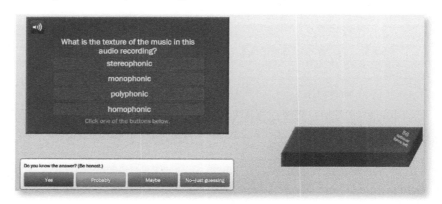

Experience Active Reading with *Smartbook*

McGraw-Hill SmartBook™ is the first and only adaptive reading experience available for the higher education market. Powered by an intelligent diagnostic and adaptive engine, SmartBook facilitates and personalizes the reading process by identifying what content a student knows and doesn't know through adaptive assessments. As the student reads, SmartBook constantly adapts to ensure the student is focused on the content he or she needs the most to close any knowledge gaps.

Experience Active Learning with Kamien and McGraw-Hill Connect Music

Connect Music offers a unique listening space for students to be active and thoughtful participants. Students connect to music through interactive assignments such as comparison listening questions, audio click drag questions, listening ID questions, Listening Outline response forms, and performance reports that support videos and concert attendances. Music selections stream in two ways: in a simple player or in interactive Listening Outlines with access to information about the piece and composer.

Instructors also connect to students in powerful ways with access to monitor the development of student comprehension and listening skills through reports at any time during the semester, instead of waiting for exam scores.

Providing alternate ways of reading the text, listening to the music, and demonstrating understanding, *Connect Music* creates a richer experience that motivates and engages students.

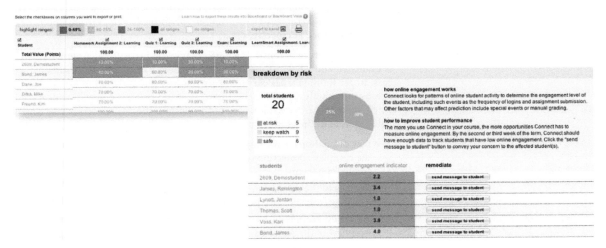

New and Updated Content

This new edition provides exciting additions to the musical selections. Always seeking to improve the breadth and depth of coverage, new pieces include:

- a new feature of **Virtual Field Trip**; students can scan the QR Code with their smartphone and experience a concert or musical performance without having to enter the concert hall, and they can respond to the performances using the **Beyond the Classroom** sections at the end of certain Parts;
- a new discussion of the song *Over the Rainbow* in Part I, section 5;
- the addition of the vocal duet *La ci da rem la mano,* from Mozart's opera *Don Giovanni,* including a **Vocal Music Guide** in Part IV, section 11;

virtual fieldtrip

La Bohème

- inclusion of the complete scene between Mimi and Rodolfo from *La Bohéme* (1896) and **Vocal Music Guide** in Part V, section 16;
- a new discussion and **Vocal Music Guide** for the song *The Year's at the Spring* by Amy Beach, the first American female composer to gain international recognition, in Part VI, section 13;
- and a new discussion and **Vocal Music Guide** for the choral work, *Lux Aurumque,* by contemporary American composer Eric Whitacre in Part VI, section 20.

Music and its appreciation is an ever-evolving process and as such it is important to introduce new artists, both historical and contemporary, to enrich the experience for both students and instructors. In **the new section on music in America** in this edition you will see new discussions and musical pieces from the following artists:

- Amy Beach, a child prodigy and the first American woman to achieve international recognition as a composer of large-scale works, discussed in Part VI, section 13,
- and Eric Whitacre, an important contemporary American composer and conductor of choral music is discussed in Part VI, section 20 with special coverage of his *"Conducting his Lux Aurumque, performed by the Virtual Choir"* in a new **Performance Perspectives** box.

The very nature of music as a performance art necessitates attentive care to how it is evaluated and what lessons are taught to today's students. Never satisfied with success, Roger Kamien takes care to assure the strong foundation of *Music: An Appreciation* by thoroughly examining his instruction and revising and adding new scholarship when appropriate. New discussions of important musical elements and time periods will be found in the following:

- new discussions of *Melody and Words* and *Song Forms* in Part I, section 5 explain the complex connection between words and melody and how the two combine to create song forms;
- updates to the discussion of *Music and Musicians in Society since 1900* to include coverage from 1950 to the present day in Part VI, section 2;
- and a new section on *Music in America* in Part VI, section 12 provides a brief overview of the American musical landscape and a context for discussion of representative American composers.

Digital Music Collection

All of the audio selections discussed in the text are now available in three ways, which makes it easier than ever to access the music on a computer or portable device:

- **Connect Music,** where selections stream via computer, tablet, or smartphone in two ways: in a simple audio player, or in interactive Listening Outlines. In the latter, students not only listen to the piece but have instant access to a visual representation of the structure of the piece.
- **MP3 download card,** which instructors can opt to package with the text. Simply use the unique code printed on the card to access and download all of the music to your music device of choice.

- **MP3 disc,** which replaces the multi-disc audio CD set. This disc contains high-quality MP3s that can be uploaded to a personal computer or other devices. Instructors can opt to package it with the text.

Simplicity in assigning and engaging your students with course materials

Craft your teaching resources to match the way you teach! With McGraw-Hill Create, **www.mcgrawhillcreate.com,** you can easily rearrange chapters, combine material from other content sources, and quickly upload content you have written, such as your course syllabus or teaching notes. Find the content you need in Create by searching through thousands of leading McGraw-Hill textbooks. Arrange your book to fit your teaching style. Create even allows you to personalize your book's appearance by selecting the cover and adding your name, school, and course information. Order a Create book and you'll receive a complimentary print review copy in 3 to 5 business days or a complimentary electronic review copy (eComp) via e-mail in about an hour. Go to **www.mcgrawhillcreate.com** today and register. Experience how McGraw-Hill Create empowers you to teach *your* students *your* way.

Tegrity Campus

Tegrity Campus is a service that makes class time available all the time by automatically capturing every lecture in a searchable format for students to review when they study and complete assignments. With a simple one-click start and stop process, users capture all computer screens and corresponding audio. Students replay any part of any class with easy-to-use browser-based viewing on a PC or Mac.

Educators know that the more students can see, hear, and experience class resources, the better they learn. With Tegrity Campus, students quickly recall key moments by using Tegrity Campus's unique search feature. This search helps students efficiently find what they need, when they need it, across an entire semester of class recordings. Help turn all your students' study time into learning moments immediately supported by your lecture.

CourseSmart

This text is available as an eTextbook at **www.CourseSmart.com.** At CourseSmart your students can take advantage of significant savings off the cost of a print textbook, reduce their impact on the environment, and gain access to powerful Web tools for learning. CourseSmart eTextbooks can be viewed online or downloaded to a computer. The eTextbooks allow students to do full text searches, add highlighting and notes, and share notes with classmates. CourseSmart has the largest selection of eTextbooks available anywhere. Visit **www.CourseSmart.com** to learn more and to try a sample chapter.

Supplements

For Listening

Virtually all of the selections covered by the Listening Outlines and Vocal Music Guides are contained on:

- MP3 download card for the Brief 8th edition: 978-1-25-924329-5
- Basic MP3 disc (which replaces the 5-disc audio CD set in previous editions): 978-1-25-915863-6

An expanded collection of music, containing every musical example discussed in the text is also available:

- MP3 download card for the comprehensive 11th edition: 978-1-25-924330-1
- Basic MP3 disc (which replaces the 9-disc audio CD set in previous editions): 978-1-25-920315-2

Each option delivers high-quality MP3s that can be uploaded to a personal computer or other devices.

For Instructors

Instructor resources on the Online Learning Center (www.mhhe.com/kamien8e) include an instructor's manual, test bank, computer test materials, and PowerPoint presentations. With the introduction of LearnSmart—an adaptive student study aid—to this edition, learning objective tags from LearnSmart have been added to test bank questions for synchronization across the learning tools. This alignment will benefit both students and instructors by creating cohesion between key concepts that are read, practiced, assessed, and ultimately, understood.

Acknowledgments

My deep thanks go to John d'Armand (University of Alaska), for class-testing the section on music in America; Catherine Coppola (Hunter College, CUNY), for suggestions concerning *Don Giovanni*; Hubert Howe (Queens College, CUNY), for updating the discussions of electronic music and instruments; James Hurd (El Camino College), for assistance in choosing repertoire; Daniel Kamien, for suggestions concerning the guitar; Roger Vetter (Grinnell College), Edwin Seroussi, and Amazia Bar-Yosef (The Hebrew University of Jerusalem), for identifying an Indonesian instrument.

A number of other instructors were instrumental in the development of this edition. Thank you to those reviewers whose input and ideas were invaluable in the process:

Candace Bailey, North Carolina Central University
Chris Bartley, University of Pittsburgh-Greensburg
Scott Blankenbaker, Riverland Community College
Chris Davis, North Greenville University
Eugene Greco, Miami Dade College-Kendall
Erin Haupt, Saint Charles Community College
Jonathan Kulp, University of Louisiana-Lafayette
Jennifer Ladkani Fryns, College of Central Florida
Max Lifchitz, University at Albany-SUNY
Susan Lindahl, Central Michigan University
Kathy Mayer, Northeast Lakeview College
Myrna Meeroff, Broward College-Central
Tom O'Neal, University of Missouri-Columbia

Carolyn Ponce, Arkansas State University-State University
Christine Poythress, Middle Tennessee State
Todd Quinlan, Blinn College
James Siddons, Liberty University
Jeff Triplett, Northwest Mississippi Community College-Senatobia
Robyn Wilkes, State College of Florida-Manatee
Suzanne Wong, Fullerton College

And, special thanks to the subject matter experts who helped to build LearnSmart for Music:

Molly Breckling, Austin Peay State University
James Boeckle, Gloucester County College
Chris Davis, North Greenville University
Eugene Greco, Miami Dade College-Kendall
Jonathan Kulp, University of Louisiana-Lafayette
Jennifer Ladkani Fryns, College of Central Florida
Max Lifchitz, University at Albany-SUNY
Susanna Loewy, Kutztown University of Pennsylvania
Jim Loos, Des Moines Area Community College
Myrna Meeroff, Broward College-Central
Claudio Osorio, Miami Dade College-North
Frank Ponce, Indiana Wesleyan University-CAPS
Carolyn Ponce, Arkansas State University-State University
Todd Quinlan, Blinn College
Alice Schmid, Georgia Southern University
James Siddons, Liberty University

A very special thank you goes to Steven Kreinberg at Temple University for helping me create the Part Summary and Beyond the Classroom features and for many valuable suggestions during the revision process.

I want to express my thanks for the assistance of my brand manager at McGraw-Hill, Sarah Remington, the development editor, Barbara Heinssen, the digital development editor, Betty Chen, and the director of development, Dawn Groundwater. I am grateful for the superb work of the copyeditor, Kay Mikel, Jennifer Gehl, content project manager, and Margarite Reynolds, the designer. I'd like to thank Tom Laskey at Sony Music Special Products for providing an outstanding package of MP3 recordings.

My wife, the conductor-pianist Anita Kamien, has contributed to every aspect of this book. She clarified ideas, helped choose representative pieces, and worked tirelessly to improve the Listening Outlines. Her advice and encouragement were essential to the completion of *Music: An Appreciation, Eighth Brief Edition*.

Roger Kamien

■ All musical elements come together when people play or sing

PART I

Rhythm and harmony find their way into the inward places of the soul . . .

—Plato

Elements

LEARNING OBJECTIVES

- Describe the properties of sound and explain how music is part of the world of sound

- Identify basic voice ranges for men and women and the categories of instruments in western music

- Explain how rhythm is basic to life and how it forms the lifeblood of music

- Recognize how music notation indicates pitch and rhythm

- Discuss some elements of melody

- Explain basic principles of chords and harmony

- Compare and contrast major and minor scales

- Identify and describe the three kinds of musical texture

- Explain the techniques that create musical form

- Discuss the different meanings of the term "musical style"

Music plays a vital role in human society. It provides entertainment and emotional release, and it accompanies activities ranging from dances to religious ceremonies. Music is heard everywhere: in auditoriums, homes, elevators, sports arenas, places of worship, and on the street.

Recorded performance was a sensational innovation of the twentieth century. Today, the Internet gives access to a practically unlimited variety of recorded sounds and images. Portable audio and media players permit us to hear and watch what we want, wherever we want.

Live performances provide special excitement. In a live performance, artists put themselves on the line; training and magnetism must overcome technical difficulties to involve the listener's emotions. What is performed, how it sounds, how the artist feels about it that evening—all this exists for a fleeting moment and can never be repeated. An audience responds to the excitement of such a moment, and feelings are exchanged between stage and hall.

Our response to a musical performance or an artist is subjective and rooted in deep feeling. Even professional critics may differ strongly in their evaluations of a performance. There is no one "truth" about what we hear and feel. Does the performer project a concept, an overall idea, or an emotion? Do some sections of a piece, but not others, communicate something to you? Can you figure out why? It's up to us as listeners to evaluate performances of music. Alert and repeated listening will enhance our ability to compare performances and judge music so that we can fully enjoy it.

People listen to music in many different ways. Music can be a barely perceived background or a totally absorbing experience. Part I of this book, "Elements," introduces concepts that can contribute to your enjoyment of a wide range of musical styles. For example, awareness of tone color—the quality that distinguishes one instrument from another—can heighten your pleasure when a melody passes from a clarinet to a trumpet. Perceptive, aware listening makes any musical experience more intense and satisfying.

Informal music making is a source of pleasure for players and listeners.

The audience at an outdoor concert in Atlanta, Georgia. Whether in a public park or a concert hall, live performances have a special electricity.

Elvis Presley: The exchange between singer and audience contains something magical, direct, and spellbinding.

The use of computers and electronics has revolutionized the way we create, play, and listen to music.

Music making transcends boundaries of many kinds. Pictured here are musicians playing in a gamelan, an ensemble found in Indonesia.

1 Sound: Pitch, Dynamics, and Tone Color

Sounds bombard our ears every day—the squeaks and honks of traffic, a child's laugh, the bark of a dog, the patter of rain. Through them we learn what's going on; we need them to communicate. By listening to speech, cries, and laughter, we learn what others think and how they feel. But silence, an absence of sound, also communicates. When we hear no sound in the street, we assume no cars are passing. When someone doesn't answer a question or breaks off in the middle of a sentence, we quickly notice, and we draw conclusions from the silence.

Sounds may be perceived as pleasant or unpleasant. Fortunately, we can direct our attention to specific sounds, shutting out those that don't interest us. At a party, for instance, we can choose to ignore the people near us and focus instead on a conversation across the room. Actually, we shut out most sounds, paying attention only to those of interest. The composer John Cage (1912–1992) may have meant to show this with his "composition" entitled *4'33"*, in which a musician sits at a piano for 4 minutes and 33 seconds—and does nothing. The silence forces the people in the audience to direct their attention to whatever noises, or sounds, they themselves are making. In a sense, the audience "composes" this piece. To get the effect, listen to the sounds that fill the silence around you right now.

What are these sounds that we hear? What is "sound"? What causes it, and how do we hear it?

Sound begins with the vibration of an object, such as a table that is pounded or a string that is plucked. The vibrations are transmitted to our ears by a *medium,* which is usually air. As a result of the vibrations, our eardrums start vibrating too, and *impulses,* or signals, are transmitted to the brain. There the impulses are selected, organized, and interpreted.

Music is part of this world of sound, an art based on the organization of sounds in time. We distinguish music from other sounds by recognizing the four main properties of musical sounds: *pitch, dynamics* (loudness or softness), *tone color,* and *duration.* We'll look now at the first three of these properties of musical sound. Duration—the length of time a musical sound lasts—is discussed in Section 3, "Rhythm."

Pitch: Highness or Lowness of Sound

Pitch is the relative highness or lowness that we hear in a sound. When you sing the beginning of *The Star-Spangled Banner,* the pitch on *see* is higher than the one on *say:*

see,

Oh,   you

                            can

        .

say!

The pitch of a sound is determined by the frequency of its vibrations—that is, their speed, which is measured in cycles per second. The faster the vibrations, the higher the pitch; the slower the vibrations, the lower the pitch. All other things being equal, smaller objects vibrate faster and have higher pitches; thus plucking a short string produces a higher pitch than plucking a long string.

In music, a sound that has a definite pitch is called a **tone.** It has a specific frequency, such as 440 cycles per second. The vibrations of a tone are regular and reach the ear at equal time intervals. On the other hand, noiselike sounds (squeaking brakes or clashing cymbals) have an indefinite pitch because they are produced by irregular vibrations.

Two tones will sound different when they have different pitches. The "distance" in pitch between any two tones is called an **interval.** When tones are separated by the interval called an **octave,** they sound very much alike. Sing the opening of *The Star-Spangled Banner* again. Notice that the tone you produce on *see* sounds like your tone on *say,* even though it's higher. (Sing the *say* and *see* tones several times.) An octave lies between them. The vibration frequency of the *say* tone is exactly half that of the *see* tone. If the *say* tone was 440 cycles per second, the *see* tone—an octave higher—would be 880 cycles per second. A tone an octave lower than the *say* tone would be half of 440, or 220 cycles per second. When sounded at the same time, two tones an octave apart blend so well that they almost seem to merge into one tone.

The interval of an octave is important in music. It is the interval between the first and last tones of the familiar scale. Sing this scale slowly:

```
                                            do
                                        ti
                                    la
                                sol
                            fa
                        mi
                    re
                do
```

You will notice that you fill the octave with seven different pitches before arriving at the high *do,* which "duplicates" the low *do* you start on. You do not slide up as a siren does; you fill the octave with a specific number of pitches. This group of seven tones was the basis of music in western civilization for centuries. The seven tones are produced by the white keys of the piano keyboard, as shown in the illustration at the left.

As time passed, five pitches were added to the original seven. These five are produced by the black keys of the keyboard. All twelve tones, like the original seven, are "duplicated" in higher and lower octaves. (In nonwestern music, the octave may be divided into a different number of tones.)

The distance between the lowest and highest tones that a voice or instrument can produce is called its **pitch range,** or simply its **range.** The range of the average untrained voice is about 1½ octaves; a piano's range is over 7 octaves.

Organization of pitch is a composer's first resource. In Sections 5 and 6, where melody and harmony are explored, we look at how pitch is organized. For now, we'll simply observe that composers can create a special mood by using very low or very high pitches. For example, low pitches can intensify the sadness of a funeral march; high pitches can make a dance sound lighter. And a steady rise in pitch often increases musical tension.

Though most music we know is based on definite pitches, indefinite pitches—such as those made by a bass drum or by cymbals—are important as well. Some percussion instruments, such as gongs, cowbells, and woodblocks, come in different sizes and therefore produce higher or lower indefinite pitches. Contrasts between higher and lower indefinite pitches play a vital role in contemporary western music and in musical cultures around the world.

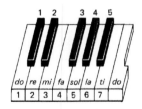

Seven different tones are produced by the white keys of the piano.

Dynamics

Degrees of loudness or softness in music are called **dynamics**—our second property of sound. Loudness is related to the amplitude of the vibration that produces the sound. The harder a guitar string is plucked (the farther it moves from the fingerboard), the louder its sound. When instruments are played more loudly or more softly, or when there is a change in how many instruments are heard, a dynamic change results; such a change may be made either suddenly or gradually. A gradual increase in loudness often creates excitement, particularly when the pitch rises too. On the other hand, a gradual decrease in loudness can convey a sense of calm.

A performer can emphasize a tone by playing it more loudly than the tones around it. We call an emphasis of this kind an **accent.** Skillful, subtle changes of dynamics add spirit and mood to performances. Sometimes these changes are written in the music; often, though, they are not written but are inspired by the performer's feelings about the music.

When notating music, composers have traditionally used Italian words, and their abbreviations, to indicate dynamics. The most common terms are

Term	Abbreviation	Meaning
pianissimo	*pp*	*very soft*
piano	*p*	*soft*
mezzo piano	*mp*	*moderately soft*
mezzo forte	*mf*	*moderately loud*
forte	*f*	*loud*
fortissimo	*ff*	*very loud*

For extremes of softness and loudness, composers use *ppp* or *pppp* and *fff* or *ffff*. The following notations indicate gradual changes in dynamics:

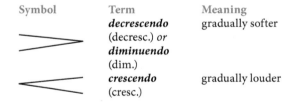

Symbol	Term	Meaning
	decrescendo (decresc.) *or* **diminuendo** (dim.)	gradually softer
	crescendo (cresc.)	gradually louder

Like many elements of music, a dynamic indication is not absolutely precise. A tone has a dynamic level—is soft or loud—in relation to other tones around it. The loudest sound of a single violin is tiny compared with the loudest sound of an entire orchestra, and even tinier compared with an amplified rock group. But it can be considered fortissimo (very loud) within its own context.

Tone Color

We can tell a trumpet from a flute even when each of them is playing the same tone at the same dynamic level. The quality that distinguishes them—our third property of musical sound—is called **tone color,** or **timbre** (pronounced *tam'-ber*). Tone color is described by words such as *bright, dark, brilliant, mellow,* and *rich.*

Changes in tone color create variety and contrast: for example, the same melody will have different expressive effects when it is played by one instrument and then another, or a new tone color may be used to highlight a new melody. Tone colors also build a sense of continuity; it is easier to recognize the return of a melody when the same instruments play it each time. Specific instruments can reinforce a melody's emotional impact—in fact, composers often create a melody with a particular instrument's tone color in mind.

A practically unlimited variety of tone colors is available to composers: instruments (see Section 2) can be combined in various ways, and modern electronic techniques allow composers to invent entirely new tone colors.

Listening Outlines, Vocal Music Guides, and the Properties of Sound

Reading about pitch, dynamics, and tone color without hearing music is too abstract. To understand and recognize the properties of sound, we must *listen for them*. In this book, Listening Outlines (for instrumental music) and Vocal Music Guides (for music with vocal texts) will help focus your attention on musical events as they unfold. These outlines and guides must be read *as you listen to the music;* otherwise, their value to you is limited.

In a Listening Outline, each item describes some musical sound. It may point out dynamics, instruments, pitch level, or mood. (Remember, though, that indications of mood in music are subjective. What one person calls "triumphant," for instance, someone else may call "determined.") In a Vocal Music Guide, the vocal text appears with brief marginal notes that indicate the relationship between words and music and help the listener follow the thought, story, or drama.

The outlines and guides are preceded by descriptions of the music's main features. Within the guide or outline, timings appear in the margin. In addition, the outlines include instrumentation, notes about our recordings (where important), and the duration of selections in our recordings.

Before you listen to a piece of music, you will find it helpful to glance over the entire Listening Outline or Vocal Music Guide. Then, while hearing one passage, look ahead to learn what's next. For example, in the Listening Outline for the second scene of Igor Stravinsky's ballet *The Firebird*, the first item (1a) is "Slow melody in French horn, soft (*p*), quivering string accompaniment." While listening to the music described by item *a*, glance at item 1b: "Violins, soft, melody an octave higher. Flutes join."

Sometimes, not all the instruments playing are listed; instead, only those that are prominent at a given moment are shown. For example, item 2a in the Listening Outline for *The Firebird* reads "Brasses, very loud (*ff*), melody in quick detached notes, timpani." Although other instruments can be heard, this description focuses attention on the instruments that play the melody.

Music selection in the text with an outline or guide can be streamed in Connect Music or downloaded after purchasing the mp3 card or mp3 disc set. See page xxviii for details.

The Firebird, Scene 2 (1910), by Igor Stravinsky

In the second—and final—scene of the ballet *The Firebird*, Igor Stravinsky (1882–1971) repeats one melody over and over, creating variety and contrast through changes of dynamics, tone color, and rhythm. During this scene, the hero triumphs and becomes engaged to a beautiful princess.

The second scene begins softly but becomes increasingly grand as the music gradually grows louder (crescendo), more instruments play, and the melody is repeated at higher pitches. After this slow buildup to a climax, there's a sudden quiet as all the instruments but the strings stop playing. A quick crescendo then leads to a brilliant concluding section.

Listening Outline

STRAVINSKY, *The Firebird,* Scene 2

Piccolo, 3 flutes, 3 oboes, English horn, 3 clarinets, bass clarinet, 3 bassoons, contrabassoon, 4 French horns, 6 trumpets, tuba, timpani, triangle, cymbals, bass drum, 3 harps, 1st violins, 2d violins, violas, cellos, double basses
(Duration, 3:06)

0:00	**1. a.**	Slow melody in French horn, soft (*p*), quivering string accompaniment.
0:29	**b.**	Violins, soft, melody an octave higher. Flutes join.
0:43	**c.**	Grows louder (crescendo) as more instruments enter.
1:03	**d.**	Violins and flutes, loud (*f*), melody at even higher octave, crescendo to
1:17	**e.**	Full orchestra, melody very loud (*ff*), timpani (kettledrums).
1:34	**f.**	Suddenly very soft (*pp*), strings, quick crescendo to
1:41	**2. a.**	Brasses, very loud (*ff*), melody in quick detached notes, timpani.
2:04	**b.**	Melody in slower, accented notes, brasses, *ff*, timpani, music gradually slows.
2:35	**c.**	High held tone, *ff*, brass chords, extremely loud (*fff*), lead to sudden *pp* and crescendo to extremely loud close.

C-Jam Blues (1942), by Duke Ellington and His Famous Orchestra

A succession of different tone colors contributes to the variety within *C-Jam Blues* (1942), as performed by Duke Ellington and His Famous Orchestra. A repeated-note melody is played first by the piano and then by saxophones. Then we hear solos by the violin, cornet, tenor saxophone, trombone, and clarinet. These solos are improvised by the players. *Improvisation* is the term used for music created at the same time as it is performed. Each instrument is first heard alone and then heard with accompaniment. The cornet and trombones are played with mutes, devices inserted into the instrument to alter its sound. *C-Jam Blues* ends climactically when the full band is heard for the first time.

Listening Outline

ELLINGTON, *C-Jam Blues*

Piano (Duke Ellington), violin (Ray Nance), 2 trumpets (Wallace Jones, Ray Nance), cornet (Rex Stewart), 2 trombones (Joe "Tricky Sam" Nanton, Lawrence Brown), valve trombone (Juan Tizol), clarinet (Barney Bigard), 2 alto saxophones (Johnny Hodges, Otto Hardwick), 2 tenor saxophones (Barney Bigard, Ben Webster), baritone saxophone (Harry Carney), guitar (Fred Guy), bass (Junior Raglin), percussion (Sonny Greer)
(Duration, 2:38)

0:00	**1.**	Piano, repeated-note melody, accompanied by bass, guitar, drums.
0:17	**2.**	Saxophones, repeated-note melody, accompanied by rhythm section (piano, bass, guitar, percussion).

0:33	**3.** Violin alone, then accompanied by rhythm section.
0:54	**4.** Muted cornet alone, then accompanied by rhythm section.
1:15	**5.** Tenor saxophone alone, then accompanied by rhythm section.
1:37	**6.** Muted trombone alone, then accompanied by rhythm section.
1:59	**7.** Clarinet alone, then accompanied by band.
2:20	**8.** Full band.

2 Performing Media: Voices and Instruments

Voices

Throughout history, singing has been the most widespread and familiar way of making music. Singers seem always to have had a magnetic appeal, and the exchange between singer and audience contains a bit of magic, something direct and spellbinding. The singer becomes an instrument with a unique ability to fuse words and musical tones.

For many reasons, it is difficult to sing well. In singing we use wider ranges of pitch and volume than in speaking, and we hold vowel sounds longer. Singing demands a greater supply and control of breath. Air from the lungs is controlled by the lower abdominal muscles and the diaphragm. The air makes the vocal cords vibrate, and the singer's lungs, throat, mouth, and nose come into play to produce the desired sound. The pitch of the tone varies with the tension of the vocal cords; the tighter they are, the higher the pitch.

The range of a singer's voice depends both on training and on physical makeup. Professional singers can command 2 octaves or even more, whereas an untrained voice is usually limited to about 1½ octaves. Men's vocal cords are longer and thicker than women's, and this difference produces a lower range of pitches. The classification of voice ranges for women and men follows, arranged from highest to lowest. (The four basic ranges are soprano, alto, tenor, and bass.)

Women	Men
soprano	*tenor*
mezzo-soprano	*baritone*
alto (or contralto)	*bass*

Methods and styles of singing vary widely from culture to culture and even within a culture: for instance, in the west, classical, popular, jazz, folk, and rock music are all sung differently.

Until the late 1600s, most music of western culture was vocal. Since then, instrumental music has rivaled vocal music in importance; but composers have continued to write vocal works—both solo and choral—with and without instrumental accompaniment (which can range from a single guitar or piano to an entire orchestra).

Throughout history, singing has been the most widespread way of making music. Shown here are the Westminster Choir and the New Jersey Symphony Orchestra, conducted by Bernard Labadie.

Musical Instruments

An *instrument* may be defined as any mechanism—other than the voice—that produces musical sounds. Western musicians usually classify instruments in six broad categories: **string** (such as guitar and violin); **woodwind** (flute, clarinet); **brass** (trumpet, trombone); **percussion** (bass drum, cymbals); **keyboard** (organ, piano); and **electronic** (synthesizer).

An instrument is often made in different sizes that produce different ranges. For instance, the saxophone family includes sopranino, soprano, alto, tenor, baritone, and bass saxophones. An instrument's tone color may vary with the **register** (part of the total range) in which it is played. A clarinet sounds dark and rich in its low register, but its high register is brilliant and piercing. Most instruments have a wider range of pitches than the voice does. A trained singer's range is about 2 octaves, but many instruments command 3 or 4 octaves, and some have 6 or 7. Also, instruments usually produce tones more rapidly than the voice. When writing music for a specific instrument, composers have to consider its range of pitches and dynamics and how fast it can produce tones.

People around the world use musical instruments that vary greatly in construction and tone color, and instruments have had many functions—at different times and in different cultures. They may provide entertainment; they may accompany song, dance, ritual, and drama; they have sometimes been considered sacred or thought to have magical powers; they have been used for communication; and they have even been status symbols.

Instruments' popularity rises and falls with changing musical tastes and requirements. Today only a fraction of all known instruments are used. However, interest in music of earlier times has led to the resurrection of instruments such as the harpsichord, an ancestor of the piano; and the recorder, a relative of the flute. In fact, modern musicians are flexible and far-ranging in their choice of instruments. Rock composers have used nonwestern instruments such as the Indian sitar (a plucked string instrument). Jazz musicians are turning to classical instruments such as the flute, and classical composers are using instruments associated with jazz, such as the vibraphone.

Compositions may be written for solo instruments, for small groups, and for orchestras with more than 100 musicians. Modern symphony orchestras contain string,

A symphony orchestra.

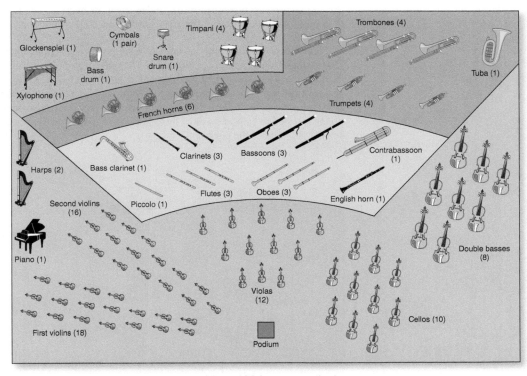

Typical seating plan for a large orchestra (about 100 instrumentalists), showing the distribution of instruments.

woodwind, brass, and percussion instruments. (The previous page shows a photograph of a symphony orchestra and a typical seating plan for a large orchestra.) Keyboard instruments also find their way into the modern orchestra as needed. Bands consist mainly of brass, woodwind, and percussion instruments.

Orchestras and bands—as well as choruses—are usually led by a **conductor,** who coordinates the performers and shapes the interpretation of a musical composition. Many conductors hold a thin stick called a **baton** in one hand to beat time and indicate pulse and tempo. With the other hand they control the balance among the instruments—or voices—so that the most important musical ideas will be brought out. In an orchestra, the principal first violinist, the **concertmaster,** plays solo violin passages and coordinates the bowing of string instruments.

Instruments commonly used for western music are described in this chapter, by categories. Nonwestern instruments are discussed in Part VII.

String Instruments

The **violin, viola, cello** (*violoncello*), and **double bass** (sometimes called simply a *bass*) form the symphony orchestra's string section. They vary in tone color as well as in size and range: the violin is the smallest and has the highest range; the double bass is the largest and has the lowest range. For symphonic music the strings are usually played with a **bow,** a slightly curved stick strung tightly with horsehair (see the illustration below.) Symphonic strings also may be plucked with the finger.

Of all the instrumental groups, the strings have the greatest versatility and expressive range. They produce many tone colors and have wide ranges of pitch and dynamics. String players can produce tones that are brilliant and rapid or slow and throbbing; they can control tone as subtly as a singer. Orchestral works tend to rely more on the strings than on any other group. Even with their differing tone colors, the four string instruments blend beautifully. Here it will be helpful to consider the construction and tone production of the string instruments; the violin can represent the entire family.

The hollow wooden body of the violin supports four strings made of gut or wire. The strings stretch, under tension, from a *tailpiece* on one end over a wooden *bridge* to the other end, where they are fastened around wooden *pegs.* The bridge holds the strings away from the *fingerboard* so that they can vibrate freely; the bridge also transmits the strings' vibrations to the *body,* which amplifies and colors the tone. Each string is tuned to a different pitch by tightening or loosening the pegs. (The greater the tension, the higher the pitch.)

Violin and bow.

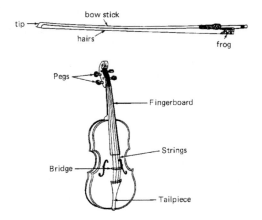

Strings

The violin is often used as a solo instrument. In the orchestra, the violins are divided into first and second violins, with the first violins frequently playing the main melody. The violinist shown here is Gil Shaham.

The body of the viola is about two inches longer than that of the violin, and thus the viola's range is somewhat lower. Its tone color is darker, thicker, and a little less brilliant than the violin's. The violist here is Tabea Zimmermann.

Although eighteenth-century composers generally used the cello in its bass and baritone registers, later composers exploited its upper registers as well. The cellist shown here is Yo-Yo Ma.

The double bass (or bass) has a very heavy tone and is less agile than other string instruments. It is generally played with a bow in symphonic music, but in jazz and popular music it is commonly played by plucking the strings.

The harp—with forty-seven strings stretched on a triangular frame—has a wide range of six octaves. The harpist plucks with the fingers of both hands.

The guitar has six strings, which are plucked with the fingers or strummed with a plectrum, or pick. The frets on the fingerboard mark the places where the strings must be pressed with the fingers of the other hand. John Williams is the guitarist shown here.

The musician makes a string vibrate by drawing the bow across it with the right hand. The speed and pressure of the bow stroke control the dynamics and tone color of the sound produced. Pitch is controlled by the musician's left hand. By pressing a string against the fingerboard, the player varies the length of its vibrating portion and so changes its pitch. This is called *stopping* a string (because the vibrations are stopped at a certain point along the string's length). Thus, a range of pitches can be drawn from each of the four strings.

Basically the viola, cello, and double bass are made in the same manner and produce sound by similar means. How the string instruments are played—what string performance techniques are used—determines which of many musical effects they will produce. The most frequently used techniques are listed here.

Pizzicato (plucked string): The musician plucks the string, usually with a finger of the right hand. In jazz, the double bass is played mainly as a plucked instrument, rather than being bowed.

Double stop (two notes at once): By drawing the bow across two strings, a string player can sound two notes at once. And by rotating the bow rapidly across three strings (*triple stop*) or four strings (*quadruple stop*), three or four notes can be sounded almost—but not quite—together.

Vibrato: The string player can produce a throbbing, expressive tone by rocking the left hand while pressing the string down. This causes small pitch fluctuations that make the tone warmer.

Mute: The musician can veil or muffle the tone by fitting a clamp (mute) onto the bridge.

Tremolo: The musician rapidly repeats tones by quick up-and-down strokes of the bow. This can create a sense of tension, when loud; or a shimmering sound, when soft.

Harmonics: Very high-pitched tones, like a whistle's, are produced when the musician lightly touches certain points on a string.

Though the violin, viola, cello, and double bass are similar, they, like members of any family, have their differences. The photographs in this section show why each adds something distinctive to the orchestra's total sound.

Some string instruments are not played with a bow but are plucked instead, with the fingers or with a *plectrum* (plural, *plectra*). The most important of these are the *harp* and the *guitar.* The harp is the only plucked string instrument that has gained wide acceptance in the symphony orchestra.

Woodwind Instruments

The woodwind instruments are so named because they produce vibrations of air within a tube that traditionally was made of wood. During the twentieth century, however, piccolos and flutes came to be made of metal. All the woodwinds have little holes along their length that are opened and closed by the fingers or by pads controlled by a key mechanism. By opening and closing these holes, the woodwind player changes the length of the vibrating air column and so varies the pitch.

The main woodwind instruments of the symphony orchestra are as follows, arranged in four families, in approximate order of range from highest (piccolo) to lowest (contrabassoon). (Only the two most frequently used instruments of each family are listed.)

Flute Family	Clarinet Family	Oboe Family	Bassoon Family
piccolo			
flute	*clarinet*		
		oboe	
		English horn	
	bass clarinet		*bassoon*
			contrabassoon

A woodwind instrument (unlike a string instrument) can produce only one note at a time. In symphonic music, woodwinds are frequently given melodic solos.

Woodwind instruments are great individualists and are much less alike in tone color than the various strings. The woodwinds' unique tone colors result largely from the different ways in which vibrations are produced. Flute and piccolo players blow across the edge of a mouth hole (players of the *recorder,* a relative of the flute, blow through a "whistle" mouthpiece); but the rest of the woodwind instruments rely on a vibrating reed. A *reed* is a very thin piece of cane, about 2½ inches long, that is set into vibration by a stream of air.

In *single-reed woodwinds* the reed is fastened over a hole in the mouthpiece and vibrates when the player blows into the instrument. The clarinet and bass clarinet are single-reed woodwinds. The *saxophone,* too, an instrument used mainly in bands, has a single reed. In *double-reed woodwinds* two narrow pieces of cane are held between the musician's lips. The oboe, English horn, bassoon, and contrabassoon are double-reed woodwinds.

Tone colors differ greatly not only between single-reed and double reed woodwinds, but also among the various registers of each woodwind instrument. In general, low registers tend to be breathy and thick, and top registers are more penetrating.

Woodwinds

The piccolo—whose name is short for *flauto piccolo,* or small flute—is half the size of the flute and plays an octave higher. The piccolo's high register is shrill and whistlelike.

The flute has a high range and is extremely agile, capable of producing a rapid succession of tones. Its tone is full and velvety in the low register and bright and sparkling at the top. Shown here is the flutist James Galway.

The oboe has a nasal, intense, expressive tone. Because the oboe's pitch is difficult to adjust, the entire orchestra is tuned to its A.

The English horn is neither English nor a horn, but simply a low, or alto, oboe. The English horn player is Dmitry Malkin.

The clarinet can produce tones very rapidly and has a wide range of dynamics and tone color. Pictured here is Benny Goodman.

The recorder, like the flute and piccolo, has no reed. The recorder's tone resembles a flute's but is softer and gentler. It is commonly found in five sizes: sopranino, soprano, alto, tenor, and bass.

The contrabassoon can produce the lowest pitch in the orchestra.

The tone of the bassoon is deeply nasal. The bassoonist is Richard Paley.

The bass clarinet is larger than the clarinet and has a much lower range.

The saxophone has a single-reed piece like a clarinet, but its tube is made of brass. Its tone is rich, husky, and speechlike. Shown here is the jazz saxophonist Sonny Rollins.

Brass Instruments

From high register to low, the main instruments of the symphony orchestra's brass section are the **trumpet, French horn** (sometimes called simply a *horn*), **trombone,** and **tuba.** Trumpets and trombones are often used in jazz and rock groups. Other instruments, such as the **cornet, baritone horn,** and **euphonium** are used mainly in concert and marching bands.

The vibrations of brass instruments come from the musician's lips as he or she blows into a cup- or funnel-shaped *mouthpiece.* The vibrations are amplified and colored in a tube that is coiled (to make it easy to carry and play). The tube is flared at the end to form a *bell.* The pitch of brass instruments is regulated both by varying lip tension and by using *slides* and *valves* to change the length of the tube through which the air vibrates. The trombone uses a slide, a U-shaped tube that fits into two parallel straight tubes. By pulling the slide in or pushing it out, the player changes the length of tubing and makes it possible to play different pitches. The trumpet, French horn, and tuba use three or four valves to divert air through various lengths of tubing. When valves came into use around 1850, these instruments could produce many more tones and became much more flexible. Brass players can alter the tone color of their instruments by inserting a **mute** into the bell. Mutes for brass instruments come in different shapes and are made of wood, plastic, or metal. They are most common in jazz, where they create a variety of effects, including a buzzing sound, a mellowing of the tone, and the comical "wah-wah."

Brasses are powerful instruments, often used at climaxes and for bold, heroic statements. Since the late nineteenth century, they are frequently given rapid solo passages as well. Today, brass instruments are very popular, owing to ensembles such as the Canadian Brass and soloists like the trumpeter Wynton Marsalis.

Brass

The French horn has a tone that is less brassy, more mellow, and more rounded than the trumpet's.

The thick, heavy tone of the tuba is used to add weight to the lowest register of an orchestra or band.

The trumpet sounds brilliant, brassy, and penetrating. The trumpeter shown here is Wynton Marsalis.

The trombone has a tone that combines the brilliance of a trumpet with the mellowness of a French horn.

Percussion Instruments

Most percussion instruments of the orchestra are struck by hand, with sticks, or with hammers. Some are shaken or rubbed. Percussion instruments are subdivided into instruments of definite and indefinite pitch, depending on whether they produce a tone or a noiselike sound.

Definite Pitch	Indefinite Pitch
timpani (kettledrums)	*snare drum (side drum)*
glockenspiel	*bass drum*
xylophone	*tambourine*
celesta	*triangle*
chimes	*cymbals*
	gong (tam-tam)

The vibrations of percussion instruments are set up by stretched membranes, like the calfskin of the kettledrum, or by plates or bars made of metal, wood, or other sonorous materials. Extremely loud sounds may be drawn from percussion instruments like the bass drum or cymbals. In a symphony orchestra, one percussionist may play several different instruments.

Percussion instruments have long been used to emphasize rhythm and to heighten climaxes. But until the twentieth century, they played a far less important role in western music than strings, woodwinds, or brasses. Since 1900, composers have been more willing to exploit the special colors of the percussion group and have occasionally written entire pieces to show it off, such as *Ionisation* (1931) by Edgard Varèse. Jazz and rock musicians, of course, have made good use of percussion instruments. Yet, for all these recent explorations, western musicians barely approach the incredibly varied use of percussion found in Africa and Asia, where subtle changes of rhythm, tone color, and dynamics are used with great imagination.

Percussion

The timpani (kettledrums) are the only orchestral drums of definite pitch. A calfskin head is stretched over a hemispherical copper shell. Varying the tension of the head using adjustable screws around the head or a pedal changes the pitch of the timpani. One percussionist generally plays two to four timpani, each tuned to a different pitch.

The xylophone consists of a set of wooden bars that are struck with two hard hammers to produce a dry, wooden tone.

The metal bars of the glockenspiel (orchestral bells) are struck with two hammers to produce a tone that is bright and silvery.

The bass drum—the largest of the orchestral drums—is almost three feet in diameter.

The celesta looks like a small upright piano, but its sounding mechanism is like a glockenspiel's. Metal bars are struck by hammers that are controlled by a keyboard. The celesta's tone is tinkling and graceful.

Chimes are a set of metal tubes hung from a frame. They are struck with a hammer and sound like church bells.

The triangle is struck with a metal beater and makes a tinkling, bell-like sound.

The dry rattling sound of the snare drum (or side drum) is produced by the vibration of snares—strings that are tightly stretched against the bottom head. The snare drum is often used in marches.

When struck by a beater, the gong (or tam-tam) produces long-lasting sounds that can seem solemn, mysterious, or frightening.

Cymbals are round brass plates. They usually are struck together with a sliding motion, and their sound penetrates like a sharp crash.

The tambourine is often used to create a Spanish or Italian effect. The player shakes it or strikes it with the knuckles.

Keyboard Instruments

The piano, harpsichord, organ, and accordion are the best-known keyboard instruments. Although they are quite different from each other, each has a keyboard that permits the performer to play several tones at the same time easily and rapidly.

The *piano* was invented around 1700 and mechanically perfected by the 1850s. It produces sound through vibrating strings held under tension by an iron frame: striking a key causes a felt-covered hammer to hit a string (the harder the pianist strikes the key, the louder the sound); releasing the key causes a felt damper to come down on the string and end the tone. Pianos have two or three pedals: the *damper pedal* lets the pianist sustain a tone after releasing the key; the *una corda pedal* (*soft pedal*) veils the sound; the *sostenuto pedal* (which not all pianos have) sustains some tones but not others.

The piano is exceptionally versatile. A pianist can play many notes at once, including both a melody and its accompaniment. Its eighty-eight keys span more than 7 octaves. The dynamic range is broad, from a faint whisper to a powerful fortissimo. Today it is among the most popular instruments and is used for solos, for accompaniments, and in combination with one other instrument or many other instruments.

The *harpsichord* was important from about 1500 to 1775 (when it was gradually replaced by the piano) and was revived in the twentieth century for performance of early music and some new works. It has strings that are plucked by a set of *plectra* (little wedges of plastic, leather, or quill). These are controlled by one or two keyboards.

Keyboard

The piano is exceptionally versatile. Shown here is the pianist Lang Lang.

The harpsichord has plucked strings controlled by one or two keyboards.

The **pipe organ** was most prominent from 1600 to 1750 (when it was known as the "King of instruments") but is still in wide use today, particularly in religious services. It has a wide range of pitch, dynamics, and tone color. There are many sets of pipes controlled from several keyboards, including a pedal keyboard played by the organist's feet. The keys control valves from which air is blown across or through openings in the pipes. Various sets of pipes are brought into play by pulling knobs called *stops*. Each set of pipes has a particular tone color that the organist uses alone or with others. Dynamic change is produced by adding to or reducing the number of pipes being played,

A pipe organ has many sets of pipes controlled from several keyboards and pedals. The organist varies the sound by selecting different combinations of the pipes.

by moving from one keyboard to another, or by opening and closing shutters around some of the pipes.

The *accordion* has free steel reeds that are controlled by a treble keyboard with piano keys, played by the right hand; and a bass keyboard with buttons, played by the left hand. The reeds are caused to vibrate by air pressure from a bellows.

Electronic Instruments

The **electric guitar** uses a built-in pickup to convert the vibration of its strings into electrical impulses for amplification. Keith Richards is the guitarist shown here.

Electronic instruments produce or amplify sound through electronic means; they were invented as early as 1904 but have had a significant impact on music only since 1950. Today, electronic and computer technologies are developing rapidly, changing continually, and increasingly blending together. Electronic instruments for performing and composing music include amplified instruments, such as the electric piano, organ, and guitar; tape studios; synthesizers; computers; and various "hybrid" technologies.

The *tape studio* was the main tool of composers of electronic music during the 1950s. (In Part VI we study Edgard Varèse's *Poème électronique*, which was created in a tape studio.) The raw material in tape studios consisted of recorded sounds that might be electronic or from "real life"—flutes, birdcalls, percussion, church bells, people singing and so forth. The composer manipulated these in various ways: by speeding them up or slowing them down, altering their pitch and duration, giving them echoes, filtering them to change tone color, mixing them, and editing the tape (as by cutting and splicing) to play them in any desired order. Rhythm could be fully controlled because the duration of a sound depended only on the length of a tape segment. However, tape splicing and rerecording were difficult, inaccurate, and time-consuming processes, and many composers of the 1960s turned to synthesizers, which appeared around 1955.

Today's electronic music studios create a wide range of sounds.

Synthesizers are systems of electronic components that generate, modify, and control sound. They can generate a huge variety of musical sounds and noises, and the composer has complete control over pitch, tone color, loudness, and duration. Most synthesizers can be "played" by means of a keyboard—an addition to the mechanisms of the tape studio.

Synthesizers vary in size and capacity. The mid-1950s saw the invention of the RCA Mark II synthesizer, an enormous (and unique) vacuum-tube synthesizer occupying an entire wall of the Columbia-Princeton Electronic Music Center in New York City. During the 1960s and 1970s, smaller, less expensive transistorized synthesizers such as the Moog and Buchla were developed; these were installed in electronic music studios at universities and advertising agencies, played in live rock concerts and concerts of electronic music, and used to create film and television scores. They permit manipulation of the sounds, such as adding reverberation. Highly sophisticated synthesizers using computer capabilities have now been developed, and several different technologies are in use.

Analog synthesis—the earliest of the synthesizer technologies, which predominated until about 1980—uses a mixture of complex sounds that are shaped by filtering. Like all analog technology, it is based on representing data in terms of measurable physical quantities, in this case sound waves.

Digital frequency modulation (FM) synthesis, invented by John Chowning, was patented by Yamaha and has been associated with Yamaha instruments. Like all digital technology, it is based on representing physical quantities—here, points on sound waves—as numbers.

Effects devices, which include reverberators, echo devices, and stereo splitters, are often integrated into synthesizers and the synthesis process. They are used in almost all recorded music (especially popular music) and in some live music.

Sampling is considered a synthesizer technology because it involves placing brief digital recordings of live sounds under the control of a synthesizer keyboard; but although the sounds can be modified during playback, no actual synthesis is present. Sampling allows the composer to record short segments of sounds (these are the "samples") digitally and then manipulate them. Sampling has been integrated into relatively inexpensive computer-linked keyboards and is one of the most important aspects of today's electronic music making.

A significant development in synthesizing technology is known as *musical instrument digital interface (MIDI):* this is a standard adopted by manufacturers for interfacing synthesizer equipment. MIDI has allowed the device actually played to be separated from tone generation; thus there are now keyboards that look, feel, and play like a piano; wind controllers played like a woodwind instrument; and string controllers played like a violin or cello. Also, control signals can be fed to and from a MIDI instrument into and out of a personal computer, and users can store and edit music and convert to and from musical notation.

Historically, **computers** were the third means of producing sounds on audiotape; they were developed for this purpose after the tape studio and synthesizers. Computers are used both as control devices to drive MIDI equipment and for direct digital synthesis.

The 1970s and 1980s saw the development of small computers with which composers could instantly hear the music they programmed; since then, computers have become even more sophisticated. Computers are used for music synthesis, live performance, to help composers write scores, to generate parts, to store samples of audio signals, to control synthesizing mechanisms, and so on. In **computer music,** some or all of the sounds are generated and manipulated by computer.

To increase the variety of sound and the composer's control over it, today's electronic music studios often contain and integrate a wide variety of equipment, including synthesizers, computers, and devices for mixing and filtering sound.

All this equipment enables the composer to exploit the entire spectrum of sound as never before. But the quality of the music produced still depends on the imagination and organizing power of the human mind.

The Young Person's Guide to the Orchestra, Op.* 34 (1946), by Benjamin Britten

Benjamin Britten (1913–1976), an English composer, wrote the attractive *Young Person's Guide to the Orchestra* in 1946 as an introduction to the instruments of the orchestra. He used a theme by Henry Purcell, a great English composer of the seventeenth century. (A **theme** is a melody used as the basis for a musical composition.) The majestic theme is presented first by the full orchestra, and then by each section of the orchestra in turn: woodwinds, brasses, strings, and percussion. Thirteen **variations,** or varied repetitions of the theme, are then heard. Each highlights a different instrument. The variations differ in dynamics, speed, and tone color, as well as mood. They follow each other without pause and last from about 30 seconds to 1 minute each. (Variation 13, however, which features many percussion instruments, lasts almost 2 minutes.) Woodwind, string, and brass instruments are generally presented from highest to lowest in range.

Variation 13 is followed immediately by a concluding section beginning with a lively new tune played by an unaccompanied piccolo. Then other instruments enter, each playing the same tune. After woodwind, string, brass, and percussion instruments have had their turn, the brasses bring back the main theme and provide an exciting ending.

---

*The abbreviation *op.* stands for *opus,* Latin for *work.* An opus number is a way of identifying a piece or set of pieces. Usually, within a composer's output, the higher a composition's opus number, the later it was written.

Listening Outline

BRITTEN, *The Young Person's Guide to the Orchestra*

Piccolo, 2 flutes, 2 oboes, 2 clarinets, 2 bassoons, 4 horns, 2 trumpets, 3 trombones, tuba, timpani, bass drum, snare drum, cymbals, tambourine, triangle, Chinese block, xylophone, castanets, gong, whip, harp, 1st violins, 2d violins, violas, cellos, double basses
(Duration, 17:23)

Theme

0:00	**a.** Full orchestra
0:41	**b.** Woodwind section
1:11	**c.** Brass section
1:42	**d.** String section
2:07	**e.** Percussion section
2:26	**f.** Full orchestra

Woodwinds

3:00	**Variation 1:**	Flutes and piccolo
3:30	**Variation 2:**	Oboes
4:33	**Variation 3:**	Clarinets
5:16	**Variation 4:**	Bassoons

Strings

6:13	**Variation 5:**	Violins
6:58	**Variation 6:**	Violas
7:46	**Variation 7:**	Cellos
8:43	**Variation 8:**	Double basses
9:41	**Variation 9:**	Harp

Brasses

10:31	**Variation 10:**	French horns
11:14	**Variation 11:**	Trumpets
11:48	**Variation 12:**	Trombones and tuba

Percussion

12:48	**Variation 13:**	**a.** Timpani (kettledrums); bass drum and cymbals
13:20		**b.** Tambourine and triangle; snare drum (side drum) and Chinese block (a hollow wooden block that is struck with a drumstick)
13:38		**c.** Xylophone
13:49		**d.** Castanets and gong
14:03		**e.** Whip (two hinged pieces of wood that are slapped against each other)
14:08		**f.** Entire percussion section; xylophone and triangle

Concluding Section

14:44	**a.** Unaccompanied piccolo, lively new tune, tune played in turn by flutes, oboes, clarinets, and bassoons, crescendo.
15:22	**b.** Lively tune played in turn by 1st violins, *p*; 2d violins, violas, cellos, double basses, woodwinds accompany, crescendo; quick decrescendo introduces
15:51	**c.** Harp, lively tune, crescendo in strings and woodwinds.
16:03	**d.** Lively tune played in turn by French horns, *ff*, trumpets, trombones and tuba, orchestra accompanies.
16:21	**e.** Percussion, *f*, accompanied by orchestra, *p*, crescendo to
16:31	**f.** Main theme in brasses, *ff*, together with lively tune in high woodwinds and strings. Full orchestra, percussion, long-held closing chord, *fff*.

Dancing is closely linked to the rhythms of music. The ballet dancer Mikhail Baryshnikov is shown here in a performance of Tchaikovsky's *The Nutcracker.*

© Jack Vartoogian

3 Rhythm

Rhythm is basic to life. We see it in the cycle of night and day, the four seasons, the rise and fall of tides. More personally, we feel rhythm as we breathe. We find it in our heartbeats and our walking.

The essence of rhythm is a recurring pattern of tension and release, of expectation and fulfillment. This rhythmic alternation seems to pervade the flow of time. Time, as we live it, has fantastic diversity; each hour has sixty minutes, but how different one hour may seem from another!

Rhythm forms the lifeblood of music too. In its widest sense, ***rhythm*** is the flow of music through time. Rhythm has several interrelated aspects, which we'll consider in turn: beat, meter, accent and syncopation, and tempo.

Beat

When you clap your hands or tap your foot to music, you are responding to its beat. ***Beat*** is a regular, recurrent pulsation that divides music into equal units of time. Beats can be represented by marks on a time line:

Beats can be shown as a succession of marks on a time line.

In music, beats occur as often as every ¼ second or as seldom as every 1½ seconds. Sometimes the beat is powerful and easy to feel, as in marches or rock music; but sometimes it may be barely noticeable, suggesting feelings like floating or aimlessness.

The pulse of music is communicated in different ways. Sometimes the beat is explicitly pounded out—by a bass drum in a marching band, for instance. At other times the beat is sensed rather than actually heard.

Sing the beginning of *America* up to the words *Land where my fathers died*:

Each of the marks represents a beat. Did you notice that you automatically held *sing* for 3 beats? You *sensed* the beat because you were aware of it and expected it to continue.

Beats form the background against which the composer places notes of varying lengths. Beats are basic units of time by which all notes are measured. A note may last a fraction of a beat, an entire beat, or more than a beat. In the excerpt from *America,* for example, we have notes ranging in length from ½ beat to 3 beats.

When we talk about the combination of different note lengths in *America,* we are considering its rhythm. Earlier, rhythm was broadly defined as the flow of music through time. More specifically, **rhythm** can be defined as the particular arrangement of note lengths in a piece of music. The rhythm of a melody is an essential feature of its personality. Indeed, we might recognize *America* merely by clapping out its rhythm without actually singing the tones. The *beat* of *America* is an even, regular pulsation. But its *rhythm* flows freely, sometimes matching the beat, sometimes not.

Meter

When we sing *America,* some beats feel stronger or more stressed than others. The stress comes regularly on the first of every 3 beats:

My	coun-	try,	'tis		of	thee,
beat	beat	beat	**beat**	beat		beat

Therefore we count the beats of *America* as **1**–2–3, **1**–2–3:

My	coun-	try,	'tis		of	thee,
1	2	3	**1**	2		3
Sweet	land	of	lib-		er-	ty,
1	2	3	**1**	2		3
Of	thee	I	sing.			
1	2	3	**1**	2		3

In music we find a repeated pattern of a strong beat plus one or more weaker beats. The organization of beats into regular groups is called **meter.** A group containing a fixed number of beats is called a **measure.** There are several types of meter, which are based on the number of beats in a measure.

When a measure has 2 beats, it is in **duple meter;** we count **1**–2, **1**–2, and so on:

Ma-	ry	had	a	lit-	tle	lamb,	lit-	tle	lamb,	lit-	tle	lamb,
1	2			**1**	2		**1**	2		**1**	2	

The vertical lines mark the beginning or end of the measure. The first, or stressed, beat of the measure is known as the **downbeat.**

A pattern of 3 beats to the measure is known as **triple meter.** As we have seen in *America,* we count **1**–2–3, **1**–2–3, and so on. All waltzes are in triple meter.

Another basic metrical pattern is **quadruple meter,** which has 4 beats to the measure. As usual, the downbeat is strongest; but there is another stress on the third beat, which is stronger than the second and fourth beats and weaker than the first: **1**–2–*3*–4, **1**–2–*3*–4. In the following example of quadruple meter, the first word is on the **upbeat,** an unaccented pulse preceding the downbeat:

Mine eyes have seen the	glo- ry	of the	com- ing of	the Lord;	He is
|**1**	2	*3*	4	|**1**	2	*3*	4		

Jazz and rock are usually in quadruple meter. Both duple and quadruple meter reflect the left-right, left-right pattern of walking or marching.

Sextuple meter contains 6 rather quick beats to the measure. The downbeat is strongest, and the fourth beat also receives a stress: **1**–2–3–**4**–5–6. For example:

Oh, give	me	a	home		where the buf-		fa- lo	roam,		where the
|**1**	2	3	4	5	6	|**1**	2 3	4	5 6	|

Note that the measure is subdivided into two groups of 3 beats each: **1**–2–3/**4**–5–6. Thus, sextuple meter is a combination of duple and triple meter. Melodies in sextuple meter often create a feeling of smooth flow, as in *Silent Night.*

Quintuple meter, with 5 beats to the measure, and *septuple meter,* with 7 beats to the measure, occur frequently in twentieth-century music and in today's music and are found occasionally in earlier music. Each of these meters combines duple and triple meter. In quintuple meter, for example, the measure is subdivided into groups of 2 and 3 beats: **1**–2–3/**4**–5 or **1**–2/**3**–4–5.

Accent and Syncopation

An important aspect of rhythm is the way individual notes are stressed—how they get special emphasis. A note is emphasized most obviously by being played louder than the notes around it, that is, by receiving a dynamic *accent.* A note is sometimes especially accented when it is held longer or is higher in pitch than those notes near it.

When an accented note comes where we normally would *not* expect one, the effect is known as *syncopation.* A syncopation occurs when an "offbeat" note is accented—that is, when the stress comes *between* two beats. In the following example, syncopation occurs on the accented *my,* which comes between beats 1 and 2:

Give	**my**	re-	gards	to	Broad-		way	
1		2	3	4	|**1**	2	3	4	|

A syncopation also occurs when a weak beat is accented, as in 1–**2**–3–4 or 1–2–3–**4**. Such contradictions of the meter surprise the listener and create rhythmic excitement. Syncopation is a characteristic feature of jazz.

Tempo

Tempo—the speed of the beat—is the basic pace of the music. A fast tempo is associated with a feeling of energy, drive, and excitement. A slow tempo often contributes to a solemn, lyrical, or calm mood.

A *tempo indication* is usually given at the beginning of a piece. As with dynamics, the terms that show tempo (at the left) are in Italian.

largo	very slow, broad
grave	very slow, solemn
adagio	slow
andante	moderately slow, a walking pace
moderato	moderate
allegretto	moderately fast
allegro	fast
vivace	lively
presto	very fast
prestissimo	as fast as possible

Qualifying words are sometimes added to tempo indications to make them more specific. The two most commonly used are *molto* (*much*) and *non troppo* (*not too much*).

We thus get phrases like *allegro molto* (*very fast*) and *allegro non troppo* (*not too fast*). The same tempo is not always used throughout a piece. A gradual quickening of tempo may be indicated by writing **accelerando** (*becoming faster*), and a gradual slowing down of tempo by **ritardando** (*becoming slower*).

All these terms (again like dynamics) are relative and approximate; different performers interpret them differently, and there is no "right" tempo for a piece. This is true even though, since about 1816, composers have been able to indicate their preferred tempos by means of a **metronome**, an apparatus that produces ticking sounds or flashes of light at any desired musical speed. The metronome setting indicates the exact number of beats per minute.

4 Music Notation

We use written words to express our thoughts and communicate with others when we can't be with them. In music, ideas are also written down, or *notated*, so that performers can play pieces unknown to them.

Notation is a system of writing music so that specific pitches and rhythms can be communicated. It is explained here—very briefly—primarily to help you recognize rising and falling melodic lines and long and short notes so that you can follow the music examples in this book. (You will find it helpful to review the material on pitch and rhythm in Sections 1 and 3.)

Notating Pitch

With music notation, we can indicate exact pitches by the upward or downward placement of symbols—called *notes*—on a *staff*. A **note** is an oval. (Its duration is indicated by whether it is black or white or has a *stem* and *flags*, as will be explained later, under "Notating Rhythm.") A **staff** (plural, *staves*) is a set of five horizontal lines. Notes are positioned either on the lines of the staff or between them, in the spaces; the higher a note is placed on the staff, the higher its pitch:

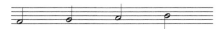

If a pitch falls above or below the range indicated by the staff, short, horizontal **ledger lines** are used:

Seven of the twelve pitches (tones) that fill the octave in western music are named after the first seven letters of the alphabet: A, B, C, D, E, F, G. This sequence is repeated over and over to represent the "same" tones in higher and lower octaves, and it corresponds to the white keys of the piano. The other five tones of the octave correspond to the black keys of the piano and are indicated by one of the same seven letters plus a **sharp sign** (♯) or a **flat sign** (♭) (see the illustration on the next page). Thus, the pitch between C and D may be called C sharp (C♯; higher than C) or D flat (D♭; lower than D). A **natural sign** (♮) is used to cancel a previous sharp or flat sign.

A **clef** is placed at the beginning of the staff to show the pitch of each line and space. The two most common clefs are the **treble clef,** used for relatively high ranges (such as

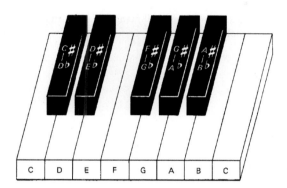

The twelve pitches of the octave and their positions on the piano keyboard.

those played by a pianist's right hand), and the **bass clef,** used for relatively low ranges (played by the pianist's left hand):

Treble Clef

Bass Clef

Keyboard music calls for a wide range of pitches to be played by both hands; for such music, the **grand staff**—a combination of the treble and bass staves—is used. The following illustration shows how the notes on the grand staff are related to the piano keyboard. Note that the C nearest to the middle of the keyboard is called **middle C.**

Notes on the grand staff and their positions on the piano keyboard.

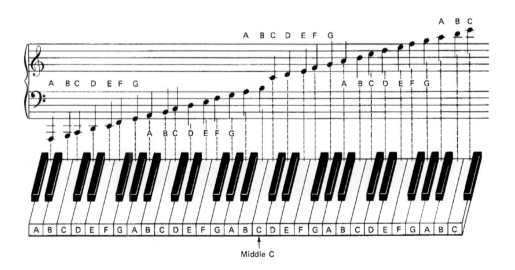

Middle C

Notating Rhythm

Music notation does not indicate the exact duration of tones; instead, it shows how long one tone lasts in relation to others in the same piece. A single note on the staff lasts longer or shorter depending on how it looks—on whether it is white or black and has a **stem** or **flags.** Following is a chart that shows the relationships of the duration symbols:

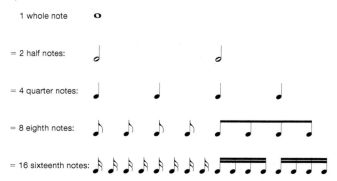

One whole note lasts as long as 2 half notes or 4 quarter notes, and so on. As shown, the flags of several eighth notes or sixteenth notes in succession are usually joined by a horizontal **beam.**

To lengthen the duration of a tone (and add rhythmic variety), we can make it a **dotted note**; adding a dot (·) to the right of a note increases its duration by half. Thus, 1 quarter note ordinarily equals 2 eighth notes, but 1 dotted quarter note equals 3 eighth notes:

Frequently, a dotted note is followed by one that is much shorter; this long-short pattern, called **dotted rhythm,** strongly emphasizes the beat (and is therefore often used in marches).

A **tie** (⌢) is another way to lengthen the duration of a note. When two notes in a row are the same pitch and are connected by a tie, the first note is lengthened by the duration of the second. In the following example, the note on *dell* lasts as long 1 dotted quarter note plus 1 quarter note; the two tied notes become one continuous sound:

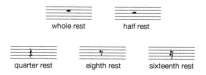

The farm - er in the dell, ___ The farm - er in the dell, ___

We also can add rhythmic variety by shortening the duration of a note. One method is the **triplet,** three notes of equal duration notated as a group within a curved line and the number 3. Such a group lasts only as long as if it were two notes of equal value:

$$\overset{3}{\underset{\bullet\bullet\bullet}{\rule{0.9cm}{0.4pt}}} = \underset{\bullet\bullet}{\rule{0.6cm}{0.4pt}}$$

Notating Silence (Rests)

Duration of silence is notated by using a symbol called a **rest.** Rests are pauses; their durations correspond to those of notes:

whole rest   half rest

quarter rest   eighth rest   sixteenth rest

Notating Meter

A *time signature* (or *meter signature*) shows the meter of a piece. It appears at the beginning of the staff at the start of a piece (and again later if the meter changes) and consists of two numbers, one on top of the other. The upper number tells how many beats fall in a measure; the lower number tells what kind of note gets the beat (2 = half note, for instance, and 4 = quarter note). Thus the time signature $\frac{2}{4}$ shows that there are 2 beats to the measure (duple meter) and a quarter note gets 1 beat. Duple meter may also be shown as $\frac{2}{2}$ (or by its symbol, ¢); quadruple meter is usually $\frac{4}{4}$ (or C). The most common triple meter is $\frac{3}{4}$.

The Score

A *score* shows the music for each instrumental or vocal category in a performing group; often, an orchestral score will show more than fifteen different staves of notation (see the illustration on the next page).

5 Melody

For many of us, music means melody. Though it is easier to recognize than to define, we do know that a *melody* is a series of single tones that add up to a recognizable whole. A melody begins, moves, and ends; it has direction, shape, and continuity. The up-and-down movement of its pitches conveys tension and release, expectation and arrival. This is the melodic *curve,* or *line.* As you get deeper into the music explored in this book, you'll find a wealth of melodies: vocal and instrumental, long and short, simple and complex. This section will help you sort them out by introducing some terms and basic melodic principles.

A melody moves by small intervals called *steps* or by larger ones called *leaps.* A step is the interval between two adjacent tones in the *do-re-mi* scale (from *do* to *re, re* to *mi,* etc.). Any interval larger than a step is a leap (*do* to *mi,* for example). Besides moving up or down by step or leap, a melody may simply repeat the same note. A melody's *range* is the distance between its lowest and highest tones. Range may be wide or narrow. Melodies written for instruments tend to have a wider range than those for voices, and they often contain wide leaps and rapid notes that would be difficult to sing. Often the highest tone of a melody will be the *climax,* or emotional focal point.

Note durations, as well as pitches, contribute to the distinctive character of a melody, and the specific order of long and short notes is important. A well-known melody can be almost unrecognizable if it is not sung or played in proper rhythm.

How the tones of a melody are performed can vary its effect too. Sometimes they are sung or played in a smooth, connected style called *legato.* Or they may be performed in a short, detached manner called *staccato.*

Many melodies are made up of shorter parts called *phrases.* These short units may have similar pitch and rhythm patterns that help unify the melody. On the other hand, contrasting phrases can furnish variety. Phrases often appear in balanced pairs; a first phrase of rising pitches may be followed by a second phrase of falling pitches. In analyzing music, letters are customarily used to represent sections of a piece: lowercase letters (a, b, etc.) for phrases and other relatively short sections, and capital letters (A, B, etc.) for longer sections. If two sections, such as phrases, differ significantly, we use different letters: a b. If one exactly repeats another, the letter is

A page from the orchestral score of Tchaikovsky's *Romeo and Juliet.*

repeated: a a. If one section is a varied repetition of a previous section, the repeated letter has a prime mark: a a′. A repetition of a melodic pattern at a higher or lower pitch is called a ***sequence.***

A resting place at the end of a phrase—a point of arrival—is called a ***cadence;*** it may be partial, setting up expectations (an ***incomplete cadence***), or it may give a sense of finality (a ***complete cadence***).

Now let's consider some examples of familiar melodies, starting with *Row, Row, Row Your Boat* (a b):

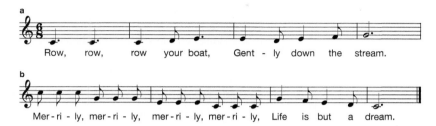

Sing the tune only up to the word *stream*. Notice that on *stream* the melody comes to a resting place, which ends the first phrase (a); but it seems incomplete, as though it had posed a question. Now sing the rest—the second phrase (b), beginning on *merrily*—and notice how it ends conclusively and seems to answer the question. The first phrase ends with an *incomplete cadence*, which sets up expectations; the second phrase ends with a *complete cadence*, which gives an answer, a sense of finality. Each phrase is the same length, a formula typical of many melodies called *tunes*. The two phrases create a feeling of symmetry and balance, one beginning with repeated notes and then moving upward by step, the second moving downward by leap and then by step. The climax comes on the first *merrily*.

Next sing the nursery tune *Mary Had a Little Lamb*:

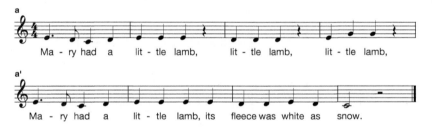

It also has two balancing phrases, the first phrase (a) ending with an incomplete cadence, and the second with a complete cadence. But here the second phrase (a′) begins exactly like the first before proceeding to a different, more conclusive ending. Melodic repetition, both exact and (as here) varied, plays an important unifying role in all kinds of music.

Our final example, *America* (a b), differs from the other songs in that its phrases are not of equal length: the second phrase (starting from *Land*) is longer than the first and creates a feeling of continuation rather than balance or symmetry. An interesting aspect of *America* is that a repeated rhythmic pattern is used to unify the melody. The rhythmic pattern for *My country 'tis of thee* is repeated for *Sweet land of liberty, Land where my fathers died,* and *Land of the Pilgrims' pride*. Notice that the melody for *Land of the Pilgrims' pride* is simply a repetition a little lower of the preceding *Land where my fathers died*. Such a repetition of a melodic pattern on a higher or lower pitch is called a *sequence*.

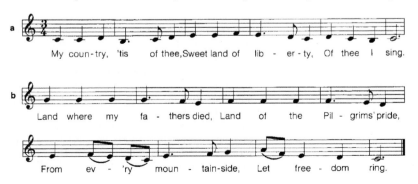

We've considered three melodies that are complete in themselves. Frequently, however, a melody will serve as the starting point for a more extended piece of music and, in stretching out, will go through all kinds of changes. This kind of melody is called a ***theme.***

Over the Rainbow (1938), by Harold Arlen

A beautiful legato melody creates a feeling of wonderment in *Over the Rainbow,* by Harold Arlen (1905–1986) with words by E.Y. Harburg (1896–1981). This song is from the movie *The Wizard of Oz* (1939), starring the seventeen-year-old Judy Garland as the Kansas farm girl Dorothy Gale. Like many popular songs, *Over the Rainbow* has a main melody (A) and a contrasting one (B). The song can be outlined as A A B A, followed by a closing part. The main melody (A: *Somewhere over the rainbow way up high . . .*) is presented and then repeated with different words (A: *Somewhere over the rainbow skies are blue . . .*). Then we hear the contrasting melody (B: *Someday I'll wish upon a star . . .*), and then a return of the main melody (A: *Somewhere over the rainbow bluebirds fly . . .*). The closing part of the song (*If happy little bluebirds fly. . .*) is a varied and abridged return of the contrasting melody.

The main melody (A) grows out of the opening upward leap of an octave that beautifully expresses Dorothy's daydreams which fly upward *over the rainbow.*

Main melody (A)
0:00
Contrasting melody (B)
0:45
Return of main melody (A)
1:13

Selection available on:
Connect Music
Mp3 download card
Mp3 disc

Melody A

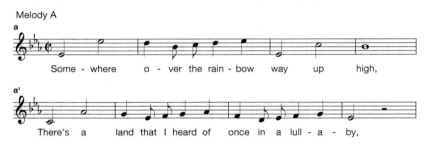

A large upward leap followed by a downward step appears three times, with changes of pitch, giving the melody a sense of unity and direction.

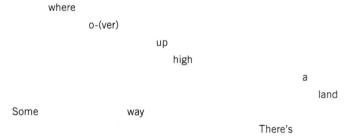

The second upward leap, which is slightly smaller than the first, is appropriate for the words *way up.* In all, the melody features upward leaps from low tones to higher tones that gradually descend.

Melody A is made up of two related phrases that can be symbolized as a (*Somewhere over the rainbow . . .*) and a′ (*There's a land . . .*). The second phrase (a′) begins somewhat like the first; but it starts on a lower pitch, and its upward leap is smaller. Whereas the first phrase (a) ends up in the air with an incomplete cadence (on *high*), the second phrase (a′) ends definitively with a complete cadence (on *lullaby*). The feeling given by A of motion to a conclusion is heightened by a sequence: the melodic pattern for *land that I heard of* is repeated on a lower pitch for *once in a lulla(by).*

Melody B is more speechlike in character.

Melody B

Some day I'll wish up - on a star and
wake up where the clouds are far be - hind me. _____
Where troub - les melt like lem - on drops, a -
way, a - bove the chim-ney tops that's where you'll find me.

It moves in a narrower range, uses quicker rhythms, and repeats two-note patterns. Like the main tune, melody B contains two phrases: b (*Someday I'll wish . . .*) and b′ (*Where troubles melt . . .*). It rises to a climax on its next-to-last tone (*find*). Together, melodies A and B produce a satisfying feeling of balance in this enchanting song.

Melody and Words

In most songs, the melody—along with the accompaniment—expresses the meaning and emotion of the words. Song texts deal with topics ranging from the pleasures and pains of love and the beauties of nature to the realm of the supernatural and the approach of death. A melody can evoke the overall mood of a text and call forth the feelings and images of individual words and lines. Changes of mood in the text often give rise to changes of tempo, rhythm, melody, and accompaniment in the music.

Song lyrics usually are poetry, rather than prose. Because of its rhythmic quality, emotional intensity, and artful use of vowel and consonant sounds, composers tend to prefer verse. Poetry is often characterized by a more or less regular rhythmic structure called *poetic meter.* (See the discussion of musical meter in Part I, Section 3.) Poetic meter involves the regular recurrence of a unit—called a *foot*—of two or three syllables: stressed, unstressed, or both. For example, in the nursery rhyme, *Mary Had a Little Lamb,* stressed syllables (*Ma, had, lit*) regularly alternate with unstressed syllables (*ry, a, tle*). In this song, as in most others, the rhythm, meter, and contour of the melody reinforce the natural emphases of the text. The accented syllable *Ma* is reinforced by a note that falls on the downbeat and is higher and longer than the immediately following notes. Conversely, the unaccented syllable *ry* is set to an unaccented note that is shorter and lower than the preceding note for *Ma.*

Song lyrics often include rhymes, as in the words *high, lullaby,* and *fly* in *Over the Rainbow,* studied previously. Rhymed syllables are often highlighted by similarities of rhythm and melody. In *America,* for example, the words *tis of thee,* and *liberty* are set to the same long-short-long rhythmic pattern. The melodic shape is similar as well: "'tis of thee" moves upward by step, whereas *liberty* moves downward by step.

```
                          lib-

              thee                er-
       of                              ty
'tis
```

Composers sometimes use **word painting,** the musical representation of specific poetic images. For example, the words *descending from heaven* might be set to a descending melodic line, and the word *running* might be heard as a series of rapid notes. We have already seen that in the song *Over the Rainbow,* the opening upward octave leap expresses the words of the title, and the word *up* appears on a high note.

In most kinds of vocal music, melodies are composed to preexisting texts. However, lyricists or composers have also written words especially to fit existing melodies; this is true of most popular songs of the twentieth century. For example, Harold Arlen first wrote the melody of *Over the Rainbow* and then E. Y. Harburg fitted his lyrics to the music. Sometimes a composer and a lyricist collaborate on the lyrics of a song, and occasionally a composer will write both words and music.

After receiving the melody, lyricists often begin by setting it to "dummy" words— perhaps trivial or meaningless—that help them remember the rhythm and shape of the melodic line. For example, it took Paul McCartney a long time to find the words *Yesterday all my troubles seemed so far away,* which open the Beatles' song *Yesterday*: His dummy line was "Scrambled eggs, oh baby how I love your legs."

Song Forms

Composers have used many different methods to set music to poems made up of several stanzas. They may employ **strophic form,** repeating the same music for each stanza of the poem. Strophic form makes a song easy to remember and is used in almost all folk songs. Or composers might use **through-composed form,** writing new music for each stanza. (*Through-composed* is a translation of the German term *durchkomponiert.*) Through-composed form allows music to reflect a poem's changing moods.

Songs are not restricted to strophic or through-composed form. There are many techniques by which music can be molded to the structure and feeling of a poem. We will consider other song forms when discussing specific songs.

6 Harmony

When folksingers accompany themselves on a guitar, they add support, depth, and richness to the melody. We call this *harmonizing.* Most music in western culture is a blend of melody and harmony (much nonwestern music, on the other hand, emphasizes melody and rhythm rather than harmony).

Harmony refers to the way chords are constructed and how they follow each other. A **chord** is a combination of three or more tones sounded at once. Essentially, a chord is a group of simultaneous tones, and a melody is a series of individual tones heard one after another. As a melody unfolds, it provides clues for harmonizing, but it does not always dictate a specific series, or **progression,** of chords. The same melody may be harmonized in several musically convincing ways. Chord progressions enrich a melody by adding emphasis, surprise, suspense, or finality.

New chords and progressions continually enter the language of music, but the basic chordal vocabulary has remained fairly constant. We'll look now at a few principles of harmony.

Consonance and Dissonance

Some chords have been considered stable and restful, others unstable and tense. A tone combination that is stable is called a **consonance.** Consonances are points of arrival, rest, and resolution. A tone combination that is unstable is called a **dissonance.** Its tension demands an onward motion to a stable chord. Dissonant chords are "active"; traditionally they have been considered harsh and have expressed pain, grief, and conflict. A dissonance has its **resolution** when it moves to a consonance. When this resolution is delayed or accomplished in unexpected ways, a feeling of drama, suspense, or surprise is created. In this way a composer plays with the listener's sense of expectation.

Consonance and dissonance can exist in varying degrees. Some consonant chords are more stable than others, and some dissonant chords are more tense than others. Dissonant chords have been used with increasing freedom over the centuries, so that often a chord considered intolerably harsh in one period has later come to seem rather mild.

Taylor Swift blends melody and harmony by accompanying herself on the guitar.

The Triad

A great variety of chords have been used in music. Some chords consist of three different tones; others have four, five, or even more. The simplest, most basic chord is the **triad** (pronounced *try'-ad*), which consists of three tones. To indicate that a triad's three tones are played at one time, it is notated as follows:

A triad is made up of alternate tones of the scale, such as the first tone (*do*), the third (*mi*), and the fifth (*sol*). The bottom tone is called the *root*; the others are a third and a fifth above the root. (From *do* to *mi* in the scale is the interval of a third; from *do* to *sol* is the interval of a fifth.)

A triad built on the first, or tonic, note of the scale (*do*) is called the **tonic chord** (*do- mi-sol*); it is the main chord of a piece, the most stable and conclusive. Traditionally, the tonic chord would usually begin a composition and almost always end it.

The triad built on the fifth note of the scale (*sol*) is next in importance to the tonic. It is called the **dominant chord** (*sol-ti-re*). The dominant chord is strongly pulled toward the tonic chord. This attraction has great importance in music. A dominant chord sets up tension that is resolved by the tonic chord. The progression from dominant to tonic gives a strong sense of conclusion, and that's why it is used so often at the end of a phrase, a melody, or an entire piece. A progression from dominant chord to tonic chord is called a **cadence.** The word *cadence* means both the resting point at the end of a melodic phrase (as was noted in Section 5) and a chord progression that gives a sense of conclusion.

Broken Chords (Arpeggios)

When the individual tones of a chord are sounded one after another, it is called a **broken chord,** or an **arpeggio.** *The Star-Spangled Banner* begins with such a broken chord:

In this example, the notes of the tonic chord are heard in succession rather than together. Throughout this book, the importance of harmony will become more and more apparent. It helps give music variety and movement; and its effects are endless, varying with the style of a particular era and the desires of individual composers.

Prelude in E Minor for Piano, Op. 28, No. 4 (1839), by Frédéric Chopin

Chopin's harmony makes a vital contribution to the brooding quality of this miniature lasting around two minutes. Without the pulsating chords of its accompaniment, the melody might seem aimless and monotonous. It hardly moves, alternating obsessively between a long note and a shorter one right above it. But the returning long note seems to change in color, because each time there is a different dissonant chord below it. The dissonant chords underscore the melancholy of this prelude, which is meant to be played *espressivo* (*expressively*).

In the middle of the prelude, a return of the opening melody leads to a brief but passionate climax with a crescendo, faster rhythm, and an acceleration of tempo (accelerando). The agitation rapidly subsides as we again hear returning long notes in the melody. Toward the end of the piece, a mildly dissonant chord is followed by a brief pause. This silence is filled with expectancy, as we wait for the dissonance to resolve. Finally the tension is released in the three solemn chords of the closing cadence.

Listening Outline

CHOPIN, Prelude in E Minor for Piano

Largo, Duple meter (²⁄₂), E minor
Piano
(Duration, 2:16)

0:00   **1.** Sad melody with obsessively returning long notes, accompanied by pulsating dissonant chords, *p*,

accompaniment stops, melody rises to

1:00   **2. a.** Return of sad melody; tempo acceleration and crescendo to *f* climax, decrescendo.
1:25   **b.** Obsessive long notes in melody, *p*, soft dissonant chord, brief pause.
1:56   **c.** Final cadence of three low chords.

Performance Perspectives

Roger Kamien, Pianist, Playing Chopin's Prelude in E Minor

A performer conveys to the listener the sound and emotional message of music. Like an actor playing a role, a performer breathes life into symbols on a page. Both actors and musicians move their audiences through changes of pace and emphasis.

Because indications of tempo, dynamics, legato, and staccato are not absolutely precise, much is left to the interpretation of the performer. A composition marked allegro (fast), for example, might be played more rapidly by one performer than another. Fine singers or instrumentalists put a personal stamp on the music they perform, so the same piece can sound quite different when interpreted by different artists.

To illustrate the role of the performer, I would like to share with you some of the decisions involved in my performance of Chopin's Prelude in E Minor, Op. 28, No. 4, included in the recording set (see the discussion and Listening Outline on page 42). For me, the Prelude in E Minor is an emotional journey from the profound grief of the beginning, through a climactic outburst of despair, to a final

acceptance of death. My tempo is very slow (largo), as Chopin indicates, but not excessively so. To emphasize the changes in color of the long notes in the melody, which return obsessively, I play each one at a slightly different dynamic level. In the pulsating accompanying chords, I stress the dissonant tones, either by subtly lengthening them, or by playing them a little louder than the consonant tones. To intensify the climax that grows out of the return of the opening melody, I momentarily quicken the tempo, as Chopin indicates. Toward the end of the Prelude, I give extra time to the pause following the questioning dissonant chord, thus heightening expectancy before the final low cadence.

You may find it interesting to compare my recorded performance of Chopin's Prelude in E Minor with performances by two other pianists. How do the three performances differ in expression, tempo, dynamic range, and relationship between melody and accompaniment? All three pianists have played the same notes, and yet they have made three different statements. That is what molding an interpretation means.

7 Key

Practically all familiar melodies are built around a central tone toward which the other tones gravitate and on which the melody usually ends. To feel this gravitational pull (which is rooted in cultural conditioning), sing *America* (page 37), pausing for a few seconds between *freedom* and *ring*.

You will probably feel uneasy until you supply the last tone. This central tone is the **keynote**, or **tonic**. A keynote can be any of the twelve tones of the octave. When a piece is in the key of C, for example, C is the keynote, or tonic.

Key involves not only a central tone but also a central scale and chord. (*Chord* was defined in Section 6.) The basic chord of a piece in C is a tonic triad with C as its root, or bottom tone. A *scale* is made up of the basic pitches of a piece of music arranged in order from low to high or from high to low. A piece in the key of C has a basic scale, *do-re-mi-fa-sol-la-ti-do*, with C as its *do*, or tonic. *Key*, then, refers to the presence of a central note, scale, and chord within a piece, with all the other tones heard in relationship to them. Another term for key is **tonality**.

After 1900, some composers abandoned tonality, but even today much of the music we hear is tonal.

The Major Scale

The basic scales of western music from the late 1600s to 1900 were the *major* and *minor*, and they continue to be widely used today.

The **major scale**—the familiar *do-re-mi-fa-sol-la-ti-do*—has two kinds of intervals in a specific pattern: *half steps* and *whole steps*. The **half step** is the smallest interval traditionally used in western music. The **whole step** is twice as large as the half step. Here is the pattern of whole and half steps making up the major scale:

whole step	whole step	half step	whole step	whole step	whole step	half step

do   *re*   *mi*   *fa*   *sol*   *la*   *ti*   *do*

Pattern of whole and half steps making up the major scale.

The illustration that follows shows a major scale with C as the beginning tone. The C major scale uses only the white keys of the piano. There are half steps between the tones E and F, and between B and C; these pairs of tones are not separated by black keys.

We can construct similar major scales by starting on any one of the twelve tones that fill an octave, thus there are twelve possible major scales. The other major scales use one or more black keys of the piano, but the pattern sounds the same.

The Minor Scale

Along with the major scale, the minor scale is fundamental to western music.

The **minor scale**—like the major—consists of seven different tones and an eighth tone that duplicates the first an octave higher; but it differs from the major scale in

Major scale beginning on C.

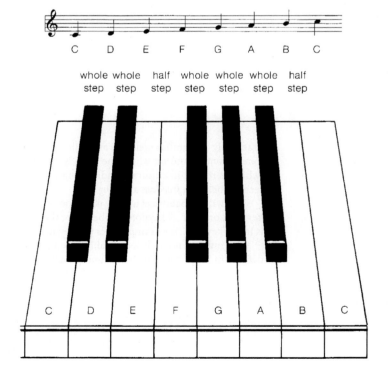

its pattern of intervals, or whole and half steps. Because (again, like the major) it can begin on any of the twelve tones in an octave, there are twelve possible minor scales. Here is a comparison between a major and a minor scale both starting on C:*

The crucial difference is that in the minor scale there is only a half step between the second and third tones. This small difference greatly changes the sound of a scale and the mood of music using that scale. Music based on minor scales tends to sound serious or melancholy. Also, the tonic triad built from a minor scale is a minor chord, which sounds darker than a major chord.

Joshua Fought the Battle of Jericho is a tune based on a minor scale:

Josh-ua fought the bat-tle of __ Jer-i - cho, Jer-i - cho, Jer-i - cho;

Josh-ua fought the bat-tle of __ Jer-i - cho, and the walls came tum-bl-ing down.

The Key Signature

When a piece of music is based on a major scale, we say it is in a **major key;** when it is based on a minor scale, it is said to be in a **minor key.** For instance, a piece based on a major scale with D as its keynote is in the key of D major. Similarly, if a composition is based on a minor scale with the keynote F, the composition is in the key of F minor. Each major or minor scale has a specific number of sharps or flats ranging from none to seven. To indicate the key of a piece of music, the composer uses a **key signature,** consisting of sharp or flat signs immediately following the clef sign at the beginning of the staff.

To illustrate, here is the key signature for D major, which contains two sharps:

By using a key signature, a composer avoids having to write a sharp or a flat sign before every sharped or flatted note in a piece.

---

* The minor scale shown in this example is the *natural minor,* one of the three minor scales. The other two kinds are the *harmonic minor* and the *melodic minor* scales. The three types of minor scales have slight variations in their patterns of intervals, but all can begin on any tone of the octave, and all will produce a sound that contrasts with the major scale as described here.

The Chromatic Scale

The twelve tones of the octave—*all* the white and black keys in one octave on the piano—form the **chromatic scale.** Unlike those of the major or minor scales, tones of the chromatic scale are all the same distance apart, one half step:

The word *chromatic* comes from the Greek word *chroma* (color). The traditional function of the chromatic scale is to color or embellish the tones of the major and minor scales. The chromatic scale does not define a key. Its tones contribute a sense of motion and tension. Composers throughout history have used the chromatic scale to evoke strong feelings of grief, loss, and sorrow. Since 1900 it has become independent of major and minor scales and has been used as the basis for entire compositions.

Modulation: Change of Key

Most short melodies remain in a single key from beginning to end. However, in longer pieces of music, variety and contrast are created by using more than one key. Shifting from one key to another within the same piece is called **modulation.**

A modulation is like a temporary shift in the center of gravity—it brings a new central tone, chord, and scale. Though modulations are sometimes subtle and difficult to spot, they produce subconscious effects that increase our enjoyment of the music.

Tonic Key

No matter how often a piece changes key, there is usually one main key, called the **tonic** or **home key.** The tonic key is the central key around which the whole piece is organized. Traditionally, a piece would usually begin in the home key and practically always end in it. A composition in the key of C major, for example, would begin in the home key, modulate to several other keys—say, G major and A minor—and finally conclude in the home key of C major. The other keys are subordinate to the tonic.

Modulating away from the tonic key is like visiting: we may enjoy ourselves during the visit, but after a while we're glad to go home. In music, modulations set up tensions that are resolved by returning to the home key. For centuries, the idea of a central key was a basic principle of music. But after 1900, some composers wrote music that ignored the traditional system. The results of this revolutionary step are explored in Part VI, "The Twentieth Century and Beyond."

8 Musical Texture

At a particular moment within a piece, we may hear one unaccompanied melody, several simultaneous melodies, or a melody with supporting chords. To describe these various possibilities, we use the term **musical texture;** it refers to how many different layers of sound are heard at once, to what kind of layers they are (melody or harmony), and to how they are related to each other. Texture is described as transparent, dense, thin, thick, heavy, or light; and variations in texture create contrast and drama. We'll look now at the three basic musical textures—*monophonic, polyphonic,* and *homophonic.*

Monophonic Texture

The texture of a single melodic line without accompaniment is **monophonic,** meaning literally *having one sound.* If you sing alone, you make monophonic music. Performance of a single melodic line at the same pitch by more than one instrument or voice is playing or singing in **unison** and results in a fuller, richer-sounding monophonic texture.

Polyphonic Texture

Simultaneous performance of two or more melodic lines of relatively equal interest produces the texture called **polyphonic,** meaning *having many sounds.* In polyphony several melodic lines compete for attention. Polyphony adds a dimension that has been compared to perspective in painting: each line enriches the others.

The technique of combining several melodic lines into a meaningful whole is called **counterpoint.** (The term *contrapuntal texture* is sometimes used in place of *polyphonic texture.*) To fully enjoy polyphony, you may have to hear a piece of music a few times. It's often helpful to listen first for the top line, then for the bottom line, and then for the middle lines.

Polyphonic music often contains **imitation,** which occurs when a melodic idea is presented by one voice or instrument and is then restated immediately by another. A *round*—a song in which several people sing the same melody but each starts at a different time—uses imitation. *Row, Row, Row Your Boat* is a familiar example:

Here the imitation is "strict"; each voice sings exactly the same melody. But in polyphonic texture imitation is often freer, with the imitating line starting like the first one but going off on its own.

Homophonic Texture

When we hear one main melody accompanied by chords, the texture is **homophonic.** Attention is focused on the melody, which is supported and colored by sounds of subordinate interest. *Row, Row, Row Your Boat,* when harmonized by chords, is an example of homophonic texture:

Accompaniments in homophonic music vary widely in character and importance, from subdued background chords to surging sounds that almost hide the main melody. When a subordinate line asserts its individuality and competes for the listener's attention, the texture is probably best described as being between homophonic and polyphonic.

Changes of Texture

A composer can create variety and contrast by changing textures within a composition. He or she might begin with a melody and a simple accompaniment and later weave the melody into a polyphonic web, or create drama by contrasting a single voice with massive chords sung by a chorus. *Farandole* by Georges Bizet (1838–1875), from *L'Arlésienne* Suite No. 2, is a good example of textural variety.

Farandole from *L'Arlésienne* Suite No. 2 (1879), by Georges Bizet*

The *Farandole* comes from music by Georges Bizet for the play *L'Arlésienne* (*The Woman of Arles*), set in southern France. Two contrasting themes are heard in this exciting orchestral piece. The first, in minor, is a march theme adapted from a southern French folksong. The lively second theme, in major, has the character of the *farandole,* a southern French dance.

---

*L'Arlésienne Suites No. 1 and No. 2 are sets of pieces from the theater music composed by Bizet. Suite No. 2 was arranged by Bizet's friend Ernest Guiraud in 1879, after the composer's death.

Many changes of texture contribute to the *Farandole*'s exciting mood. The piece contains two kinds of homophonic texture: in one, the accompaniment and melody have the same rhythm; in the other, the rhythm of the accompaniment differs from that of the melody. The *Farandole* opens with the march theme and its accompaniment in the same rhythm. But when the lively dance theme is first presented, its accompanying chords do not duplicate the rhythm of the melody; instead, they simply mark the beat.

The *Farandole* also includes two kinds of polyphony: with and without imitation. Soon after the opening, the march theme is presented by the violins and then is imitated by the violas. At the end of the piece, polyphony results when the march and dance themes—previously heard in alternation—are presented simultaneously. In this concluding section, both themes are in major.

The *Farandole* also contains monophonic texture, which sets off the homophony and polyphony. Monophony is heard when the march theme is played by the strings in unison.

Listening Outline

BIZET, *Farandole* from *L'Arlésienne* Suite No. 2

Allegro deciso (forceful allegro), march tempo, quadruple meter ($\frac{4}{4}$), D minor
Piccolo, 2 flutes, 2 oboes, 2 clarinets, 2 bassoons, 4 French horns, 2 trumpets, 2 cornets, 3 trombones, timpani, tambourine, bass drum, cymbals, 1st violins, 2d violins, violas, cellos, double basses
(Duration, 3:08)

0:00   **1. a.** Full orchestra, ***ff***, march theme; homophonic (accompaniment in same rhythm as melody), minor.

0:16   **b.** Violins imitated by violas, march theme; polyphonic, minor.

0:33   **2. a.** High woodwinds, ***ppp***, dance theme; faster tempo, homophonic (accompanying chords on beat), major; decorative rushes in violins, long crescendo to ***ff*** as dance theme is repeated.

1:17   **b.** Full orchestra, ***fff***, dance theme.

1:28   **3. a.** Strings only, ***ff***, march theme in faster tempo; monophonic, minor.

1:39   **b.** High woodwinds, ***ppp***, dance theme; homophonic.

1:45   **c.** Strings only, ***ff***, continue march theme; monophonic, then homophonic as lower strings accompany melody.

1:56   **d.** High woodwinds, ***ppp***, dance theme; homophonic. Crescendo to

2:19   **4.** Full orchestra, ***fff***, dance and march themes combined; polyphonic, major. Homophonic ending.

9 Musical Form

The word *form* is associated with shape, structure, organization, and coherence. Form calls to mind the human body or a balanced arrangement of figures in a painting. **Form** in music is the organization of musical elements in time. In a musical composition, pitch, tone color, dynamics, rhythm, melody, and texture interact to produce a sense of shape and structure. All parts of the composition are interrelated. Our memory lets us perceive the overall form by recalling the various parts and how they relate to each other. The form becomes clearer as we develop awareness and recall these parts through repeated listening. As listeners, we can respond more fully to the emotional power and meaning of a musical composition when we appreciate its form.

Techniques That Create Musical Form

Repetition, contrast, and variation are essential techniques in short tunes as well as in compositions lasting much longer. **Repetition** creates a sense of unity; **contrast** provides variety; and **variation,** in keeping some elements of a musical thought while changing others, gives a work unity and variety at the same time.

Repetition

Musical repetition appeals to the pleasure we get in recognizing and remembering something. In music the repetition of melodies or extended sections is a technique widely used for binding a composition together.

The passage of time influences our reaction to repetition: when a musical idea returns, the effect is not duplication but balance and symmetry.

Contrast

Forward motion, conflict, and change of mood all come from contrast. Opposition—of loud and soft, strings and woodwinds, fast and slow, major and minor—propels and develops musical ideas. Sometimes such contrast is complete, but at other times the opposites have common elements that give a sense of continuity.

Variation

In the variation of a musical idea, some of its features will be retained while others are changed. For example, the melody might be restated with a different accompaniment. Or the pitches of a melody might stay the same while its rhythmic pattern is changed. A whole composition can be created from a series of variations on a single musical idea.

Types of Musical Form

Composers have traditionally organized musical ideas by using certain forms or patterns, and listeners can respond more fully when they recognize these patterns. It's important to note, however, that two compositions having the same form may be different in every other respect. We'll look now at two basic types of musical form. (Remember from Section 5, that lowercase letters represent phrases or short sections and capital letters represent longer sections.)

Three-Part (Ternary) Form: A B A

During the last few centuries *three-part form* (**A B A**) has probably been used most frequently. This form can be represented as *statement* (A), *contrast* or *departure* (B), *return* (A). When the return of A is varied, the form is outlined A B A′. The contrast between A and B can be of any kind; A and B can be of equal or unequal length; and the way A returns after B differs from piece to piece—A may come back unexpectedly, or it may be clearly signaled (if B comes to a definite end with a cadence and a pause), or there may be a transition smoothly linking the two.

The sections of an A B A composition can be subdivided, for example, as follows:

A   B   A

a b a   c d c   a b a

In some pieces, a listener might mistake subsection b within the first A for the arrival of B; but as the music progresses, the greater contrast one hears with B will make it clear that b is a subsection. (For example, in Tchaikovsky's *Dance of the Reed Pipes*, studied next, the English horn melody in item 1*c* in the Listening Outline introduces a brief contrast within the A section, whereas the trumpet melody in item 2*a* brings a greater contrast and initiates the B section.)

Dance of the Reed Pipes from *Nutcracker* Suite (1892), by Peter Ilyich Tchaikovsky

The *Nutcracker* Suite is a set of dances from the fairytale ballet *The Nutcracker* by Peter Ilyich Tchaikovsky (1840–1893). *Dance of the Reed Pipes* is a particularly clear example of A B A′ form. Section A features three flutes playing a staccato melody that conveys a light, airy feeling and is repeated several times. The B section contrasts in tone color, melody, and key—it features a trumpet melody accompanied by brasses and cymbals. This melody moves by step within a narrow range, in contrast to the opening flute melody, which has a wide range and many leaps as well as steps. The F sharp minor key of the middle section contrasts with the D major key of the opening section. The concluding A′ section, in D major, is a shortened version of the opening A section.

Listening Outline

TCHAIKOVSKY, *Dance of the Reed Pipes* from *Nutcracker* Suite

Three-part (ternary) form: A B A′
Moderato assai (very moderate), duple meter (²/₄), D major
3 flutes, 2 oboes, English horn, 2 clarinets, bass clarinet, 2 bassoons, 4 French horns, 2 trumpets, 3 trombones, tuba, timpani, cymbals, 1st violins, 2d violins, violas, cellos, double basses
(Duration, 2:05)

A

0:00   **1. a.** Low pizzicato strings, *p*, introduce
0:03   **b.** 3 flutes, staccato melody in major, pizzicato strings accompany. Melody repeated.

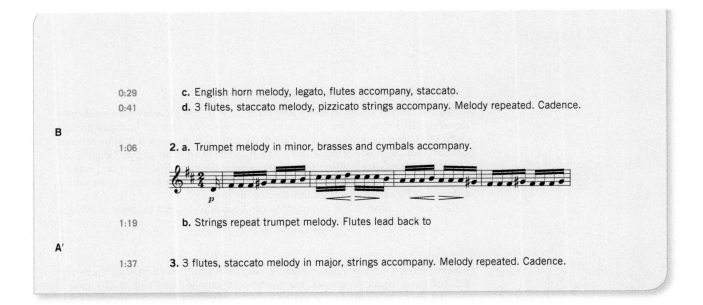

0:29   **c.** English horn melody, legato, flutes accompany, staccato.

0:41   **d.** 3 flutes, staccato melody, pizzicato strings accompany. Melody repeated. Cadence.

B

1:06   **2. a.** Trumpet melody in minor, brasses and cymbals accompany.

1:19   **b.** Strings repeat trumpet melody. Flutes lead back to

A′

1:37   **3.** 3 flutes, staccato melody in major, strings accompany. Melody repeated. Cadence.

Two-Part (Binary) Form: A B

A composition made up of two sections is in **two-part form** (**A B**). Two-part form, frequently called **binary form,** gives a sense of *statement* (A) and *counterstatement* (B). Usually, compositions in two-part form repeat both parts: A A B B. Like the sections in three-part form, parts A and B in two-part form are often divided into subsections.

The two sections of a composition in binary form are often similar in rhythm, melody, and texture. However, the conclusion of each section is usually signaled by a cadence, held tones, or a brief pause. Part A begins in the tonic (home) key and ends either in the tonic or in a new key. Part B ends in the home key and brings a feeling of completion.

Bourrée from Suite in E Minor for Lute (probably around 1710), by Johann Sebastian Bach

This lighthearted bourrée—a type of dance-inspired piece in duple meter—comes from the Suite in E minor for lute, by Johann Sebastian Bach (1685–1750). The *lute* is a plucked string instrument popular during the sixteenth and seventeenth centuries. In our recording, Julian Bream performs this bourrée—a favorite of classical guitarists—on an acoustic guitar.

Lasting about 1½ minutes, this bourrée is in two-part (binary) form, and is outlined A A B B because each section is repeated. Throughout the bourrée, a lilting three-note rhythm, short-short-long, pervades the dancelike melody, which is supported by a steadily moving bass line. Within each section, rhythmic motion is almost continuous except for long, held tones that close parts A and B. These longer notes help define the conclusion of each section.

Part A, about 15 seconds in duration, is made up of two brief balancing phrases (a a′). The melody of these phrases gradually descends, almost entirely by step. The first phrase (a), in minor, closes with a quick downward scale pattern in the melody. The second phrase (a′) begins exactly like the first but proceeds to a different ending on a held major chord. In our recording, the guitarist chooses to repeat part A more loudly. (There are no indications of dynamics in Bach's score of the bourrée.)

Part B, about 30 seconds in length, is twice as long as A. The melody of B is more playful because it moves by leap as well as by step. It contains four brief phrases, each ending with a held note in the melody. The fourth phrase of B differs from the previous phrases because it quickly descends, repeating a three-note melodic pattern at increasingly lower pitches. (This is a downward *sequence.*) Part B ends in minor with a low, held octave. In our recording, the guitarist plays part B at a fairly soft dynamic level and concludes the repetition of B with a slight slowing of tempo to heighten the feeling of finality.

Listening Outline

BACH, Bourrée from Suite in E Minor for Lute

Two-part (binary) form: A A B B
Duple meter (²⁄₂), E minor
Acoustic guitar
(Duration, 1:32)

A

0:00

1. Dancelike melody (a) in minor, short-short-long rhythm, moves downward mostly by step. Melody repeats (a'), descends to long, low, major chord. Soft dynamic level.

A

0:14

Part A repeated more loudly.

B

0:26

2. Three soft phrases with skips and steps, short-short-long rhythm continues; each brief phrase ends with long note in melody.

Fourth phrase quickly descends in sequential repetition of short-short-long pattern; minor key, long low octave ends B.

Downward sequence

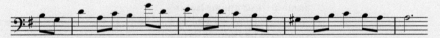

B

0:57

Part B repeated.

Listening for Form

The musical patterns covered in this section fall into clearly defined units. However, music is continuous in its flow and sometimes can't be subdivided quite so easily. Some music seems to fit none of the frequently used patterns. But such music is not formless—it has a unique form that can be discovered through repeated hearings.

Again, it's important to lean on memory when you listen to music. Spotting musical ideas when they occur is fine, but it's only the beginning. The goal is to put the related ideas together by recognizing and remembering them and by finding the relationships between them. Through alert, repeated listening their overall shape will be made clear, and your response to music will be more satisfying.

10 Musical Style

We use the word *style* in reference to everything from clothing to cooking, automobiles to paintings. In music, **style** refers to a characteristic way of using melody, rhythm, tone color, dynamics, harmony, texture, and form. The particular way these elements are combined can result in a total sound that's distinctive or unique. We speak of the musical style of an individual composer, a group of composers, a country, or a particular period in history. Compositions created in the same geographical area or around the same time are often similar in style, but individuals using the same musical vocabulary can create a personal manner of expression.

Musical styles change from one era in history to the next. These changes are continuous, and so any boundary line between one stylistic period and the next can be only an approximation. Though sudden turning points do occur in the history of music, even the most revolutionary new styles are usually foreshadowed in earlier compositions; and few changes of style sweep away the past entirely.

The history of western art music can be divided into the following stylistic periods:

Middle Ages (450–1450)
Renaissance (1450–1600)
Baroque (1600–1750)
Classical (1750–1820)
Romantic (1820–1900)
Twentieth century to 1945
1945 to the present

The chapters that follow describe the general features of each period and show how that period differs from the preceding one. An awareness of the characteristics of a style helps you to know what to listen for in a composition and help you recognize innovative or unique features.

Music is not created in a vacuum. To fully understand the style of a composition, one has to be aware of its function in society. Is a piece meant to provide entertainment in an aristocrat's castle, a concert hall, or a middle-class home? Is it designed to accompany singing, dancing, religious rites, or drama? Musical style is shaped by political, economic, social, and intellectual developments as well. And often, similar features of style can be found in different arts of the same period.

Music is probably as old as the human race itself. There is pictorial evidence of musical activity in Egypt as early as 3000 BC. We know that music played an important role in the cultures of ancient Israel, Greece, and Rome. But hardly any notated music has survived from these ancient civilizations.

The first stylistic period to be considered in this book is the European Middle Ages, from which notated music has come down to us. Through the power of notation, music created more than 1,000 years ago can come alive today.

Elements: Summary

IMPORTANT TERMS

Sound, p. 4
Pitch, p. 4
Tone, p. 5
Interval, p. 5
Octave, p. 5
Pitch range (range), p.5
Dynamics, p. 6
  pianissimo
  piano
  mezzo piano
  mezzo forte
  forte
  fortissimo
  decrescendo (diminuendo)
  crescendo
Accent, p. 6
Tone color (timbre), p. 6
improvisation, p. 8
Voices, p. 9
  Women
    soprano
    mezzo-soprano
    alto (contralto)
  Men
    tenor
    baritone
    bass
Musical instruments
  string, p. 10
  woodwind, p. 10
  brass, p. 10
  percussion, p. 10
  keyboard, p. 10
  electronic, p. 10
  register, p. 10
  conductor, p. 12
  baton, p. 12
  concertmaster, p. 12
String instruments
  violin, p. 12
  viola, p. 12
  cello, p. 12
  double bass, p. 12
  bow, p. 12
  pizzicato, p. 14
  stop (double, triple, quadruple), p. 14
  vibrato, p. 14
  mute, p. 15
  tremolo, p. 15
  harmonics, p. 15
  plectrum, p. 15
  harp, p. 15
  guitar, p. 15

Woodwind instruments
  piccolo, p. 15
  flute, p. 15
  clarinet, p. 15
  bass clarinet, p. 15
  oboe, p. 15
  English horn, p. 15
  bassoon, p. 15
  contrabassoon, p. 15
  recorder, p. 15
  reed, p. 15
  single-reed woodwinds, p. 15
  saxophone, p. 15
  double-reed woodwinds, p. 15
Brass instruments
  trumpet, p. 18
  French horn, p. 18
  trombone, p. 18
  tuba, p. 18
  cornet, p. 18
  baritone horn, p. 18
  euphonium, p. 18
  mute, p. 18
Percussion instruments
  Definite pitch
    timpani (kettledrums), p. 20
    glockenspiel, p. 20
    xylophone, p. 20
    celesta, p. 20
    chimes, p. 20
  Indefinite pitch
    snare drum (side drum), p. 20
    bass drum, p. 20
    tambourine, p. 20
    triangle, p. 20
    cymbals, p. 20
    gong (tam-tam), p. 20
Keyboard instruments
  piano, p. 23
  harpsichord, p. 23
  pipe organ, p. 24
  accordion, p. 25
Electronic instruments
  electric guitar, p. 25
  tape studio, p. 25
  synthesizer, p. 26
  computer, p. 28
  computer music, p. 28
Theme, p. 28
Variation, p. 28
Rhythm, p. 29
Beat, p. 29
Meter, p. 30
  duple meter

  triple meter
  quadruple meter
  quintuple meter
  sextuple meter
  septuple meter
Measure, p. 30
Downbeat, p. 30
Upbeat, p. 30
Accent, p. 31
Syncopation, p. 31
Tempo, p. 31
Tempo indication, p. 31
  largo
  grave
  adagio
  andante
  moderato
  allegretto
  allegro
  vivace
  presto
  prestissimo
Accelerando, p. 32
Ritardando, p. 32
Metronome, p. 32
Notation, p. 32
Note, p. 32
Staff, p. 32
Ledger lines, p. 32
Sharp sign, p. 32
Flat sign, p. 32
Natural sign, p. 32
Clef (treble and bass), p. 32
Grand staff, p. 33
Middle C, p. 33
Stem, p. 34
Flag, p. 34
Beam, p. 34
Dotted note, p. 34
Dotted rhythm, p. 34
Tie, p. 34
Triplet, p. 34
Rest, p. 34
Time signature (meter signature), p. 35
Score, p. 35
Melody, p. 35
Step, p. 35
Leap, p. 35
Climax, p. 35
Legato, p. 35
Staccato, p. 35
Phrase, p. 35
Sequence, p. 35

FEATURED COMPOSERS

Igor Stravinsky (1882–1971)
Duke Ellington (1899–1974)
Benjamin Britten (1913–1976)
Harold Arlen (1905–1986)
Frédéric Chopin (1810–1849)
Georges Bizet (1838–1875)
Peter Ilyich Tchaikovsky (1840–1893)
Johann Sebastian Bach (1685–1750)

Beyond the Classroom: What to Listen For in Music

We hear music all the time, but we don't always *listen* to music. Separating the various elements of music into their different component parts, then integrating them back together, is an exercise that benefits all students of music listening. Describing accurately what is happening in the music at any moment helps us enjoy music more deeply by understanding it more completely.

The American composer Aaron Copland (1900–1990), called by some the "dean of American music," frequently spoke and wrote about music listening. In his book *What to Listen For in Music* (1939), Copland describes three planes of music listening: the sensuous, the expressive, and the purely musical.

At the sensuous level, one bathes in the sound of music, enjoying music simply for the sheer pleasure and beauty of the sound. Copland explains that everyone listens to one degree or another on this plane; even seasoned music listeners do so, particularly when they seek consolation or an escape. Copland notes that the sensuous sound plane is an important aspect of understanding any composer's individual style.

At the expressive level, one considers the meaning behind the notes themselves. By *meaning*, Copland refers not to music describing a specific object or event, such as a storm or a battle, but rather to the uniquely personal aspect of what the music "says" to us. This plane is far easier to understand intuitively than it is to articulate. Copland explains that the meaning of a great musical work may change for us as we change over time.

At the purely musical level, the listener listens to music to understand the individual musical components, how they are used, and how they interact. Though this might seem like an academic exercise, the more one understands about music and how it functions, the greater one's listening pleasure can be.

Copland's three planes of listening are not mutually exclusive; we frequently shift between these planes as we listen to music. In particular, great works of music require repeated listening to fully comprehend all that is there to discover and enjoy.

When you attend a concert or listen to any musical selection, ask yourself the following questions:

- What individual musical elements do you hear? What words might you use to describe each one?
- Does the music use instruments, voices, or both? Which specific instruments or voices do you hear? How many of each do you notice?
- Do any elements change as the composition progresses? If so, which elements change and in what way do they change?
- If you listen to a song, how does the music express the words through its melody, harmony, rhythm, tempo, dynamics, and accompaniment?
- On which of Copland's music listening planes did you listen?

qui non abyit in confilio
impiorum & in uia pecca

■ Most medieval music was vocal, though musicians also performed on a wide variety of instruments. A page from the Peterborough Psalter.

PART II

The man that hath no music in himself, Nor is not mov'd with concord of sweet sounds, Is fit for treasons, strategems and spoils.

—William Shakespeare

The Middle Ages and Renaissance

LEARNING OBJECTIVES

- Explain the roles of musicians in medieval society

- Discuss the texture, melody, rhythm, mood, and texts of Gregorian chant

- Describe different types of secular music in the middle ages

- Trace the development of polyphonic music in the middle ages

- Identify the musical innovations in music of the fourteenth century

- Explain the shift in musical patronage during the Renaissance

- Compare and contrast polyphonic vocal music of the middle ages and the Renaissance

- Describe two types of sacred vocal music during the Renaissance

- Compare and contrast two types of secular vocal music during the Renaissance

- Discuss the development of Renaissance instrumental music

TIME LINE

Middle Ages 450–1450

450–1000	1000–1300	1300–1450

Historical and Cultural Events

455 Sack of Rome by Vandals

590–604 Reign of Pope Gregory I (the Great)

800 Charlemagne crowned Holy Roman Emperor

1066 Norman Conquest

1096–1099 First Crusade

1215 Magna Carta signed

1337–1453 Hundred Years' War

1347–1352 Black death

1431 Joan of Arc executed by the English

Arts and Letters

c. 700 *Beowolf*

c. 800 *Book of Kells*

1163 Beginning of Notre Dame Cathedral in Paris

1273 Thomas Aquinas, *Summa Theologica*

1321 Dante, *The Divine Comedy*

351 Boccaccio, *Decameron*

1387–1400 Chaucer, *The Canterbury Tales*

Music

c. 900 Earliest notated Gregorian chant manuscripts

c. 1100–1300 Troubadours and trouvères

c. 1150 Hildegard of Bingen, *O successores*

begun c. 1170 School of Notre Dame

c. 1360 Guillaume de Machaut *Notre Dame* Mass

TIME LINE

Renaissance 1450–1600

1450–1500	1500–1600

Historical and Cultural Events

1453 Fall of Constantinople
1456 Gutenberg Bible
1492 Columbus reaches America

1517 Martin Luther's ninety-five theses, start of the Reformation
1545–1563 Council of Trent
1558–1603 Elizabeth I, queen of England
1588 Spanish Armada defeated

Arts and Letters

c. 1482 Botticelli, *La Primavera*

c. 1503 Leonardo da Vinci, *Mona Lisa*
1504 Michelangelo, *David*
1505 Raphael, *School of Athens*
c. 1570 Titian, *Venus and the Lute Player*
1596 Shakespeare, *Romeo and Juliet*

Music

c. 1475 Josquin Desprez, *Ave Maria . . . Virgo Serena*

1563 Giovanni Pierluigi da Palestrina, *Pope Marcellus Mass*
c. 1600 John Dowland, *Flow My Tears*
1601 Thomas Weelkes, *As Vesta Was Descending*

The Middle Ages
(450–1450)

A thousand years of European history are spanned by the phrase *Middle Ages*. Beginning around 450 with the disintegration of the Roman empire, the early Middle Ages was a time of migrations, upheavals, and wars. But the later Middle Ages (until about 1450) were a period of cultural growth: Romanesque churches and monasteries (1000–1150) and Gothic cathedrals (1150–1450) were constructed, towns grew, and universities were founded. The later Middle Ages also witnessed the crusades, a series of wars undertaken by European Christians—primarily between 1096 and 1291—to recover the holy city of Jerusalem from the Muslims.

During the Middle Ages a very sharp division existed among three main social classes: nobility, peasantry, and clergy. Nobles were sheltered within fortified castles surrounded by moats. During wars, noblemen engaged in combat as knights in armor, while noblewomen managed estates, ran households, and looked after the

Architecture changed during the Middle Ages from the Romanesque style, seen in the eleventh-century nave at left, to the Gothic style of the thirteenth-century Cathedral of Reims, at right.

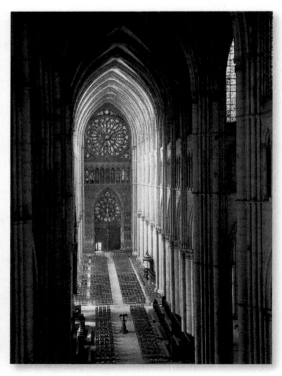

Choir of Cathedral of Reims. During the Middle Ages, religious teachings were imparted, and beliefs were strengthened, by biblical scenes depicted in stained-glass windows.

During the Middle Ages, artists were more concerned with religious symbolism than with lifelike representation. Madonna and Child Enthroned by an anonymous Byzantine artist of the thirteenth century.

sick. In peacetime, the nobles amused themselves with hunting, feasting, and tournaments. Peasants—the vast majority of the population—lived miserably in one-room huts. Many were serfs, bound to the soil and subject to feudal overlords. All segments of society felt the powerful influence of the Roman Catholic church. In this age of faith, hell was very real, and heresy was the gravest crime. Monks in monasteries held a virtual monopoly on learning; most people—including the nobility—were illiterate.

In the fourteenth century, an age of disintegration, Europe suffered through the Hundred Years' War (1337–1453) and the black death—or bubonic plague (around 1350)—which killed one-fourth of its population. By this time, both the feudal system and the authority of the church had been weakened. From 1378 to 1417, two rival popes claimed authority; and at one time there were three. Even devout Christians were confused. Literature of the time, such as Chaucer's *Canterbury Tales* (1387–1400) and Boccaccio's *Decameron* (after 1348), stressed graphic realism and earthly sensuality rather than virtue and heavenly rewards.

The Renaissance
(1450–1600)

The fifteenth and sixteenth centuries in Europe have come to be known as the *Renaissance*. People then spoke of a "rebirth," or *renaissance,* of human creativity. It was a period of exploration and adventure—consider the voyages of Christopher Columbus (1492), Vasco da Gama (1498), and Ferdinand Magellan (1519–1522). The Renaissance was an age of curiosity and individualism, too, as can be seen in the remarkable life of Leonardo da Vinci (1452–1519), who was a painter, sculptor, architect, engineer, and scientist—and a fine musician as well.

During the Renaissance, the Virgin Mary was depicted as a beautiful, idealized young woman. Renaissance painters emphasized balance and used perspective to create an illusion of depth. *Madonna del Granduca* (c. 1505) by Raphael.

Renaissance sculptors and painters once again depicted the nude human body, which had been an object of shame and concealment during the Middle Ages. *David* (1504) by Michelangelo.

Classical mythology was an important source of inspiration for Renaissance art. *La Primavera* (*Spring*; c. 1482) by Sandro Botticelli depicts Venus (center), the Three Graces and Mercury (left), and Flora, Spring, and Zephyrus (right).

During the Renaissance, the dominant intellectual movement, which was called **humanism,** focused on human life and its accomplishments. Humanists were not concerned with an afterlife in heaven or hell. Though devout Christians, they were captivated by the cultures of ancient Greece and Rome. They became intoxicated with the beauty of ancient languages—Greek and Latin—and with the literature of antiquity. Humanism strongly influenced art throughout the Renaissance. Painters and sculptors were attracted to subjects drawn from classical literature and mythology. Once again they depicted the nude human body, which had been a favorite theme of antiquity but an object of shame and

concealment during the Middle Ages. Medieval artists had been concerned more with religious symbolism than with lifelike representation.

They had conceived of a picture as a flat, impenetrable surface on which persons or objects were shown. Renaissance painters like Raphael (1483–1520) and Leonardo da Vinci were more interested in realism and used linear perspective, a geometrical system for creating an illusion of space and depth. During the Renaissance, painters no longer treated the Virgin Mary as a childlike, unearthly creature; they showed her as a beautiful young woman.

The Catholic church was far less powerful during the Renaissance than

it had been during the Middle Ages, for the unity of Christendom was exploded by the Protestant Reformation led by Martin Luther (1483–1546). No longer did the church monopolize learning. Aristocrats and the upper middle class now considered education a status symbol, and they hired scholars to teach their children. The invention of printing with movable type (around 1450) accelerated the spread of learning. Before 1450, books were rare and extremely expensive because they were copied entirely by hand. But by 1500, 15 million to 20 million copies of 40,000 editions had been printed in Europe.

Renaissance artists were strongly influenced by the cultures of ancient Greece and Rome.
The School of Athens (1505) by Raphael, showing the Greek philosophers Aristotle and
Plato (center). Plato is painted in the likeness of Leonardo da Vinci.

1 Music in the Middle Ages (450–1450)

Just as the cathedral dominated the medieval landscape and mind, so was it the center of musical life. Most of the important musicians were priests and worked for the church. An important occupation in thousands of monasteries was liturgical singing. Boys received music education in schools associated with churches and cathedrals. Women were not allowed to sing in church but did make music in convents. Nuns learned to sing, and some—like Hildegard of Bingen (1098–1179), abbess of Rupertsberg—wrote music for their choirs. With this preeminence of the church, it is not surprising that for centuries only sacred music was notated.

Most medieval music was vocal, though musicians also performed on a wide variety of instruments. Church officials required monks to sing with proper pronunciation, concentration, and tone quality. For example, Saint Bernard, the twelfth-century mystic and head of the abbey at Clairvaux in France, ordered his monks to sing vigorously, "pronouncing the words of the Holy Spirit with becoming manliness and resonance and affection; and correctly, that while you chant you ponder on nothing but what you chant."

The church frowned on instruments because of their earlier role in pagan rites. After about 1000, however, organs and bells became increasingly common in cathedrals and monastic churches. For three centuries or so, organs were played mainly on feast days and other special occasions. Sometimes the clergy complained about noisy organs that distracted worshippers. "Whence hath the church so many Organs," complained St. Aethelred, a twelfth-century abbot. "To what purpose, I pray you, is that terrible blowing of bellows, expressing rather the cracks of thunder than the sweetness of a Voyce." Aethelred criticized people who watched the organ as if "in a theater not a place of worship."

Today, we know relatively little about how medieval music sounded. Few medieval instruments have survived; and music manuscripts of the time do not indicate tempo, dynamics, or names of instruments. In some kinds of medieval music, the notation indicates pitch, but not rhythm. Singers and instrumentalists often appear together in pictures and in literary descriptions, but it is not certain whether polyphonic music was performed with voices alone or with voices and instruments.

Gregorian Chant

For over 1,000 years, the official music of the Roman Catholic church has been *Gregorian chant,* which consists of melody set to sacred Latin texts and sung without accompaniment. (The chant is monophonic in texture.) The melodies of Gregorian chant were meant to enhance specific parts of religious services. They set the atmosphere for prayers and ritual actions. For centuries, composers have based original compositions on chant melodies. (Since the Second Vatican Council of 1962–1965, however, most Roman Catholic services have been celebrated in the native language of each country, and so today Gregorian chant is no longer common.)

Gregorian chant conveys a calm, otherworldly quality; it represents the voice of the church, rather than that of any single individual. Its rhythm is flexible, without meter, and has little sense of beat. The exact rhythm of chant melodies is uncertain, because precise time values were not notated. But its free-flowing rhythm gives Gregorian chant a floating, almost improvisational character. The melodies tend to move by step within a narrow range of pitches. Depending on the nature and importance of the text, they are simple or elaborate; some are little more than recitations on a single tone; others contain complex melodic curves.

Gregorian chant is named after Pope Gregory I (the Great), who reorganized the Catholic liturgy during his reign from 590 to 604. Although medieval legend credits Pope Gregory with the creation of Gregorian chant, we know that it evolved over many centuries. Some of its practices, such as the singing of psalms, came from the Jewish synagogues of the first centuries after Christ. Most of the several thousand melodies known today were created between AD 600 and 1300.

At first Gregorian melodies were passed along by oral tradition, but as the number of chants grew to the thousands, they were notated to ensure musical uniformity throughout the western church. (The illustration on page 69 shows an example of medieval chant notation.) The earliest surviving chant manuscripts date from about the ninth century. The composers of Gregorian chant—like the sculptors who decorated early medieval churches—remain almost completely unknown.

Medieval monks and nuns spent several hours of each day singing Gregorian chant in two types of services: the office and the mass. Each type included both sung and spoken texts in Latin. The office consisted of eight services, the first before sunrise and the last at sunset. The **mass,** the highlight of the liturgical day, was a ritual reenactment of the Last Supper. Some texts of the mass remained the same from day to day throughout most of the church year, whereas other texts were meant only for particular feasts, such as Christmas, Epiphany, or Easter.

The Church Modes

The "otherworldly" sound of Gregorian chant results partly from the unfamiliar scales used. These scales are called **church modes** (or sometimes simply *modes*). Like major and minor scales, church modes consist of seven different tones and an eighth tone that duplicates the first an octave higher. However, their patterns of whole and half steps are different. The church modes were the basic scales of western music during the Middle Ages and Renaissance and were used in secular as well as sacred music. Much western folk music follows the patterns of the church modes. For example, the sea chantey *What Shall We Do with the Drunken Sailor?* is in a mode called *Dorian*.

Alleluia: Vidimus stellam (We Have Seen His Star)

An elaborate and jubilant Gregorian chant is the Alleluia from the Mass for Epiphany. The word *alleluia* is a Latinized form of the Hebrew *hallelujah* (*praise ye the Lord*). In this chant (shown on page 70 in medieval notation), many notes are sung to single syllables of text. The long series of tones on *ia* is a wordless expression of joy and religious ecstasy. The monophonic texture of the chant is varied by an alternation between a soloist and a choir singing in unison. The chant is in A B A form; the opening *alleluia* melody is repeated after a middle section that is set to a biblical verse.

Manuscript page with a Gregorian chant in medieval notation. The illustration within the initial R depicts the resurrection of Christ.

Vocal Music Guide

Alleluia: Vidimus stellam

A

0:00

Solo, opening melody, many tones on *ia*

Alleluia.

Hallelujah.

Choir repeats melody

Alleluia.

Hallelujah.

B

0:39

Solo, second melody

Vidimus stellam ejus in Oriente et venimus cum muneribus adorare Dominum.

We have seen his star in the east and are come with gifts to worship the Lord.

A

1:48

Choir, opening melody

Alleluia.

Hallelujah.

Medieval chant notation for *Alleluia: Vidimus stellam.*

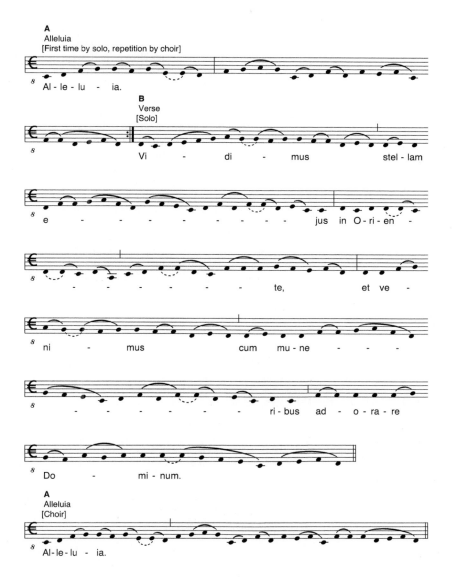

A
Alleluia
[First time by solo, repetition by choir]

Al - le - lu - ia.

B
Verse
[Solo]

Vi - di - mus stel - lam

e - - - - - - - - - jus in O - ri - en -

- - - - - - te, et ve -

ni - mus cum mu - ne - - -

- - - - - ri - bus ad - o - ra - re

Do - mi - num.

A
Alleluia
[Choir]

Al - le - lu - ia.

O successores (You successors), by Hildegard of Bingen

A late, highly expressive example of Gregorian chant is *O successores* (*You successors*) by the nun Hildegard of Bingen (1098–1179), abbess of Rupertsberg in Germany. Hildegard was one of the most creative and many-sided personalities of the Middle Ages. A visionary and mystic, she was active in religious and diplomatic affairs. She also wrote poetry and music; treatises on theology, science, and medicine; and a musical drama, *Ordo virtutum* (*Play of the Virtues*), which is the earliest known morality play. She was the first woman composer from whom a large number of works—monophonic sacred songs—have survived.

The chant *O successores* was composed to be sung by the nuns in Hildegard's convent. It is in praise of the holy confessors who are successors of Christ. (Christ is referred to as *lion* and *lamb* in the text.) Hildegard explained that the words came to her in a vision: "Then I saw the lucent sky, in which I heard different kinds of music. . . . I heard the praises of the joyous citizens of heaven, steadfastly persevering in the ways of truth."

The chant is notated in the manuscript as a single melodic line, without accompaniment. However, in our recording the performers have added a drone accompaniment. A **drone** consists of one or more long, sustained tones accompanying a melody. In *O successores,* two simultaneous sustained notes at the interval of a fifth are played on a fiddle, a medieval bowed string instrument. It may well be that such an accompaniment accords with medieval performance practice.

The melody is sung by a women's choir and is made up of several different phrases. This chant usually has one to four notes to each syllable; only at the end are many notes sung on the final syllable. The melody creates a sense of progression and growth as it moves gradually through a wide pitch range (an octave and a sixth). At first, the melody seems calm as it proceeds primarily by step within a low register. However, beginning with the word *sicut* there are several ascents to high notes and wide upward leaps of a fifth (on the words *et, vos, qui,* and *semper*). The climactic tone (on the important word *officio, service*) is reserved for the concluding phrase, which gently descends by step (on the word *agni, lamb*) to the original low register. *O successores* seems more speechlike than *Alleluia: Vidimus stellam,* where many tones are sung to single syllables of text. Hildegard's chant has a larger pitch range, more wide leaps, and a greater feeling of motion toward a climax near the end.

Vocal Music Guide

HILDEGARD OF BINGEN, *O successores*

Low register	O successores fortissimi leonis *inter templum et altare—* *dominantes in ministratione eius—*	You successors of the mightiest lion between the temple and the altar— you the masters in his household—
Melody rises and falls	*sicut angeli sonant in laudibus,* *et sicut adsunt populis in adiutorio,* *vos estis inter illos,* *qui haec faciunt,* *semper curam habentes*	as the angels sound forth praises and are here to help the nations, you are among those who accomplish this, forever showing your care
Climax on *officio,* long descent on *agni*	*in officio agni.*	in the service of the lamb.

Secular Music in the Middle Ages

Despite the predominance of Gregorian chant throughout the Middle Ages, there was also much music outside the church. The pleasures of secular music and dance were vividly evoked by the thirteenth-century theologian Henri de Malines, as he reminisced about his life as a young student in Paris. "This servant of God gladly heard music performed upon reed instruments, pipes, and every kind of musical instrument."

Henri "knew how to play a fiddle, bringing together in harmonious fashion, a melodious touching of the strings and drawing of the bow. He was familiar with and willingly sang all kinds of monophonic songs in various languages." Henri created poems and melodies and was a "merry and amorous leader . . . of dances in wooded places, arranging parties and games, and interspersing the sport of dancing with others."

The first large body of secular songs surviving in decipherable notation were composed during the twelfth and thirteenth centuries by French nobles called *troubadours* and *trouvères*. Among the best-known of these poet-musicians were the troubadour Guillaume IX, duke of Aquitaine, from southern France; and the trouvère Chastelain de Couci, from northern France. During this age of chivalry, knights gained great reputations as musical poets, as they might have done earlier by fighting bravely. Many of their love songs have been preserved because nobles had clerics write them down. These songs were usually performed by court minstrels, and most of them deal with love; but there are also songs about the Crusades, dance songs, and spinning songs. In southern France, there were women troubadours—such as Beatriz de Dia—who addressed their songs to men.

Some 1,650 troubadour and trouvère melodies have been preserved. The notation does not indicate rhythm, but it's likely that many had a regular meter with a clearly defined beat. They thus differ from the free, nonmetrical rhythm of Gregorian chant.

During the Middle Ages, wandering minstrels (or *jongleurs*—*juggler* comes from this French word) performed music and acrobatics in castles, taverns, and town squares. Minstrels had no civil rights and were on the lowest social level, with prostitutes and slaves; only a lucky few found steady work in the service of the nobility. But they were an important source of information in a time when there were no newspapers. They usually sang songs written by others and played instrumental dances on harps, fiddles (ancestors of the violin), and lutes (plucked string instruments).

Many secular songs in the Middle Ages dealt with love. The illustration shows the German poet-composer Frauenlob (c. 1255–1318) with a group of musicians.

Dances in the Middle Ages were often accompanied by instrumental music.

Selection available on:
Connect Music
Mp3 download card
Mp3 disc

Estampie (Thirteenth Century)

The *estampie,* a medieval dance, is one of the earliest surviving forms of instrumental music. In the manuscript for this **estampie,** a single melodic line is notated and, as usual, no instrument is specified. In our recording, the melody is played on a *rebec* (a bowed string instrument) and a *pipe* (a tubular wind instrument). Since medieval minstrels probably improvised modest accompaniments to dance tunes, the performers have added a drone—two simultaneous, repeated notes at the interval of a fifth, played on a *psaltery* (a plucked or struck string instrument). The estampie is in triple meter and has a strong, fast beat.

The Development of Polyphony: Organum

For centuries, western music was basically monophonic, having a single melodic line. But sometime between 700 and 900, the first steps were taken in a revolution that eventually transformed western music. Monks in monastery choirs began to add a second melodic line to Gregorian chant. In the beginning, this second line was improvised, not written down; it duplicated the chant melody at a different pitch. The two lines were in parallel motion, note against note, at the interval of a fourth or a fifth. (The interval from *do* to *fa* is a fourth; from *do* to *sol* is a fifth.)

Sit   glo   -   ri - a   Do - mi - ni   in   se - cu - la

Medieval music that consists of Gregorian chant and one or more additional melodic lines is called **organum.** Between 900 and 1200, organum became truly polyphonic, and the melody added to the chant became more independent. Instead of moving strictly parallel to the chant, it developed a melodic curve of its own. Sometimes this line was in contrary motion to the chant, moving up as the chant moved down. The second line became even more independent around 1100, when the chant and the added melody were no longer restricted to a note-against-note style. Now the two lines could differ rhythmically as well as melodically. The chant, on the bottom, was generally sung in very long notes while the added melody, on top, moved in shorter notes.

Medieval listeners must have been startled to hear religious music in which the added melody was more attractive than the chant. In fact, at times the chant tones were so slow and dronelike that the original melody was hardly recognizable. Nonetheless, the chant represented the authority of the church. And respect for the church was so great that for centuries most polyphonic music was created by placing new melodic lines against known chants.

School of Notre Dame: Measured Rhythm

After 1150, Paris—the intellectual and artistic capital of Europe—became the center of polyphonic music. The University of Paris attracted leading scholars, and the Cathedral of Notre Dame (begun in 1163) was the supreme monument of Gothic architecture. Two successive choirmasters of Notre Dame, Leonin and Perotin, are among the first notable composers known by name. They and their followers are referred to as the *school of Notre Dame.*

The Cathedral of Notre Dame in Paris.

From about 1170 to 1200, the Notre Dame composers developed rhythmic innovations. Earlier polyphonic music was probably performed in the free, unmeasured rhythms of Gregorian chant. But the music of Leonin and Perotin used *measured rhythm,* with definite time values and clearly defined meter. For the first time in music history, notation indicated precise rhythms as well as pitches. At first the new notation was limited to only certain rhythmic patterns, and the beat had to be subdivided into threes, the symbol of the Trinity. Despite these limitations, much fine polyphonic music was composed during the late twelfth century and in the thirteenth century.

Modern listeners sometimes find medieval polyphony hollow and thin, probably because it has relatively few triads, which in later periods became the basic consonant chords. The triad contains two intervals of a third; medieval music theorists considered this interval a dissonance. (An interval of a third separates *do* and *mi,* and *mi* and *sol.*) But as the Middle Ages advanced, triads and thirds were used more often, and polyphonic music gradually became fuller and richer by our standards.

Fourteenth-Century Music: The "New Art" in France

As we have seen in the opening to Part II (page 63), the fourteenth century was an age of disintegration that witnessed the Hundred Years' War, the catastrophic plague known as the black death, and a weakening of the feudal system and the Catholic church. Literary works of the fourteenth century stressed sensuality more than virtue.

Given this atmosphere, it's not surprising that secular music became more important than sacred music in the fourteenth century. Composers wrote polyphonic music that was *not* based on Gregorian chant, including drinking songs and pieces in which birdcalls, dogs' barks, and hunters' shouts were imitated.

By the early fourteenth century, a new system of music notation had evolved, and a composer could specify almost any rhythmic pattern. Now beats could be subdivided into two as well as three. Syncopation—rarely used earlier—became an important rhythmic practice. Changes in musical style in the fourteenth century were so profound that music theorists referred to Italian and French music as the **new art** (**ars nova** in Latin).

As contrasting examples of fourteenth-century music, we'll study a love song and a mass by Guillaume de Machaut, the leading French composer of the time.

Guillaume de Machaut

Guillaume de Machaut (about 1300–1377), who was famous as both a musician and a poet, was born in the French province of Champagne. He studied theology and spent much of his life in the service of various royal families. Around 1323, he became secretary and chaplain to John, king of Bohemia, whom he accompanied on trips and military campaigns throughout Europe. In his later years he lived mainly in Reims, where he served as a church official.

Machaut traveled to many courts and presented beautifully decorated copies of his music and poetry to noble patrons. These copies make Machaut one of the first important composers whose works have survived. The decline of the church in the fourteenth century is reflected in Machaut's output, which consists mainly of courtly love songs for one to four performers. We'll consider, first, one of his love songs, and then the *Notre Dame* Mass, the best-known composition of the fourteenth century.

Puis qu'en oubli sui de vous *(Since I am forgotten by you; around 1363)*

When he was about sixty, Machaut fell in love with Peronne, a beautiful young noblewoman. For several years they exchanged poems and letters, but the difference in age eventually proved too great and their relationship ended in mutual disappointment. Machaut immortalized their love in his greatest narrative poem, *Le Livre Dou Voir Dit* (*The Book of the True Poem,* 1363–1365). Along with the narrative, the *Voir Dit* contains lyric poems and letters by Machaut and Peronne as well as nine musical compositions, including the song *Puis qu'en oubli sui de vous* (*Since I am forgotten by you*).

This melancholy work expresses Machaut's "farewell to joy," because he has been forgotten by his beloved. The song consists of a vocal melody and two accompanying parts in an exceptionally low pitch range. These lower parts have no texts in the medieval manuscript, so it is not certain whether they are meant to be sung or to be played by instruments. In our recording, they are performed by two solo voices.

Puis qu'en oubli sui de vous is a **rondeau,** one of the main poetic and musical forms in fourteenth- and fifteenth-century France. The poem has eight lines, each ending with either the syllable *mis* or the syllable *mant* (see the French text in the Vocal Music Guide below). Lines 1–2 constitute the poetic refrain, which returns as lines 7–8; line 1 appears again as line 4.

The music consists of two phrases, a and b. (These phrases are indicated to the left of the French text in the Vocal Music Guide.) Phrase a is used for lines ending with *mis.* It begins with long notes, pauses in the middle, and ends with an incomplete cadence.

Phrase a

Puis qu'en ou - - bli　　sui　　de　vous, dous a -

- mis,

Phrase b is set to lines ending with *mant*. It begins with short notes, flows continuously, and ends with a complete cadence.

Phrase b

Vie　a_mou_reu_se　et　joie　　a Dieu　com _ mant.

The endings of both phrases contain syncopation, a rhythmic feature of fourteenth-century music. *Puis qu'en oubli* is a heartfelt message of courtly love.

Vocal Music Guide

MACHAUT, *Puis qu'en oubli*

a	*Puis qu'en oubli sui de vous dous amis*	Since I am forgotten by you, sweet friend,
b	*Vie amoureuse et joie a dieu commant*	I say farewell to joy and a life of love.
a	*Mar vi le jour que m'amour en vous mis*	Ill-fated was the day I placed my love in you,
a	*Puis qu'en oubli sui de vous dous amis*	Since I am forgotten by you, sweet friend.
a	*Mais ce tenray que je vous ay promis*	But what I have promised you I will maintain,
b	*C'est que jamais n'aray nul autre amant*	Which is that I shall never have any other lover.
a	*Puis qu'en oubli sui de vous dous amis*	Since I am forgotten by you, sweet friend.
b	*Via amoureuse et joie a dieu commant*	I say farewell to joy and a life of love.

Notre Dame Mass (Mid-Fourteenth Century)

Machaut's *Notre Dame* Mass, one of the finest compositions known from the Middle Ages, is also of great historical importance: it is the first polyphonic treatment of the mass ordinary by a known composer.

The ***mass ordinary*** consists of texts that remain the same from day to day throughout the church year. The five sung prayers of the ordinary are the Kyrie, Gloria, Credo, Sanctus, and Agnus Dei. Since the fourteenth century, these five texts have often been set to polyphonic music and have inspired some of the greatest choral works. (In the service, the Kyrie and Gloria were sung in succession, whereas the Credo, Sanctus, and Agnus Dei were separated by liturgical activity and by other texts sung as Gregorian chant.) In each age, composers have responded to the mass in their own particular style. This centuries-old tradition of the mass gives invaluable insight into the long span of music and its changing styles.

The *Notre Dame* Mass is written for four voice parts. How Machaut wanted his mass to be performed in unknown, but it is likely that four solo voices were employed. In our recording, the four voice parts are sung by a small group of male singers. The *Notre Dame* Mass was probably composed in the early 1360s for performance at the cathedral of Reims. We'll examine the Agnus Dei of the mass as an example of fourteenth-century polyphony.

Agnus Dei

Machaut's music for the Agnus Dei—a prayer for mercy and peace—is solemn and elaborate. It is in triple meter. Complex rhythmic patterns contribute to its intensity. The two upper parts are rhythmically active and contain syncopation, a characteristic of fourteenth-century music. The two lower parts move in longer notes and play a supporting role.

The Agnus Dei is based on a Gregorian chant, which Machaut furnished with new rhythmic patterns and placed in the tenor, one of the two lower parts. Because the chant, or cantus firmus, is rhythmically altered within a polyphonic web, it is more a musical framework than a tune to be recognized. The harmonies of the Agnus Dei include stark dissonances, hollow-sounding chords, and full triads.

Like the chant melody on which it is based, the Agnus Dei is in three sections. It may be outlined as follows:

Agnus Dei (I)	Agnus Dei (II)	Agnus Dei (III)
A	B	A

The same text appears in each section, except for a change from *miserere nobis (have mercy on us)* to *dona nobis pacem (grant us peace)* in the concluding Agnus Dei (III). A and B are similar in mood, rhythm, and texture and end with the same hollow-sounding chord. The division into three sections is thought to symbolize the Trinity. In Machaut's time, music was meant to appeal to the mind as much as to the ear.

Vocal Music Guide

MACHAUT, Agnus Dei from *Notre Dame* Mass

A	0:00	*Agnus Dei, qui tollis peccata mundi: miserere nobis.*	Lamb of God, who taketh away the sins of the world, have mercy on us.
B	1:01	*Agnus Dei, qui tollis peccata mundi: miserere nobis.*	Lamb of God, who taketh away the sins of the world, have mercy on us.
A	2:15	*Agnus Dei, qui tollis peccata mundi: dona nobis pacem.*	Lamb of God, who taketh away the sins of the world, grant us peace.

Performance Perspectives

Paul Hillier Conducting the Agnus Dei from Machaut's *Notre Dame* Mass

The distinguished choral conductor and singer Paul Hillier performs highly diverse vocal works ranging from Machaut's *Notre Dame* Mass (c. 1360) to *The Little Match Girl Passion* (2007) by the American composer David Lang. "I've always been equally interested in contemporary music as in early music," Hillier has said.

Hillier was born in 1949 in the English town of Dorchester, where he sang in the local church choir. In his early teens, he became a fan of Elvis Presley and won a dance competition doing the twist. He later studied singing and acting at the Guildhall School of Music and Drama in London, where he developed his interest in medieval and renaissance music. After graduating, Hillier became a singer at St. Paul's Cathedral and in 1973 founded the Hilliard Ensemble, an unaccompanied male vocal quartet specializing in early music. His many CDs with this and other choral ensembles have gained worldwide acclaim, and he won Grammys in 2007 and 2010. In addition to conducting and singing, he has been active as a writer and a music educator, including a decade spent teaching in California and Indiana.

The 1987 recording by the Hilliard Ensemble of Machaut's *Notre Dame* Mass uses six unaccompanied male voices (including Hillier himself). Hillier has written, "this Mass for four voices was almost certainly written to be sung by a small group of singers,

and without any instruments." He believes that the work poses special challenges for the singer: "The music is fun to sing, but also quite difficult. It needs to be sung very much in tune, and not all singers can do that! . . . The rhythms too are not very easy, especially in the top two voices which dance around with endless syncopations and flourishes. And yet the music needs to sound graceful and easy!" Hillier finds it helpful in rehearsal to have the two lower voices sung separately, without the upper parts. "The lower two voices," he writes, "are supports, like pillars in architecture; yet these also need to be phrased gracefully. . . . This is one way I rehearse the music—and it helps me to find the right tempo, one at which the lower voices make sense, even though the top voices have to go quite fast." Hillier stresses the importance of maintaining musical direction and flow. "I also enjoy the moments when all four voices come to rest just for a moment in the middle of a phrase, before setting off again in a new direction." For Hillier, the *Notre Dame* Mass "still speaks strongly to us as music. It may sound 'medieval' (whatever that means), but I think it comes across as being both strange and yet inevitable—and as fresh as if it had been composed yesterday." His performance with the Hilliard Ensemble of the *Agnus Dei* from the Mass is included on our recording sets.

2 Music in the Renaissance (1450–1600)

The Renaissance in music occurred between 1450 and 1600. (Some historians place the beginning of the Renaissance as early as 1400.) As in the other arts, the horizons of music were greatly expanded. The invention of printing widened the circulation of music too, and the number of composers and performers increased.

In keeping with the Renaissance ideal of the "universal man," every educated person was expected to be trained in music. "I am not pleased with the courtier if he be not also a musician," Castiglione wrote in *The Book of the Courtier* (1528). Shakespeare's stage directions call for music more than 300 times, and his plays are full of beautiful tributes to music:

> The man that hath no music in himself,
> Nor is not mov'd with concord of sweet sounds,
> Is fit for treasons, stratagems and spoils.
> *(The Merchant of Venice)*

As in the past, musicians worked in churches, courts, and towns. Church choirs grew in size. (The papal choir in Rome increased from ten singers in 1442 to twenty-four in 1483.) Although polyphonic church music in the Middle Ages was usually sung by several soloists, during the Renaissance it was performed by an entire (male) choir. The church remained an important patron of music, but musical activity gradually shifted to the courts. Kings, princes, and dukes competed for the finest composers. A single court might have ten to sixty musicians, including singers as well as instrumentalists. Women functioned as virtuoso singers at several Italian courts during the late Renaissance. A court music director would compose secular pieces to entertain the nobility and sacred works for the court chapel. The nobility often brought their musicians along when traveling from one castle to another.

Renaissance town musicians played for civic processions, weddings, and religious services. In general, musicians enjoyed higher status and pay than ever before. Composers were no longer content to remain unknown; like other artists, they sought credit for their work.

Many leading Renaissance composers came from the Low Countries (Flanders), an area which now includes parts of the Netherlands, Belgium, and northern France. These Flemish composers were regarded highly and held important positions throughout Europe, but especially in Italy, which became the leading music center in the sixteenth century. Other countries with a vibrant musical life in the Renaissance were Germany, England, and Spain.

Characteristics of Renaissance Music

Words and Music   In the Renaissance, as in the Middle Ages, vocal music was more important than instrumental music. The humanistic interest in language influenced vocal music, creating a close relationship between words and music. Renaissance composers wrote music to enhance the meaning and emotion of the text. "When one of the words expresses weeping, pain, heartbreak, sighs, tears and other similar things, let the harmony be full of sadness," wrote Zarlino, a music theorist of the sixteenth century. By contrast, medieval composers had been relatively uninterested in expressing the emotions of a text.

Renaissance composers often used ***word painting,*** a musical depiction of specific words. For example, the word *high* might be set to a high note, and the word *arch* might be heard with a series of notes that form the curved shape of an arch. Yet despite this emphasis on capturing the emotion and imagery of a text, Renaissance music may seem calm and restrained to us. While there *is* a wide range of emotion in Renaissance music, it is usually expressed in a moderate, balanced way, with *no* extreme contrasts of dynamics, tone color, or rhythm.

Texture   The texture of Renaissance music is chiefly polyphonic. A typical choral piece has four, five, or six voice parts of nearly equal melodic interest. Imitation among the voices is common: each presents the same melodic idea in turn, as in a round.

Homophonic texture, with successions of chords, is also used, especially in light music, like dances. The texture may vary within a piece to provide contrast and bring out aspects of the text as it develops.

Renaissance music sounds fuller than medieval music. The bass register was used for the first time, expanding the pitch range to more than four octaves. With this new emphasis on the bass line came richer harmony. Renaissance music sounds mild and relaxed, because stable, consonant chords are favored; triads occur often, while dissonances are played down.

Renaissance choral music did not need instrumental accompaniment. For this reason, the period is sometimes called the "golden age" of unaccompanied—*a cappella*—choral music. Even so, on special occasions instruments were combined with voices. Instruments might duplicate the vocal lines to reinforce the sound, or they might take the part of a missing singer. But parts written exclusively for instruments are rarely found in Renaissance choral music.

Rhythm and Melody In Renaissance music, rhythm is more a gentle flow than a sharply defined beat. This is because each melodic line has great rhythmic independence: when one singer is at the beginning of his or her melodic phrase, the others may already be in the middle of theirs. This technique makes singing Renaissance music both a pleasure and a challenge, for each singer must maintain an individual rhythm. But pitch patterns in Renaissance melodies are easy to sing. The melody usually moves along a scale with few large leaps.

Sacred Music in the Renaissance

The two main forms of sacred Renaissance music are the motet and the mass. They are alike in style, but a mass is a longer composition. The Renaissance **motet** is a polyphonic choral work set to a sacred Latin text other than the ordinary of the mass. The Renaissance **mass** is a polyphonic choral composition made up of five sections: Kyrie, Gloria, Credo, Sanctus, and Agnus Dei.

Josquin Desprez and the Renaissance Motet

Josquin Desprez (about 1440–1521), a contemporary of Leonardo da Vinci and Christopher Columbus, was a master of Renaissance music. Like many Flemish composers, he had an international career. Josquin was born in the province of Hainaut—today part of Belgium—and spent much of his life in Italy, serving in dukes' private chapels and in the papal choir at Rome. In his later years, he worked for Louis XII of France and held several church posts in his native land.

Josquin's compositions, which include masses, motets, and secular vocal pieces, strongly influenced other composers and were praised enthusiastically by music lovers. Martin Luther, for example, remarked: "God has His Gospel preached also through the medium of music; this may be seen from the compositions of Josquin, all of whose works are cheerful, gentle, mild, and lovely; they flow and move along and are neither forced nor coerced and bound by rigid and stringent rules, but, on the contrary, are like the song of the finch."

Ave Maria . . . virgo serena
(Hail, Mary . . . serene virgin; c. 1475)

Josquin's four-voice motet *Ave Maria . . . virgo serena* is an outstanding Renaissance choral work. This Latin prayer to the Virgin is set to delicate and serene music. The opening uses polyphonic imitation, a technique typical of the period.

The short melodic phrase on *Ave Maria* is presented by the soprano voice and then imitated in turn by the alto, tenor, and bass. The next two words, *gratia plena (full of grace*), have a different melody, which also is passed from voice to voice. Notice that each voice enters while the preceding one is in the middle of its melody. This overlapping creates a feeling of continuous flow. Josquin adapted the melody for the opening phrases from a Gregorian chant, but the rest of the motet was not based on a chant melody.

Josquin skillfully varies the texture of this motet; two, three, or four voices are heard at one time. In addition to the imitation among individual voices, there is imitation between pairs of voices: duets between the high voices are imitated by the two lower parts. Sometimes the texture almost becomes homophonic, as at the words *Ave, vera virginitas.* Here, also, is a change from duple to triple meter, and the tempo momentarily becomes more animated. But soon the music returns to duple meter and a more peaceful mood. *Ave Maria* ends with slow chords that express Josquin's personal plea to the Virgin: *O Mother of God, remember me. Amen.*

Vocal Music Guide

JOSQUIN, *Ave Maria . . . virgo serena*

0:00	Each soprano phrase imitated in turn by alto, tenor, and bass. Duple meter.	*Ave Maria gratia plena dominus tecum, virgo serena.*	Hail Mary, full of grace, the Lord is with thee, serene Virgin.
0:49	High duet imitated by three lower voices.	*Ave, cuius conceptio,*	Hail, whose conception,
	All four voices. Increased rhythmic animation reflects "new joy."	*solemni plena gaudio, coelestia terrestria nova replet laetitia.*	full of great jubilation, fills Heaven and Earth with new joy.

1:32	High duet imitated by low duet. Soprano phrase imitated by alto, tenor, and bass.	*Ave, cuius nativitas nostra fuit solemnitas, ut lucifer lux oriens verum solem praeveniens.*	Hail, whose birth brought us joy, as Lucifer, the morning star, went before the true sun.
2:17	High duet imitated by low duet. High duet. Low duet.	*Ave, pia humilitas, sine viro fecunditas, cuius annuntiatio nostra fuit salvatio.*	Hail, pious humility, fruitful without a man, whose Annunciation brought us salvation.
2:50	Triple meter.	*Ave, vera virginitas, immaculata castitas, cuius purificatio nostra fuit purgatio.*	Hail, true virginity, immaculate chastity, whose purification brought our cleansing.
3:16	Duple meter, high duets imitated by lower voices.	*Ave praeclara omnibus angelicis virtutibus, cuius assumptio nostra glorificatio.*	Hail, glorious one in all angelic virtues, whose Assumption was our glorification.
	Brief pause. Sustained chords.	*O mater Dei, memento mei. Amen.*	O Mother of God, remember me. Amen.

Palestrina and the Renaissance Mass

During the sixteenth century, Italian composers attained the excellence of such earlier Flemish musicians as Josquin Desprez. Among the most important Italian Renaissance composers was Giovanni Pierluigi da Palestrina (about 1525–1594), who devoted himself to music for the Catholic church. His career was thus centered in Rome, where he held important church positions, including that of music director for St. Peter's.

Palestrina's music includes 104 masses and some 450 other sacred works; it is best understood against the background of the Counter-Reformation. During the early 1500s, the Catholic church was challenged and questioned by the Protestants and, as a result, sought to correct abuses and malpractices within its structure, as well as to counter the move toward Protestantism. This need to strengthen the church led to the founding of the Jesuit order (1540) and the convening of the Council of Trent (1545–1563), which considered questions of dogma and organization.

During its deliberations, the council discussed church music, which many felt had lost its purity. Years before, the scholar Desiderius Erasmus (about 1466–1536) had complained: "We have introduced an artificial and theatrical music into the church, a bawling and agitation of various voices, such as I believe had never been heard in the theaters of the Greeks and Romans. . . . Amorous and lascivious melodies are heard such as elsewhere accompany only the dances of courtesans and clowns." At the council sessions, church music was attacked because it used secular tunes, noisy instruments, and theatrical singing. Some complained that complex polyphony made it impossible to understand the sacred texts; they wanted only monophonic music—Gregorian chant—for the mass. The council finally decreed that church music should be composed not "to give empty pleasure to the ear," but to inspire religious contemplation.

The restraint and serenity of Palestrina's works reflect this emphasis on a more spiritual music. For centuries, church authorities have regarded his masses as models of church music because of their calmness and otherworldly quality. Even today, the technical perfection of his style is a model for students of counterpoint.

A miniature showing a mass at the court of Philip the Good in Burgundy.

Pope Marcellus Mass (1562–1563)

Palestrina's *Pope Marcellus* Mass, his most famous mass, was long thought to have convinced the Council of Trent that polyphonic masses should be kept in Catholic worship. While we now know that this work did *not* play that role, it does reflect the council's desire for a clear projection of the sacred text. It is dedicated to Pope Marcellus II, who reigned briefly in 1555 while Palestrina was a singer in the papal choir.

The *Pope Marcellus* Mass is written for an a cappella choir of six voice parts: soprano, alto, two tenors, and two basses. We'll focus on the first section of the mass, the Kyrie.

Kyrie

The Kyrie has a rich polyphonic texture. Its six voice parts constantly imitate each other, yet blend beautifully. This music sounds fuller than Josquin's *Ave Maria*, in part because six voices are used rather than four. The elegantly curved melodies summon the spirit of Gregorian chant. They flow smoothly and can be sung easily. Upward leaps are balanced at once by downward steps, as in the opening melody:

Soprano

Ky - rie e - lei - - - - - son,

The Kyrie of the *Pope Marcellus* Mass is written in three different sections:

1. *Kyrie eleison.*   Lord, have mercy.
2. *Christe eleison.*   Christ, have mercy.
3. *Kyrie eleison.*   Lord, have mercy.

This text is short, and words are repeated with different melodic lines to express calm supplication. The rhythm flows continuously to the end of each section, when all voices come together on sustained chords. Each of the three sections begins in a thin texture with only some of the voices sounding; but as the other voices enter, the music becomes increasingly full and rich. In our recording, the third section sounds climactic because it is performed in a somewhat faster tempo and at a louder dynamic level than the first two sections.

Vocal Music Guide

PALESTRINA, Kyrie from *Pope Marcellus* Mass

0:00	Tenor quickly imitated in turn by three other voice parts; remaining two voice parts join. Voices imitate each other and repeat words. Sustained chord, pause end section.	1. *Kyrie eleison.*	Lord, have mercy.
1:35	Three voice parts begin at same time; other three voice parts join in turn. Voices imitate each other. Sustained chord, pause.	2. *Christe eleison.*	Christ, have mercy.
3:29	Soprano phrase quickly imitated in turn by three lower voice parts; two other voice parts join. Voices imitate each other.	3. *Kyrie eleison.*	Lord, have mercy.
4:35	Sustained chord ends *Kyrie.*		

Secular Music in the Renaissance

Vocal Music

During the Renaissance, secular vocal music became increasingly popular. Throughout Europe, music was set to poems in various languages, including Italian, French, Spanish, German, Dutch, and English.

The development of music printing helped spread secular music, and thousands of song collections became available. Music was an important leisure activity; every educated person was expected to play an instrument and read notation. The Elizabethan composer Thomas Morley describes the embarrassment of being unable to participate in after-dinner music making: "But supper being ended, and Musicke bookes (according to the custome) being brought to the tables, the mistresse of the house presented me with a part, earnestly requesting me to sing. But when, after many excuses, I protested unfainedly that I could not: every one began to wonder. Yea, some whispered to others, demanding how I was brought up."

Renaissance secular music was written for groups of solo voices and for solo voice with the accompaniment of one or more instruments. Word painting—musical illustration of a text—was common. Composers delighted in imitating natural sounds such as birdcalls and street cries. In a famous piece entitled *La Guerre* (*The War*), the Frenchman Clément Janequin (about 1485–1560) vividly imitated battle noises, drumbeats, and fanfares. Secular music contained more rapid shifts of mood than sacred music. As Morley advised one composer, "You must in your music be wavering like the wind, sometimes wanton, sometimes drooping, sometimes grave and staid; . . . and the more variety you show the better shall you please."

An important kind of secular vocal music during the Renaissance was the **madrigal,** a piece for several solo voices set to a short poem, usually about love. A madrigal, like a motet, combines homophonic and polyphonic textures. But the madrigal uses word painting and unusual harmonies more often.

The Renaissance madrigal originated in Italy around 1520, during a creative explosion in Italian poetry. Madrigals were published by the thousands in sixteenth-century Italy, where they were sung by cultivated aristocrats. Among the many Italian madrigalists were Luca Marenzio (1553–1599) and Carlo Gesualdo (about 1560–1613), the infamous prince of Venosa who had his wife and her lover murdered after finding them together in bed.

In 1588—the year of the defeat of the Spanish Armada—a volume of translated Italian madrigals was published in London. This inspired a spurt of madrigal writing by English composers, and for about thirty years there was a steady flow of English madrigals and other secular vocal music. The time of Queen Elizabeth I (1533–1603) and William Shakespeare (1564–1616) was as much a golden age in English music as it was in English literature. The impetus for both arts arose in Italy. But the English madrigal became lighter and more humorous than its Italian model, and its melody and harmony were simpler.

As Vesta Was Descending (1601), by Thomas Weelkes

Among the finest English madrigalists was Thomas Weelkes (about 1575–1623), an organist and church composer. Weelkes's *As Vesta Was Descending* comes from *The Triumphes of Oriana* (1601), an anthology of English madrigals written to honor Queen Elizabeth, who was often called Oriana. The text of this six-voice madrigal pictures Vesta (the Roman goddess of the hearth) coming down a hill with her attendants, "Diana's darlings." (Diana was the Roman goddess of chastity, hunting, and the moon.) At the same time, the "maiden queen," Oriana (Elizabeth), is climbing the hill with her shepherd gallants. Vesta's attendants desert her and race down the hill to join Oriana.

As Vesta Was Descending has the light mood typical of English madrigals. Word painting is plentiful. For example, the word *descending* is sung to downward scales, and *ascending* to upward ones.

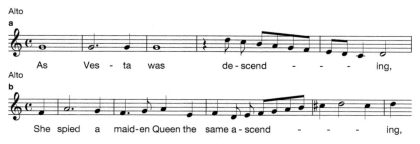

When Vesta's attendants run down the hill, "first *two* by *two*, then *three* by *three together*, leaving their goddess all *alone*," we hear first *two* voices, then *three* voices, then *six* voices, and finally a *solo* voice. In the extended concluding section, "*Long* live fair Oriana," a joyous phrase is imitated among the voices. And in the bass this phrase is sung in long notes, with the longest note on the word *long*.

Vocal Music Guide

WEELKES, *As Vesta Was Descending*

Descending scales.	As Vesta was from Latmos hill *descending*,
Ascending scales.	she spied a maiden queen the same *ascending*,
Rapid descending figures.	attended on by all the shepherds swain, to whom Diana's darlings came *running down* amain.
Two voices,	First *two* by *two*,
Three voices; all voices.	then *three* by *three together*,
Solo voice.	leaving their goddess *all alone*, hasted thither, and mingling with the shepherds of her train with mirthful tunes her presence entertain. Then sang the shepherds and nymphs of Diana,
Brief joyful phrase imitated among voices; long notes in bass.	*Long* live fair Oriana!

The Renaissance Lute Song

A simpler type of secular music than the madrigal is the song for solo voice and lute. The **lute,** which derives from the Arab instrument known as the *'ūd* (literally, *the wood*), is a plucked string instrument with a body shaped like half a pear. The lute's versatility—like that of the guitar today—made it the most popular instrument in the Renaissance home. It could be used for solos or for accompaniments; to play chords, melodies, and rapid scales; and even in polyphonic music.

In England the lute song was widely cultivated from the late 1590s to the 1620s. In contrast to much Renaissance music, lute songs are mostly homophonic in texture.

The lute accompaniment is secondary to the vocal melody. During the Renaissance, singers could accompany themselves, or have the lute accompaniment played by another musician.

Flow My Tears (about 1600), by John Dowland (1563–1626)

The leading English composer of lute songs was John Dowland, a virtuoso performer on the lute famous throughout Europe. His lute song *Flow My Tears* was extraordinarily popular in Shakespeare's time, and in our own day it has been recorded by many singers, including the rock star Sting.

Flow My Tears expresses the intense melancholy of someone whose happiness has been abruptly shattered. Such emotionally charged words as *tears, despair, woes, sighs, groans, fear,* and *grief* dominate the song's text, a poem that may have been written by Dowland himself. The expression of melancholy was a prominent feature of English literature and music in the time of Elizabeth I and Shakespeare. Dowland, especially, seems to have cultivated a melancholy public image, and he composed many pieces with sad titles such as *Semper Dowland semper dolens* (*Always Dowland, Always Sorrow*).

Flow My Tears consists of three brief musical sections (A, B, C) that are each immediately repeated: AA (stanzas 1 and 2), BB (stanzas 3 and 4), CC (stanza 5 repeated to the same melody). Dowland's music heightens the mood of grief through its slow tempo, minor key, and descending four-note melodic pattern that represents falling tears. This descending pattern appears throughout the song with variations of pitch and rhythm.

The opening four-note descent, in minor, on *Flow my tears,* is immediately repeated—with greater emotional intensity—on higher, slower notes to the words *fall from your springs.*

Part B begins with a contrasting major-key version of the four-note descent on the words *Never may my.*

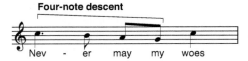

Dowland creates variety by opening part C with a stepwise *ascent,* turning the four-note pattern upside down on the words *Hark you shadows.*

In much of the song, the lute accompaniment is subordinate to the voice. However, in part B, the lute momentarily gains prominence as it imitates the voice's gasping upward skips on *and tears, and sighs,* heightening the agitated mood.

As Sting has observed, even though *Flow My Tears* is "a song about hopelessness, it is strangely uplifting."

Vocal Music Guide

DOWLAND, *Flow My Tears*

0:00	**A**	Minor key.	Flow my tears, fall from your springs, 　　Exiled for ever: Let me mourn where night's black bird her sad infamy sings, 　　there let me live forlorn.
0:38	**A**	Minor.	Down vain lights, shine you no more, 　　No nights are dark enough for those That in despair their lost fortunes deplore, 　　light doth but shame disclose.
1:18	**B**	Major. Minor. Lute imitates voice.	Never may my woes be relieved, 　　since pity is fled, and tears, and sighs, and groans my weary days, 　　of all joys have deprived.
1:55	**B**	Major. Minor. Lute imitates voice.	From the highest spire of contentment, 　　my fortune is thrown; and fear, and grief, and pain for my deserts, 　　are my hopes since hope is gone.
2:31	**C**	Minor.	Hark you shadows that in darkness dwell, 　　learn to condemn light, Happy, happy they that in hell 　　feel not the world's despite.
3:13	**C**	Minor.	Hark you shadows that in darkness dwell, 　　learn to condemn light, Happy, happy they that in hell 　　feel not the world's despite.

Instrumental Music

Though still subordinate to vocal music, instrumental music did become more important during the Renaissance. Traditionally, instrumentalists accompanied voices or played music intended for singing. Even in the early 1500s instrumental music was largely adapted from vocal music. Instrumental groups performed polyphonic vocal pieces, which were often published with the indication *to be sung or played*. Soloists used the harpsichord, organ, or lute to play simple arrangements of vocal works.

During the sixteenth century, however, instrumental music became increasingly emancipated from vocal models. More music was written specifically for instruments. Renaissance composers began to exploit the particular capacities of the lute or organ for instrumental solos. They also developed purely instrumental forms, such as theme and variations.

A wide variety of instruments were used during the Renaissance. Hans Burgkmair's woodcut of the emperor Maximilian with his musicians (1505–1516) shows (left) an organ and a cornett; (center) a harp; (on floor) a drum, a kettledrum, a trumsheit (string instrument), and a sackbut; (on table) a viola da gamba, an oblong keyboard instrument, a flute, recorders, a cornett, and a krummhorn.

Much of this instrumental music was intended for dancing, a popular Renaissance entertainment. Every cultivated person was expected to be skilled in dance, which was taught by professional dancing masters. Court dances were often performed in pairs. A favorite pair was the stately *pavane,* or *passamezzo,* in duple meter, and the lively *galliard,* in triple meter. Dance music was performed by instrumental groups or by soloists like harpsichordists and lutenists. A wealth of dance music published during the sixteenth century has come down to us.

Renaissance musicians distinguished between loud, outdoor instruments like the trumpet and the *shawm* (a double-reed ancestor of the oboe), and soft, indoor instruments like the lute and the *recorder* (an early flute). The many instruments used in the Renaissance produced softer, less brilliant sounds than we hear from instruments today; most came in families of from three to eight instruments, ranging from soprano to bass. Among the most important Renaissance instruments were recorders, shawms, *cornetts* (wooden instruments with cup-shaped mouthpieces), *sackbuts* (early trombones), lutes, *viols* (bowed string instruments), organs, *regals* (small organs with reed pipes), and harpsichords. Often several members of the same instrumental family were played together, but Renaissance composers did not specify the instruments they wanted. A single work might be performed by recorders, viols, or several different

Much instrumental music of the Renaissance was intended for dancing. This illustration is from a book of hours produced in Tours, France, c. 1530–1535.

instruments, depending on what was available. Today's standardized orchestra did not exist. Large courts might employ thirty instrumentalists of all types. On state occasions such as a royal wedding, guests might be entertained by woodwinds, plucked and bowed strings, and keyboard instruments all playing together.

Selection available on:
Connect Music
Mp3 download card
Mp3 disc

Passamezzo and Galliard, by Pierre Francisque Caroubel, from *Terpsichore* (1612), by Michael Praetorius

This passamezzo and galliard illustrate the Renaissance practice of pairing contrasting court dances in duple and triple meter. These dances come from *Terpsichore,* a collection of over 300 dance tunes arranged for instrumental ensemble by Michael Praetorius (1571–1621), a German composer and theorist. (Terpsichore was the Greek muse, or goddess, of the dance.) A few dances in the collection, including the passamezzo and galliard studied here, were composed by the French violinist Pierre Francisque Caroubel (1576–1611). Both dance types originated in Italy and were popular during the sixteenth century and the early seventeenth century.

The passamezzo is a stately dance in duple meter and the galliard is a quick dance in triple meter. The dance-pair studied here is written for five unspecified instrumental parts. In our recording the two dances are performed by a Renaissance string ensemble including violins, violas, and bass violins (ancestors of the cello), lutes, and harpsichord. Both the passamezzo and galliard are made up of three brief sections (a, b, c). The two dances can be outlined as follows:

Passamezzo: aa bb cc abc
Galliard: aa bb cc

The music of the galliard is a variation of the preceding passamezzo, but sounds very different because its tempo is faster and its meter is triple rather than duple.

Passamezzo, section a

Galliard, section a

In each dance, section b brings greater rhythmic animation. Section b of the passamezzo introduces quicker note values (eighth notes).

Section b of the galliard brings delightful rhythmic irregularity because $\frac{6}{4}$ meter alternates with the prevailing $\frac{3}{2}$ meter. That is, six fast pulses divide alternatively into *two* groups of three pulses (1-2-3 4-5-6) and *three* groups of two pulses (**1**-2 *3*-4 *5*-6).

A similar alternation can be heard in *America,* from Leonard Bernstein's *West Side Story,* studied in Part VI, "The Twentieth Century and Beyond," in Section 20, "Music for Stage and Screen."

The Middle Ages and Renaissance: Summary

IMPORTANT TERMS

Renaissance, p. 64
Humanism, p. 65
Church modes, p. 68
Drone, p. 72
Ars nova ("new art"), p. 76
Mass ordinary, p. 77
Word painting, p. 80
A cappella, p. 81
Lute, p. 87

FEATURED GENRES

Gregorian chant, p. 67
Estampie, p. 74
Organum, p. 74
Rondeau, p. 76
Motet, p. 81
Mass, p. 81
Madrigal, p. 86
Lute song, p. 87
Instrumental music, p. 89

FEATURED COMPOSERS

Hildegard of Bingen
  (1098–1179)
Guillaume de Machaut
  (1300–1377)
Josquin Desprez (about
  1440–1521)
Giovanni Pierluigi da Palestrina
  (about 1525–1594)
Thomas Weelkes (1575–1623)
John Dowland (1563–1626)
Pierre Francisque Caroubel
  (1576–1611)

Music in Society—Middle Ages

- Musicians worked for churches, courts, and towns.
- Churches and cathedrals were the center of musical life and education during the Middle Ages.
- Vocal music was more important than instrumental music.
- Women were not permitted to sing in church, but they could make music in convents, where they also could receive musical training.
- Secular music and dance flourished.

Important Style Features—Middle Ages

Mood and Emotional Expression
- Gregorian chant conveys a calm, otherworldly, spiritual quality.
- Medieval composers were relatively uninterested in expressing the emotions of a text.

Rhythm
- Gregorian chant rhythm is flexible, without meter, and has little sense of beat; as a result, the music has a floating quality.
- Notre Dame composers developed the first instances of western notation that indicated specific pitches as well as measured rhythms with definite time values.
- Dances have a regular, clearly defined beat.
- In ars nova, the beat could be subdivided into two as well as three, and syncopation became an important rhythmic practice.

Tone Color
- Occasionally vocal or instrumental music will be accompanied by a drone.

Melody and Harmony
- For centuries, medieval composers based original compositions on chant melodies.
- Chant melodies of the Middle Ages often move by step within a narrow range.
- Medieval music theorists considered the interval of a third a dissonance; thus, the music occasionally can sound hollow to us.
- Music is based on church modes rather than major and minor scales.

Texture
- For hundreds of years, western music was basically monophonic.
- Sometime between 700 and 900 CE, a second line of music was added to Gregorian chant, creating organum.
- Starting around 1200, composers wrote polyphonic music in three- and four-voice parts.

Performance Practice

- We know very little about how medieval music sounded and how it was performed.
- Music manuscripts do not indicate tempo, dynamics, or names of instruments.
- Much music was passed down for generations through oral tradition and memorization because music notation was either nonexistent or primitive.

Music in Society—Renaissance

- Musical patronage gradually shifted from the church to the courts.
- Music was an important leisure activity, and every educated person was expected to be trained in music.
- As in the Middle Ages, vocal music was more important than instrumental music; however, instrumental music increased in importance.
- The invention of printing during the Renaissance widened the circulation of music.
- Secular music and dance continued to flourish.

Important Style Features—Renaissance

Mood and Emotional Expression
- Renaissance composers wrote vocal music to enhance the meaning and emotion of a text.
- Renaissance madrigals express a wide range of emotions and imagery through word painting.
- Secular music contains more rapid shifts of mood than sacred music.

Rhythm
- Rhythm is more of a gentle flow than a sharply defined beat, particularly in a cappella choral music. Each line of music has great rhythmic independence.
- Secular music, both vocal and instrumental, usually has a more clearly defined beat.

Tone Color
- In Renaissance music, instruments may or may not accompany vocal music by doubling one or more of the parts.

Melody and Harmony
- Compared with music of the Middle Ages, Renaissance music sounds mild and relaxed because stable, consonant triads occur frequently and are favored over dissonances.
- Melodies usually move stepwise along a scale, with few large leaps.
- The bass register was used for the first time, resulting in a fuller sound and richer harmonies.
- In Renaissance vocal music especially, each melodic line has great independence; phrases often overlap to create a seamless flow of sound among the parts.

Texture
- The main texture of Renaissance vocal music is polyphonic, with a typical choral piece having four to six different parts of nearly equal melodic interest.
- Imitation among voices is common, particularly in a cappella choral music.
- Homophonic texture is also used, especially in light music, like dances.
- Secular music written for solo voices and for solo voice with accompaniment of one or more instruments was popular.

Performance Practice
- Sacred choral music was sung by an a cappella male choir; women were excluded from participating in liturgical services, although nuns could perform music in convents.
- In courts, the number of musicians could be from ten to as many as sixty, and women functioned as virtuoso singers in several Italian courts during the late Renaissance.
- Renaissance music does not indicate tempos and dynamics, or the specific instruments or number of performers on a part.

Beyond the Classroom: Listening to Medieval and Renaissance Music

Over the past several years, recorded performances of Gregorian chant and other music of medieval composers have attracted great interest throughout the world, posting record-breaking sales of CDs and Internet downloads. A variety of speculation exists over why this music would become so popular all of a sudden; however, one reason may be that the calm, spiritual quality of the music soothes the nerves of a world caught up by the frenetic pace of modern day life.

The Renaissance period produced music, both sacred and secular, that modern audiences and performers find enjoyable. Renaissance fairs, at which one can hear music by performers who wear period clothing and use authentic instruments are held in many communities throughout the year. Watch plays by Shakespeare and his contemporaries to observe how they often include songs and dance music. Madrigal dinners, in which entertainers dress in period clothing and perform Renaissance madrigals, secular songs, and instrumental pieces, are especially popular during the Christmas season. And the sacred a cappella choral works of Palestrina and his contemporaries are among the most glorious music produced in any era.

When listening to music from the Middle Ages or the Renaissance at a concert or on a recording, ask yourself these questions:

- What are the performing forces? Only voices, only instruments, or a combination of the two?
- What is the texture of the music? Do you notice the use of a drone?
- How would you characterize the rhythm? Does it seem to float, or flow smoothly, or is there a clearly defined beat?
- If the music has more than one part, do you hear instances of imitation between the parts, particularly in choral music?
- In vocal music, is the text sacred or secular? In what language is it sung? Are there instances of word painting that enhance the meaning of the text?
- For instrumental music, what instruments are performing? What do the instruments look like? What kinds of sounds do they produce?
- Are the performers dressed in clothing of the period? Are there any dancers?

■ Baroque vocal music was often composed for ceremonial occasions and meant to flatter the aristocracy. *The Celebration of the Marriage of the Dauphin of France at the Teatro Argentina in Rome* (1747), by the Italian painter Giovanni Paolo Panini.

PART III

The figured bass is the most perfect foundation of music, being played with both hands in such a manner that the left hand plays the notes written down while the right adds consonances and dissonances, in order to make a well-sounding harmony to the Glory of God and the permissible delectation of the spirit.

—Johann Sebastian Bach

LEARNING OBJECTIVES

- Identify key features of the late baroque style in music
- Explain how composers were an integral part of baroque society
- Discuss baroque concerto grosso and ritornello form
- Describe the main elements of a fugue
- List the special characteristics of opera, and opera of the baroque period
- Enumerate the features of a baroque suite
- Discuss the chorale and church cantata during the baroque era
- Compare and contrast baroque opera and baroque oratorio

The Baroque Period

TIME LINE

Baroque Period 1600–1750

1600–1680	1680–1750

Historical and Cultural Events

1607 Jamestown founded

1610 Galileo confirms that the earth revolves around the sun

1611 King James Bible

1618–1648 Thirty Years' War

1643–1715 Louis XIV reigns in France

1687 Newton, *Principia Mathematica*

1692 Witchcraft trials in Salem, Massachusetts

1715–1774 Louis XV reigns in France

1740–1786 Frederick the Great reigns in Prussia

Arts and Letters

1600 Shakespeare, *Hamlet*

1605 Cervantes, *Don Quixote*

1612–1615 Rubens, *Descent from the Cross*

1613 Gentileschi, *Judith Slaying Holofernes*

1623 Bernini, *David Slaying Goliath*

1630 Poussin, *Mars and Venus*

1659 Rembrandt, *Self-Portrait*

1667 Milton, *Paradise Lost*

1689 Locke, *Essay Concerning Human Understanding*

1717 Watteau, *The Embarkation for Cythera*

1719 Defoe, *Robinson Crusoe*

1726 Swift, *Gulliver's Travels*

Music

1607 Monteverdi, *Orfeo*

1642 Monteverdi, *The Coronation of Poppea*

1689 Purcell, *Dido and Aeneas*

1689 Corelli, Trio Sonata in A Minor, Op. 3, No. 10

c. 1709 Bach, Organ Fugue in G Minor (*Little Fugue*)

c. 1721 Bach, *Brandenburg* Concerto No. 5 in D Major

1725 Vivaldi, *La Primavera* (*Spring*), Concerto for Violin and Orchestra, Op. 8, No. 1

1731 Bach, Cantata No. 140: *Wachet auf, ruft uns die Stimme*

1741 Handel, *Messiah*

The Baroque Style (1600–1750)

Though the word *baroque* has at various times meant bizarre, flamboyant, and elaborately ornamented, modern historians use it simply to indicate a particular style in the arts. An oversimplified but useful characterization of baroque style is that it fills space—canvas, stone, or sound—with action and movement. Painters, sculptors, and architects became interested in forming a total illusion, like a stage setting. Artists such as Caravaggio, Gentileschi, Bernini, Rubens, and Rembrandt exploited their materials to expand the dramatic potential of color, depth, and contrasts of light and dark; they wanted to create totally structured worlds.

Such a style was very well suited to the wishes of the aristocracy, who also thought in terms of completely integrated structures. In France, for example, Louis XIV held court in the palace of Versailles, a magnificent setting that fused baroque painting, sculpture, architecture, and garden design into a symbol of royal wealth and power.

The aristocracy was enormously rich and powerful during the seventeenth and eighteenth centuries. While most of the population barely managed to survive, European rulers surrounded themselves with luxury. There were many such rulers. Germany, for example, was divided into about 300 territories, each governed separately.

Judith Slaying Holofernes (c. 1612–1613) by the Italian painter Artemisia Gentileschi (1593–1652). Baroque artists emphasized motion and drama.

Bernini's *David Slaying Goliath* (1623) fills space with action and movement. It is far more dynamic than Michelangelo's *David* shown on page 64.

Kings and princes proclaimed their greatness by means of splendid palaces and magnificent court entertainments like balls, banquets, ballets, operas, and plays. Indeed, entertainment was a necessity; most courtiers did no real work and tried to avoid boredom as much as possible.

The baroque period (1600–1750) is also known as the "age of absolutism" because many rulers exercised absolute power over their subjects. In Germany, for example, the duke of Weimar could throw his court musician Johann Sebastian Bach into jail for a month because Bach stubbornly asked to leave his job.

Along with the aristocracy, religious institutions powerfully shaped the baroque style. Churches used the emotional and theatrical qualities of art to make worship more attractive and appealing. During the baroque period, Europe was divided into Catholic and Protestant areas: France, Spain, Italy, and the Austrian empire were primarily Catholic; England, Holland, Denmark, Sweden, and parts of Germany were Protestant.

The middle class, too, influenced the development of the baroque style. In the Netherlands, for example, prosperous merchants and doctors commissioned realistic landscapes and scenes from everyday life.

It is also helpful to think of baroque style against the backdrop of scientific discoveries during the seventeenth and eighteenth centuries. The work of Galileo (1564–1642) and Newton (1642–1727) represented a new approach to science based on the union of mathematics and experiment; they discovered mathematical laws governing bodies in motion. Such scientific advances led to new inventions and the gradual improvement of medicine, mining, navigation, and industry during the baroque era.

Mars and Venus (c. 1630) by the French painter Nicholas Poussin. The subject matter, harmonious colors, and balanced composition reflect Poussin's love of classical antiquity and Renaissance art.

The Flemish painter Peter Paul Rubens used diagonal motion and theatrical lighting in *Descent from the Cross* (1612–1615). Baroque artists became interested in forming a total illusion, like a stage setting. Often baroque painting and baroque opera were created for the nobility and were designed to display magnificent extravagance.

Self-Portrait (1659) by Rembrandt van Rijn. Rembrandt's use of light and dark contributes to the poetry, drama, and psychological truth of his portraits.

The palace of Versailles, in France, fused baroque architecture, sculpture, and painting into a symbol of royal wealth and power.

1 Baroque Music (1600–1750)

In music, the baroque style flourished during the period from 1600 to 1750. The two giants of baroque composition were George Frideric Handel and Johann Sebastian Bach. Bach's death in 1750 marks the end of the period. Other baroque masters—Claudio Monteverdi, Henry Purcell, Arcangelo Corelli, Antonio Vivaldi—were largely forgotten until the twentieth century. But the appearance of long-playing records in the late 1940s spurred a "baroque revival" that made these musicians familiar to many music lovers.

The baroque period can be divided into three phases: early (1600–1640), middle (1640–1690), and late (1690–1750). Though the baroque music best known today comes from the latest phase, the earliest was one of the most revolutionary periods in music history. Monteverdi (1567–1643), for instance, strove to create unprecedented passion and dramatic contrast in his works. In Italy, especially, music was composed for texts conveying extreme emotion, and the text ruled the music. With this stress on drama and text, it is not surprising that Italian composers of the early baroque created opera—a drama sung to orchestral accompaniment. Their melodic lines imitated the rhythms and inflections of speech.

Early baroque composers favored homophonic texture over the polyphonic texture typical of Renaissance music. They felt that words could be projected more clearly by using just one main melody with a chordal accompaniment. But note that this new emphasis on homophonic texture characterizes only the *early* baroque; by the *late* baroque period, polyphonic texture returned to favor.

To depict extreme emotions in their texts, early baroque composers used dissonance with a new freedom. Never before were unstable chords so prominent and emphatic. Contrasts of sound were stressed—one or more solo singers against a chorus, or voices against instruments. In Renaissance choral music, instruments—if used at all—duplicated a singer's melody. But in the early baroque, voices were accompanied by melodic lines designed for instruments.

During the middle phase of the baroque (1640–1690), the new musical style spread from Italy to practically every country in Europe. The medieval or church modes—scales that had governed music for centuries—gradually gave way to major and minor scales. By about 1690, major or minor scales were the tonal basis of most compositions. Another feature of the middle baroque phase was the new importance of instrumental music. Many compositions were written for specific instruments, the violin family being most popular.

We focus mainly on the late baroque period (1690–1750), which produced most of the baroque music heard today. Many aspects of harmony—including an emphasis on the attraction of the dominant chord to the tonic—arose in this period. During the late baroque, instrumental music became as important as vocal music for the first time. Early baroque composers had emphasized homophonic texture; late baroque composers gloried in polyphony. Let's look more closely at some features of late baroque style. (From now on the word *baroque* will pertain to the late baroque phase.)

Characteristics of Baroque Music

Unity of Mood A baroque piece usually expresses one basic mood: what begins joyfully will remain joyful throughout. Emotional states like joy, grief, and agitation were represented—at the time, these moods were called **affections.** Composers molded a musical language to depict the affections; specific rhythms or melodic patterns were associated with specific moods. This common language gives a family resemblance to much late baroque music.

The prime exception to this baroque principle of unity of mood occurs in vocal music. Striking changes of emotion in a text may inspire corresponding changes in the music. But even in such cases, one mood is maintained at some length before it yields to another.

Rhythm   Unity of mood in baroque music is conveyed, first of all, by continuity of rhythm. Rhythmic patterns heard at the beginning of a piece are repeated throughout it. This rhythmic continuity provides a compelling drive and energy—the forward motion is rarely interrupted. The beat, for example, is emphasized far more in baroque music than in most Renaissance music.

Melody   Baroque melody also creates a feeling of continuity. An opening melody will be heard again and again in the course of a baroque piece. And even when a melody is presented in varied form, its character tends to remain constant. There is a continuous expanding, unfolding, and unwinding of melody. This sense of directed motion is frequently the result of a melodic sequence, that is, successive repetition of a musical idea at higher or lower pitches. Many baroque melodies sound elaborate and ornamental, and they are not easy to sing or remember. A baroque melody gives an impression of dynamic expansion rather than of balance or symmetry. A short opening phrase is often followed by a longer phrase with an unbroken flow of rapid notes.

Dynamics   Paralleling continuity of rhythm and melody in baroque music is continuity of dynamics: the level of volume tends to stay fairly constant for a stretch of time. When the dynamics do shift, the shift is sudden, like physically stepping from one level to another. This alternation between loud and soft is called *terraced dynamics.* *Gradual* changes through crescendo and decrescendo are *not* prominent features of baroque music. However, singers and instrumentalists no doubt made some subtle dynamic inflections for expressive purposes.

The main keyboard instruments of the baroque period were the organ and harpsichord, both well suited for continuity of dynamics. An organist or harpsichordist could not obtain a crescendo or decrescendo by varying finger pressure, as can pianists today. A third keyboard instrument, the *clavichord,* could make gradual dynamic changes, but only within a narrow range—from about *ppp* to *mp*. (The clavichord produced sound by means of brass blades striking the strings. It was usually not used in large halls because its tone was too weak. But for home use by amateurs it was ideal; its cost was low and its expressive sound satisfying. It had especially wide popularity in Germany.)

Texture   We've noted that late baroque music is predominantly polyphonic in texture: two or more melodic lines compete for the listener's attention. Usually, the soprano and bass lines are the most important. Imitation between the various lines, or "voices," of the texture is very common. A melodic idea heard in one voice is likely to make an appearance in the other voices as well.

However, not all late baroque music was polyphonic. A piece might shift in texture, especially in vocal music, where changes of mood in the words demand musical contrast. Also, baroque composers differed in their treatment of musical texture. Bach inclined toward a consistently polyphonic texture, whereas Handel used much more contrast between polyphonic and homophonic sections.

Chords and the Basso Continuo   Chords became increasingly important during the baroque period. In earlier times, there was more concern with the beauty of individual melodic lines than with chords formed when the lines were heard together. In a sense, chords were mere by-products of the motion of melodic lines. But in the baroque period chords became significant in themselves. As composers wrote a melodic line, they thought of chords to mesh with it. Indeed, sometimes they composed a melody to fit a specific chord progression. This interest in chords gave new prominence to the bass part, which served as the foundation of the harmony. The whole musical structure rested on the bass part.

The new emphasis on chords and the bass part resulted in the most characteristic feature of baroque music, an accompaniment called the **basso continuo** (Italian for *continuous bass*). The *continuo*—to use the common abbreviation for basso continuo— is usually played by at least two instruments: a keyboard instrument like an organ or a harpsichord and a low melodic instrument like a cello or bassoon. With the left hand the organist or harpsichordist plays the bass part, which is also performed by the cellist or bassoonist. With the right hand the keyboard player improvises chords following the indications of numbers (figures) above the bass part. This bass part with numbers (figures) is called a **figured bass.** The numbers specify only basic chords, not the exact way in which the chords should be played. Thus the performer is given a great deal of freedom. (This shorthand system is similar in principle to the chord indications found on the modern song sheets from which jazz pianists improvise.) Shown here is the beginning of the continuo part of Bach's *Brandenburg* Concerto No. 5, first movement (studied in Section 3), and one possible performance or *realization* of this part by a harpsichordist.

The basso continuo offered the advantage of emphasizing the all-important bass part, besides providing a steady flow of chords. Practically, the use of numbers, rather than chords with all their notes written out, saved time for busy baroque composers. It also saved paper during a period when paper was expensive.

Words and Music   Like their predecessors in the Renaissance, baroque composers used music to depict the meaning of specific words. *Heaven* might be set to a high tone, and *hell* to a low tone. Rising scales represented upward motion; descending scales depicted the reverse. Descending chromatic scales were associated with pain and grief. This descriptive musical language was quite standardized: a lament for a lost love might call forth the same descending chromatic scale used to depict suffering in the *Crucifixus* of the mass.

Baroque composers often emphasized words by writing many rapid notes for a single syllable of text; this technique also displayed a singer's virtuosity. The individual words and phrases of a text are repeated over and over as the music continuously unfolds.

The Baroque Orchestra

During the baroque period, the orchestra evolved into a performing group based on instruments of the violin family. By modern standards, the baroque orchestra was small, consisting of from ten to thirty or forty players. Its instrumental makeup was flexible and could vary from piece to piece. At its nucleus were the basso continuo (harpsichord plus cello, double bass, or bassoon) and upper strings (first and second violins and violas). Use of woodwind, brass, and percussion instruments was variable. To the strings and continuo could be added recorders, flutes, oboes, trumpets, horns, trombones, or timpani. One piece might use only a single flute, whereas another would call for two oboes, three trumpets, and timpani. Trumpets and timpani joined the orchestra mainly when the music was festive. This flexibility contrasts with the standardized orchestra of later periods, consisting of four sections: string, woodwind, brass, and percussion.

The baroque trumpet (like the early French horn) had no valves but was given rapid, complex melodic lines to play in a high register. Because the instrument was difficult to play and had a traditional association with royalty, the trumpeter was the aristocrat of the baroque orchestra. When prisoners of war were exchanged, trumpeters, if they had been captured, were treated like military officers.

Bach, Handel, Vivaldi, and others chose their orchestral instruments with care and obtained beautiful effects from specific tone colors. They loved to experiment with different combinations of instruments. However, in the baroque period tone color was distinctly subordinate to other musical elements—melody, rhythm, and harmony. Composers frequently rearranged their own or other composers' works for different instruments. A piece for string orchestra might become an organ solo, losing little in the process. Often, one instrument was treated like another. An oboe would play the same melody as the violins, or the flute and trumpet would imitate each other for extended sections of a piece.

Baroque Forms

It has been noted that a piece of baroque music—particularly instrumental music—usually has unity of mood. Yet many baroque compositions include a set of pieces, or movements, that contrast. A ***movement*** is a piece that sounds fairly complete and independent but is part of a larger composition. Usually, each movement has its own themes, comes to a definite end, and is separated from the next movement by a brief pause. Thus, a baroque composition in three movements may contain contrasts between a fast and energetic opening, a slow and solemn middle, and a conclusion that is quick, light, and humorous.

All the forms described in Part I, Section 9, "Musical Form," appear in baroque music. Three-part form (A B A), two-part form (A B), and continuous or undivided form are all common. We consider examples of these and other forms in the sections that follow.

Regardless of form, baroque music features contrasts between bodies of sound. Often there is a quite regular alternation between a small and a larger group of instruments, or between instruments and voices with instrumental accompaniment. This exploration of contrasting sounds was pursued with great imagination and provides a key to the understanding and enjoyment of baroque music.

2 Music in Baroque Society

Before 1800, most music was written to order, to meet specific demands that came mainly from churches and aristocratic courts. Opera houses and municipalities also required a constant supply of music. In every case, the demand was for *new* music; audiences did not want to listen to pieces in an "old-fashioned" style.

Music was a main source of diversion in the courts of the aristocracy. One court might employ an orchestra, a chapel choir, and opera singers—the size of the musical staff depending on the court's wealth. Bach directed about eighteen players in the orchestra of a small German court in 1717, but a large court might have more than eighty performers, including the finest opera singers of the day. The music director supervised performances and composed much of the music required, including operas, church music, dinner music, and pieces for court concerts. This overworked musician also was responsible for the discipline of the other musicians, and for the upkeep of the instruments and the music library.

During the baroque period, musicians often played with amateurs in music clubs or university music societies, getting together in private homes, coffeehouses, and taverns. *The Concert* by Nicholas Tournier (1590–1639) shows one such gathering.

The music director's job had good and bad features. Pay and prestige were quite high, and anything the composer wrote would be performed. But no matter how great, the composer was still a servant who could neither quit nor even take a trip without the patron's permission. Like everyone in baroque society, musicians had to curry favor with the aristocracy.

It is in this light that we must understand dedications like the one Bach addressed to a nobleman along with his *Brandenburg* Concertos: "Begging Your Highness most humbly not to judge their imperfection with the rigor of the fine and delicate taste which the whole world knows Your Highness has for musical pieces; but rather to infer from them in benign Consideration the profound respect and the most humble obedience which I try to show Your Highness." Yet sometimes musicians formed personal friendships with their patrons, as did Arcangelo Corelli, who thus gained a private apartment in a palace.

Some rulers were themselves good musicians. Frederick the Great, king of Prussia during the mid-eighteenth century, was a flutist and good composer, as well as a feared general. At his nightly court concerts, Frederick played his own works and some of the hundreds of pieces supplied by his flute teacher, Johann Quantz. (Quantz was "granted the privilege" of shouting "Bravo!" after a royal performance.)

Churches also needed music, and church music was often very grand. Along with an organ and a choir, many baroque churches had an orchestra to accompany services. Indeed, it was in church that most ordinary citizens heard music. There were few public concerts, and the populace was rarely invited to the palace. The music director of a church, like the music director at a court, had to produce a steady flow of new music and was also responsible for the musical training of choristers in the church school. Fine church music contributed to the prestige of a city, and cities often competed to attract the best musicians.

Still, church musicians earned less and had lower status than court musicians. Their meager income was supplemented by allotments of firewood and grain and by irregular fees for weddings and funerals. They suffered a financial pinch when a "healthy wind" blew and there were fewer funerals than usual, a situation Bach once complained about.

Large towns employed musicians for a variety of functions—to play in churches, in processions, in concerts for visiting dignitaries, and for university graduations. These town musicians often played with amateurs in music clubs or university music societies, getting together at private homes, coffeehouses, and taverns.

Some baroque musicians earned money by writing operas for commercial opera houses; such houses were located mainly in Italy. In Venice, a city of 125,000 people, six opera companies performed simultaneously between 1680 and 1700. In London, Handel became music director of a commercial opera company in 1719. Backed by English nobles, this company was a corporation with shares listed on the London stock exchange. When the company went bankrupt in 1728, Handel formed his own company, for which he wrote operas and served as conductor, manager, and impresario. In filling these many roles, Handel became one of the first great "freelance" musicians.

How did one become a musician in the baroque period? Often the art was handed from father to son; many leading composers—such as Bach, Vivaldi, Purcell, Couperin, and Rameau—were sons of musicians. Sometimes boys were apprenticed to a town musician and lived in his home. In return for instruction, the boys did odd jobs, such as copying music. Many baroque composers began their studies as choirboys, learning music in the choir school. In Italy, music schools were connected with orphanages. (*Conservatory* comes from the Italian for *orphans' home.*) There, orphans, foundlings, and poor children—boys and girls—were given thorough musical training, and some became the most sought-after opera singers and instrumentalists in Europe. Eminent composers such as Vivaldi were hired to teach and direct concerts in these schools. Vivaldi's all-female orchestra in Venice was considered one of the finest ensembles in Italy. During the baroque period, women were not permitted to be employed as music directors or as instrumentalists in court or opera orchestras. Nevertheless, a number of women—including Francesca Caccini, Barbara Strozzi, and Elisabeth-Claude Jacquet de la Guerre—succeeded in becoming respected composers.

To get a job, musicians usually had to pass a difficult examination, performing and submitting compositions. Sometimes there were nonmusical job requirements too. An applicant might be expected to make a "voluntary contribution" to the town's treasury, or even to marry the daughter of a retiring musician. Bach and Handel turned down the same job because one of the conditions was marriage to the organist's daughter. Italian musicians held the best posts in most European courts and were frequently paid twice as much as local musicians.

Composers were an integral part of baroque society, working for courts, churches, towns, and commercial opera houses. Though they wrote their music to fit specific needs, its quality is so high that much of it has become standard in today's concert repertoire.

3 The Concerto Grosso and Ritornello Form

We've seen that the contrast between loud and soft sounds—between relatively large and small groups of performers—is a basic principle of baroque music. This principle governs the concerto grosso, an important form of orchestral music in the late baroque period. In a **concerto grosso,** a small group of soloists is pitted against a larger group of players called the **tutti** (*all*). Usually, between two and four soloists play with anywhere from eight to twenty or more musicians for the tutti. The tutti consists mainly of string instruments, with a harpsichord as part of the basso continuo. A concerto grosso presents a contrast of texture between the tutti and the soloists, who assert their individuality and appeal for attention through brilliant and fanciful melodic lines. The soloists were the best and highest-paid members of the baroque orchestra because their parts were more difficult than those of the other players. Concerti grossi were frequently performed by private orchestras in aristocratic palaces.

A concerto grosso consists of *several movements that contrast in tempo and character.* Most often there are three movements: (1) fast, (2) slow, (3) fast. The opening movement is usually vigorous and determined, clearly showing the contrast between tutti and soloists. The slow movement is quieter than the first, often lyrical and intimate. The last movement is lively and carefree, sometimes dancelike.

The first and last movements of concerti grossi are often in **ritornello form,** which is based on alternation between tutti and solo sections. In ritornello form the tutti opens with a theme called the **ritornello** (*refrain*). This theme, always played by the tutti, returns in different keys throughout the movement. But it usually returns in fragments, not complete. Only at the end of the movement does the entire ritornello return in the home key. Although the number of times a ritornello (tutti) returns varies from piece to piece, a typical concerto grosso movement might be outlined as follows:

1. a. Tutti (*f*), ritornello in home key
   b. Solo

2. a. Tutti (*f*), ritornello fragment
   b. Solo

3. a. Tutti (*f*), ritornello fragment
   b. Solo

4. Tutti (*f*), ritornello in home key

In contrast to the tutti's ritornello, the solo sections offer fresh melodic ideas, softer dynamics, rapid scales, and broken chords. Soloists may also expand short melodic ideas from the tutti. The opening movement of Bach's *Brandenburg* Concerto No. 5 is a fine example of ritornello form in the concerto grosso.

Brandenburg Concerto No. 5 in D Major (about 1721), by Johann Sebastian Bach

With his set of six *Brandenburg* Concertos, Bach brought immortality to a German aristocrat, the margrave of Brandenburg. Bach and the margrave met in 1718, when Bach was music director for another patron. The margrave loved music and asked Bach to send him some original compositions. About three years later, Bach sent him the *Brandenburg* Concertos with the flattering dedication quoted in Section 2, probably hoping for money or favors in return. (We don't know whether he got any.) These concertos had been composed for, and performed by, the orchestra of Bach's employer, the prince of Cöthen. Each of the concertos is written for a different and unusual combination of instruments.

Brandenburg Concerto No. 5 uses a string orchestra and a group of soloists consisting of a flute, a violin, and a harpsichord. This was the first time that a harpsichord had been given the solo role in a concerto grosso. In 1719, the prince of Cöthen bought a new harpsichord; Bach probably wanted to show off this instrument (as well as his own skill as a keyboard player), and so he gave it a solo spot. The tutti is written for violins, violas, cellos, and double bass. During the tutti sections the solo violinist plays along, as does the harpsichordist, who realizes the figured bass.

The *Brandenburg* Concerto No. 5 has three movements: (1) fast, (2) slow, (3) fast. We focus on the first movement.

First Movement:
Allegro

The allegro movement opens with the ritornello, which is an almost continuous flow of rapid notes. After the ritornello ends—very definitely—the soloists present short melodic ideas, the flute and violin imitating each other playfully. The appearance of the soloists brings a lower dynamic level and a new tone color—the flute. After a while, the tutti returns loudly with a brief fragment of the ritornello, only to give way again to the soloists. This alternation between brief, relatively loud ritornello fragments in the tutti and longer, softer solo sections continues throughout the movement.

The soloists' music tends to be brilliant, fanciful, and personal as compared with the more vigorous and straightforward tutti sections. Solo sections are also more polyphonic in texture than the tutti and stress imitation between the flute and violin. The soloists play new material of their own or varied fragments from the ritornello. These solo sections build tension and make the listener anticipate the tutti's return. Listen especially for the suspenseful solo section that begins with a new theme in minor and ends with long notes in the flute.

Only the harpsichord plays during the long final solo section. And it is spectacular! Bach builds to a tense high point for the movement through irresistible rhythm and dazzling scale passages that require a virtuoso's skill. His audience must have marveled at this brilliant harpsichord solo within a concerto grosso. Audiences are still dazzled by it.

Listening Outline

BACH, *Brandenburg* Concerto No. 5

First Movement: Allegro
Ritornello form, duple meter (²⁄₂), D major
Flute, violin, harpsichord (solo group); string orchestra, continuo (tutti)
(Duration, 9:58)

Tutti

0:00   **1. a.** Strings, *f*, ritornello.

Solo

0:20   **b.** Flute, violin, harpsichord, major key.

Tutti

0:44   **2. a.** Strings, *f*, ritornello fragment.

Solo

0:49   **b.** Flute, violin, harpsichord, varied ritornello fragment.

Tutti

1:09   **3. a.** Strings, *f*, ritornello fragment.

Solo

1:16   **b.** Violin, flute, harpsichord.

Tutti

1:36   **4. a.** Strings, *f*, ritornello fragment, minor.

Solo

1:42   **b.** Harpsichord, flute, violin.

Tutti

2:23   **5. a.** Strings, *f*, ritornello fragment, major.

Solo

2:30   **b.** Flute, harpsichord, violin, varied ritornello fragment, ***pp***.

2:55   **c.** New theme in minor, ***pp***, tossed between flute and violin.

Tension mounts, long notes in flute lead to

Tutti

4:11   **6. a.** Strings, *f*, ritornello fragment, major.

Solo

4:16   **b.** Violin, flute, harpsichord.

Tutti

5:01   **7. a.** Strings, *f*, longer ritornello fragment.

Solo

5:12   **b.** Violin, harpsichord, flute, varied ritornello fragment.

Tutti

5:40   **8. a.** Strings, *f*, ritornello fragment.

Solo

5:47   **b.** Violin and flute play carefree idea with rapid harpsichord scales in background.

6:24   **c.** Long harpsichord solo featuring virtuoso display. Mounting tension resolved in

Tutti

9:32   **9.** Strings, *f*, ritornello.

4 The Fugue

One cornerstone of baroque music is the fugue, which can be written for a group of instruments or voices, or for a single instrument like an organ or harpsichord. A *fugue* is a polyphonic composition based on one main theme, called a *subject.* Throughout a fugue, different melodic lines, called *voices,* imitate the subject. The top melodic line—whether sung or played—is the soprano voice, and the bottom is the bass. The texture of a fugue usually includes three, four, or five voices. Though the subject remains fairly constant throughout, it takes on new meanings when shifted to different keys or combined with different melodic and rhythmic ideas.

The form of a fugue is extremely flexible; in fact, the only constant feature of fugues is how they begin—the subject is almost always presented in a single, unaccompanied voice. By thus highlighting the subject, the composer tells us what to remember and listen for. In getting to know a fugue, try to follow its subject through the different levels of texture. After its first presentation, the subject is imitated in turn by all the remaining voices.

The opening of a fugue in four voices may be represented as follows:

Soprano Subject ....etc.

Alto   Subject ....etc.

Tenor   Subject ....etc.

Bass   Subject ....etc.

In this case, the top voice announces the subject and then the lower voices imitate it. However, the subject may be announced by *any* voice—top, bottom, or middle—and the order in which the remaining voices imitate it is also completely flexible.

This may seem reminiscent of a round like *Row, Row, Row Your Boat,* but in a fugue the game of follow the leader (exact imitation of the subject) does not continue indefinitely. The dotted lines in the diagram indicate that *after a voice has presented the subject, it is free to go its own way with different melodic material.* The opening of a fugue differs from that of a round in another way: in a round, each voice presents the melody on the same tones. If the melody begins with the tones C–D–E, each voice will begin with these tones, whether at a higher or a lower register. But in the opening of a fugue, *the subject is presented in two different scales.* The first time, it is based on the notes of the *tonic scale.* But when the second voice presents the subject, it is in the *dominant scale*—five scale steps higher than the tonic—and it is then called the ***answer.*** A subject beginning with the notes C–D–E, for example, would be imitated by an answer five steps higher, on G–A–B. This alternation of subject and answer between the two scales creates variety.

In many fugues, the subject in one voice is constantly accompanied in another voice by a different melodic idea called a ***countersubject.*** A constant companion, the countersubject always appears with the subject, sometimes below it, sometimes above it.

After the opening of a fugue, when each voice has taken its turn at presenting the subject, a composer is free to decide how often the subject will be presented, in which voices, and in which keys. Between presentations of the subject, there are often transitional sections called ***episodes,*** which offer either new material or fragments of the subject or countersubject. Episodes do *not* present the subject in its entirety. They lend variety to the fugue and make reappearances of the subject sound fresh. Bach called one composer of fugues "pedantic" because he "had not shown enough fire to reanimate the theme by episodes."

Several musical procedures commonly appear in fugues. One is ***stretto,*** in which a subject is imitated before it is completed; one voice tries to catch the other. Another common procedure is ***pedal point*** (or ***organ point***), in which a single tone, usually in the bass, is held while the other voices produce a series of changing harmonies against it. (The term is taken from organ music, where a sustained low tone is produced by the organist's foot on a key of the pedal keyboard.)

A fugue subject can be varied in four principal ways:

1. It can be turned upside down, a procedure known as ***inversion.*** If the subject moves *upward* by leap, the inversion will move *downward* the same distance; if the subject moves *downward* by step, the inversion will move *upward* by step. In inversion, each interval in the subject is reversed in direction.

2. The subject may be presented ***retrograde,*** that is, by beginning with the last note of the subject and proceeding backward to the first.

3. The subject may be presented in ***augmentation,*** in which the original time values are lengthened.

4. The subject may appear in ***diminution,*** with shortened time values.

Fugues usually convey a single mood and a sense of continuous flow. They may be written as independent works or as single movements within larger compositions. Very often an independent fugue is introduced by a short piece called a ***prelude.***

Bach and Handel each wrote hundreds of fugues; their fugues represent the peak among works in the form. In the baroque period, as a friend of Bach's observed, "Skill in fugue was so indispensable in a composer that no one could have attained a musical post who had not worked out a given subject in all kinds of counterpoint and in a regular fugue." Fugal writing continued into the nineteenth and twentieth centuries. It is not used as frequently today as in the baroque period; yet to this day, as part of their training, musicians study how to write fugues.

Organ Fugue in G Minor (*Little Fugue;* about 1709), by Johann Sebastian Bach

One of Bach's best-known organ pieces is the *Little Fugue* in G Minor, so called to differentiate it from another, longer fugue in G minor. The opening section of the *Little Fugue* corresponds to the diagram on page 112. Each of the fugue's four voices takes its turn presenting the tuneful subject, which is announced in the top voice and then appears in progressively lower voices, until it reaches the bass, where it is played by the organist's feet on the pedal keyboard. Like many baroque melodies, the subject gathers momentum as it goes along, beginning with relatively long time values (quarter notes) and then proceeding to shorter ones (eighth and sixteenth notes). Starting with its second appearance, the subject is accompanied by a countersubject that moves in short time values.

After the opening section, the subject appears five more times, each time preceded by an episode. The first episode uses both new material and a melodic idea from the countersubject. This episode contains downward sequences, which are melodic patterns repeated in the same voice but at lower pitches.

For harmonic contrast, Bach twice presents the subject in major keys rather than minor. The final statement of the subject—in minor—exploits the powerful bass tones of the pedal keyboard. Though the fugue is in minor, it ends with a major chord. This was a frequent practice in the baroque period; major chords were thought more conclusive than minor chords.

Listening Outline

BACH, Organ Fugue in G Minor (*Little Fugue*)

Fugue, quadruple meter (4/4), G minor
Organ
(Duration, 4:04)

0:00   **1. a.** Subject, soprano voice alone, minor key.

0:18   **b.** Subject in alto, countersubject in running notes in soprano.

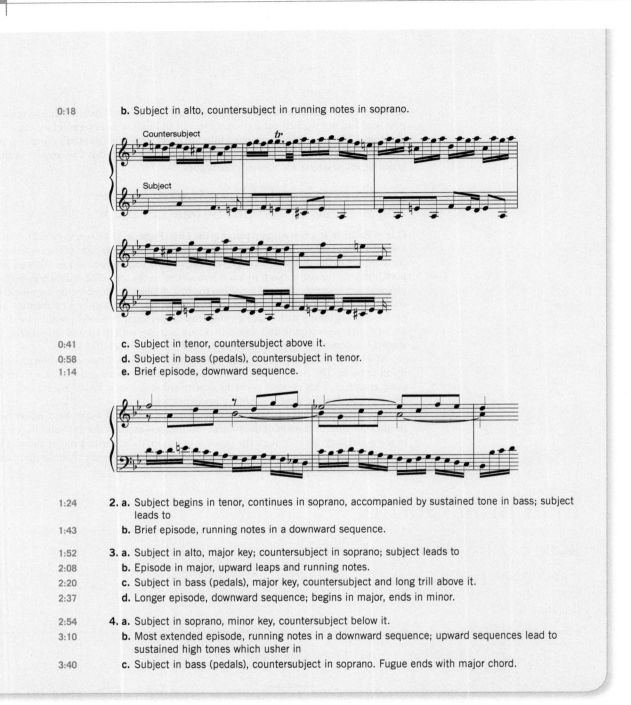

0:41   **c.** Subject in tenor, countersubject above it.
0:58   **d.** Subject in bass (pedals), countersubject in tenor.
1:14   **e.** Brief episode, downward sequence.

1:24   **2. a.** Subject begins in tenor, continues in soprano, accompanied by sustained tone in bass; subject leads to
1:43   **b.** Brief episode, running notes in a downward sequence.

1:52   **3. a.** Subject in alto, major key; countersubject in soprano; subject leads to
2:08   **b.** Episode in major, upward leaps and running notes.
2:20   **c.** Subject in bass (pedals), major key, countersubject and long trill above it.
2:37   **d.** Longer episode, downward sequence; begins in major, ends in minor.

2:54   **4. a.** Subject in soprano, minor key, countersubject below it.
3:10   **b.** Most extended episode, running notes in a downward sequence; upward sequences lead to sustained high tones which usher in
3:40   **c.** Subject in bass (pedals), countersubject in soprano. Fugue ends with major chord.

5 The Elements of Opera

The baroque era witnessed the development of a major innovation in music—*opera*, or drama that is sung to orchestral accompaniment. This unique fusion of music, acting, poetry, dance, scenery, and costumes is a theatrical experience offering overwhelming excitement and emotion. Since its beginnings in Italy around 1600, opera has spread to many countries, and even today it remains a powerful form of musical theater. In Section 6, we look closely at opera in the baroque period; but first, a general discussion of opera is in order.

In an opera, characters and plot are revealed through song, rather than the speech used in ordinary drama. Once we accept this convention, opera provides great pleasure; its music both delights the ear and heightens the emotional effect of the words and story. Music makes even an unlikely plot believable by depicting mood, character, and dramatic action. The flow of the music carries the plot forward. In opera, the music *is* the drama.

Opera demands performers who can sing and act simultaneously. Onstage are star solo singers, secondary soloists, a chorus, and sometimes dancers—all in costume. In addition to the chorus of professional singers, there may be "supers" (supernumeraries, or "extras"), who don't sing but who carry spears, fill out crowds, drink wine, or do other things that add to the effect. Scenery, lighting, and stage machinery are intricate and are used to create the illusion of fires, floods, storms, and supernatural effects. In the orchestra pit are the instrumentalists and the conductor, whose awesome responsibility it is to hold everything together. The personnel for a large opera—from conductor to stage director and assorted vocal coaches, rehearsal accompanists, technicians, and stagehands—may reach a startling total of several hundred people.

The capacity of this combined force to create spectacle and pageantry accounts for much of opera's appeal. Historically, opera has been associated with high social status. It originated in the courts of kings and princes (who could afford it) and long continued as a form of aristocratic entertainment. But as opera became more concerned with "real" people and less with royal figures, it attracted popular audiences. Today, radio and television broadcasts, videos, DVDs, recordings, iPods, and smartphones have changed opera's image as an exotic and expensive diversion for the very rich. Millions of people from every economic background know opera for what it is: a powerful and pleasurable emotional experience.

The creation of an opera involves the joint efforts of a composer and a dramatist. The *libretto,* or text, of the opera is usually written by the *librettist,* or dramatist, and set to music by the composer. But composers often collaborate with dramatists to ensure that the texts meet their musical needs. W. H. Auden once said that a good libretto "offers as many opportunities as possible for the characters to be swept off their feet by placing them in situations which are too tragic or too fantastic for words. No good opera plot can be sensible, for people do not sing when they are feeling sensible." And that is true—opera characters are people overwhelmed by love, lust, hatred, and revenge. They wear fantastic disguises and commit extraordinary acts of violence. Yet the music makes them human and real. It evokes the haughtiness of a countess or the simplicity of a peasant girl. It creates a dramatic entrance for an outraged father, depicts the tension behind sword thrusts in a duel, and portrays the bleakness of a winter dawn. A great opera composer is a master of musical timing and characterization and has a keen sense of theater, knowing just when to have a character sing a simple phrase or a soaring melody, when to provide a stirring chorus or a graceful dance. Through the music, the composer paces the drama, controlling the speed of gestures, entrances, exits, and stage movements.

Some operas are serious, some comic, some both. Operas may contain spoken dialogue, but most are entirely sung. (Spoken dialogue is used mainly in comic opera, where stage action must be performed quickly for the most humorous effect.) Because singing normally takes longer than speaking words, the text of a three-hour opera is shorter than that of a three-hour play. The librettist allows time for the composer's musical elaboration.

The range of characters found in opera is broad and varied; gods, empresses, dukes, servants, priests, prostitutes, peasants, clowns, and cowboys all make appearances. Opera soloists must create all these characters and so need acting skill as well as vocal

A scene from a production of *Aida* (1871), by Giuseppe Verdi, at the Théàtre Antique in Orange, France.

artistry. During rehearsals, the stage director coaches the singers to move well, gesture meaningfully, and identify with their characters.

The basic voice ranges (soprano, alto, tenor, bass) are divided more finely in opera. Some of the **voice categories of opera** are as follows:

Coloratura soprano	Very high range; can execute rapid scales and trills
Lyric soprano	Rather light voice; sings roles calling for grace and charm
Dramatic soprano	Full, powerful voice; is capable of passionate intensity
Lyric tenor	Relatively light, bright voice
Dramatic tenor	Powerful voice; is capable of heroic expression
Basso buffo	Takes comic roles; can sing very rapidly
Basso profondo	Very low range, powerful voice; takes roles calling for great dignity

Like a play, an opera has from one to five acts subdivided into scenes. A single act presents a variety of vocal and orchestral contrasts. For example, a tenor solo might be followed by a duet for soprano and bass, and then by a chorus or an orchestral interlude. A section may end definitely—and provide an opportunity for applause—or it may be linked with the next section to form a continuous flow of music within the act.

The main attraction for many opera fans is the **aria,** a song for solo voice with orchestral accompaniment. It's an outpouring of melody that expresses an emotional state. In an aria, *I love you* might be sung ten times to accommodate the expansion of the idea. Often the action stops while the character's feelings are revealed through music. An aria usually lasts several minutes. It is a complete piece with a definite beginning, high point, and end. If the performance of an aria is brilliant, the audience responds with an ovation at its conclusion. This breaks the dramatic flow but allows the audience to release its feelings through applause and shouts of *bravo!* or *brava!*

Opera composers often lead into an aria with a **recitative,** a vocal line that imitates the rhythms and pitch fluctuations of speech. In a recitative (from the Italian word for *recite*), words are sung quickly and clearly, often on repeated tones. There is usually only one note to each syllable in a recitative—as opposed to an aria, where one syllable may be stretched over many notes. Recitative is used for monologues and dialogues that connect the more melodic sections of the opera. It carries the action forward and presents routine information quickly.

Besides arias, the soloists in an opera will sing compositions for two or more singers: duets (for two singers), trios (for three), quartets (for four), quintets (for five), and sextets (for six). When three or more singers are involved, the composition is called an **ensemble.** In a duet or ensemble, the performers either face the audience or move through action that develops the plot. Each character expresses his or her own feelings. Conflicting emotions like grief, happiness, and anger can be projected simultaneously when different melodies are combined. This special blend of feelings is the glory of opera and is possible only through music; it cannot be duplicated in spoken drama.

An opera **chorus** generates atmosphere and makes comments on the action. Its members might be courtiers, sailors, peasants, prisoners, ballroom guests, and so on. Their sound creates a kind of tonal background for the soloists.

Rising just over the edge of center stage, near the footlights, is the prompter's box. In this cramped space, invisible to the audience, is the **prompter,** who gives cues and reminds the singers of words or pitches if they momentarily forget. Occasional memory lapses are inevitable with so much activity onstage.

Dance in opera is generally incidental. It provides an ornamental interlude that contrasts with and relaxes the thrust of the plot. By and large, dance is used as part of the setting—in a ballroom, at a country fair, in a pagan court—while the soloists, downstage, advance the action of the plot and work out their destinies.

The nerve center of an opera in performance is the orchestra pit—a sunken area directly in front of the stage. An opera orchestra has the same instruments as a full symphony orchestra, but usually it has a smaller string section. Covered lights attached to the players' music stands leave the orchestra in a deep shadow that doesn't interfere with the audience's view of the stage. The orchestra not only supports the singers but depicts mood and atmosphere and comments on the stage action. During the performance, the conductor shapes the entire work. He or she sets tempos, cues in singers, and indicates subtle dynamic gradations.

Most operas open with a purely orchestral composition called an **overture** or a **prelude.** Since the eighteenth century, the music for an overture has been drawn from material heard later in the opera. The overture is thus a short musical statement that involves the audience in the overall dramatic mood. Orchestral introductions to acts in the opera other than the first are always called *preludes.* Because overtures and preludes, like arias, are complete compositions, they frequently appear on symphony orchestra programs.

Should opera be translated? This question has long aroused controversy, and the battle continues. Most of the best-loved operas are in Italian, German, or French. Champions of translations into English argue that an audience should be able to understand the plot as it develops. Why tell jokes in a comic opera if they can't be understood? On the other hand, a composer takes pains to make a special fusion of pitch and the original words. This results in tonal color that seems absolutely right. But no matter how well a singer articulates, some words are bound to be lost, whatever the language. For example, a sung melody can stretch one vowel over many notes; it takes a while to get to the end of a word. If the melody is placed in a soprano's highest range, the listener is really aware only of the silvery vowel and not of the word as a whole. Some operas seem to work well in translation; others don't. Much depends on the style of the opera and on the sensitivity of the translator.

In many recent opera productions, a translation of the libretto is projected above the stage. This device—called *supertitles*—has also been a source of controversy. Its advocates say that it provides the best of both worlds because it allows an opera to be sung in the original language while the audience is enabled to understand the words. But its opponents feel that it detracts from the music and the action onstage.

Before you attend a live opera performance, in any language and with or without su-pertitles, it's a good idea to read the libretto or a synopsis of the plot. Even better, watch a video or DVD, or listen to a recording while following the libretto. This way, you will be freer at the performance to appreciate the quality of production and interpretation.

6 Opera in the Baroque Era

Opera was born in Italy. Its way was prepared by musical discussions among a small group of nobles, poets, and composers who began to meet regularly in Florence around 1575. This group was known as the **Camerata** (Italian for *fellowship* or *society*) and included the composer Vincenzo Galilei, father of the astronomer Galileo.

The Camerata wanted to create a new vocal style modeled on the music of ancient Greek tragedy. No actual dramatic music had come down to them from the Greeks, so they based their theories on literary accounts that had survived. It was believed that the Greek dramas had been sung throughout in a style that was midway between melody and speech. The Camerata wanted the vocal line to follow the rhythms and pitch fluctuations of speech. Because it was modeled after speech, the new vocal style became known as *recitative* (*recited*). It was sung by a soloist with only a simple chordal accompaniment. The new music was therefore homophonic in texture. Polyphony was rejected by the Camerata because different words sounding simultaneously would ob-scure the all-important text.

Euridice by Jacopo Peri is the earliest opera that has been preserved. It was composed for the wedding of King Henri IV of France and Marie de' Medici and was performed in Florence in 1600. Seven years later Monteverdi composed *Orfeo*—the first *great* opera— for the court of the Gonzaga family in Mantua. Both these operas are based on the Greek myth of Orpheus's descent into Hades to bring back his beloved Eurydice.

Much baroque opera was composed for ceremonial occasions at court and was de-signed as a display of magnificence and splendor. The subject matter was drawn from Greek mythology and ancient history. Not only were aristocratic patrons of the ba-roque fascinated by the classical civilizations of Greece and Rome, but they identified with Greek and Roman heroes and divinities. Opera did indeed reflect the creative urge of composer and librettist, but it also was a way to flatter the aristocracy. The radiant appearance of Apollo (god of poetry, music, and the sun) might symbolize a prince's enlightened rule.

The first public opera house opened in Venice in 1637; now anyone with the price of admission could attend an opera performance. Between 1637 and 1700 there were seventeen opera houses in Venice alone, as well as many in other Italian cities—ample evidence that opera had been born in the right place at the right time. Hamburg, Leipzig, and London had public opera houses by the early 1700s, but, on the whole, public opera outside Italy took longer to develop.

Venetian opera became a great tourist attraction. An English traveler wrote in 1645 about the opera and its "variety of scenes painted and contrived with no less art of perspective, and machines for flying in the air, and other wonderful motions; taken together, it is one of the most magnificent and expensive diversions the wit of man can invent." The stage machinery of baroque opera bordered on the colossal; stage effects might include gods descending on clouds or riding across the sky in chariots, ships tossing, boulders splitting. And set design was an art in itself. Painters turned back-drops into cities with arches and avenues that stretched into the distant horizon.

Much baroque opera was designed to display magnificent extravagance. Pietro Domenico Olivero's painting of the Royal Theater, Turin (1740), shows a performance of Francesco Feo's opera *Arsace.*

Baroque opera marked the rise of virtuoso singers. Chief among these was the *castrato,* a male singer who had been castrated before puberty. (Castration of boy singers was common in Italy from 1600 to 1800; it was usually done with the consent of impoverished parents who hoped their sons would become highly paid opera stars.) A castrato combined the lung power of a man with the vocal range of a woman. His agility, breath control, and unique sound (which was not like a woman's) intrigued listeners. Castrati received the highest fees of any musicians. With their soprano or alto vocal ranges, they played male roles such as Caesar and Nero—baroque audiences evidently were more interested in vocal virtuosity than dramatic realism. Today, a castrato part in a baroque opera is often sung by a *countertenor,* a male who sings in a female pitch range using a special kind of voice production.

During the late baroque, operas consisted largely of arias linked by recitatives. These recitatives were usually accompanied only by a basso continuo, in which case they are called *secco recitatives.* At emotional high points and moments of tension, however, they might be supported by the orchestra; they are then called *accompanied recitatives.*

All action stopped during the aria, when the singer faced the audience, expressed the feelings of the character, and displayed vocal virtuosity. The form of a typical late baroque aria is A B A. An aria in A B A form is called a *da capo aria*: after the B section, the term *da capo* is written; this means *from the beginning* and indicates a repetition of the opening A section. However, the repetition was usually not literal, because the singer was expected to embellish the returning melody with ornaments.

By combining virtuosity, nobility, and extravagance, baroque opera perfectly expressed the spirit of a grand age.

7 Claudio Monteverdi

Claudio Monteverdi (1567–1643), one of the most important composers of the early baroque era, was born in Cremona, Italy. He served at the court of Mantua for twenty-one years, first as a singer and violist, then as music director. For this court Monteverdi created the earliest operatic masterpiece, *Orfeo* (*Orpheus,* 1607). Though widely recognized as a leading composer in Mantua, Monteverdi received little pay or respect: "I have never suffered greater humiliation," he wrote, "than when I had to go and beg the treasurer to obtain what was due me."

Claudio Monteverdi (c. 1640), in a portrait by Bernardo Strozzi.

Life improved for Monteverdi in 1613, when he was appointed music director at St. Mark's in Venice, the most important church position in Italy. He stayed at St. Mark's for thirty years, until his death in 1643. There he composed not only the required sacred music but also secular music for the aristocracy. He wrote operas for San Cassiano in Venice, the first public opera house in Europe. At the age of seventy-five, Monteverdi wrote his last opera, *L'incoronazione di Poppea* (*The Coronation of Poppea,* 1642).

Monteverdi is a monumental figure in the history of music. His works form a musical bridge between the sixteenth and seventeenth centuries and greatly influenced composers of the time. All his music—madrigals, church music, opera—is for voices, ordinarily supported by a basso continuo and other instruments.

Monteverdi wanted to create music of emotional intensity. He felt that earlier music had conveyed only moderate emotion, and he wanted to extend its range to include agitation, excitement, and passion. To achieve this intensity, he used dissonances with unprecedented freedom and daring. And to evoke the angry or warlike feelings in some of his texts, he introduced new orchestral effects, including pizzicato and tremolo.

Monteverdi was the first composer of operatic masterpieces. Only three of the twelve operas he wrote are preserved, but they truly blend music and drama. His vocal lines respond marvelously to the inflections of Italian while maintaining melodic flow.

Orfeo (*Orpheus,* 1607)

Fittingly enough, Monteverdi's first opera is about Orpheus, the supremely gifted musician of Greek myth. Orpheus, son of the god Apollo, is ecstatically happy after his marriage to Eurydice. But his joy is shattered when his bride is killed by a poisonous snake. Orpheus goes down to Hades hoping to bring her back to life. Because of his beautiful music, he is granted this privilege—on the condition that he not look back at Eurydice while leading her out of Hades. During a moment of anxiety, however, Orpheus does look back, and Eurydice vanishes. Nonetheless, there is a happy ending, of sorts. Apollo pities Orpheus and brings him up to heaven, where he can gaze eternally at Eurydice's radiance in the sun and stars.

Orpheus and Euridice
(c. 1625), by Jacopo Vignali.
The painting depicts Orpheus
leading Eurydice out of Hades
while a winged demon reaches
out to her from behind.

Orfeo was composed in 1607 for the Mantuan court, and no expense was spared to make it a lavish production. There were star soloists, a chorus, dancers, and a large orchestra of about forty players. The aristocratic audience was wildly enthusiastic and recognized the historic significance of the performance.

Monteverdi creates variety in *Orfeo* by using many kinds of music—recitatives, arias, duets, choruses, and instrumental interludes. He uses the opera orchestra to establish atmosphere, character, and dramatic situations. With the simplest of musical means, Monteverdi makes his characters come alive. Through vocal line alone he quickly characterizes the hero's joy and despair. Monteverdi sets his text in a very flexible way, freely alternating recitatives with more melodious passages, depending on the meaning of the words.

We now consider one well-known passage from this opera, Orpheus's recitative *Tu se' morta* (*You are dead*).

Act II:
Recitative: *Tu se' morta* (*You are dead*)

Monteverdi's mastery of the then novel technique of recitative is shown in *Tu se' morta,* sung by Orpheus after he is told of Eurydice's death. Orpheus resolves to bring her back from Hades, and he bids an anguished farewell to the earth, sky, and sun. His vocal line is accompanied only by a basso continuo played by a small portable organ and a bass lute. (In modern performances, other instruments are sometimes substituted.)

The texture is homophonic: the accompaniment simply gives harmonic support to the voice. The vocal line is rhythmically free, with little sense of beat or meter, and its phrases are irregular in length. This flexible setting of text is meant to suggest the passionate speech of an actor declaiming his lines.

Monteverdi frequently uses word painting, the musical representation of poetic images that was favored by baroque composers. For example, words like *stelle* (*stars*) and *sole* (*sun*) are sung to climactic high tones, whereas *abissi* (*abysses*) and *morte* (*death*) are sung to somber, low tones. Three times during the recitative the melodic line rises to a climax and then descends. Through such simple means, Monteverdi expresses Orpheus's passion.

Vocal Music Guide

MONTEVERDI, *Tu se' morta* from *Orfeo*

		Tu se' morta, se' morta, mia vita,	You are dead, you are dead, my dearest,
		ed io respiro; tu se' da me partita,	And I breathe; you have left me,
		se' da me partita per mai più,	You have left me forevermore,
		mai più non tornare, ed io rimango—	Never to return, and I remain—
		no, no, che se i versi alcuna cosa ponno,	No, no, if my verses have any power,
1:12	Low tone on *abissi*.	n'andrò sicuro a' più profondi abissi,	I will go confidently to the deepest abysses,
		e, intenerito il cor del re de l'ombre,	And, having melted the heart of the king of shadows,
1:38	High tone on *stelle*.	meco trarotti a riverder le stelle,	Will bring you back to me to see the stars again,
		o se ciò negherammi empio destino,	Or, if pitiless fate denies me this,
2:00	Low tone on *morte*.	rimarrò teco in compágnia di morte.	I will remain with you in the company of death.
2:17	High tone on *sole*.	Addio terra, addio cielo, e sole, addio.	Farewell earth, farewell sky, and sun, farewell.

8 Henry Purcell

Purcell mastered all the musical forms of late seventeenth-century England. His opera *Dido and Aeneas* was written for students at a girls' boarding school.

Henry Purcell (about 1659–1695), called the greatest of English composers, was born in London; his father was a musician in the king's service. At about the age of ten, Purcell became a choirboy in the Chapel Royal, and by the time he was in his late teens his extraordinary talents were winning him important musical positions. In 1677, at about eighteen, he became composer to the king's string orchestra; two years later he was appointed organist of Westminster Abbey; and in 1682, he became an organist of the Chapel Royal. During the last few years of his short life, Purcell was also active composing music for plays.

Acclaimed as *the* English composer of his day, Purcell, who died at thirty-six, was buried beneath the organ in Westminster Abbey. He was the last native English composer of international rank until the twentieth century.

Purcell mastered all the musical forms of late seventeenth-century England. He wrote church music, secular choral music, music for small groups of instruments, songs, and music for the stage. His only true opera is *Dido and Aeneas* (1689), which many consider the finest ever written to an English text. His other dramatic works are spoken plays with musical numbers in the form of overtures, songs, choruses, and dances.

Few composers have equaled Purcell's handling of the English language. His vocal music is faithful to English inflection and brings out the meaning of the text. Purcell developed a melodious recitative that seems to grow out of the English language. His music is filled with lively rhythms and has a fresh melodic style that captures the spirit of English folk songs. He treated the chorus with great variety and was able to obtain striking effects through both simple homophonic textures and complex polyphony. His music is spiced with dissonances that seemed harsh to the generation of musicians who followed him. Some of Purcell's finest songs use a variation form found in many baroque works—a ground bass.

Ground Bass

Often in baroque works, a musical idea in the bass is repeated over and over while the melodies above it change. The repeated musical idea is called a ***ground bass,*** or ***basso ostinato*** (*obstinate* or *persistent bass*). The ground bass pattern may be as short as four notes or as long as eight measures. In this type of variation form, the constant repetition of the bass pattern gives unity, while the free flow of the melodic lines above it results in variety.

Composers have used a ground bass in both vocal and instrumental music. We'll hear a ground bass in Purcell's opera *Dido and Aeneas.*

Dido and Aeneas (1689)

Purcell's *Dido and Aeneas,* a masterpiece of baroque opera, was written for students at a girls' boarding school. It lasts only an hour, is scored only for strings and harpsichord continuo, and requires no elaborate stage machinery or virtuoso soloists. Most of its solo roles are for women. Purcell used many dances in *Dido and Aeneas,* because the director of the school was a dancing master who wanted to display the students' accomplishments. The chorus plays a prominent role, both participating in the action and commenting on it.

The libretto of *Dido and Aeneas,* by Nahum Tate, was inspired by the *Aeneid,* an epic poem by the Roman poet Virgil (70–19 BC). The opera's main characters are Dido, queen of Carthage; and Aeneas, king of the defeated Trojans. After the destruction of his native Troy, Aeneas has been ordered by the gods to seek a site for building a new city. He sets out on the search with twenty-one ships. After landing at Carthage, a north African seaport, Aeneas falls in love with Dido. A sorceress and two witches see this as an opportunity to plot Dido's downfall. (In Purcell's time, people really believed in witches: nineteen supposed "witches" were hanged in Massachusetts in 1692, three years after *Dido's* first performance.) A false messenger tells Aeneas that the gods command him to leave Carthage immediately and renew his search. Aeneas agrees but is desolate at the thought of deserting Dido.

In the last act, which takes place at the harbor, Aeneas's sailors sing and dance before leaving, and the witches look on in glee. An emotional scene follows between Aeneas and Dido, who enters with her friend Belinda. Dido calls Aeneas a hypocrite and refuses his offer to stay. After he sails, Dido sings a noble, deeply tragic lament and kills herself. The opera concludes with the mourning of the chorus.

Now let's look at *Dido's Lament.*

Act III: *Dido's Lament*

A melodic recitative accompanied only by the basso continuo sets the sorrowful mood for *Dido's Lament,* the climax of the opera. This aria is built on a chromatically descending ground bass that is stated eleven times. (In the baroque period, such chromatic ground basses were commonly used to show grief.) As shown in the music example, Dido's melody moves freely above this repeated bass line, creating touching dissonances with it.

Dido's repeated *Remember me* reaches the highest note of the aria and haunts the listener. The emotional tension is sustained in the orchestral conclusion, where a chromatically descending violin melody movingly expresses the tragedy of Dido's fate.

Vocal Music Guide

PURCELL, *Dido's Lament*

0:00

Recitative, descending melody, basso continuo accompanies.

Thy hand, Belinda, darkness shades me,
On thy bosom let me rest;
More I would but Death invades me;
Death is now a welcome guest.

0:46

Dido's Lament (aria), lute introduces chromatically descending ground bass.

Upper strings join.

When I am laid, am laid in earth, may my wrongs create
No trouble, no trouble in thy breast.
Remember me! But ah! forget my fate.

Orchestral conclusion, violin melody descends chromatically.

9 The Baroque Sonata

Instrumental music gained importance rapidly and dramatically during the baroque period. One of the main developments in instrumental music was the **sonata,** a composition in several movements for one to eight instruments. (In later periods, the term *sonata* took on a more restricted meaning.)

Composers often wrote **trio sonatas,** so-called because they had three melodic lines: two high lines and a basso continuo. Yet the word *trio* is misleading, because the "trio" sonata actually involves *four* instrumentalists. There are two high instruments (commonly, violins, flutes, or oboes) and two instruments for the basso continuo—a keyboard instrument (organ or harpsichord) and a low instrument (cello or bassoon).

The sonata originated in Italy but spread to Germany, England, and France during the seventeenth century. Sonatas were played in palaces, in homes, and even in churches—before, during, or after the service. Sometimes composers differentiated between the *sonata da chiesa* (*church sonata*), which had a dignified character and was suitable for sacred performance; and the *sonata da camera* (*chamber sonata*), which was more dancelike and was intended for performance at court.

Trio Sonata in A Minor, Op. 3, No. 10 (1689), Arcangelo Corelli

The most prominent Italian violinist and composer of string music around 1700 was Arcangelo Corelli (1653–1713). Corelli was also an eminent teacher who laid the foundations of modern violin technique. He wrote only instrumental music: sixty sonatas and twelve concertos, all for strings.

Trio Sonata in A Minor, Op. 3, No. 10 (1689)

Movements 1 and 2
available in Connect Music

Corelli's Trio Sonata in A Minor, Op. 3, No. 10, is written for two violins and basso continuo. The violins play the two upper lines in the same high register and are the center of attention; they seem to be rivals, taking turns at the melodic ideas, intertwining, and sometimes rising above each other in pitch. The basso continuo is for organ and cello or *theorbo* (bass lute), a plucked string instrument which is capable of producing chords as well as the bass line. Though the bass line is subordinate to the two upper voices, it is not merely an accompaniment. It imitates melodic ideas presented by the violins.

The sonata consists of four short movements:

1. Fast
2. Fast
3. Slow
4. Fast

All are in the same minor key, but they differ in meter, mood, and tempo. Each movement alone has only a single basic mood, as is typical in baroque instrumental music.

The lively opening movement is in quadruple meter and features dotted rhythms. It is played twice, each time ending with an incomplete cadence on the dominant that creates a feeling of expectancy.

	6		7	7	6	♯	7 6 ♯

The second movement, a vigorous allegro, is fuguelike and also in quadruple meter. Fugal second movements were characteristic of baroque trio sonatas. The subject begins with a pervasive repeated-note motive.

This subject is introduced by the first violin and then is successively imitated in lower registers by the second violin and the cello (doubled by the organ). The second movement, like the first, ends with an incomplete cadence on the dominant that creates expectancy.

The third movement is songlike and soulful, a very brief adagio in triple meter. It opens with a descending leap in the first violin that is immediately imitated a step higher by the second violin.

The longest and most brilliant movement of this sonata is the concluding allegro, a dancelike piece in quadruple meter in which each beat is subdivided into three. This fourth movement is in two-part form, and each part is repeated: A A B B. Section B is three times longer than section A. At the end of section B, Corelli calls for the only dynamic change in the sonata: the concluding phrase is repeated more softly, like an echo.

10 Antonio Vivaldi

Vivaldi's most popular work is the concerto *La Primavera (Spring)* from *The Four Seasons,* a set of four solo concertos for violin, string orchestra, and continuo.

Antonio Vivaldi (1678–1741), a towering figure of the late Italian baroque, was born in Venice; his father was a violinist at St. Mark's Cathedral. Along with his musical training, Vivaldi prepared for the priesthood. He took holy orders at the age of about twenty-five, but poor health caused him to leave the ministry after a year. Because of his religious background and his red hair, Vivaldi was known as the "red priest" (*il prete rosso*).

For most of his life, Vivaldi was a violin teacher, composer, and conductor at the music school of the Pietà, an institution for orphaned or illegitimate girls in Venice. Every Sunday and holiday, about forty young women presented a concert of orchestral and vocal music in the chapel. They were placed in a gallery, "hid from any distinct view of those below by a lattice of ironwork." It was for this all-female group—considered one of the finest orchestras in Italy—that Vivaldi composed many of his works. He also wrote for Venetian opera houses and sometimes took leave to visit foreign courts.

Vivaldi was famous and influential as a virtuoso violinist and composer. Bach arranged some of his concertos. Emperor Charles VI, a passionate music lover, was said to have talked longer to Vivaldi "alone in fifteen days, than he talked to his ministers in two years."

But Vivaldi's popularity waned shortly before his death in 1741, and he died in poverty. Although he had been acclaimed during his lifetime, he was almost forgotten for 200 years after his death. The baroque revival of the 1950s established his reputation among modern music lovers.

Although Vivaldi composed operas and fine church music, he is best known for his 450 or so concerti grossi and solo concertos. A **solo concerto** is a piece for a *single* soloist and an orchestra. Vivaldi exploited the resources of the violin as well as other instruments. (There are Vivaldi concertos for solo flute, piccolo, cello, bassoon, and even mandolin.) His fast movements feature tuneful themes in vigorous rhythms, and his slow movements have impassioned, lyrical melodies that would be appropriate in an opera aria.

La Primavera (Spring), Concerto for Violin and String Orchestra, Op. 8, No. 1, from The Four Seasons (1725)

Vivaldi's most popular work is the concerto *La Primavera (Spring)* from *The Four Seasons,* a set of four solo concertos for violin, string orchestra, and basso continuo. Each of these concertos depicts sounds and events associated with one of the seasons, such as the birdsong heard in spring and the gentle breezes of summer. The descriptive effects in the music correspond to images and ideas found in the sonnets that preface each of the four concertos. To make his intentions absolutely clear, Vivaldi placed lines from the poems at the appropriate passages in the musical score and even added such descriptive labels as *sleeping goatherd* and *barking dog.* The concertos *Spring, Summer, Autumn,* and *Winter* are examples of baroque *program music,* or instrumental music associated with a story, poem, idea, or scene. They are forerunners of the more elaborate program music that developed during the romantic period.

Spring was as popular in Vivaldi's time as it is in ours and was a special favorite of Louis XV, king of France. Once, when the violinist Guignon gave a concert at the court, the king asked for *Spring* as an encore. This posed a problem because the king's orchestra was not present. Rising to the occasion, a group of nobles at the court volunteered to accompany the violin soloist. A Parisian newspaper reported that "this beautiful piece of music was performed perfectly."

Like most of Vivaldi's concertos, *Spring* has three movements: (1) fast, (2) slow, (3) fast. Both the first and last movements are in ritornello form.

First Movement: Allegro

> Spring has come, and joyfully,
> The birds greet it with happy song.
> And the streams, fanned by gentle breezes,
> Flow along with a sweet murmur.
> Covering the sky with a black cloak,
> Thunder and lightning come to announce the season.
> When these have quieted down, the little birds
> Return to their enchanting song.

The allegro, in E major, opens with an energetic orchestral ritornello depicting the arrival of spring. Each of the ritornello's two phrases is played loudly and then repeated softly, in the terraced dynamics typical of baroque music. After the ritornello, the movement alternates between extended solo sections containing musical tone painting and brief tutti sections presenting part of the ritornello theme. In the first solo section, birdsongs are imitated by high trills and repeated notes played by the violin soloist and two violins from the orchestra. (A **trill** is an ornament consisting of the rapid alternation of two tones that are a whole or half step apart.) In the second descriptive episode, murmuring streams are suggested by soft running notes in the violins. The next solo section contains string tremolos and rapid scales representing thunder and lightning. Following the storm, the ritornello appears in minor instead of in major. All the pictorial passages in this movement provide contrasts of texture and dynamics between returns of the ritornello theme. The allegro's tunefulness, rhythmic vitality, and light, homophonic texture evoke the feeling of springtime.

Listening Outline

VIVALDI, *La Primavera,* from *The Four Seasons*

First Movement: Allegro
Ritornello form, quadruple meter ($\frac{4}{4}$), E major
Solo violin, string orchestra, harpsichord (basso continuo)
(Duration, 3:38)

Spring has come

0:00   **1. a.** Tutti, ritornello opening phrase, *f*, repeated *p*

        closing phrase with syncopations, *f*, repeated *p*, major key.

Song of the birds

0:31   **b.** Solo violin joined by two violins from orchestra, high trills and repeated notes.

1:06   **2. a.** Tutti, ritornello closing phrase, *f*.

Murmuring streams

1:14   **b.** Violins, *p*, running notes, cellos, *p*, running notes below sustained tones in violins.

1:38   **3. a.** Tutti, ritornello closing phrase, *f*.

Thunder and lightning

1:46   **b.** String tremolos, *f*, upward rushing scales introduce high solo violin, brilliant virtuoso passages answered by low string tremolos.

2:15   **4. a.** Tutti, ritornello closing phrase in minor key, *f*.

Song of the birds

2:23   **b.** Solo violin joined by two violins from orchestra, high repeated notes and trills, minor key.

2:43   **5. a.** Tutti, ritornello opening phrase varied, *f*, ends in major key.
2:55   **b.** Solo violin, running notes accompanied by basso continuo.

3:11   **6.** Tutti, ritornello closing phrase, *f*, repeated *p*, major key.

Second Movement:
Largo e pianissimo sempre
(very slow and very soft throughout)

> And then, on a pleasant meadow covered with flowers,
> Lulled by the soft murmuring of leaves and branches,
> The goatherd sleeps, his faithful dog at his side.

Selection available on:
Connect Music
Mp3 download card
Mp3 disc

The peaceful slow movement, in C sharp minor, is much quieter than the energetic opening movement. It uses only the solo violin and the orchestral violins and violas, omitting the cellos, basses, and harpsichord. A tender, expansive melody for the solo violin depicts the goatherd's slumber, while a soft, rocking figure in the violins suggests the rustling of leaves. The violas imitate the barking of the goatherd's "faithful dog" with a repeated-note figure in short-long rhythm. The tranquility of this pastoral scene is evoked by the movement's unchanging texture, rhythm, and dynamic level.

In the performance of this movement on our recordings, the violin soloist Jeanne Lamon decorates the melody with ornaments, or embellishing notes. During the baroque period, performers were often expected to add embellishments not indicated in the printed music. Vivaldi's notated melody and the decorated version of the melody you hear in the recording are shown in the following music examples.

(a) Notated melody

(b) Ornamented melody

(a)

(b)

Third Movement:
Danza pastorale (Pastoral Dance)

> To the festive sounds of country bagpipes,
> Dance nymphs and shepherds in their beloved fields,
> When spring appears in all its brilliance.

Selection available on:
Connect Music
Mp3 download card
Mp3 disc

Like the first movement, the concluding *Danza pastorale (Pastoral Dance),* in E major, alternates between tutti and solo sections. The playful ritornello theme, with its dotted rhythms, suggests nymphs and shepherds dancing in the fields. Sustained tones in the lower strings imitate the drone of country bagpipes. The sections for solo violin contain brilliant passages with many melodic sequences, which are typical of baroque style.

Performance Perspectives

Jeanne Lamon, Violinist, Plays and Conducts Vivaldi's *Spring* Concerto

One of the leading performers on the baroque violin is Jeanne Lamon, who conducts and directs the Canadian period-instrumental group Tafelmusik. During the past few decades, many performers of baroque music have chosen to use baroque instruments—originals and reproductions—rather than the later counterparts. Baroque instruments differ somewhat from their later counterparts in construction and in the way they are played. Baroque violins, for example, usually have strings of gut rather than metal. The strings are held under less tension and produce sounds that are softer and less brilliant.

Jeanne Lamon, who was raised in New York state, began to play the violin at age seven and later studied music at Brandeis University in Boston. After graduating, she studied baroque violin in the Netherlands, a center for the performance of early music. In 1973, she returned to North America, where she performed as soloist and concertmaster with many ensembles. Under her direction since 1981, Tafelmusik has made many award-winning recordings, including Vivaldi's *The Four Seasons* and Bach's *Brandenburg* Concertos.

In Lamon's performance of Vivaldi's *Spring* Concerto—included in the recordings—she conducts from the concertmaster's seat, playing the solo violin part at the same time. She points out that "most orchestral music of the baroque was led by the first violinist or the harpsichordist. This suits the music very well, as do the original instruments. It is in many ways easier for string players to follow a violinist than a conductor."

As we have seen, Vivaldi's *Spring* Concerto contains episodes suggesting birdsongs and murmuring streams. Lamon believes that such passages pose special problems for the performer: "How rhythmically strict should an imitation of birds be? How literally would Vivaldi have wished it to be played? Should the birdcalls be played as literally as possible, or should we take whatever freedom we see fit to make them as realistic as we can? I chose a middle ground, probably a bit more strict than free, but with the intention of applying humor and charm to this music. I see it not as literal music, but as playful and evocative."

In the peaceful second movement, Lamon enriches the written solo violin melody with decorative tones. She points out that she "chose to ornament in a way that was comfortable for me as a player and reflected the mood of the musical picture." The second movement poses special interpretive problems for the conductor. "The biggest challenge in this movement, writes Lamon, "is the viola part, which imitates dogs barking and is indicated *ff e strappato* ('very loud and ripped'). If we really do this, we hear nothing else, but the polite version where the violas play softly and roundly doesn't sound at all like dogs." Lamon's solution is to have the violists play *forte* rather than *fortissimo*. She thinks that Vivaldi marked the part *fortissimo* because he was "frustrated that his violists were playing too softly and without any edge or roughness (barking). Our violists are much meatier players perhaps!"

How can the performer breathe new life into such a well-known work as Vivaldi's *Spring* Concerto? Lamon answers, "Our challenge as performers is to keep sometimes very familiar works 'new' and fresh by remembering what was new and fresh about them: . . . when they were heard for the first time; what surprised the audience; what was innovative, shocking, humorous."

The following outline will clarify the movement's ritornello form:

1. a. Tutti, ritornello, lilting melody in major.
   b. Solo violin accompanied by basso continuo.
2. a. Tutti, varied ritornello in minor.
   b. Solo violin joined by violin from orchestra, major.
   c. Solo violin, staccato, accompanied by violins, faster rhythms.
3. a. Tutti, ritornello, major, varied in minor.
   b. Solo violin accompanied by sustained tone in cellos and basses, minor.
4. Tutti, ritornello in major.

11 Johann Sebastian Bach

The masterpieces of Johann Sebastian Bach (1685–1750) mark the high point of baroque music. Bach came from a long line of musicians and passed on this musical heritage; four of his sons were also composers. He was born in Eisanach, Germany, and began his musical career as a church organist and then as court organist and later concertmaster of the court orchestra in Weimar.

His most lucrative and prestigious post was as court conductor for the prince of Cöthen. This was the first time in Bach's career that he was not involved with church or organ music. For the six years from 1717 to 1723, Bach directed the prince's small orchestra. The *Brandenburg* Concertos grew out of this productive period.

Bach's next position was as cantor (director of music) of St. Thomas Church in Leipzig, a position that involved responsibility for Leipzig's four main municipal churches. Bach remained here for the last twenty-seven years of his life. He rehearsed, conducted, and usually composed an extended composition for chorus, soloists, and orchestra for each Sunday and holiday of the church year. He was responsible for the musical education of some fifty-five students in the St. Thomas school. After some years in Leipzig he became director of the Leipzig Collegium Musicum, a student organization that gave concerts every Friday night at a coffeehouse. He was also an eminent teacher of organ and composition, gave organ recitals, and was often asked to judge the construction of organs. In his last years, Bach's eyesight deteriorated, yet he continued to compose, conduct, and teach. In 1750, the year of his death, he became blind.

Bach was a deeply religious man—a Lutheran—who wrote the letters *J. J.*, standing for *Jesu Juva* (*Jesus help*), at the beginning of each of his sacred compositions and *S. D. G.* for *Soli Deo Gloria* (*to God alone the glory*) at the end. His love of music was so great that as a young man he would walk up to thirty miles to hear a famous organist. He was married twice and had twenty children, of whom nine survived him and four (as noted above) became well-known musicians.

Though recognized as the most eminent organist, harpsichordist, improviser, and master of the fugue, Bach was by no means considered the greatest composer of his day; his music was largely forgotten and remained unpublished for years after his death.

Bach was by no means considered the greatest composer of his day, though he was recognized as the most eminent organist, harpsichordist, and improviser (**improvisation** is the term used for music created at the same time as it is performed). He was little known outside Germany; and by the time of his maturity, the baroque style had started to go out of fashion and many people thought his works too heavy, complex, and polyphonic. His music was largely forgotten for years after his death, though a few later composers were aware of his genius; but in 1829 Felix Mendelssohn presented the *St. Matthew Passion,* and Bach's music has been the daily bread of every serious musician since then.

Bach's Music

Bach created masterpieces in every baroque form except opera. Throughout, he fused technical mastery and emotional depth. His instrumental music includes pieces for orchestra, for small groups, and for solo organ, harpsichord, clavichord, violin, and cello.

The excellence and number of these works show how prominent instrumental music had become in the baroque period. Bach's vocal music—the bulk of his output—was written mostly for the Lutheran church and was often based on familiar hymns. But his personal style was drawn from Italian concertos and French dance pieces, as well as the church music of his native Germany.

Bach's music is unique in its combination of polyphonic texture and rich harmony. His works show an astounding mastery of harmony and counterpoint, and are used as models by music students today. Baroque music leans toward unity of mood, and this is particularly true of Bach, who liked to elaborate a single melodic idea in a piece, creating unity of mood by an insistent rhythmic drive. By Bach's time there was little difference in style between secular and sacred music. In fact, he often created sacred music simply by rearranging instrumental pieces or works originally written for secular texts. His church music also uses operatic forms like the aria and recitative. Sometimes Bach composed music to demonstrate what he could do with a specific form (his *Art of the Fugue,* for example, displays all the resources of fugue writing), or a particular instrument (for instance his suites for cello solo). His *Well-Tempered Clavier,* a collection of forty-eight preludes and fugues, two in each major key and each minor key, was composed to explain and demonstrate a system of tuning (the title means, roughly, the *Well-Tuned Keyboard Instrument*).

12   The Baroque Suite

Instrumental music has always been closely linked with dancing; in the past, much of it was written for use in palace ballrooms. During the Renaissance, dances often came in pairs—a dignified dance in quadruple meter was often followed by a lively one in triple meter. In the baroque period and later, music was written that—while meant for listening, not dancing—was related to specific dance types in tempo, meter, and rhythm.

Baroque composers wrote *suites,* which are sets of dance-inspired movements. Whether for solo instruments, small groups, or orchestra, a baroque suite is made up of movements that are all written in the same key but differ in tempo, meter, and character. The dancelike movements also have a variety of national origins: the moderately paced *allemande* (from Germany) might be followed by a fast *courante* and a moderate *gavotte* (from France), a slow and solemn *sarabande* (from Spain), and a fast *gigue* (jig, from England and Ireland). Suites were played in private homes, at court concerts, or as background music for dinner and outdoor festivities.

Dance pieces have a diverse past. Some began as folk dances, and others sprang from aristocratic ballrooms. Even the character of a dance might show dramatic evolution. The slow, solemn sarabande grew out of a sexually suggestive song and dance that a sixteenth-century moralist condemned as "so lascivious in its words, so ugly in its movements, that it is enough to inflame even very honest people." In the seventeenth century, however, the sarabande became respectable enough to be danced by a cardinal at the French court.

The movements of a suite are usually in two-part form with each section repeated; that is, in the form A A B B. The A section, which opens in the tonic key and modulates to the dominant, is balanced by the B section, which begins in the dominant and returns to the tonic key. Both sections use the same thematic material, and so they contrast relatively little except in key.

Suites frequently begin with a movement that is *not* dance-inspired. One common opening is the French overture, which is also the type of piece heard at the beginning of baroque oratorios and operas. Usually written in two parts, the **French overture** first presents a slow section with dotted rhythms that is full of dignity and grandeur. The second section is quick and lighter in mood, often beginning like a fugue. Sometimes part of the opening section will return at the end of the overture.

The suite was an important instrumental form in the baroque. Even compositions not called "suite" often have several dance-inspired movements. Music influenced by dance tends to have balanced and symmetrical phrases of the same length, because formal dancing has a set of steps in one direction symmetrically balanced by a similar motion in the opposite direction.

Bach wrote four suites for orchestra. We don't know exactly when they were composed, but it seems likely that the Collegium Musicum performed them in a coffee-house in Leipzig.

Suite No. 3 in D Major (1729–1731), by Johann Sebastian Bach

First Movement: Overture

Suite No. 3 in D Major—scored for two oboes, three trumpets, timpani, strings, and basso continuo—opens with a majestic French overture, which exploits the bright sounds of trumpets. After a slow opening section with dotted rhythms, we hear the energetic fast section. This begins like a fugue, with an upward-moving theme introduced by the first violins and then imitated by the other instruments.

The fast section is like a concerto grosso in its alternation of solid tutti passages with lightly scored passages highlighting the first violins. After the fast section, the slow tempo, dotted rhythms, and majestic mood of the opening return.

Second Movement: Air

The second movement, the air, contains one of Bach's best-loved melodies. It is scored for only strings and continuo and is serene and lyrical, in contrast to the majestic and then bustling French overture. The title suggests that the movement is written in the style of an Italian aria. Like the opening movement, the air is not related to dance. It is in A A B B form, with the B section twice as long as the A section. The air combines a steadily moving bass (which proceeds in upward and downward octave leaps) with a rhapsodic and rhythmically irregular melody in the violins.

Third Movement: Gavotte

All the movements that follow the overture and the air are inspired by dance, beginning with the gavotte, which is written in duple meter and in a moderate tempo and uses the full orchestra again. It may be outlined as follows: gavotte I (A A B B); gavotte II (C C D D); gavotte I (A B). Notice the contrast between the sections for full orchestra and those without trumpets and timpani.

Fourth Movement: Bourrée

The bourrée is an even livelier dance, also in duple meter; it is the shortest movement of the suite. Its form is A A B B. Section A uses the full orchestra, including trumpets and timpani. Section B is three times as long as section A and alternates loud tutti passages with softer passages for strings and oboes.

Fifth Movement: Gigue

The suite concludes with a rollicking gigue in $\frac{6}{8}$ time, which is also in the form A A B B. Here, Bach's manner is simple and direct. Listen for the splendid effect when timpani and trumpets periodically join the rest of the orchestra.

Air, Bourrée, and Gigue available on Connect Music Bourrée available on Mp3 download card and Mp3 disc

Air
Section A
0:00
Section B
1:14

Bourrée
Section A
0:00
Section B
0:16

Gigue
Section A
0:00
Section B
0:49

13 The Chorale and Church Cantata

In Leipzig in Bach's time, the Lutheran church service on Sunday was the social event of the week: it started at seven in the morning and lasted about four hours. The sermon alone could take an hour.

Music was a significant part of the Lutheran service. Most religious services today use no more than a chorus and an organ, but Bach's church had a small orchestra of between fourteen and twenty-one players to accompany the twelve or so men and boys of the choir. The service was filled with music; single compositions might last half an hour.

Lutheranism stressed direct communication between the believer and Christ; to further this communication, the rite was largely in the vernacular—German. Each service included several hymns, or chorales. The **chorale,** or hymn tune, was sung to a German religious text. Chorales were easy to sing and remember, having only one note to a syllable and moving in steady rhythm. They were tunes that had been composed in the sixteenth and seventeenth centuries or had been adapted from folk songs and Catholic hymns. The members of the congregation had sung these tunes since childhood, and each tune carried religious associations. Congregational singing of chorales was an important way for people to participate directly in the service. These melodies were often harmonized for church choirs. The hymn melody was sung in the top part, and the tones of the supporting harmonies were sung in the three lower parts.

New church music was often based on traditional melodies written as far back as two centuries earlier. Before the congregation began to sing a hymn, the organist might play a **chorale prelude,** a short composition based on the hymn tune that reminded the congregation of the melody. By using traditional tunes in their works, composers could involve the congregation and enhance the religious associations.

Music was a significant part of the Lutheran church service in Germany during the baroque period. This engraving shows a performance of a cantata in Bach's time.

The Church Cantata

The principal means of musical expression in the Lutheran service, and one which used chorales, was the church **cantata.** *Cantata* originally meant a piece that was *sung,* as distinct from a sonata, which was *played.* Many kinds of cantatas were being written in Bach's day, but we shall focus only on the cantata designed for the Lutheran service in Germany in the early 1700s. It was usually written for chorus, vocal soloists, organ, and a small orchestra. It had a German religious text, either newly written or drawn from the Bible or familiar hymns. In the Lutheran services, there were different Gospel and Epistle readings for each Sunday and holiday, and the cantata text was related to them. In a sense, the cantata was a sermon in music that reinforced the minister's sermon, which was also based on the Gospel and Epistle readings. The cantata of Bach's day might last twenty-five minutes and include several different movements—choruses, recitatives, arias, and duets. You'll see that in its use of aria, duet, and recitative, the cantata closely resembled the opera of the time and thus is typical of the baroque fusion of sacred and secular elements in art and music.

The cantor, or music director, had to provide church cantatas for every Sunday and holiday. Bach wrote about 295; about 195 are still in existence. In his first few years as cantor in Leipzig, he composed cantatas at the staggering rate of almost three a month. During the remaining twenty-five years of his tenure, he was inclined to reuse cantatas, and so his output dropped.

Movements 1, 4 and 7 available in Connect Music

Movements 4 and 7 available on Mp3 download card and Mp3 disc

Cantata No. 140: *Wachet auf, ruft uns die Stimme (Awake, a Voice Is Calling Us; 1731)* by Johann Sebastian Bach

Wachet auf, ruft uns die Stimme (Cantata No. 140), one of Bach's best-known cantatas, is based on a chorale that was then about 130 years old and widely familiar. The melody has the form A A B, and the last movement of the cantata presents it unadorned. (The text of the chorale is translated on page 140.)

There are nine melodic phrases, of which the first three (making up the A section) are repeated immediately. The last phrase of the A section (phrase 3) reappears at the end of the B section (phrase 9) and beautifully rounds off the chorale melody.

Now let's consider movements 1, 4, and 7, which use the chorale melody in different ways.

First Movement: Chorus and Orchestra

The opening movement is scored for chorus and a small orchestra of two oboes, English horn, French horn, strings, and basso continuo (organ, bassoon, and cello). In the chorale text of this movement, watchmen on the towers of Jerusalem call on the wise virgins (Christians) to awake because the bridegroom (Christ) is coming. The movement opens with an orchestral ritornello that may have been intended to suggest a procession or march. As shown in the music example that follows, there are dotted rhythms (long-short, long-short), a rising figure with syncopation, and a series of rising scales.

At the ritornello's closing cadence the sopranos enter and sing the first phrase of the chorale in long notes. Soon the three lower voices engage in an imitative dialogue based on a new motive in shorter note values. Throughout, the orchestra continues to play still shorter notes.

Thus there are three layers of sound: the chorale phrases in long notes in the soprano; the imitative dialogue in shorter note values in the three lower voices; and the ever-busy orchestra playing motives from the ritornello in even shorter notes. The chorale tune (in the soprano) is presented not as a continuous whole but rather phrase by phrase, with breaks between phrases. After each phrase, the voices pause while the orchestra continues to play interludes made up of either the whole ritornello or sections from it. Sometimes the motives in the three lower voices illustrate the text, as when they have rising scale figures at the word *hoch* (*high*) and exclamations at the repeated *wo* (*where*).

Once during the movement, the three lower voices become emancipated from the soprano and jubilantly sing a melody in rapid notes on *Alleluja*. This, perhaps, is the most exciting moment in the movement.

Vocal Music Guide

BACH, *Wachet auf, ruft uns die Stimme*

First Movement

      0:00

Orchestral ritornello.

      0:28   *Wachet auf, ruft uns die Stimme*   "Awake," the voice of watchmen

**Brief orchestral
interlude.**

      0:49   *der Wächter sehr hoch auf der Zinne*   calls us from high on the tower,

**Rising scales
in lower voices
depict *hoch* (high).
Brief orchestral
interlude.**

                       wach auf, du Stadt Jerusalem!   "Awake, you city of Jerusalem!"

      1:32

Orchestral ritornello.

      2:00   *Mitternacht heisst diese Stunde;*   Midnight is this very hour;

**Brief orchestral
interlude.**

                       sie rufen uns mit hellem Munde: they call to us with bright voices:

**Brief orchestral
interlude.**

                       wo seid ihr klugen Jungfrauen?   "Where are you, wise virgins?"

      3:04

**Long orchestral
interlude.**

                       Wohl auf, der Bräut'gam kömmt,   Take cheer, the Bridegroom comes,

**Brief orchestral
interlude.**

                       steht auf, die Lampen nehmt!   arise, take up your lamps!

      3:56   *Alleluja!*   Hallelujah!

**Altos, jubilant
melody in
rapid notes.
Imitation by
tenors, then
basses.**

      4:22   *Alleluja!*   Hallelujah!

Sopranos, chorale in long notes.		
Orchestral interlude.		
	Macht euch bereit	Prepare yourselves
Orchestral interlude.		
	zu der Hochzeit	for the wedding,
Brief orchestral interlude.		
5:14	*ihr müsset ihm entgegen gehn.*	you must go forth to meet him.
Orchestral ritornello.		

Fourth Movement: Tenor Chorale

The fourth movement is scored for tenors; violins and violas in unison; and basso continuo. The chorale tune returns in this movement, the most popular of the cantata. Bach liked this section so much that toward the end of his life he rearranged it as a chorale prelude for organ. With miraculous ease, he sets two contrasting melodies against each other. First we hear the unison strings supported by the continuo playing the ritornello, a warm, flowing melody that Bach may have intended as a dancelike procession of the maidens as they "all follow to the joyful hall and share in the Lord's supper." This melody is repeated and varied throughout while the tenors sing the chorale tune against it.

The chorale tune moves in faster rhythmic values here than in the opening movement, but, again, it is broken into component phrases linked by the instrumental melody. It's helpful to listen several times to this movement, focusing first on the rapid rhythms of the graceful string melody, then on the sturdy, slower rhythms of the chorale tune, and finally on all lines at once.

Vocal Music Guide

BACH, *Wachet auf, ruft uns die Stimme*

Fourth Movement

0:00

String ritornello.

0:39	*Zion hört die Wächter singen,*	Zion hears the watchmen singing,
	das Herz tut ihr vor Freuden springen,	for joy her very heart is springing,
	sie wachet und steht eilend auf.	she wakes and rises hastily.

Ritornello.

1:52	*Ihr Freund kommt von Himmel prächtig,*	From heaven comes her friend resplendent,
	von Gnaden stark, von Wahrheit mächtig,	sturdy in grace, mighty in truth,
	Ihr Licht wird hell, ihr Stern geht auf.	her light shines bright, her star ascends.

Ritornello.

2:46	*Nun komm, du werte Kron,*	Now come, you worthy crown,
	Herr Jesu, Gottes Sohn.	Lord Jesus, God's own Son.
3:04	*Hosianna!*	Hosanna!

Ritornello in minor.

| 3:28 | *Wir folgen all' zum Freudensaal* | We all follow to the joyful hall |
| | *und halten mit das Abendmahl.* | and share the Lord's Supper. |

Ritornello.

Seventh Movement: Chorale

Bach rounds off Cantata No. 140 by bringing back the chorale once more. For the first time since the first movement, all voices and instruments take part. Here the chorale is set in a relatively simple, homophonic texture for four voices, with the instruments simply duplicating them, not playing melodies of their own. Now the chorale is heard as a continuous melody, without interludes between its phrases. The rich sound, full harmonies, and regular rhythms express praise of God, faith in him, and joy in being in his kingdom. No doubt the congregation joined in the singing of the final chorale, which so firmly expressed their unity and belief.

Vocal Music Guide

BACH, *Wachet auf, ruft uns die Stimme*

Seventh Movement

A

Gloria sei dir gesungen	Gloria be sung to you
mit Menschenund englischen Zungen,	with men's and angel's tongues,
mit Harfen und mit Zimbeln schon.	with harps and beautiful cymbals.

A

Von zwölf Perlen sind die Pforten	Of twelve pearls are the gates
an deiner Stadt; wir sind Konsorten	at your city; we are consorts
der Engel hoch um deinen Thron.	of the angels high about your throne.

B

Kein Aug' hat je gespürt,	No eye has ever sensed,
kein Ohr hat je gehört	no ear has ever heard
solche Freude.	such a delight.
Des sind wir froh,	Of this we rejoice,
io, io!	io, io!
ewig in dulci jubilo.	forever in sweet joy.

14 The Oratorio

Together with the opera and cantata, the oratorio stands as a major development in baroque vocal music. Like an opera, an ***oratorio*** is a large-scale composition for chorus, vocal soloists, and orchestra; it is usually set to a narrative text. Oratorio differs from opera in that it has no acting, scenery, or costumes. Most oratorios are based on biblical stories, but usually they are not intended for religious services. Today they are performed in either concert halls or churches.

An oratorio contains a succession of choruses, arias, duets, recitatives, and orchestral interludes. The chorus is especially important and serves either to comment on or to participate in the drama. A narrator's recitatives usually relate the story and connect one piece with another. Oratorios (which sometimes last more than two hours) are longer than cantatas and have more of a story line.

Oratorios first appeared in early seventeenth-century Italy as musical dramatizations of biblical stories and were performed in prayer halls called *oratorios*. During the baroque period, the oratorio spread to other countries and assumed many forms. *Messiah,* by George Frideric Handel, has for decades been the best-known and most-loved oratorio.

15 George Frideric Handel

George Frideric Handel (1685–1759), a master of Italian opera and English oratorio, was born in Halle, Germany, one month before J. S. Bach. Handel was not from a musical family—his father wanted him to study law—but by the time he was nine, his musical talent was so outstanding that he was allowed to study with a local organist and composer. By eleven, Handel was able not only to compose but also to give organ lessons. At eighteen, he set out for Hamburg, where he was drawn to the renowned opera house. There he became a violinist and harpsichordist in the orchestra. When he was twenty, one of his operas was successfully produced.

Handel's triple career as impresario, composer, and performer brought him success and fame but led to political infighting and two nervous breakdowns.

At twenty-one, Handel went to Italy. There he wrote widely acclaimed operas and mingled with princes, cardinals, and famous musicians. Returning to Germany in 1710, Handel took a well-paid position as music director for Elector Georg Ludwig of Hanover. After just a month, he asked for a leave to go to London, where his opera *Rinaldo* was being produced. *Rinaldo* was a triumph, and a year later Handel asked for another English leave—which was granted for a "reasonable time" that turned out to be the next half-century (1712–1759).

Handel became England's most important composer and a favorite of Queen Anne. He was the director of the Royal Academy of Music (a commercial opera company) and composed a number of brilliant operas for outstanding sopranos and castrati. When the Royal Academy folded, he formed a company to produce his works. (For years he had a triple career as impresario, composer, and performer.) The company eventually went bankrupt and Handel suffered a breakdown, but he recovered, returned to London, and—though heavily in debt—managed again to produce operas on his own. To these he added his oratorios, opening a glowing new chapter in music history.

Late in life, Handel was still conducting and giving organ concerts, though he was almost blind. When he died in 1759, 3,000 mourners attended his funeral in Westminster Abbey. He was wealthy, generous, cultivated—and stubborn. But above all, he was a master composer whose dramatic sense has rarely been equaled.

Handel's Music

Handel shares Bach's stature among composers of the late baroque. Although he wrote a great deal of instrumental music—suites, organ concertos, concerti grossi—the core of his huge output consists of Italian operas and English oratorios.

Handel's thirty-nine Italian operas are not as well known today as his oratorios. But after two centuries of neglect, these operas are being revived successfully by modern opera companies. Their arias—often written to display the virtuosity of singers—show his outstanding ability to evoke a mood or an emotion.

Handel's English oratorios are usually based on stories from the Old Testament and have titles like *Israel in Egypt, Saul,* and *Joshua.* They are *not* church music, however; they were composed to entertain paying audiences in public theaters. Most have plots and characters, even though they are performed without acting, scenery, or costumes. As we'll see, *Messiah* is an exception, in that it deals with a New Testament subject and is without a plot. The chorus is the focus of Handel's oratorio and is combined flexibly and imaginatively with the orchestra. Changes in texture are more frequent in Handel's music than in Bach's. He liked to combine two different melodic ideas polyphonically and he achieved sharp changes of mood by shifting between minor keys and major keys.

Messiah (1741)

Messiah lasts about two and a half hours and was composed in just twenty-four days. Handel wrote it before going to Ireland to attend performances of his own works that were being given to dedicate a concert hall. About five months after his arrival in Dublin (in 1742), Handel gave the first performance of *Messiah;* the occasion was a benefit for people languishing in debtors' prisons. The rehearsals attracted wide attention: one newspaper commented that *Messiah* was thought "by the greatest Judges to be the finest Composition of Musick that ever was heard." Normally, the concert hall held 600 people; but to increase the capacity, women were asked not to wear hoopskirts, and men were asked to leave their swords at home.

Although the premiere was a success, the first performance in London (1743) was poorly received, mainly because of religious opposition to using a Christian text in a theater. It took *Messiah* almost a decade to find popularity in London. Not until it was performed yearly at a benefit for a London orphanage did it achieve its unique status. A contemporary wrote that *Messiah* "fed the hungry, clothed the naked, fostered the orphan."

Messiah is in three parts. Part I starts with the prophecy of the Messiah's coming and makes celestial announcements of Christ's birth and the redemption of humanity through his appearance. Part II has been aptly described by one Handel scholar as "the accomplishment of redemption by the sacrifice of Jesus, mankind's rejection of God's offer and mankind's utter defeat when trying to oppose the power of the Almighty." Part III expresses faith in the certainty of eternal life through Christ as redeemer.

Unlike most of Handel's oratorios, *Messiah* is meditative rather than dramatic; it lacks plot, action, and specific characters. *Messiah* is Handel's only English oratorio that uses the New Testament as well as the Old. Charles Jennings, a millionaire and amateur literary man, compiled the text by taking widely separated passages from the Bible—Isaiah, Psalms, and Job from the Old Testament; Luke, I Corinthians, and Revelations from the New.

Over the years, Handel rewrote some movements in *Messiah* for different performers and performances. In his own time, it was performed with a smaller orchestra and chorus than we are used to. His chorus included twenty singers, all male; and his small orchestra had only strings and continuo, with trumpets and timpani used in some sections. Today we sometimes hear arranged versions; Mozart made one, and still later versions are often played by orchestras of one hundred and choruses of several hundred.

Messiah has over fifty movements, and Handel ensures variety by skillfully contrasting and grouping them. We focus on two movements from Part I and the famous *Hallelujah* Chorus, which ends Part II.

Ev'ry Valley Shall Be Exalted,
Aria for tenor, strings, and continuo
Andante

The aria *Ev'ry Valley Shall Be Exalted* is based on a verse from Isaiah (40:4) describing the creation of a desert highway on which God will lead his people back to their homeland. Like many baroque arias, it opens and closes with a string ritornello. This aria is striking in its vivid word painting, so characteristic of baroque music. On a single syllable of *exalted* (*raised up*), forty-six rapid notes form a rising musical line.

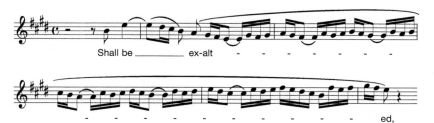

Shall be _____ ex-alt - - - - - -

- - - - - - - - - ed,

Notice, too, the rising and falling direction of the phrase *and every mountain and hill made low:*

and ev-'ry moun-tain and hill _____ made low;

The crooked straight is represented as follows:

the crook-ed __ straight,

In the line *and the rough places plain,* the word *plain* (*smooth* or *level*) is expressed by sustained tones and a long, legato melodic line.

Vocal Music Guide

HANDEL, *Ev'ry Valley Shall Be Exalted,* from *Messiah*

0:00	Orchestral ritornello.	
0:20	Voice alone.	Ev'ry valley
	Orchestra imitates voice.	
	Ascending rapid notes on *exalted.*	Ev'ry valley shall be exalted,
0:54	High tone on *mountain.*	and ev'ry mountain
	Low tone on *low.*	and hill made low,
	Wavy melody on *crooked.*	the crooked straight,
	Legato melody on *plain.*	and the rough places plain.
	Orchestra alone, cadence.	
	New word painting on	Ev'ry valley shall be exalted,
1:37	*exalted, mountain, low.*	and ev'ry mountain and hill
	crooked, plain.	made low, the crooked straight,
		and the rough places plain.
2:46	Slow, ornamented	The crooked straight,
	vocal cadence.	and the rough places plain.
	Orchestral ritornello.	

For unto Us a Child is Born available on Connect Music

For unto Us a Child Is Born, Chorus, strings, continuo

The twelfth movement, *For unto Us a Child Is Born,* is among Handel's most joyful music. This chorus is based on a verse from Isaiah (9:6) that celebrates the birth of a royal child whose names predict salvation. The texture is light, often with only one or two voices singing at a time. Handel uses a transparent polyphonic texture for the words *For unto us a Child is born, unto us a Son is given.* He sets two contrasting ideas against each other. One voice part sings fifty-six rapid notes on the single syllable of *born* while another sings *unto us a Son is given,* with one note to each syllable.

The words *and the government shall be upon His shoulder* bring a new melodic idea in dotted rhythm.

Handel keeps the dynamics subdued until the striking chordal outburst on *Wonderful, Counsellor.* This change from *p* to *ff* and from polyphonic to homophonic texture is a masterstroke.

   For unto Us a Child Is Born divides into four sections, each with the same text and musical ideas. The first three sections all begin with a light texture, but the climactic final section uses the full chorus almost from the very beginning.

   With such a close fusion of words and music, it may be disconcerting to learn that most of the melodic ideas in this chorus came from Handel's Italian duet for the words *No, I will not trust you, blind love, cruel Beauty! You are too treacherous, too charming a deity!* (The musical idea for *Wonderful* is new.) But remember that in Handel's time there was little difference in style between sacred and secular music. Amorous joy and religious joy could therefore be conveyed in the same manner.

> *For unto us a Child is born, unto us a Son*
> *is given,*
> Sopranos imitated by tenors.
> Sopranos, rapid notes (*born*) against
> tenors (*unto us a Son is given*).
> Altos (*For unto us*) imitated by basses.
> altos (*unto us a Child is given*).
> Basses, rapid notes (*born*) against altos (*unto us a Son is given*).

and the government shall be upon His shoulder,
and His Name shall be called:

Wonderful, Counsellor, the Mighty God,
the Everlasting Father, the Prince of Peace.

Hallelujah Chorus

The *Hallelujah* Chorus is one of the world's most famous choral pieces. In this vigorous chorus, Handel offers sweeping variety by sudden changes among monophonic, polyphonic, and homophonic textures. The monophonic texture is very full-sounding as all the voices and instruments perform in unison at the proclamation *for the Lord God Omnipotent reigneth.* The texture becomes polyphonic when this majestic proclamation is set against joyful repeated exclamations of *Hallelujah* in quick rhythms. Polyphony gives way to homophony as the chorus sings *The kingdom of this world* to hymnlike music.

In the *Hallelujah* Chorus, words and phrases are repeated over and over, as has been common practice in choral music for several centuries. (In the following text, braces connect lines sung at the same time.) Handel took his text from the Revelation of St. John, which celebrates God as the almighty and everlasting ruler.

Vocal Music Guide

HANDEL, *Hallelujah* Chorus, from *Messiah*

	Orchestral introduction.	
	Chorus joins, homophonic, quick exclamations.	Hallelujah!
0:23	Monophonic, longer notes.	for the lord God Omnipotent reigneth;
	Homophonic, quick exclamations.	Hallelujah!
	Monophonic, longer notes.	for the Lord God Omnipotent reigneth;
	Homophonic, quick exclamations.	Hallelujah!
0:44	Longer-note melody against quick exclamations, polyphonic.	{ for the Lord God Omnipotent reigneth; Hallelujah!
1:09	Hymnlike in longer notes, homophonic.	The kingdom of this world is become the Kingdom of our Lord and of His Christ:
1:26	Bass melody, monophonic. Other voices imitate, polyphonic.	and He shall reign for ever and ever,

1:48	Long repeated tones against quick exclamations; phrases repeated at higher pitches.	{ King of Kings, and Lord of Lords, for ever and ever, Hallelujah, Hallelujah!
2:28	Polyphonic, imitation.	and He shall reign for ever and ever,
2:40	Long repeated tones against quick exclamations. Polyphonic.	King of Kings, and Lord of Lords, for ever and ever, Hallelujah, Hallelujah! and He shall reign for ever and ever,
2:55	Homophonic. Polyphonic.	King of Kings, and Lord of Lords, and He shall reign for ever and ever.
3:10	Quick exclamations.	{ King of Kings, and Lord of Lords, for ever and ever, for ever and ever, Hallelujah, Hallelujah, Hallelujah, Hallelujah!
3:20	Pause. Sustained chords, homophonic.	Hallelujah!

The Baroque Period: Summary

Music in Society

- Music was composed to order for specific events.
- The primary areas of employment for musicians were in aristocratic courts, the church, and the opera house. Composers working in aristocratic courts were considered servants.
- Some aristocrats became accomplished musicians.
- Large towns employed musicians for a variety of functions.

Important Style Features

Mood and Emotional Expression
- In instrumental music, a section or entire movement will express one basic mood throughout ("unity of mood").
- In vocal music, changes of mood in the text are often accompanied by changes in the music.

Rhythm
- Rhythmic patterns heard at the beginning of a piece are often repeated throughout.
- The rhythmic pulse is regular, consistent, and strong, typically featuring a constantly moving bass line, even when the music is in a slow tempo.
- The unity of rhythm provides compelling drive and energy that are characteristic of baroque music.

Dynamics
- Terraced dynamics change suddenly rather than gradually and are a major feature of baroque music.

Tone Color
- The basso continuo—consisting of a bass melodic instrument, such as the cello or bassoon; and a keyboard instrument, such as the organ or harpsichord—is one of the most distinctive instrumental features of baroque music.
- The instruments of baroque orchestras, typically ten to forty players, vary from piece to piece.
- Stringed instruments predominate, along with the basso continuo. Woodwind, brass, and percussion instruments are optional and variable in number when used.
- Purely instrumental music grows in importance as a genre throughout the baroque period.

Melody and Harmony
- Melodies are often complex and are not easy to remember on one hearing.
- Melodies recur as a whole or in part throughout a movement or aria.
- Melodies give an impression of continuous expansion, even within a slow tempo.
- Vocal melodies frequently use wide leaps and contain striking chromatic intervals.
- Harmony is based on major and minor scales but may contain passages of striking chromaticism.

IMPORTANT TERMS

Affections, p. 102
Terraced dynamics, p. 103
Clavichord, p. 103
Basso continuo, p. 104
Figured bass, p. 104
Movement, p. 105
Tutti, p. 108
Ritornello form, p. 108
Ritornello, p. 108
Subject, p. 111
Answer, p. 112
Countersubject, p. 112
Episode, p. 112
Stretto, p. 112
Pedal point (organ point), p. 112
Inversion, p. 112
Retrograde, p. 112
Augmentation, p. 112
Diminution, p. 112
Prelude, p. 112
Libretto, p. 115
Librettist, p. 115
Voice categories of opera, p. 116
Aria, p. 116
Recitative, p. 116
Ensemble, p. 117
Chorus, p. 117
Prompter, p. 117
Overture (prelude), p. 117
Camerata, p. 118
Castrato, p. 119
Countertenor, p. 119
Secco recitative, p. 119
Accompanied recitative, p. 119
Da capo aria, p. 119
Da capo, p. 119
Ground bass, p. 123
Basso ostinato, p. 123
Trill, p. 127
Improvisation, p. 131
Suite, p. 132
French overture, p. 132
Chorale, p. 134
Chorale prelude, p. 134

FEATURED COMPOSERS

Johann Sebastian Bach
     (1685–1750)
Claudio Monteverdi
     (1567–1643)
Henry Purcell (1659–1695)
Arcangelo Corelli (1653–1713)
Antonio Vivaldi (1678–1741)
George Frideric Handel
     (1685–1759)

Texture

- In late baroque music, the texture is predominantly polyphonic, with an emphasis on the lowest and highest melodic lines.
- The bass line provides a harmonic foundation for the music, often written as a figured bass that encouraged improvisation.
- Imitation between the individual melodic lines of music is very common.

Baroque Performance Practice

- Performers of baroque music face numerous choices about how they are going to play the music written on the page. Their decisions greatly affect the music you hear.
- Baroque musical scores often do not specify either the instruments to be used in a performance or the exact numbers of performers required, especially in early baroque music. Pay careful attention to the types and number of instruments or voices you hear.
- Improvisation and virtuosity by instrumentalists and vocalists were both expected and greatly prized by baroque audiences. Performing or "realizing" a basso continuo line relies heavily on this practice. Listen carefully for the distinctive sound of the basso continuo, or note if the soloist embellishes the music if a section is repeated.
- Performers of baroque music must choose to perform on either "authentic" period instruments that are typical of those used during the baroque era, or modern instruments that utilize technological advances made since the music was composed.

Beyond the Classroom: Attending an Opera

Opera was one of the most important genres invented during the baroque era. Thousands of operas have been composed since then, and they remain one of the most popular forms of entertainment today. When you attend a live opera performance or listen to a recording, you will notice that certain aspects do not change regardless of when the music was composed, whereas other features vary considerably. Pay attention to these similarities and differences. Newer productions now may incorporate computer generated projections to the set and scenery, demonstrating opera's great ability to adapt to the times. To more fully enjoy an opera performance, ask yourself the following questions:

- What features of the music might indicate when it was composed? For example, if you are listening to an opera from the baroque period, do you notice recitatives accompanied by a basso continuo? Do any of the arias repeat the opening section, as in a da capo aria, and if so, is the repeated music ornamented by the singer?
- What are the voice types of the lead singers and any secondary characters?

- Is there a chorus, and if so, what role does the chorus play in the drama?
- Are there any duets, trios, or larger ensembles of singers?
- What number and kinds of instruments are used in the orchestra?
- Does the opera feature dancing at any point?
- Are the scenery and costumes characteristic of the period and locale, or do they represent another time and place?
- Are computer-generated projections used to create scenery? Do you notice any other digital enhancements added to the projection?
- Is the opera sung in its original language or in English translation?
- If there are supertitles above the stage, are they helpful or distracting?
- Did you notice a prompter?
- Did the performance appear to go as rehearsed, or did you notice anything unusual or notable about it?

■ During the classical period, many members of the aristocracy and the wealthy middle class were good musicians. Johann Zoffany (1733–1810), *George, Third Earl Cowper with the Family of Charles Gore* (c. 1775).

PART IV

The Classical Period

I am never happier than when I have something to compose, for that, after all, is my sole delight and passion.

—Wolfgang Amadeus Mozart

LEARNING OBJECTIVES

- Compare and contrast the classical style and the late baroque style

- Trace the gradual emancipation of the composer through the careers of Haydn, Mozart, and Beethoven

- Explain the main elements of sonata form, theme and variations, minuet and trio, and rondo

- Distinguish the sonata form from the *sonata*

- Describe a typical symphony of the classical period

- List the ways in which the classical concerto differs from the classical symphony

- Discuss the key features of classical chamber music

- Explain some of the innovative features in Beethoven's music

TIME LINE

Classical Period 1750–1820

| 1750–1770 | 1770–1820 |

Historical and Cultural Events

1756–1763 Seven Years' War

1769 Watt invents
steam engine

1774–1792 Louis XVI reigns in France

1776 American Declaration
of Independence

1780–1790 Joseph II reigns in Austria

1789 French Revolution begins

1799 Napoleon becomes first consul
of France

1803–1815 Napoleonic Wars

1814–1815 Congress of Vienna

Arts and Letters

1751 Publication of the French
Encyclopedia begins

1759 Voltaire,
Candide

1762 Rousseau,
*The Social
Contract*

c. 1771–1773 Fragonard, *The
Lover Crowned*

1787 David, *Death of Socrates*

1800 David, *Napoleon at
St. Bernard*

1808 Goethe, *Faust*

1813 Austen, *Pride and
Prejudice*

1814 Goya, *The Third of May,
1808*

1819 Scott, *Ivanhoe*

Music

c. 1757 Haydn, String Quartets, Op. 1

1759 Haydn, Symphony No. 1 in D Major

1764 Mozart, Symphony No. 1 in E Flat Major,
K. 16

1772 Haydn, Symphony No. 45
in F Sharp Minor (*Farewell*)

1787 Mozart, *Don Giovanni* and
Eine kleine Nachtmusik

1788 Mozart, Symphony No. 40
in G Minor, K. 550

1791 Haydn, Symphony No. 94
(*Surprise*)

1796 Haydn, Trumpet Concerto
in E Flat Major

1798 Beethoven, Piano Sonata in
C Minor, Op. 13 (*Pathétique*)

1808 Beethoven, Symphony No. 5
in C Minor

1824 Beethoven, Symphony No. 9
in D Minor (*Choral*)

The Classical Era
(1750–1820)

In looking at the baroque era, we found that the scientific methods and discoveries of geniuses like Galileo and Newton vastly changed people's view of the world. By the middle of the eighteenth century, faith in the power of reason was so great that it began to undermine the authority of the social and religious establishment. Philosophers and writers—especially Voltaire (1694–1778) and Denis Diderot (1713–1784)—saw their time as a turning point in history and referred to it as the "age of enlightenment." They believed in progress, holding that reason, not custom or tradition, was the best guide for human conduct. Their attacks on the privileges of the aristocracy and clergy reflected the outlook of the middle class, which was struggling for its rights.

The ideas of enlightenment thinkers were implemented by several rulers during the eighteenth century. For example, Emperor Joseph II of Austria, who reigned from 1780 to 1790, abolished serfdom, closed monasteries and convents, and eliminated the nobility's special status in criminal law. He discouraged elaborate religious ceremonies and decreed that burials be simple; though this decree was soon revoked, modest funerals became customary in Vienna. In 1791, Wolfgang Amadeus Mozart—one of the greatest composers of the classical period—was buried in a sack in an unmarked communal grave.

Violent political and social upheaval marked the seventy-year period from 1750 to 1820. These years were convulsed by the Seven Years' War, the American and French revolutions, and the Napoleonic Wars. Political and economic power shifted from the aristocracy and church to the middle class.

Social mobility increased to a point that Napoleon could become emperor of France by his own genius rather than as a birthright. "Subversive" new slogans like *Liberty, equality, fraternity!* sprang from the people's lips. All established ideas were being reexamined, including the existence of God.

Revolutions in thought and action were paralleled by shifts in style in the visual arts. During the early eighteenth century, the heavy, monumental baroque style gave way to the more intimate *rococo* style, with its light colors, curved lines, and graceful ornaments. The painters Antoine Watteau (1684–1721) and Jean-Honoré Fragonard (1732–1806) depicted an enchanted world peopled by elegant men and women in constant pursuit of pleasure. But by the later eighteenth century there was yet another change

Happy Lovers (c. 1760–1765), by the French rococo painter Jean-Honoré Fragonard (1732–1806), depicts a young couple in an idealized natural setting.

Death of Socrates (1787) by Jacques-Louis David. By the late eighteenth century, the rococo style had been superseded by the neoclassical style, which attempted to recapture the "noble simplicity and calm grandeur" of ancient Greek and Roman art. Neoclassic artists, such as the French painter David, emphasized firm lines, clear structure, and moralistic subjects.

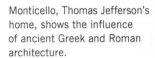

Monticello, Thomas Jefferson's home, shows the influence of ancient Greek and Roman architecture.

in taste, and rococo art was thought frivolous, excessively ornamented, and lacking in ethical content. The rococo style was superseded by the *neoclassical* style, which attempted to recapture the "noble simplicity and calm grandeur" of ancient Greek and Roman art. Neoclassical artists emphasized firm lines, clear structure, and moralistic subject matter. The painter Jacques-Louis David (1748–1825), who took part in the French Revolution, sought to inspire heroism and patriotism through his scenes of ancient Rome.

The artistic response to the decline of traditional power is evidenced further by the English painter William Hogarth (1697–1764), whose socially conscious paintings satirized the manners and morals of the British aristocracy and middle class; and by the Spanish painter Francisco Goya (1746–1828), who used his highly personal vision to create art that lashed out against hypocrisy, oppression, and inhumanity.

Napoleon at St. Bernard (1800) by Jacques-Louis David. Beethoven originally planned to name his Third Symphony (*Eroica,* 1803–1804) "Bonaparte," because he saw Napoleon as an embodiment of heroism; but when he learned that Napoleon had proclaimed himself emperor, Beethoven tore out the title page and later renamed the symphony "Heroic Symphony composed to celebrate the memory of a great man."

The Third of May, 1808 by the Spanish artist Francisco Goya. The classical period was a time of violent political and social upheaval, witnessing the American Revolution, the French Revolution, and the Napoleonic wars. In 1814 Goya painted this vivid scene of the execution of Spanish hostages by Napoleon's soldiers.

1 The Classical Style (1750–1820)

In music history, the transition from the baroque style to the full flowering of the classical is called the *preclassical* period; it extends from roughly 1730 to 1770. The shift in musical taste parallels the similar, earlier trend in the visual arts. It was developing even as Bach and Handel were creating baroque masterpieces. Among the important pioneers in this new style were Bach's sons Carl Philipp Emanuel (1714–1788) and Johann Christian (1735–1782). Around the middle of the eighteenth century, composers concentrated on simplicity and clarity, discarding much that had enriched late baroque music. Polyphonic texture was neglected in favor of tuneful melody and simple harmony. Carl Philipp Emanuel Bach described music with strict polyphonic imitation as "dry and despicable pieces of pedantry." Mid-eighteenth-century composers entertained their listeners with music offering contrasts of mood and theme. The term *style galant* (*gallant style*) was applied to this light, graceful music. The *style galant* in music is comparable to the rococo style in art.

The term *classical* is confusing because it has so many different meanings. It may refer to Greek or Roman antiquity, or it may be used for any supreme accomplishment of lasting appeal (as in the expression *movie classic*). Many people take *classical music* to mean anything that is not rock, jazz, folk, or popular music.

Music historians have borrowed the term *classical* from art history, where it is more appropriate. The painting, sculpture, and architecture of the late eighteenth century and the early nineteenth century were often influenced by Greek and Roman models. But the music of this period shows little direct relation to antiquity. The significant parallel between "classical" music and "neoclassical" art is a common stress on balance and clarity of structure. These traits can be found in the fully developed classical style in music, which is our focus. That style flourished from about 1770 to 1820, and its master composers were Joseph Haydn (1732–1809), Wolfgang Amadeus Mozart (1756–1791), and Ludwig van Beethoven (1770–1827). First, we study the characteristics of their work.

Characteristics of the Classical Style

Contrast of Mood   Great variety and contrast of mood received new emphasis in classical music. Whereas a late baroque piece may convey a single emotion, a classical composition will fluctuate in mood. Dramatic, turbulent music might lead into a carefree dance tune. Not only are there contrasting themes within a movement, but there may also be striking contrasts within a single theme.

Mood in classical music may change gradually or suddenly, expressing conflicting surges of elation and depression. But such conflict and contrast are under the firm control of the classical composer. Masters like Haydn, Mozart, and Beethoven were able to impart unity and logic to music of wide emotional range.

Rhythm   Flexibility of rhythm adds variety to classical music. A classical composition has a wealth of rhythmic patterns, whereas a baroque piece contains a few patterns that are reiterated throughout. Baroque works convey a sense of continuity and perpetual motion, so that after the first few bars one can predict pretty well the rhythmic character of an entire movement. But the classical style also includes unexpected pauses, syncopations, and frequent changes from long notes to shorter notes. And the change from one pattern of note lengths to another may be either sudden or gradual.

Texture In contrast to the polyphonic texture of late baroque music, classical music is basically homophonic. However, texture is treated as flexibly as rhythm. Pieces shift smoothly or suddenly from one texture to another. A work may begin homophonically with a melody and simple accompaniment but then change to a more complex polyphonic texture that features two simultaneous melodies or melodic fragments imitated among the various instruments.

Melody Classical melodies are among the most tuneful and easiest to remember. The themes of even highly sophisticated compositions may have a folk or popular flavor. Occasionally, composers simply borrowed popular tunes. (Mozart did, in his variations on the French song *Ah, vous dirai-je, maman,* which we know as *Twinkle, Twinkle, Little Star.*) More often, however, they wrote original themes with a popular character.

Classical melodies tend to sound balanced and symmetrical because they are frequently made up of two phrases of the same length. The second phrase in such melodies may begin like the first, but it ends more conclusively. Such a melodic type, which may be diagrammed a a′, is easy to sing. (It is frequently found in nursery tunes such as *Mary Had a Little Lamb.*) Baroque melodies, in contrast, tend to be less symmetrical, more elaborate, and harder to sing.

Dynamics and the Piano Classical composers' interest in expressing shades of emotion led to the widespread use of gradual dynamic change—crescendo and decrescendo. These composers did not restrict themselves to the terraced dynamics (abrupt shifts from loud to soft) characteristic of baroque music. Crescendos and decrescendos were an electrifying novelty; audiences sometimes rose excitedly from their seats.

During the classical period, the desire for gradual dynamic change led to the replacement of the harpsichord by the piano. By varying the finger pressure on the keys, a pianist can play more loudly or softly. Although the piano was invented around 1700, it began to replace the harpsichord only around 1775. Most of the mature keyboard compositions of Haydn, Mozart, and Beethoven were written for the piano, rather than for harpsichord, clavichord, and organ, which had been featured in baroque music. The late eighteenth-century piano—called a *fortepiano*—weighed much less than the modern piano and had thinner strings held by a frame made of wood rather than metal. Its pitch range was smaller, and its tone was smaller and lasted a shorter time.

The End of the Basso Continuo The basso continuo was gradually abandoned during the classical period. In Haydn's or Mozart's works, a harpsichordist did not need to improvise an accompaniment. One reason the basso continuo became obsolete was that more and more music was written for amateurs, who could not master the difficult art of improvising from a figured bass. Also, classical composers wanted more control; they preferred to specify an accompaniment rather than trust the judgment of improvisers.

The Classical Orchestra

A new orchestra evolved during the classical period. Unlike the baroque orchestra, which could vary from piece to piece, it was a standard group of four sections: strings, woodwinds, brass, and percussion. In the late instrumental works of Mozart and Haydn, an orchestra might consist of the following:

> *Strings:* 1st violins, 2d violins, violas, cellos, double basses
> *Woodwinds:* 2 flutes, 2 oboes, 2 clarinets, 2 bassoons
> *Brass:* 2 French horns, 2 trumpets
> *Percussion:* 2 timpani

Notice that woodwind and brass instruments are paired and that clarinets have been added. Trombones were also used by Haydn and Mozart, but only in opera and church music, not in solely instrumental works.

The number of musicians was greater in a classical orchestra than in a baroque group, though practice varied considerably from place to place. Haydn directed a private orchestra of only twenty-five players from 1761 to 1790. But for public concerts in London in 1795, he led an orchestra of sixty.

Classical composers exploited the individual tone colors of orchestral instruments. Unlike baroque composers, they did not treat one instrument like another. Classical composers would not let an oboe duplicate the violin melody for the entire length of a movement. A classical piece has greater variety—and more rapid changes—of tone color. A theme might begin in the full orchestra, shift to the strings, and then continue in the woodwinds.

Each section of the classical orchestra had a special role. The strings were the most important section, with the first violins taking the melody most of the time and the lower strings providing an accompaniment. The woodwinds added contrasting tone colors and were often given melodic solos. Horns and trumpets brought power to loud passages and filled out the harmony, but they did not usually play the main melody. Timpani were used for rhythmic bite and emphasis. As a whole, the classical orchestra had developed into a flexible and colorful instrument to which composers could entrust their most powerful and dramatic musical conceptions.

Classical Forms

Instrumental compositions of the classical period usually consist of several movements that contrast in tempo and character. There are often four movements, arranged as follows:

1. Fast movement
2. Slow movement
3. Dance-related movement
4. Fast movement

Classical symphonies and string quartets usually follow this four-movement pattern, whereas classical sonatas may consist of two, three, or four movements. A *symphony* is written for orchestra; a *string quartet* for two violins, viola, and cello; and a *sonata* for one or two instruments. (The classical symphony, string quartet, and sonata are more fully described in Sections 3 to 7 and 9.)

In writing an individual movement of a symphony, string quartet, or sonata, a classical composer could choose from several different forms. One movement of a composition might be in A B A form, whereas another might be a theme and variations. The sections that follow describe some forms used in classical movements, but now let's look at a few general characteristics of classical form.

Classical movements often contrast themes vividly. A movement may contain two, three, or even four or more themes of different character. This use of contrasting themes distinguishes classical music from baroque music, which often uses only one main theme. The classical composer sometimes uses a brief pause to signal the arrival of a new theme.

The larger sections of a classical movement balance each other in a satisfying and symmetrical way. Unstable sections that wander from the tonic key are balanced by stable sections that confirm it. By the end of a classical movement, musical tensions have been resolved.

Though we speak of the classical style, we must remember that Haydn, Mozart, and Beethoven were three individuals with dissimilar personalities. While Haydn's and Mozart's works may sound similar at first, deeper involvement reveals striking personal styles. Beethoven's music seems more powerful, violent, and emotional when compared with the apparently more restrained and elegant works of the earlier masters. But Haydn and Mozart also composed music that is passionate and dramatic. We'll see that all three composers used similar musical procedures and forms, yet their emotional statements bear the particular stamp of each.

2 Composer, Patron, and Public in the Classical Period

Haydn, Mozart, and Beethoven—three of the world's greatest composers—worked during a period of violent political and social upheaval, as we have seen in the opening of Part IV. Like everyone else, musicians were strongly affected by changes in society, and in the careers of the three classical masters we can trace the slow emancipation of the composer. First came Joseph Haydn (1732–1809), who was content to spend most of his life serving a wealthy aristocratic family. His contract of employment (1761) shows that he was considered a skilled servant, like a gardener or gamekeeper. He had to wear a uniform and "compose such music as His Highness shall order"—and was warned to "refrain from vulgarity in eating, drinking, and conversation." Wolfgang Amadeus Mozart (1756–1791), born just twenty-four years later, could not bear being treated as a servant; he broke from his court position and went to Vienna to try his luck as a freelance musician. For several years, he was very successful, but then his popularity declined; he died in debt. Ludwig van Beethoven (1770–1827) fared better than Mozart. Only a few years after Mozart's death, Beethoven was able to work as an independent musician in Vienna. His success was gained through a wider middle-class market for music and a commanding personality that prompted the nobility to give him gifts and treat him as an equal.

As the eighteenth century advanced, more people made more money. Merchants, doctors, and government officials could afford larger homes, finer clothes, and better food. But the prospering middle class wanted more than material goods; it also sought aristocratic luxuries like theater, literature, and music. In fact, during the classical period, the middle class had a great influence on music. Because palace concerts were usually closed to them, townspeople organized public concerts, where, for the price of admission, they could hear the latest symphonies and concertos. During the second half of the eighteenth century, public concerts mushroomed throughout Europe. In London, a concert series ran from 1765 to 1781, codirected by one of Bach's sons, Johann Christian Bach, who had settled in England. In Paris, around the same time, a concert organization called the *Concert des Amateurs* assembled a large orchestra, conducted during the 1770s by the Chevalier de Saint-Georges (1739–1799), a black composer and violinist who was a champion fencer as well.

But merchants and lawyers were not content to hear music only in concerts. They wanted to be surrounded by music at home. They felt that their sons and daughters deserved music lessons as much as the children of aristocrats did. Indeed, if middle-class children played instruments well enough, they might be invited to palaces and eventually marry into the aristocracy. In any event, the demand for printed music, instruments, and music lessons had vastly increased.

Composers in the classical period took middle-class tastes into account. They wrote pieces that were easy for amateur musicians to play and understand. They turned from serious to comic opera, from the heroic and mythological plots dear to the nobility to middle-class subjects and folklike tunes. Their comic operas sometimes even ridiculed the aristocracy, and their dance movements became less elegant and courtly, more vigorous and rustic.

Serious composition was flavored by folk and popular music. The classical masters sometimes used familiar tunes as themes for symphonies and variations. Mozart was delighted that people danced to waltzes arranged from melodies in his operas. Haydn, Mozart, and Beethoven all wrote dance music for public balls in Vienna.

Vienna

Vienna was one of the music centers of Europe during the classical period, and Haydn, Mozart, and Beethoven were all active there. As the seat of the Holy Roman Empire (which included parts of modern Austria, Germany, Italy, Hungary, and the Czech Republic), it was a bustling cultural and commercial center with a cosmopolitan character. Its population of almost 250,000 (in 1800) made Vienna the fourth largest city in Europe. All three classical masters were born elsewhere, but they were drawn to Vienna to study and to seek recognition. In Vienna, Haydn and Mozart became close friends and influenced each other's musical style. Beethoven traveled to Vienna at sixteen to play for Mozart; at twenty-two, he returned to study with Haydn.

Aristocrats from all over the empire would spend winters in Vienna, sometimes bringing their private orchestras. Music was an important part of court life, and a good orchestra was a symbol of prestige. Many of the nobility were excellent musicians. For

Most of Haydn's music was composed for a wealthy aristocratic family. Shown here is a performance of a comic opera by Haydn in 1775 at the palace Eszterháza.

instance, Empress Maria Theresa had sung in palace musicales when she was young, Emperor Joseph II was a competent cellist, and Archduke Rudolf was Beethoven's longtime student of piano and composition.

Much music was heard in private concerts, where aristocrats and wealthy commoners played alongside professional musicians. Mozart and Beethoven often earned money by performing in these intimate concerts. The nobility frequently hired servants who could double as musicians. An advertisement in the *Vienna Gazette* of 1789 reads: "Wanted, for a house of the gentry, a manservant who knows how to play the violin well."

In Vienna there was also outdoor music, light and popular in tone. Small street bands of wind and string players played at garden parties or under the windows of people likely to throw down money. A Viennese almanac reported that "on fine summer nights you may come upon serenades in the streets at all hours." Haydn and Mozart wrote many outdoor entertainment pieces, which they called *divertimentos* or *serenades*. Vienna's great love of music and its enthusiastic demand for new works made it the chosen city of Haydn, Mozart, and Beethoven.

3 Sonata Form

An astonishing amount of important music from the classical period to the twentieth century was composed in sonata form (sometimes called *sonata-allegro form*). The term **sonata form** refers to the form of a *single* movement. It should not be confused with the term *sonata,* which is used for a whole composition made up of *several* movements. The opening fast movement of a classical symphony, sonata, or string quartet is usually in sonata form. This form is also used in slow movements and in fast concluding movements.

A sonata-form movement consists of three main sections: the exposition, where the themes are presented; the development, where themes are treated in new ways; and the recapitulation, where the themes return. These three main sections are often followed by a concluding section, the coda (Italian for *tail*). Remember that these sections are all within *one movement*. A *single* sonata-form movement may be outlined as follows:

Exposition
First theme in tonic (home) key
Bridge containing modulation from home key to new key
Second theme in new key
Closing section in key of second theme

Development
New treatment of themes; modulations to different keys

Recapitulation
First theme in tonic key
Bridge
Second theme in tonic key
Closing section in tonic key

Coda
In tonic key

A fast movement in sonata form is sometimes preceded by a slow introduction that creates a strong feeling of expectancy.

Exposition

The **exposition** sets up a strong conflict between the tonic key and the new key, and between the first theme (or group of themes) and the second theme (or group of themes). It begins with the first theme in the tonic, or home, key. Then comes a **bridge,** or **transition,** leading to the second theme, which is in a new key. The modulation from the home key to a new key creates a feeling of harmonic tension and forward motion. The second theme often contrasts in mood with the first theme. A closing section ends the exposition in the key of the second theme. At the end of a classical exposition there is usually a repeat sign (:‖) to indicate that the whole exposition is to be played again.

Development

The **development** is often the most dramatic section of the movement. The listener may be kept off balance as the music moves restlessly through several different keys. Through these rapid modulations, the harmonic tension is heightened.

In this section, themes are *developed,* or treated in new ways. They are broken into fragments, or **motives,** which are short musical ideas developed within a composition. A motive may take on different and unexpected emotional meanings. One fragment of a comic theme, for example, may be made to sound aggressive and menacing through changes of melody, rhythm, or dynamics. Themes can be combined with new ideas or changed in texture. A complex polyphonic texture can be woven by shifting a motive rapidly among different instruments. The harmonic and thematic searching of the development builds tension that demands resolution.

Recapitulation

The beginning of the **recapitulation** brings resolution, as we again hear the first theme in the tonic key. In the recapitulation, the first theme, bridge, second theme, and concluding section are presented more or less as they were in the exposition, with one crucial difference: all the principal material is now in the tonic key. Earlier, in the exposition, there was strong contrast between the first theme in the home key and the second theme and closing section in a new key; that basis for tension is resolved in the recapitulation by presenting the first theme, second theme, and closing section all in the tonic key.

Coda

An even more powerful feeling of conclusion is attained by following the recapitulation with yet another section. The **coda** rounds off a movement by repeating themes or developing them further. It always ends in the tonic key.

The amazing durability and vitality of sonata form result from its capacity for drama. The form moves from a stable situation toward conflict (in the exposition), to heightened tension (in the development), and then back to stability and resolution of conflict. The following illustration shows an outline.

A movement in sonata form proceeds from a stable situation toward conflict, to heightened tension, and then back to stability.

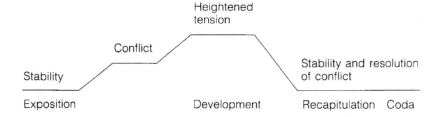

Sonata form is exceptionally flexible and subject to endless variation. It is not a rigid mold into which musical ideas are poured. Rather, it may be viewed as a set of principles that serve to shape and unify contrasts of theme and key. Haydn, Mozart, and Beethoven used sonata form repeatedly, yet each maintained individuality. Movements in sonata form may differ radically in character, in length, and in the number and treatment of themes. Sonata form is so versatile that it is no surprise to find its use spanning more than two centuries.

We'll now consider an excellent example of sonata form: the first movement of Symphony No. 40 by Wolfgang Amadeus Mozart.

Symphony No. 40 in G Minor, K. 550,* by Wolfgang Amadeus Mozart

First Movement:
Molto allegro

The rapid sonata-form opening movement of Mozart's Symphony No. 40 in G Minor, K. 550, conveys a feeling of controlled agitation. A throbbing accompaniment in the violas contributes to the tension of the opening theme, which begins softly in the violins. Dominating the violin melody is the rhythmic pattern short-short-long, first heard in the opening three-note motive.

The persistence of this rhythmic pattern gives the music a sense of urgency. Yet the melody is balanced and symmetrical. Questioning upward leaps are answered by downward scales, and the second phrase of the melody is a sequential repetition of the first, one step lower. The exposition continues with a bridge section that presents a new staccato motive played loudly by the violins.

The lyrical second theme, in B flat major, contrasts completely with the agitated G minor opening. Mozart exploits the expressive resources of tone color by dividing the theme between strings and woodwinds. In the closing section of the exposition, he uses a fragment from the opening theme to achieve a different emotional effect. The three-note motive now sounds gentle and plaintive as it is passed between clarinet and bassoon against a sighing string background.

In the development, the movement becomes feverish. The opening theme is led into different keys and is cut into smaller and smaller pieces. The development begins mysteriously as the opening phrase ends in an unexpected way and sinks lower and lower. Then a sudden explosion of polyphonic texture increases the excitement and complexity. Mozart brusquely shifts the opening phrase between low and high strings while combining it with a furious staccato countermelody. Soon after, he demolishes the opening phrase: we hear the beginning of the theme without its upward leap.

---

*In the nineteenth century, Mozart's compositions (numbering more than 600) were cataloged chronologically by Ludwig von Köchel. Hence, it is customary to refer to them by their "K." numbers.

Then the final note is lopped off.

Finally, we are left with the irreducible minimum of the original theme, the three-note motive.

The tension resolves only with the entrance of the entire opening theme in the tonic key.

In the recapitulation, material from the exposition is given new expressive meaning. The bridge is expanded and made more dramatic. The lyrical second theme, now in G minor, is touching and sad.

Listening Outline

MOZART, Symphony No. 40 in G Minor

First Movement: Molto allegro
Sonata form, duple meter ($\frac{2}{2}$), G minor
Flute, 2 oboes, 2 clarinets, 2 bassoons, 2 French horns, 1st violins, 2d violins, violas, cellos, double basses
(Duration, 8:12)

Exposition

First theme

0:00   **1. a.** Main theme in violins, *p*, throbbing accompaniment in violas, minor key.

b. Full orchestra, *f*.

Bridge

0:23   **2. a.** Violins, *p*, main theme takes new turn to
        b. Full orchestra, *f*, major key, staccato motive and insistent upward scales in violins. Pause.

Second theme

0:52 0:00   **3. a.** Lyrical melody, *p*, major key, strings and woodwinds.

1:01	0:09	**b.** Woodwinds and strings, **p**, lyrical melody somewhat varied. Crescendo in full orchestra.
		c. Staccato phrase, **f**, downward scale, **p**, to

Closing section

1:28		**4. a.** String sighs, **p**, three-note motive in woodwinds, violins, **f**. Varied repetition of string sighs and three-note motive.
		b. Downward scales, **f**, full orchestra, cadence in major key.
2:02		Exposition is repeated.

Development

4:05	0:00	**1. a.** High woodwinds, **p**, lead to
		b. Violins, **p**, main-theme phrase repeated on lower pitches.
4:21	0:16	**2.** Sudden **f**, full orchestra, main-theme phrase combined with rapid countermelody.
4:49	0:44	**3. a.** Sudden **p**, high violins and woodwinds, three-note motive.
		b. Sudden **f**, full orchestra, three-note motive.
		c. Sudden **p**, high flutes and clarinets, three-note motive carried down to

Recapitulation

First theme

5:21	0:00	**1. a.** Main theme in violins, **p**, throbbing accompaniment in violas, minor key.
		b. Full orchestra, **f**.

Bridge

5:46	0:25	**2. a.** Violins, **p**, main theme takes new turn to
		b. Full orchestra, **f**, staccato motive in violins and cellos. Insistent upward scales in violins, **f**. Pause.

Second theme

6:37	0:00	**3. a.** Lyrical melody, **p**, minor key, strings and woodwinds.
6:46	0:09	**b.** Woodwinds and strings, **p**, lyrical melody somewhat varied. Crescendo in full orchestra.
		c. Staccato phrase, **f**, downward scale, **p**, to

Closing section

7:19	0:42	**4. a.** String sighs, **p**, three-note motive in woodwinds, violins, **f**. Varied repetition of string sighs and three-note motive.
		b. Downward scales, **f**, full orchestra.

Coda

7:49		**1. a.** Sudden **p**, main-theme motive in strings.
		b. Full orchestra, **f**, cadence in minor key.

4 Theme and Variations

The form called *theme and variations* was widely used in the classical period, either as an independent piece or as one movement of a symphony, sonata, or string quartet. In a **theme and variations,** a basic musical idea—the theme—is repeated over and over and is changed each time. This form may be outlined as theme (A), variation 1 (A′), variation 2 (A″), variation 3 (A‴), and so on; each prime mark indicates a variation of the basic idea. (Another way of indicating variations is A¹, A², etc.)

Each variation, though usually about the same length as the theme, is unique and may differ in mood from the theme. Changes of melody, rhythm, harmony, accompaniment, dynamics, or tone color may be used to give a variation its own identity. The core melody may appear in the bass, or it may be repeated in a minor key instead of a major key. It may be heard together with a new melody. The variations may be connected to each other or separated by pauses. For the theme itself, a composer may invent an original melody or borrow someone else's. Beethoven once borrowed a little waltz tune and put it through thirty-three brilliant variations (the *Diabelli* variations). More modest examples of theme and variations have as few as three variations.

Symphony No. 94 in G Major (*Surprise;* 1791), by Joseph Haydn

Second Movement: Andante

The second movement (andante) of Haydn's Symphony No. 94 in G Major (*Surprise* Symphony) is a theme and variations. The theme of this movement is folklike and mostly staccato. It is primarily soft but is punctuated by an unexpected loud chord—this is the "surprise" that gave the symphony its nickname. The theme consists of two parts, sections a and b, each of which is repeated. This pattern is usually retained in the variations that follow. There are four variations, in which the theme is changed in tone color, dynamics, rhythm, and melody. In Variations 1 and 3 the original melody is accompanied by a new one called a ***countermelody.*** Such combinations of two distinctive melodies result in a polyphonic texture. In variation 2 the theme is presented in minor instead of major. The last variation is followed by a closing section in which a gently dissonant accompaniment momentarily darkens the mood of the carefree theme.

Listening Outline

HAYDN, Symphony No. 94 in G Major (*Surprise*)

Second Movement: Andante
Theme and variations, duple meter (²⁄₄), C major
2 flutes, 2 oboes, 2 bassoons, 2 French horns, 2 trumpets, timpani, 1st violins, 2d violins, violas, cellos, double basses
(Duration, 6:14)

Theme

Section a

0:00   Violins, *p*, staccato theme.

Section a repeated, *pp*, with pizzicato string accompaniment. Surprise chord, *ff*.

Section b   Violins, *p*, continuation of theme.

Section b repeated with flute and oboe.

Variation 1

1:06   **a.** Theme begins, *f*, higher countermelody in violins, *p*. Section a repeated.

b. Violins, *p*, continuation of theme and higher countermelody. Section b repeated.

Variation 2

2:13   **a.** Theme in minor, *ff*, violin phrase in major, *p*. Section a repeated.

b. Violins, *f*, rapid downward scales, orchestra *f*. Violins alone, *p*, lead into

Variation 3

3:21   **a.** Oboe, *p*, theme in faster repeated notes, major key.

Flute and oboe, *p*, legato countermelody above staccato theme in violins, *p*.

b. Continuation of theme and countermelody. Section b repeated.

Variation 4

4:28   **a.** Theme in brasses and woodwinds, *ff*, fast notes in violins, *ff*. Violins, *p*, legato version of theme, dotted rhythm (long-short).

b. Violins, *p*, continuation of theme, dotted rhythm. Full orchestra, *ff*, triumphant continuation of theme leads to suspenseful chord, *ff*, sudden *p*.

Closing section

5:52   Theme in oboe, *p*, gently dissonant chords in strings, flute joins, very soft, conclusion.

5 Minuet and Trio

The form known as **minuet and trio,** or **minuet,** is often used as the third movement of classical symphonies, string quartets, and other works. Like the movements of the baroque suite, the minuet originated as a dance. It first appeared at the court of Louis XIV of France around 1650 and was danced by aristocrats throughout the eighteenth century. The minuet was a stately, dignified dance in which the dancing couple exchanged curtsies and bows.

The minuet movement of a symphony or string quartet is written for listening, not dancing. It is in triple meter (($\frac{3}{4}$)) and usually in a moderate tempo. The movement is in A B A form: minuet (A), trio (B), minuet (A). The trio (B) is usually quieter than the minuet (A) section and requires fewer instruments. It often contains woodwind solos. The trio section got its name during the baroque period, when a set of two dances would be followed by a repetition of the first dance. The second dance was known as a "trio" because it was usually played by three instruments. Classical composers did not restrict themselves to three instruments in the B sections of their minuets, but the name *trio* remained.

The A (minuet) section includes smaller parts a, b, and a′ (variation of a). In the opening A (minuet) section, all the smaller parts are repeated, as follows: a (repeated) ba′ (repeated). (In the musical score, the repeat sign ‖ indicates each repetition.) The B (trio) section is quite similar in form: c (repeated) dc′ (repeated). At the close of the B (trio) section, the repetition of the entire A (minuet) section is indicated by the words **da capo** (*from the beginning*). This time, however, the minuet is played straight through without the repetitions: a ba′. The whole movement can be outlined like this:

Minuet	Trio	Minuet
A	B	A
a (repeated) ba′ (repeated)	c (repeated) dc′ (repeated)	a ba′

With its A B A form and its many repeated parts, the minuet is structurally the simplest movement of a symphony or string quartet.

In many of Beethoven's compositions, the third movement is not a minuet but a related form called a *scherzo.* Like a minuet, a **scherzo** is usually in A B A form and triple meter, but it moves more quickly, generating energy, rhythmic drive, and rough humor. (*Scherzo* is Italian for *joke.*)

Eine kleine Nachtmusik (*A Little Night Music;* 1787), K. 525, by Wolfgang Amadeus Mozart

Third Movement: Minuet (Allegretto)

Mozart's *Eine kleine Nachtmusik* is a **serenade,** a work that's usually light in mood, meant for evening entertainment. It is written for a small string orchestra or for a string quartet plus a double bass. (The double bass plays the cello part an octave lower.) The third movement is a courtly minuet in A B A form. The A (minuet) section is stately, mostly loud and staccato, with a clearly marked beat. In contrast, the B (trio) section is intimate, soft, and legato. Its murmuring accompaniment contributes to the smooth flow of the music.

Listening Outline

MOZART, *Eine kleine Nachtmusik*

Third Movement: Minuet (Allegretto)
A B A form, triple meter (3/4), G major
1st violins, 2d violins, violas, cellos, double basses
(Duration, 2:03)

Minuet (A)

0:00   **1.** Stately melody, *f*, predominantly staccato. Repeated.

Legato phrase, *p*, leads to stately staccato phrase, *f*. Repeated.

Trio (B)

0:42   **2.** Gracious legato melody, *p*, murmuring accompaniment. Repeated.

Climbing legato phrase, *f*, leads to legato melody, *p*. Repeated.

Minuet (A)

1:39   **3.** Stately melody, *f*, predominantly staccato.
       Legato phrase, *p*, leads to stately staccato phrase, *f*.

6 Rondo

Many classical movements are in rondo form. A ***rondo*** features a tuneful main theme (A) that returns several times in alternation with other themes. Common rondo patterns are A B A C A and A B A C A B A. The main theme is usually lively, pleasing, and simple to remember, and the listener can easily recognize its return. Because the main theme is usually stated in the tonic key, its return is all the more welcome. The rondo can be used either as an independent piece or as one movement of a symphony, string quartet, or sonata. It often serves as a finale, because its liveliness, regularity, and buoyancy bring a happy sense of conclusion.

Rondo form is often combined with elements of sonata form to produce a sonata-rondo. The **sonata-rondo** contains a development section like that in sonata form and is outlined A B A—development section—A B A.

The popularity of the rondo did not end with the classical period. It was used by twentieth-century composers such as Igor Stravinsky and Arnold Schoenberg.

String Quartet in C Minor, Op. 18, No. 4 (1798–1800), by Ludwig van Beethoven

Fourth Movement: Rondo (Allegro)

The exciting rondo movement from Beethoven's String Quartet in C Minor, Op. 18, No. 4, may be outlined A B A C A B A. Its lively main theme, A, in the style of a Gypsy dance, is made up of two repeated parts: a a b b. An unexpected held tone in part b suggests the improvisatory playing of a Gypsy fiddler. The main theme, in minor, contrasts with the other themes, which are in major. Theme B is a lyrical legato melody. Theme C is playful, with quick upward rushes. At its final return, the main theme (A) has a faster tempo, prestissimo, and leads into a frenzied concluding section.

Listening Outline

BEETHOVEN, String Quartet in C Minor, Op. 18, No. 4

Fourth Movement: Rondo (Allegro)
Duple meter (²⁄₂), C minor
1st violin, 2d violin, viola, cello
(Duration, 4:08)

A

0:00   **1.** Lively main theme in 1st violin, minor key.

B

0:29   **2.** Lyrical melody, legato, major key.

A

1:14   **3.** Lively main theme, minor key. Theme becomes more agitated.

C

1:42   **4.** Upward rushes in each instrument, playful downward phrase in 1st violin, major key.

A

2:05   **5.** Lively main theme, minor key. Crescendo to held chord, ***ff***.

B

2:43   **6.** Lyrical melody, legato, major key. Melody repeated an octave higher. Playful phrases in violins, crescendo to ***f***, sustained tones in 1st violin.

A

3:26   **7.** Lively main theme, ***ff***, faster tempo (prestissimo), minor key. Concluding section builds, downward staccato scale, high repeated tones, ***p***. Upward rushes, ***ff***, at end.

7 The Classical Symphony

The great contribution of the classical period to orchestral music is the symphony. Haydn wrote at least 104 symphonies, Mozart more than 40, and Beethoven 9. Most of Haydn's symphonies were composed for his employers, who required a steady flow of works for their palace concerts. Beethoven, on the other hand, wrote a symphony only when inspired. His symphonies are longer than Haydn's or Mozart's and were conceived for performance in large concert halls.

A *symphony* is an extended, ambitious composition typically lasting between twenty and forty-five minutes, exploiting the expanded range of tone color and dynamics of the classical orchestra. A classical symphony usually consists of four movements that evoke a wide range of emotions through contrasts of tempo and mood. A typical sequence is (1) a vigorous, dramatic fast movement; (2) a lyrical slow movement; (3) a dancelike movement (minuet or scherzo); and (4) a brilliant or heroic fast movement.

The opening movement is almost always fast and in sonata form. It is usually the most dramatic movement and stresses an exciting development of short motives. Sometimes a slow introduction leads to the opening fast movement and creates a feeling of anticipation.

It is in the slow second movement that we are most likely to find broad, song-like melodies. This movement, by and large, is in either sonata form, A B A form, or theme-and-variations form. Unlike the other movements in the symphony, the slow movement is generally *not* in the tonic key. For example, if the first, third, and fourth movements are in the tonic key of C major, the second movement may be in F major. The new key points up the expressive contrast of the slow movement.

In the symphonies of Haydn and Mozart, the third movement is generally a minuet and trio, which may be in a moderate or fairly quick tempo. This movement varies in character from a courtly dance to a peasant romp or a vigorous piece that is hardly dancelike. Beethoven liked fast, energetic scherzos for his third movements.

The fourth, concluding movement of a symphony by Haydn or Mozart is fast, lively, and brilliant, but somewhat lighter in mood than the opening movement. (The agitated final movement of Mozart's Symphony No. 40 in G minor is not typical.) Beethoven's concluding movement tends to be more triumphant and heroic in character and is sometimes meant as the climax of the whole symphony. The final movement of a classical symphony is most often in sonata or sonata-rondo form.

In most classical symphonies, each movement is a self-contained composition with its own set of themes. A theme in one movement will only rarely reappear in a later movement. (Beethoven's Fifth and Ninth Symphonies are exceptions.) But a symphony is unified partly by the use of the same key in three of its movements. More important, the movements balance and complement each other both musically and emotionally.

The importance of the symphony lasted throughout the twentieth century and into the twenty-first. Its great significance is reflected in such familiar terms as *symphonic music, symphony hall,* and *symphony orchestra.*

8 The Classical Concerto

A classical *concerto* is a three-movement work for an instrumental soloist and orchestra. It combines the soloist's virtuosity and interpretive abilities with the orchestra's wide range of tone color and dynamics. Emerging from this encounter is a contrast of ideas and sound that is dramatic and satisfying. The soloist is very much the star, and all of his or her musical talents are needed in this challenging dialogue.

The classical love of balance can be seen in the concerto, because soloist and orchestra are equally important. Between them, there's an interplay of melodic lines and a spirit of give-and-take. One moment the soloist plays the melody while the orchestra accompanies. Then the woodwinds may unfold the main theme against rippling arpeggios (broken chords) played by the soloist. Mozart and Beethoven—the greatest masters of the classical concerto—often wrote concertos for themselves to play as piano soloists; the piano is their favored solo instrument. But other solo instruments used in classical concertos include violin, cello, horn, trumpet, clarinet, and bassoon.

Like symphonies, concertos can last anywhere from twenty minutes to forty-five minutes. But instead of the symphony's four movements, a classical concerto has three: (1) fast, (2) slow, and (3) fast. A concerto has no minuet or scherzo.

In the first movement and sometimes in the last movement, there is a special unaccompanied showpiece for the soloist, the *cadenza* (Italian for *cadence*). Near the end of the movement, the orchestra suspends forward motion by briefly sustaining a dissonant chord. This is indicated in the score by a *fermata* (⌢), a sign meaning *pause,* which is placed over the chord. The suspense announces the entry of the soloist's cadenza. For several minutes, the soloist, *without orchestra,* displays virtuosity by playing dazzling scale passages and broken chords. Themes of the movement are varied and presented in new keys. At the end of a cadenza, the soloist plays a long trill followed by a chord that meshes with the reentrance of the orchestra.

In the classical era, the soloist, who was often the composer, generally improvised the cadenzas. In this case, the score contained only the fermata, indicating where the cadenza should be inserted. But after the eighteenth century, the art of improvisation declined, and composers began to write cadenzas directly into the score. This gave them more control over their compositions.

Today, performers of eighteenth-century concertos may have a choice of cadenzas. For some concertos, composers wrote cadenzas for their own performance or for that of a student. Also, many nineteenth-, twentieth-, and early twenty-first-century musicians later provided cadenzas for classical concertos. These are best when their style matches that of the concerto. For example, the cadenzas Beethoven composed for Mozart's D Minor Piano Concerto are so strong and so much in the spirit of the work that pianists still use them today.

A classical concerto begins with a movement in sonata form of a special kind, containing *two* expositions. The first is played by the orchestra, which presents several themes in the home key. This opening section sets the mood for the movement and leads us to expect the soloist's entrance. The second exposition begins with the soloist's first notes. Music for the solo entry may be powerful or quiet, but its effect is dramatic because suspense has been built. Together with the orchestra, the soloist explores themes from the first exposition and introduces new ones. After a modulation from the home key to a new key, the second exposition then moves to a development section, followed by the recapitulation, cadenza, and coda. The slow middle movement may take any one of several forms, but the finale is usually a quick rondo or sonata-rondo.

9 Classical Chamber Music

Classical **chamber music** is designed for the intimate setting of a room (chamber) in a home or palace, rather than for a public concert hall. It is performed by a small group of two to nine musicians, with one player to a part. Chamber music is lighter in sound than classical orchestral music. During the classical period, it was fashionable for an aristocrat or a member of the well-to-do middle class to play chamber music with friends and to hire professional musicians to entertain guests after dinner.

Chamber music is subtle and intimate, intended to please the performer as much as the listener. A chamber music group is a team. Each member is essential, and each may have an important share of the thematic material. Therefore much give-and-take is called for among the instruments. Classical chamber music does not need a conductor; instead, each musician must be sensitive to what goes on and must coordinate dynamics and phrasing with the other musicians. In this respect, a chamber ensemble is like a small jazz group.

The most important form in classical chamber music is the ***string quartet,*** written for two violins, a viola, and a cello. Haydn, Mozart, and Beethoven wrote some of their most important music in this form. The string quartet can be compared to a conversation among four lively, sensitive, and intelligent people. It's not surprising that the string quartet evolved when conversation was cultivated as a fine art.

Like a symphony, a string quartet usually consists of four movements: (1) fast, (2) slow, (3) minuet or scherzo, (4) fast. (Sometimes the second movement is a minuet or a scherzo and the slow movement is third.)

Other popular forms of classical chamber music are the sonata for violin and piano; the piano trio (violin, cello, and piano); and the string quintet (two violins, two violas, and cello).

Today, as in the eighteenth century, much chamber music is performed by amateurs. By consulting the Internet or the directory *Amateur Chamber Music Players,* one can find partners for chamber music almost anywhere in the United States.

10 Joseph Haydn

Joseph Haydn (1732–1809) was born in a tiny Austrian village called Rohrau. Until he was six, his musical background consisted of folksongs and peasant dances (which later had an influence on his style). Haydn's eager response to music was recognized, and he was given training. At the age of eight, he went to Vienna to serve as a choirboy in the Cathedral of St. Stephen. When his voice changed, Haydn was dismissed, penniless, from St. Stephen's. He gave music lessons to children, struggled to teach

Haydn was a pathfinder for the classical style, a pioneer in the development of the symphony and string quartet.

himself composition, and took odd jobs, including playing violin in street bands. Gradually, aristocratic patrons of music began to notice Haydn's talent. In 1761, when he was twenty-nine, his life changed for the better, permanently: he entered the service of the Esterházys, the richest and most powerful of the Hungarian noble families. For almost thirty years, most of his music was composed for performance in the palaces of the family, especially Eszterháza, which contained an opera house, a theater, two concert halls, and 126 guest rooms.

As a highly skilled servant, Haydn was to compose all the music requested by his patron, conduct the orchestra, coach singers, and oversee the instruments and the music library. This entailed a staggering amount of work; there were usually two concerts and two opera performances weekly, as well as daily chamber music. Though today this sort of patronage seems degrading, it was taken for granted at the time and had definite advantages for composers. They received a steady income and their works were performed. Haydn was conscientious about his professional duties, concerned about his musicians' interest, and—despite an unhappy marriage—good-humored and unselfish. Word spread about the Esterházys' composer, and Haydn's music became immensely popular all over Europe. In 1791–1792 and again in 1794–1795, Haydn went to London. Reports of the time say that his appearances were triumphs. (The twelve symphonies he composed for these visits are now known as the *London Symphonies.*) A servant had become a celebrity. Haydn was wined and dined by the aristocracy, given an honorary doctorate at Oxford, and received by the royal family.

In 1795, he returned to Vienna rich and honored. In his late sixties, he composed six masses and two oratorios, *The Creation* (1798) and *The Seasons* (1801). They were so popular that choruses and orchestras were formed for the sole purpose of performing them.

He died in 1809, at the age of seventy-seven.

Haydn's Music

Haydn was a pathfinder for the classical style, a pioneer in the development of the symphony and string quartet. Both Mozart and Beethoven were influenced by his style. Haydn's music, like his personality, is robust and direct; it radiates a healthy optimism. Much of it has a folk flavor, and *The Creation* and *The Seasons* reflect his love of nature. Haydn was a master at developing themes. He could build a whole movement out of a single main theme, creating contrasts of mood through changes in texture, key, rhythm, dynamics, and orchestration. The contagious joy that springs from his lively rhythms and vivid contrasts makes it clear why London went wild.

"I prefer to see the humorous side of life," Haydn once said. He produced comic effects from unexpected pauses and tempo changes and from sudden shifts in dynamics and pitch. We've heard one of his musical jokes in the second movement of the *Surprise* Symphony, where a soft theme is suddenly punctuated by a loud chord.

Haydn's 104 symphonies—along with his 68 string quartets—are considered the most important part of his enormous output. Many of them have nicknames, such as *Surprise* (No. 94), *Military* (No. 100), *Clock* (No. 101), and *Drum Roll* (No. 103).

Some scholars believe that Haydn invented the string quartet form. He began writing string quartets for a good reason—only three other musicians (two violinists and a cellist, in addition to Haydn as a violinist) were on hand during the summer of 1757, when he was invited to take part in chamber music performances at a castle.

Haydn's output also includes piano sonatas, piano trios, divertimentos, concertos, operas, and masses. The variety in his works is astounding. He was a great innovator

A performance of Haydn's oratorio *The Creation* at the University of Vienna in 1808.

and experimenter who hated arbitrary "rules" of composition. "Art is free," he said. "The educated ear is the sole authority . . . and I think that I have as much right to lay down the law as anyone."

Trumpet Concerto in E Flat Major (1796)

Haydn's Trumpet Concerto in E Flat Major has a remarkable history. After its premiere in 1800, it was forgotten for almost 130 years. It was first published only in 1929, and in the 1930s a phonograph recording brought it to a wide audience. Now, it may well be Haydn's most popular work.

Haydn wrote the concerto in 1796 for a friend, a trumpeter at the Viennese court who had recently invented a keyed trumpet that could produce a complete chromatic scale. The keyed trumpet was intended to replace the natural trumpet, which could produce only a restricted number of tones. But the keyed trumpet had a dull sound and was supplanted by the valve trumpet around 1840. Today, the concerto is performed on a valve trumpet. Like most concertos, it has three movements: (1) fast, (2) slow, (3) fast. We examine the third movement.

Third Movement: Allegro

Movement 3 available on Connect Music

The third movement is a dazzling sonata-rondo in which Haydn gives the trumpeter's virtuosity free rein. The movement combines the recurring main theme characteristic of rondo form with the development section found in sonata form. It may be outlined as A B A B′ A—development section—A B″—coda. Themes A and B are introduced by the orchestra and are then presented mainly by the trumpet, with orchestral support. The main theme, A, is a high-spirited melody that is well suited to the trumpet.

Theme B is playful; it contains a short, downward-moving phrase that is repeated several times.

Haydn's fondness for musical surprises is reflected in the coda, which contains sudden changes of dynamics, unexpected harmonic twists, and a suspenseful long pause.

11 Wolfgang Amadeus Mozart

Wolfgang Amadeus Mozart (1756–1791), one of the most amazing child prodigies in history, was born in Salzburg, Austria. By the time he was six, he could play the harpsichord and violin, improvise fugues, write minuets, and read music perfectly at first sight. At the age of eight, he wrote a symphony; at eleven, an oratorio; at twelve, an opera.

Mozart's father, Leopold, a court musician, was eager to show him off. Between the ages of six and fifteen Mozart was continually on tour. He played for Empress Maria Theresa in Vienna, Louis XV at Versailles, George III in London, and innumerable aristocrats along the way. On his trips to Italy he was able to master the current operatic style, which he later put to superb use.

When he was fifteen, Mozart returned to Salzburg, which was ruled by a new prince-archbishop. The archbishop was a tyrant who did not appreciate Mozart's music and refused to grant him more than a subordinate seat in the court orchestra. With his father's help, Mozart tried repeatedly over the next decade to find a suitable position elsewhere, but with no success.

Mozart was among the most versatile of all composers; he wrote masterpieces in all the musical forms of his time.

The tragic irony of Mozart's life was that he won more acclaim as a boy wonder than as an adult musician. Having begun his professional life as an international celebrity, he could not tolerate being treated like a servant. He became insubordinate when the prince-archbishop forbade him to give concerts or perform at the houses of the aristocracy, and his relationship with his patron went from bad to worse. Moreover, his complete dependence on his father had given him little opportunity to develop initiative, and a contemporary observed that he was "too good-natured, not active enough, too easily taken in, too little concerned with the means that may lead him to good fortune."

When he was twenty-five, Mozart could stand it no longer. He broke free of provincial Salzburg and traveled to Vienna, intending to be a freelance musician. Indeed, Mozart's first few years in Vienna were successful. His German opera *Die Entführung aus dem Serail* (*The Abduction from the Seraglio*, 1782) was acclaimed. Concerts of his own music were attended by the emperor and the nobility. Pupils paid him high fees, his compositions were published, and his playing was heard in palace drawing rooms. Contributing to the brightness of these years was Mozart's friendship with Haydn, who told Leopold, "Your son is the greatest composer that I know, either personally or by reputation; he has taste and, what is more, the most profound knowledge of composition."

In 1786, came Mozart's opera *Le Nozze di Figaro* (*The Marriage of Figaro*). Vienna loved it, and Prague was even more enthusiastic. "They talk about nothing but *Figaro*," Mozart joyfully wrote.

This success led an opera company in Prague to commission *Don Giovanni* (*Don Juan*) the following year. Although *Don Giovanni* was a triumph in Prague, its dark qualities and dissonance did not appeal to the Viennese, and Mozart's popularity in Vienna began to decline. It was a fickle city in any case, and it found Mozart's music complicated and hard to follow. His pupils dwindled, and the elite snubbed his concerts.

During his last year, Mozart was more successful. He received a commission for a German comic opera, *Die Zauberflöte* (*The Magic Flute*), and, while working on it, was visited by a stranger who carried an anonymous letter commissioning a requiem, a mass for the dead. As Mozart's health grew worse, he came to believe that the requiem was for himself and rushed to finish it while on his deathbed. (In fact, the stranger was the servant of a nobleman who intended to claim the requiem as his own composition.) *The Magic Flute* was premiered to resounding praise in Vienna, but its success came too late. Mozart died of rheumatic fever on December 5, 1791, shortly before his thirty-sixth birthday, leaving the requiem unfinished. (It was completed by his friend and pupil Franz Süssmayer.)

Mozart's Music

Mozart was among the most versatile of all composers. He wrote masterpieces in all the musical forms of his time—symphonies, string quartets, piano concertos, and operas. His music sings and conveys a feeling of ease, grace, and spontaneity, as well as balance, restraint, and perfect proportion. Yet mysterious harmonies bring dark moods that contrast with the lyricism. Mozart fuses power and elegance in a unique way.

His compositions sound effortless and were created with miraculous rapidity. For example, he completed his last three symphonies in only six weeks!

Many of Mozart's concertos are among his greatest works. His piano concertos—composed mainly for his own performances—are particularly important. He also wrote concertos for violin, horn, flute, bassoon, oboe, and clarinet.

He was also a master of opera with a supreme ability to coordinate music and stage action, a keen sense of theater, an inexhaustible gift of melody, and a genius for creating characters through tone. Most of his operas are comedies, composed to German or Italian librettos. Mozart's three masterpieces of Italian comic opera are *The Marriage of Figaro* (1786), *Don Giovanni* (1787), and *Così fan tutte* (*All Women Behave Like This*, 1790); they were all composed to librettos by Lorenzo da Ponte. Mozart's finest opera in German is *The Magic Flute* (1791). The comic operas contain both humorous and serious characters. The major characters are not mere stereotypes but individual human beings who think and feel. Emotions in his arias and ensembles continuously evolve and change.

"I am never happier," Mozart once wrote his father, "than when I have something to compose, for that, after all, is my sole delight and passion." Mozart's "delight and passion" are communicated in his works, which represent late eighteenth-century musical style at its highest level of perfection.

Don Giovanni (1787)

Don Giovanni (*Don Juan*) is a unique blend of comic and serious opera, combining seduction and slapstick with violence and the supernatural. The old tale of Don Juan, the legendary Spanish lover, had attracted many playwrights and composers before Mozart. Mozart's Don Giovanni is a seductive but ruthless nobleman who will stop at nothing to satisfy his sexual appetite. Don Giovanni's comic servant, Leporello, is a grumbling accomplice who dreams of being in his master's place.

The Don attempts to rape a young noblewoman, Donna Anna; she pursues and struggles with Don Giovanni—who conceals his face—trying to determine his identity. Her father, the Commendatore (Commandant), challenges him to a duel. Don Giovanni kills the old man, causing Donna Anna and her fiancé, Don Ottavio, to swear revenge. Pursued by his enemies, Don Giovanni seeks sexual pleasure in a series of adventures. During one of them, he hides in a cemetery, where he sees a marble statue of the dead Commandant. The unearthly statue utters threatening words, but Don Giovanni brazenly invites it to dinner. When the statue appears at the banquet hall, it orders the Don to repent. Don Giovanni defiantly refuses and is dragged down to hell.

virtual
fieldtrip

Don Giovanni

Act I:
Introduction

The overture leads directly into the action-packed opening scene. In breathless succession we witness Leporello keeping guard, Don Giovanni struggling with Donna Anna, the Commandant dueling with the Don, and the Commandant's agonized last gasps. Mozart's music vividly depicts the characters and pushes the action forward. (In the Vocal Music Guide, braces indicate that characters sing at the same time. *Etc.* indicates that previous lines of text are repeated.)

Vocal Music Guide

MOZART, *Don Giovanni*

Act I: Excerpt from Opening Scene

0:00 Orchestral introduction, molto allegro; sudden fortes suggest pacing and abrupt turns.	(Late evening outside the Commandant's palace in Seville. Don Giovanni, concealing his identity, has stolen into Donna Anna's room. Leporello paces back and forth.)	
	Leporello	
0:15	*Notte e giorno faticar,*	Night and day I slave
	Per chi nulla sa gradir;	For one who does not appreciate it.
	Piova e vento sopportar,	I put up with wind and rain,
0:29	*Mangiar male e mal dormir!*	Eat and sleep badly.
	Voglio far il gentiluomo,	I want to be a gentleman
	E non voglio più servir,	And to give up my servitude.
	No, no, no, no, no, no,	No, no, no, no, no, no,
	Non voglio più servir!	I want to give up my servitude.
0:46	*Oh che caro galantuomo!*	Oh, what a fine gentleman!
	Voi star dentro colla bella	You stay inside with your lady
0:58	*Ed io far la sentinella!*	And I must play the sentinel!
	Voglio far il gentiluomo, ecc.	Oh, what a fine gentleman, etc.
1:24	*Ma mi par che venga gente . . .*	But I think someone is coming!
	Non mi voglio far sentir, ecc.	I don't want them to hear me, etc.
1:41 Orchestral crescendo.	Leporello hides to one side. Don Giovanni and Donna Anna come down the palace stairs struggling. The Don hides his face to prevent her from recognizing him.)	

		Donna Anna
1:47	*Non sperar, se non m'uccidi.*	There's no hope, unless you kill me
	Ch'io ti lasci fuggir mai!	That I'll ever let you go!
		Don Giovanni
	Donna folle, indarno gridi:	Idiot! You scream in vain.
	Chi son io tu non saprai.	Who I am you'll never know!
		Donna Anna
	Non sperar, ecc.	There's no hope, etc.
		Don Giovanni
1:58	*Donna folle! ecc.*	Idiot! etc.
		Leporello
	Che tumulto! Oh ciel, che gridi!	What a racket! Heavens, what screams!
	Il padron in nuovi guai.	My master in another scrape.
		Donna Anna
2:07	*Gente! Servi! Al traditore!*	Help! Everyone! The betrayer!
		Don Giovanni
	Taci, e trema al mio furore!	Keep quiet! Beware my wrath!
		Donna Anna
	Scellerato!	Scoundrel!
		Don Giovanni
	Sconsigliata!	Fool!
		Donna Anna
	Scellerato!	Scoundrel!
		Don Giovanni
	Sconsigliata!	Fool!
		Leporello
	Sta a veder che il malandrino	We will see if this rascal
	Mi farà precipitar.	Will be the ruin of me!
		Donna Anna
	Gente! Servi!	Help! Everyone!
		Don Giovanni
	Taci, e trema!	Keep quiet!
		Donna Anna
2:18	*Come furia disperata*	Like a desperate fury
	Ti saprò perseguitar! ecc.	I'll know how to pursue you! etc.
	Scellerato! Gente! Servi!	Scoundrel! Help! Everyone!
	Come furia disperata, ecc.	Like a desperate fury, etc.
		Don Giovanni
	Questa furia disperata	This desperate fury
	Mi vuol far precipitar! ecc.	Is aimed at destroying me!
	Sconsigliata! Taci, e trema!	Fool! Keep quiet!
	Questa furia disperata, ecc.	This desperate fury, etc.
		Leporello
	Che tumulto! Oh ciel, che gridi!	What a racket! Heavens, what screams!
	Sta a veder che il malandrino, ecc.	We will see if this rascal, etc.

11 | Wolfgang Amadeus Mozart   **179**

3:02
String tremolo, *ff*,
shift to minor key.

(Donna Anna hears the Commandant; she leaves Don Giovanni and goes into the house. The Commandant appears.)

Commandant

3:10

Lasciala, indegno! Battiti meco!   Leave her alone, wretch, and defend yourself.

Don Giovanni

Va, non mi degno di pugnar teco.   Go away! I disdain to fight with you.

Commandant

Così pretendi da me fuggir?   Thus you think to escape me?

Leporello

Potessi almeno di qua partir.   If I could only get out of here!

3:23

Don Giovanni

Va, non mi degno, no!   Go away! I disdain you!

Commandant

Così pretendi da me fuggir?   Thus you think to escape me!

Leporello

Potessi almeno di qua partir!   If I could only get out of here!

Commandant

3:31

Battiti!   Fight!

Don Giovanni

Misero! Attendi, se vuoi morir!   So be it, if you want to die!

Dueling 3:47
music, upward
sweeps in strings.
Death blow, suspenseful,
held chord.

(They duel. The Commandant is fatally wounded.)

4:06
andante, *pp*,
pathetic minor
phrases.

Commandant

Ah, soccorso! son tradito!   Help! I've been betrayed!
L'assassino m'ha ferito,   The assassin has wounded me!
E dal seno palpitante   And from my heaving breast
Sento l'anima partir.   I feel my soul escaping!

Don Giovanni

Ah! già cade il sciagurato!   Ah, already the wretch has fallen,
Affannosa e agonizzante   And he gasps for air.
Già dal seno palpitante   From his heaving breast I already
Veggo l'anima partir, ecc.   See his soul escaping, etc.

Leporello

Qual misfatto! Qual eccesso!   What a misdeed! What a crime!
Entro il sen dallo spavento   I can feel my heart
Palpitar il cor mi sento!   Beating hard from fright!
Io non sò che far, che dir, ecc.   I don't know what to do or say, etc.

(The Commandant dies.)

5:18

Recitative, harpsichord accompanies.

	Don Giovanni	
Leporello, dove sei?		Leporello, where are you?

	Leporello	
Son qui, per mia disgrazia. E voi?		I'm here, unfortunately, and you?

	Don Giovanni	
Son qui.		Over here.

	Leporello	
Chi è morto, voi, o il vecchio?		Who's dead, you or the old man?

	Don Giovanni	
Che domanda da bestia! Il vecchio.		What an idiotic question! The old man.

5:29

	Leporello	
Bravo! Due imprese leggiadre, Sforzar la figlia, ed ammazzar il padre!		Well done! Two misdeeds! First you raped the daughter, then murdered the father!

	Don Giovanni	
L'ha voluto, suo danno.		He asked for it; too bad for him.

	Leporello	
Ma Donn' Anna cosa ha voluto?		And Donna Anna, did she ask for it too?

	Don Giovanni	
Taci, non mi seccar! Vien meco, se non vuoi qualche cosa ancor tu.		Keep quiet and don't bother me. Now come along, unless you're anxious for something for yourself.

	Leporello	
Non vo' nulla, signor, non parlo più.		I have no desires, sir, and no more to say.

virtual fieldtrip

Don Giovanni

Act I:
Duet: *Là ci darem la mano*
(*There you will give me your hand*)

The Don's seduction technique is put to use in the lovely duet *Là ci darem la mano*. Don Giovanni persuades the pretty peasant girl Zerlina to come to his palace, promising to marry her and change her life. The music magically conveys his persuasiveness and her gradual surrender, as the voices become more and more intertwined. Forgetting her fiancé, Masetto, Zerlina throws herself into the Don's arms and they sing together, "Let us go, my beloved."

As they go off together, they are suddenly intercepted by Donna Elvira, a woman whom Don Giovanni had earlier seduced and deserted. She denounces Don Giovanni as a liar, and protectively leads Zerlina away. During the opera, all of Don Giovanni's attempts at seduction or rape are frustrated.

The Korean soprano Hei-Kyung Hong as Zerlina and the Welsh baritone Bryn Terfel as Don Giovanni in a production of *Don Giovanni* at the Metropolitan Opera.

© Jack Vartoogian

Vocal Music Guide

MOZART, *Là ci darem la mano,* from *Don Giovanni*

0:00 Andante, $\frac{2}{4}$, legato melody.		**Don Giovanni**	
	Là ci darem la mano,	There you will give me your hand,	
	Là mi dirai di sì.	There you will tell me "yes."	
	Vedi, non è lontano;	You see, it is not far;	
	Partiam, ben mio, da qui.	Let us leave, my beloved.	
		Zerlina	
0:20 Legato melody repeated.	*Vorrei e non vorrei;*	I'd like to, but yet I would not.	
	Mi trema un poco il cor.	My heart trembles a little.	
	Felice è ver, sarei,	It's true I would be happy,	
	Ma può burlarmi ancor.	But he may just be tricking me.	
0:45 Quicker interchange between voices.	*Vieni, mio bel diletto!*	**Don Giovanni** Come, my dearly beloved!	
		Zerlina	
	Mi fa pietà Masetto!	I'm sorry for Masetto	
		Don Giovanni	
	Io cangierò tua sorte.	I will change your life!	

		Zerlina	
1:14	*Presto, non son più forte!*		Soon I won't be able to resist.
Legato melody now shared by both voices.		**Don Giovanni**	
	Vieni! Vieni!		Come! Come!
	Là ci darem la mano!		There you will give me your hand.

		Zerlina	
	Vorrei, e non vorrei!		I'd like to, but yet I would not.
		Don Giovanni	
	Là mi dirai di sì.		There you will tell me "yes."
		Zerlina	
	Mi trema un poco il cor!		My heart trembles a little.
		Don Giovanni	
	Partiam, mio ben, da qui!		Let us leave, my beloved.
		Zerlina	
	Ma può burlarmi ancor!		But he may just be tricking me.
1:41		**Don Giovanni**	
	Vieni, mio bel diletto!		Come, my dearly beloved!
		Zerlina	
Voices overlap.	*Mi fa pietà Masetto!*		I'm sorry for Masetto.
		Don Giovanni	
	Io cangierò tua sorte.		I will change your life.
		Zerlina	
	Presto, non son più forte!		Soon I won't be able to resist.
		Don Giovanni	
1:58	*Andiam! Andiam!*		Let us go!
		Zerlina	
	Andiam!		Let us go!
2:09		**Don Giovanni and Zerlina**	
Allegro, ⁶⁄₈; together they sing a new joyous tune.	*Andiam, andiam, mio bene,*		Let us go, let us go, my beloved,
	A ristorar le pene		To soothe the pangs
	D'un innocente amor! ecc.		Of an innocent love, etc.

Movements 1, 2, 3, and 4 available in Connect Music
Movement 1 available on Mp3 download card and Mp3 disc

Symphony No. 40 in G Minor, K. 550 (1788)

Symphony No. 40 in G Minor is the most passionate and dramatic of Mozart's symphonies. Although the work is classical in form and technique, it is almost romantic in emotional intensity. It staggers the imagination that Mozart could compose the G minor and two other great symphonies—No. 39 in E Flat and No. 41 in C (*Jupiter*)—during the short period of six weeks. They are his last three symphonies.

Like most classical symphonies, Symphony No. 40 in G Minor has four movements: (1) fast, (2) slow, (3) minuet, (4) fast.

First Movement:
Molto allegro

Mozart opens his Symphony No. 40 in G Minor with the agitated movement already described in Section 3.

Second Movement:
Andante

The mood of the andante hovers between gentleness and longing. The andante is written in sonata form and is the only movement of this symphony in major (it is in E flat). This movement develops from a series of gently pulsating notes in the opening theme.

Exposition
0:00
Development
3:39
Recapitulation
5:03

As the theme continues, the violins introduce an airy two-note rhythmic figure that will appear—with changes of dynamics and orchestration—in almost every section of the andante. The rhythmic figure will be, at different times, graceful, insistent, and forceful.

Later, Mozart uses the airy figures as a delicate countermelody to the repeated-note idea. Floating woodwinds interwoven with strings reveal Mozart's sensitivity to tone color as an expressive resource.

Third Movement:
Menuetto (Allegretto)

The minuet, in G minor, is serious and intense; it does not sound like an aristocratic dance. The form of the minuet is A B A:

Minuet	Trio	Minuet
A	B	A
a (repeated) ba' (repeated)	c (repeated) dc' (repeated)	a ba'

Section A
0:00

Powerful syncopations give a fierce character to the A section (the minuet), which is predominantly loud and in minor.

Section B
1:54

Later, Mozart increases the tension through polyphonic texture and striking dissonances. At the end of the A section, there is a sudden drop in dynamics; the flute, supported by oboes and a bassoon, softly recalls the opening melody of the minuet.

The trio section (B) brings a shift from minor to major, from fierce energy to graceful relaxation.

Return to section A
3:57

This change of mood is underscored by a soft dynamic level and pastoral woodwind interludes. After the trio, a sudden forte announces the return of the fierce A section.

Fourth Movement:
Allegro assai (very fast)

The very fast finale, in sonata form, is unusually tense. Its opening theme, in the tonic key of G minor, offers brusque contrasts of dynamics and rhythm. A soft upward arpeggio (broken chord) alternates repeatedly with a loud rushing phrase.

First theme
0:00

Bridge
0:27

Excitement is maintained throughout the long bridge, which is based on the loud rushing phrase of the first theme. The bridge ends clearly with a brief pause, as do other sections in this movement.

Second theme
1:00

The tender second theme, in the new key of B flat major, is a lyrical contrast to the brusque opening theme. It is softer, flows more smoothly, and uses longer notes.

Closing section
1:29

The exposition closes with a loud passage of continuously rushing notes in the strings.

Development
1:49

Mozart weaves almost the entire development section from the upward arpeggio of the first theme. During the opening few seconds, there is an eruption of violence as the orchestra in unison plays a variation of the arpeggio and a series of jagged downward leaps.

Recapitulation
First theme
3:03
Second theme
3:38

As the development continues, the texture becomes polyphonic and contrasts with the homophony of the exposition. Arpeggios press upon each other in quick imitation. Rapid shifts of key create restless intensity.

In the recapitulation, both the first and the second theme are in the tonic key, G minor. This minor key now adds a touch of melancholy to the tender second theme, which was heard in major before. The passion and violence of this movement foreshadow the romantic expression to come during the nineteenth century.

Piano Concerto No. 23 in A Major, K. 488 (1786)

Mozart's Piano Concerto in A Major—completed on March 2, 1786—dates from a very productive and successful period in his life. Between October 1785 and May 1786, he taught piano and composition; conducted operas; performed in concerts; and composed *The Marriage of Figaro,* the comic one-act opera *The Impresario,* two other great piano concertos (K. 482 in E Flat and K. 491 in C Minor), Quartet for Piano and Strings (K. 478), and *Masonic Funeral Music* (K. 477).

Mozart thought highly of the A Major piano concerto. In a letter to the court chamberlain of a prospective patron, he included it among "the compositions which I keep for myself or for a small circle of music-lovers and connoisseurs. . . ." Today, it is one of the best-known of his piano concertos.

Like all classical concertos, this one has three movements. The grace of the opening movement and the high spirits of the finale contrast with the melancholy of the middle movement. This concerto stresses poetry and delicacy rather than pianistic virtuosity or orchestral power. It is scored for an orchestra without trumpets or timpani and highlights the clarinets, flute, and bassoon. Mozart associated its key—A major—with tenderness, lyricism, and elegance. (He also used this key for the Clarinet Concerto and the duet between Don Giovanni and Zerlina in *Don Giovanni.*)

First Movement:
Allegro

The gentle opening movement blends lyricism with a touch of sadness, owing to many shifts between major and minor. Two main lyrical themes introduced by the orchestra in the first exposition are restated by the piano and orchestra in the second exposition. The development section is based on a new legato theme that is unexpectedly introduced by the orchestra after a dramatic pause. (In the Listening Outline, this is called the *development theme.*) Mozart creates a dramatic confrontation by juxtaposing fragments of this new theme, played by the woodwinds, with restless ideas in the piano and orchestra.

Toward the end of the allegro is a cadenza—an unaccompanied showpiece for the soloist. Exceptionally, Mozart notated the cadenza directly into the score, instead of leaving it to be improvised by the soloist. With its rapid sweeps up and down the keyboard, its alternation between brilliant and tender passages, and its concluding trill, this cadenza gives us some idea of how Mozart himself must have improvised.

Listening Outline

MOZART, Piano Concerto No. 23 in A Major

First Movement: Allegro
Sonata form, quadruple meter (⁴⁄₄), A major
Solo piano, flute, 2 clarinets, 2 bassoons, 2 French horns, 1st violins, 2d violins, violas, cellos, double basses
(Duration, 11:36)

First exposition

First theme

0:00   **1. a.** Strings, p, gracious main melody, legato, major key,

staccato ascent.

0:16   **b.** Winds, *p*, repeat opening of main melody an octave higher. Strings, *f*, answered by winds; cadence to

Bridge

0:34   **2.** Full orchestra, *f*, vigorous bridge theme,

running notes in violins, *f*. Brief pause.

Second theme group

0:58   **3. a.** Violins, *p*, tender second theme, repeated notes in dotted rhythm.

     b. Violins and bassoon, *p*, repeat second theme, flute joins.
     c. Agitated rhythms in minor lead to

1:34   **d.** Full orchestra, *f*, major; winds alternate with violins, minor, crescendo to
     e. Full orchestra, *f*, major, cadence. Brief pause.
     f. High woodwind phrase, *p*, orchestral chords, *f*. Brief pause.

Second exposition

First theme

2:11   **1. a.** Piano solo, main melody, low strings join, violins introduce
     b. Piano, varied repetition of main melody, rapid downward and upward scales.

Bridge

2:40   **2. a.** Full orchestra, *f*, bridge theme.
     b. Piano, running notes, with string accompaniment. High staccato violins, high staccato winds, downward scale in piano. Brief pause.

Second theme group

3:11   **3. a.** Piano solo, second theme, dolce.
     b. Violins and flute repeat second theme, piano joins.

3:42   **c.** Piano and orchestra.

3:53   **d.** Violins alternate with piano, minor.
     e. Piano, major. Long passage of running notes in piano culminating in short trill closing into

4:25   **4.** Full orchestra, opening of bridge theme. Sudden pause.

Development

4:39   **1. a.** Strings, *p*, legato development theme.

     b. Piano solo, development theme embellished by rapid notes.

5:05	**2. a.** Clarinet, fragment of development theme in minor, answered by piano and staccato strings.
5:13	**b.** Flute, fragment of development theme in major, answered by piano and staccato strings.
5:21	**c.** High woodwinds, development theme fragment in minor answered by piano, strings join with development theme fragment.
5:33	**3.** Piano continues with running notes; clarinet and flute, imitations of development theme fragment.
5:48	**4.** Strings, minor, repeatedly alternate with piano and woodwinds.
6:10	**5.** Piano solo, orchestra joins. Long descents and ascents, rising chromatic scale leads into

Recapitulation

First theme

| 6:30 | **1. a.** Strings, *p*, main melody, woodwinds join. |
| | **b.** Piano *p*, with woodwinds, ornamented repeat of main melody in higher octave; piano scales lead to |

Bridge

| 7:00 | **2. a.** Full orchestra, *f*, bridge theme. |
| | **b.** Piano, running notes, strings accompany; staccato violins, high staccato winds, upward scale in piano. Brief pause. |

Second theme group

7:30	**3. a.** Piano solo, second theme.
	b. Winds repeat second theme an octave higher, piano joins.
8:00	**c.** Piano and orchestra.
8:12	**d.** Violins alternate with piano, minor.
8:20	**e.** Piano, major, running-note passage interrupted by brief pause.
8:35	**4. a.** Piano alone, development theme.
	b. Clarinets and bassoons repeat development theme, accompanied by running notes in piano, staccato winds join, piano trill meshes with entrance of
9:19	**5. a.** Full orchestra, *f*, bridge theme; sudden brief pause.
9:32	**b.** Strings and winds, *p*, development theme. Full orchestra, *f*, dotted rhythm, briefly held chord.

Cadenza

| 9:48 | **c.** Extended piano solo; long trill closes into |

Coda

| 11:05 | **6. a.** Full orchestra, *f*, cadence. |
| | **b.** High woodwind phrase, *p*; full orchestra; sudden *p* ending, trills in flutes and violins. |

Performance Perspectives

Murray Perahia, Pianist, Playing and Conducting the First Movement of Mozart's Piano Concerto in A Major, K. 488

Murray Perahia, one of the world's leading pianists, was born in New York City in 1947. Though he began to play the piano at age four, his major musical interest during his teens was conducting and composition, which he studied at Mannes College of Music in New York. His career as a piano soloist soared in 1972, when he became the first American to win the Leeds International Piano Competition in England. Starting in the 1980s, Perahia began to conduct from the piano in performances and recordings of works including the piano concertos of Mozart. (His performance of the first movement of Mozart's Piano Concerto in A Major, K. 488, is included in the recordings.)

In the early 1990s, a serious thumb injury forced Perahia to stop performing for several years. "You get very depressed when you can't play, because it's your way of communicating," he later recalled. "Bach was a solace to me. . . . There is something in his music that is life-fulfilling, life-affirming." After recovering from his injury, he made a series of award-winning Bach recordings. In 2004, Perahia was knighted for his musical achievements by Queen Elizabeth II in London, where he now lives.

Perahia feels that great "music has to appeal at many different levels—intellectually, emotionally, metaphysically, spiritually. Every note has to have a reason for being. A masterpiece must be inevitable." He believes that a sense of direction is crucially important in music. Music must not be static: "It should sound spontaneous, so that it never seems mechanical. And at the same time, it must have an inner logic."

Concerning the Piano Concerto in A Major, K. 488, Perahia emphasizes that it is very different from other concertos Mozart composed at that time (1786): "They were all more symphonic in dimension, military-sounding, and they had very virtuosic piano writing—robust and strong." By contrast, in the first movement of the Piano Concerto in A Major, "the piano writing is more melodic, more obviously lyrical." The movement's "passion and ardor" are akin to the world of romantic love depicted in operas by Mozart, such as *Così fan tutte*. "There is a constant give-and-take with the orchestra, the piano decorating ideas first stated by the orchestra." The movement evokes a world "in perfect concord, an idealized world—soon to be shattered by a slow movement whose depth of pain and despair is matched by its sublimity."

12 Ludwig van Beethoven

For many people, Ludwig van Beethoven (1770–1827) represents the highest level of musical genius. He opened new realms of musical expression and profoundly influenced composers throughout the nineteenth century.

Beethoven was born in Bonn, Germany, into a family of musicians. By the age of eleven, he was serving as assistant to the court organist, and at twelve he had several piano compositions published. When he was sixteen he played for Mozart who reportedly said, "Keep your eyes on him; someday he will give the world something to talk about." Shortly before his twenty-second birthday, Beethoven left Bonn to study with Haydn in Vienna, where he spent the rest of his life.

Beethoven opened new realms of musical expression that profoundly influenced composers throughout the nineteenth century.

Beethoven's first years in Vienna brought hard work, growing confidence, and public praise (although his studies with Haydn were not entirely successful and he went secretly to another teacher). This music-loving city was dazzled by his virtuosity and moved by his improvisations. And although he rebelled against social convention, asserting that an artist deserved as much respect as the nobility, the same aristocrats who allowed Mozart to die in debt showered Beethoven with gifts. In 1809, three noblemen committed themselves to give him an annual income, their only condition being that he remain in Vienna—an arrangement unprecedented in music history. Unlike earlier composers, Beethoven was never actually in the service of the Viennese aristocracy. He earned good fees from piano lessons and concerts, and publishers were quick to buy his compositions.

Disaster struck during his twenty-ninth year: Beethoven felt the first symptoms of deafness. Doctors could do nothing to halt its progress. On October 6, 1802, Beethoven was in Heiligenstadt, a village outside Vienna where he sought solitude during the summer. That day he expressed his feelings in what is now known as the *Heiligenstadt testament,* a long, agonized letter addressed to his brothers. Beethoven wrote, "I would have ended my life—it was only my art that held me back. Ah, it seemed to me impossible to leave the world until I had brought forth all that I felt was within me."

Beethoven's victory over despair coincided with an important change in his musical style. Works that he created after his emotional crisis have a new power and heroism. In 1803 he composed the gigantic Third Symphony, the *Eroica,* a landmark in music history. At first, he planned to name it *Bonaparte,* after Napoleon; but when he learned that Napoleon had proclaimed himself emperor of the French, Beethoven crossed out the dedication and later wrote on the title page "Heroic Symphony composed to celebrate the memory of a great man."

As a man, Beethoven remains something of a mystery. He was self-educated and had read widely, but he was weak in elementary arithmetic. He claimed the highest moral principles, but he was often unscrupulous in dealing with publishers. Although orderly and methodical when composing, Beethoven dressed sloppily and lived in incredibly messy apartments. He fell in and out of love with several women, but never formed a lasting relationship. The contradictions in his personality are especially evident in his disastrous guardianship of his young nephew Karl, who eventually attempted suicide. Beethoven took consolation from nature for disappointments in his personal life. Ideas came to him while he walked through the Viennese countryside. His Sixth Symphony, the *Pastoral,* beautifully expresses his recollections of life in the country.

As Beethoven's hearing weakened, so did his piano playing and conducting. By the time he was forty-four, this once brilliant pianist was forced to stop playing in public. But he insisted on conducting his orchestral works long after he could do it efficiently. His sense of isolation grew with his deafness. Friends had to communicate with him through an ear trumpet, and during his last years he carried notebooks in which people would write questions and comments.

Despite this, and despite mounting personal problems, Beethoven had a creative outburst after 1818 that produced some of his greatest works: the late piano sonatas and string quartets, the *Missa solemnis,* and the Ninth Symphony—out of total deafness, new realms of sound.

Beethoven's Music

For Beethoven, music was not mere entertainment, but a moral force, "a higher revelation than all wisdom and philosophy." His music directly reflects his powerful, tortured personality.

Beethoven's demand for perfection meant long and hard work. Sometimes he worked for years on a single symphony, writing other works during the same period of time. He carried music sketchbooks everywhere, jotting down new ideas, revising and refining old ones. The final versions of his works were often hammered out through great labor.

Beethoven mostly used classical forms and techniques, but he gave them new power and intensity. The musical heir of Haydn and Mozart, he bridged the classical and romantic eras. Many of his innovations were used by composers who came after him.

In his works, great tension and excitement are built up through syncopations and dissonances. The range of pitch and dynamics is greater than ever before, so that contrasts of mood become more pronounced. Accents and climaxes seem titanic. Greater tension called for a larger musical framework, and so Beethoven expanded his forms. Beethoven was a musical architect who was unsurpassed in his ability to create large-scale structures in which every note seems inevitable. But not all his music is stormy and powerful; much is gentle, humorous, noble, or lyrical.

More than his predecessors, Beethoven tried to unify the contrasting movements by means of musical continuity. Sometimes one movement leads directly into the next, without the traditional pause. He also greatly expanded the development section and coda of sonata-form movements and made them more dramatic. His works often have climactic, triumphant finales, toward which the previous movements seem to build. Beethoven's finales mark an important departure from the light, relaxed ending movement favored by Haydn and Mozart.

Beethoven's most popular works are the nine symphonies, written for larger orchestras than Haydn's or Mozart's. Each is unique in character and style. There is a curious alternation of mood between his odd-numbered symphonies, which tend to be forceful and assertive, and his even-numbered ones, which are calmer and more lyrical. In the finale of the Ninth Symphony (*Choral*), Beethoven took the unprecedented step of using a chorus and four solo vocalists who sing the text of Schiller's *Ode to Joy.*

His thirty-two piano sonatas are far more difficult than the sonatas of Haydn and Mozart and exploit the stronger, tonally improved piano of Beethoven's time, drawing many new effects from it. In these sonatas, he experimented with compositional techniques that he would later expand in the symphonies and string quartets. The sixteen string quartets are among the greatest music composed, and each of the five superb piano concertos is remarkable for its individuality.

Most of Beethoven's important works are for instruments, but his sense of drama was also expressed in vocal music, including two masses and his only opera, *Fidelio.*

Beethoven's total output is usually divided into three periods: early (up to 1802), middle (1803–1814), and late (1815–1827). The music of Haydn and Mozart influenced some works of the early period, but other pieces clearly show Beethoven's personal style. The compositions of the middle period are longer and tend to be heroic in tone. And the sublime works of the last period well up from the depths of a man almost totally deaf. During this period Beethoven often used the fugue to express new musical concepts. The late works contain passages that sound surprisingly harsh and "modern." When a violinist complained that the music was very difficult to play, Beethoven reportedly replied, "Do you believe that I think of a wretched fiddle when the spirit speaks to me?"

Piano Sonata in C Minor, Op. 13 (*Pathétique;* 1798)

The title *Pathétique,* coined by Beethoven, suggests the tragically passionate character of his famous Piano Sonata in C Minor, Op. 13. Beethoven's impetuous playing and masterful improvisational powers are mirrored in the sonata's extreme dynamic contrasts, explosive accents, and crashing chords. At the age of twenty-seven, during his early period, Beethoven had already created a powerful and original piano style that foreshadowed nineteenth-century romanticism.

First Movement: Grave (solemn, slow introduction); Allegro molto e con brio (very fast and brilliant allegro)

The *Pathétique* begins in C minor with an intense, slow introduction, dominated by an opening motive in dotted rhythm: long-short-long-short-long-long.

Slow introduction
0:00

This six-note idea seems to pose a series of unresolved questions as it is repeated on higher and higher pitch levels. The tragic mood is intensified by dissonant chords, sudden contrasts of dynamics and register, and pauses filled with expectancy. The slow introduction is integrated in imaginative and dramatic ways into the allegro that follows it.

First theme
1:41

The tension of the introduction is maintained in the allegro con brio, a breathless, fast movement in sonata form. The opening theme, in C minor, begins with a staccato idea that rapidly rises up a two-octave scale. It is accompanied by low broken octaves, the rapid alternation of two tones an octave apart.

Bridge motive
1:57

Growing directly out of the opening theme is a bridge that is also built from a climbing staccato motive.

This bridge motive has an important role later in the movement.

Second theme
2:08

The contrasting second theme, which enters without a pause, is spun out of a short motive that is repeatedly shifted between low and high registers.

High running passage
2:53

This restless idea begins in E flat minor but then moves through different keys. The exposition is rounded off by several themes, including a high running passage and a return of the opening staccato idea in E flat major.

Development
3:11

Bridge and introduction motives
3:54

The development section begins with a dramatic surprise: Beethoven brings back the opening bars of the slow introduction. This reappearance creates an enormous contrast of tempo, rhythm, and mood. After four bars of slow music, the fast tempo resumes as Beethoven combines two different ideas: the staccato bridge motive and a quickened version of the introduction motive. The introduction motive is presented in a rhythmically altered form: short-short-short-long-long.

Recapitulation
4:34

Opening of slow introduction
5:51

The bridge motive is then developed in the bass, played by the pianist's left hand while the right hand plays high broken octaves. After several high accented notes, the brief development concludes with a running passage that leads down to the recapitulation.

For a while, the recapitulation runs its usual course as themes from the exposition are presented in the tonic key of C minor. But Beethoven has one more surprise for the coda—after a loud dissonant chord and a brief pause, he again brings back the opening of the slow introduction. This time the slow music is even more moving, as it is punctuated by moments of silence. Then the fast tempo resumes, and the opening staccato idea and powerful chords bring the movement to a decisive close.

Symphony No. 5 in C Minor, Op. 67 (1808)

The Fifth Symphony opens with one of the most famous rhythmic ideas in all music, a short-short-short-long motive. Beethoven reportedly explained this four-note motive as "fate knocking at the door." It dominates the first movement and also plays an important role later in the symphony. The entire work can be seen as an emotional progression from the conflict and struggle of the first movement, in C minor, to the exultation and victory of the final movement, in C major. The finale is the climax of the symphony; it is longer than the first movement and more powerful in sound.

Through several different techniques, Beethoven brilliantly welds four contrasting movements into a unified work. The basic rhythmic motive of the first movement (short-short-short-long) permeates the symphony. It is prominent in a marchlike theme in the third movement. And this third-movement theme is later quoted dramatically within the finale. The last two movements are also connected by a bridge passage.

Beethoven jotted down a few themes for the Fifth Symphony in 1804 but mainly worked on it during 1807 and 1808, an amazingly productive period when he also composed his Mass in C Major; Sonata for Cello and Piano, Op. 69; and Symphony No. 6.

First Movement:
Allegro con brio (allegro with vigor)

The allegro con brio is an enormously powerful and concentrated movement in sonata form. Its character is determined by a single rhythmic motive, short-short-short-long, from which Beethoven creates an astonishing variety of musical ideas. Tension and expectation are generated from the very beginning of the movement. Three rapid notes of the same pitch are followed by a downward leap to a held, suspenseful tone. This powerful idea is hammered out twice by all the strings in unison; the second time, it is a step lower in pitch.

As the opening theme continues in C minor, Beethoven maintains excitement by quickly developing his basic idea. He crowds varied repetitions of the motive together and rapidly shifts the motive to different pitches and instruments.

The second theme, in E flat major, dramatically combines different ideas. It begins with an unaccompanied horn call that asserts the basic motive in a varied form (short-short-short-long-long-long).

This horn-call motive announces a new legato melody, which is calm and contrasts with the preceding agitation. Yet even during this lyrical moment, we are not allowed to forget the basic motive; now it is muttered in the background by cellos and double basses.

Beethoven generates tension in the development section by breaking the horn-call motive into smaller and smaller fragments until it is represented by only a single tone. Supported by a chord, this tone is echoed between woodwinds and strings in a breathtaking decrescendo. The recapitulation comes as a tremendous climax as the full orchestra thunders the basic motive. The recapitulation also brings a new expressive oboe solo at the end of the first theme. The heroic closing section of the recapitulation, in C major, moves without a break into a long and exciting coda in C minor. This coda is like a second development section in which the basic motive creates still greater power and energy.

Listening Outline

BEETHOVEN, Symphony No. 5

First Movement: Allegro con brio
Sonata form, duple meter (²⁄₄), C minor
2 flutes, 2 oboes, 2 clarinets, 2 bassoons, 2 French horns, 2 trumpets, timpani, 1st violins, 2d violins, violas, cellos, double basses
(Duration, 7:37)

Exposition

First theme

0:00   **1. a.** Basic motive, *ff*, repeated a step lower, strings in unison.

0:06   **b.** Sudden *p*, strings quickly develop basic motive, minor key, powerful chords, high held tone.

Bridge

0:19   **2. a.** Basic motive, *ff*, orchestra in unison.
0:22   **b.** Sudden *p*, strings quickly develop basic motive, crescendo, *ff*, powerful chords.

Second theme

0:43   **3. a.** Solo French horns, *ff*, horn-call motive.

0:46   **b.** Violins, *p*, lyrical melody in major. Basic motive accompanies in low strings.

Crescendo to

1:07   **4. a.** Triumphant melody, **ff**, violins.

1:17   **b.** Woodwinds and horns, basic motive rushes downward. Cadences in basic rhythm. Pause.
1:27   Exposition is repeated.

Development

2:54   **1. a.** Basic motive, **ff**, horns, strings.

      b. Sudden **p**, strings and woodwinds, basic motive quickly developed. Motive climbs to rapidly repeated chords, **ff**.

3:30   **2. a.** Violins, **ff**, horn-call motive, low strings, descending line.

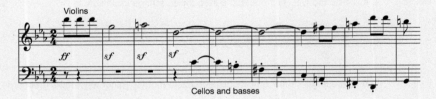

3:40   **b.** High woodwinds, **ff**, in dialogue with lower strings, **ff**. Horn-call motive broken into tiny fragments. Decrescendo to **pp**.

4:03   **c.** Sudden **ff**, horn-call rhythm.

      d. Sudden **pp**, repeated motive drives into

      e. Sudden **ff**, woodwinds echoed by strings.

Recapitulation

First theme

4:17   **1. a.** Climactic basic motive, full orchestra, **ff**, repeated a step lower.

      b. Sudden **p**, strings quickly develop basic motive, minor key, chords lead to

4:37   **c.** Oboe solo.

Bridge

4:51   **2.** Basic motive quickly developed in strings, crescendo to **ff**, full orchestra.

Second theme

5:12   **3. a.** Horn-call motive, solo bassoons, **ff**.

      b. Lyrical major melody, **p**, violins and flutes alternate. Basic motive accompanies in timpani, **p**. Crescendo to

5:41   **4. a.** Triumphant melody, *ff*, violins.

      b. Woodwinds, basic motive rushes downward.
Cadences in basic rhythm.

Coda

5:58   **1. a.** Rapidly repeated chords, *ff*.

6:14   **b.** Horn-call motive, lower strings, *f*, with higher violin melody, minor.

Descending violin melody, staccato, leads to

6:30   **2. a.** New, rising theme in strings, legato and staccato.

6:41   **b.** High woodwinds, *ff*, answered by lower strings in powerful interchange. Rapidly repeated notes lead to

7:07   **3. a.** Basic motive, *ff*, repeated a step lower, full orchestra.

      b. Sudden *p*, basic motive quickly developed in strings and woodwinds.

      c. Sudden *ff*, powerful concluding chords.

Second Movement:
Andante con moto (moderately slow, with movement)

The second movement, in A flat major, is mostly relaxed and lyrical, but it includes moments of tension and heroism. It is an extended set of variations based on two themes, A and B, and may be outlined as follows:

    theme A   theme B   variation A′   variation B′   variation A″   middle section variation A‴   coda.

The main theme (A), softly introduced by the cellos and violas, is a long, legato melody of great nobility. It includes many dotted-rhythm (long-short) patterns. The second theme (B) begins very gently in the clarinets with rising phrases in A flat major. Soon a startling contrast of mood results when the full orchestra suddenly bursts in, and the clarinet melody is transformed into a triumphant trumpet fanfare in the new key of C major. This emphasis of C major by loud brasses foreshadows the triumphant C major opening of the finale. In Variations A′ and A″ the melody flows evenly in increasingly rapid notes.

The middle section contrasts with earlier parts of the movement in that it uses only varied segments of themes A and B, and highlights woodwind instruments more prominently. The movement concludes with a final variation of the main melody (A‴)—now majestically proclaimed by the full orchestra—and a coda that poetically recalls what has come before.

Listening Outline

BEETHOVEN, Symphony No. 5

Second Movement: Andante con moto
Theme and variations, triple meter (⅜), A flat major
2 flutes, 2 oboes, 2 clarinets, 2 bassoons, 2 French horns, 2 trumpets, timpani, 1st violins, 2d violins, violas, cellos, double basses
(Duration, 9:58)

Theme A

0:00   **1.** Lyrical melody, violas and cellos, *p*.

Melody continues in higher register, violins alternate with flute.

Theme B

0:52   **2. a.** Clarinets, *p*, rising phrases.

            Violins, *pp*, sudden *ff*, full orchestra

1:14   **b.** Trumpets, *ff*, rising phrases.

            Violins, *pp*, sustained notes.

Variation A¹

1:58   **3.** Violas and cellos, *p*, lyrical melody in even-flowing rhythm.

Melody continues in higher register, violins alternate with flute.

Variation B¹

2:48   **4. a.** Clarinets, *p*, rising phrases. Violins, *pp*, sudden *ff*, full orchestra.
3:10   **b.** Trumpets, *ff*, rising phrases. Violins, *pp*, sustained notes, cellos, low repeated notes.

Variation A²

3:51   **5. a.** Violas and cellos, *p*, lyrical melody decorated by quick, even-flowing notes.

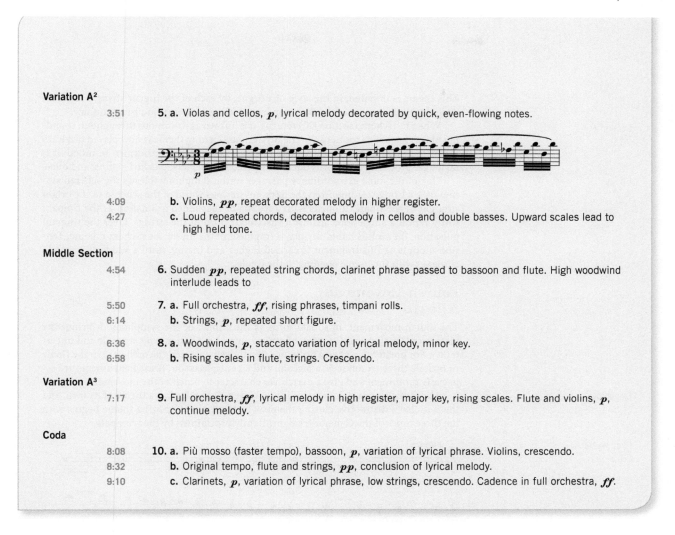

4:09   **b.** Violins, *pp*, repeat decorated melody in higher register.
4:27   **c.** Loud repeated chords, decorated melody in cellos and double basses. Upward scales lead to high held tone.

Middle Section

4:54   **6.** Sudden *pp*, repeated string chords, clarinet phrase passed to bassoon and flute. High woodwind interlude leads to

5:50   **7. a.** Full orchestra, *ff*, rising phrases, timpani rolls.
6:14   **b.** Strings, *p*, repeated short figure.
6:36   **8. a.** Woodwinds, *p*, staccato variation of lyrical melody, minor key.
6:58   **b.** Rising scales in flute, strings. Crescendo.

Variation A³

7:17   **9.** Full orchestra, *ff*, lyrical melody in high register, major key, rising scales. Flute and violins, *p*, continue melody.

Coda

8:08   **10. a.** Più mosso (faster tempo), bassoon, *p*, variation of lyrical phrase. Violins, crescendo.
8:32   **b.** Original tempo, flute and strings, *pp*, conclusion of lyrical melody.
9:10   **c.** Clarinets, *p*, variation of lyrical phrase, low strings, crescendo. Cadence in full orchestra, *ff*.

Third Movement:
Allegro (scherzo)

The rapid third movement is a scherzo, in C minor, with three sections: A (scherzo) B (trio) A′ (scherzo). The scherzo opens with a hushed, mysterious broken-chord theme played by cellos and double basses in a low register.

Section A
0:00

Soon, in sharp contrast, a bold repeated-note theme is hammered out loudly by the horns.

0:19

This theme is dominated by the rhythmic pattern short-short-short-long and recalls the basic motive of the first movement.

    The B section (trio), in major, brings a gruff, hurried theme, played by cellos and double basses.

Section B
1:49

This theme is imitated, in the style of a fugue, by each of the higher strings. The bustling rhythmic motion of the B section has a feeling of energy and rough humor.

When the scherzo section (A′) returns, it is hushed and ominous throughout, sounding like a ghost of its former self. The mysterious opening theme is now played pizzicato rather than legato. The repeated-note theme is completely transformed in mood; it is no longer proclaimed by horns but is whispered by clarinets, plucked violins, and oboe.

One of the most extraordinary passages in the symphony follows the scherzo section (A′): a bridge leading from the dark, mysterious world of the scherzo to the bright sunlight of the finale. It opens with a feeling of suspended animation as the timpani softly repeat a single tone against a sustained chord in the strings. Over the timpani pulsation, the violins hesitantly play a fragment of the mysterious scherzo theme. Tension mounts as this fragment is carried higher and higher, until a sudden crescendo climaxes with the heroic opening of the finale.

Fourth Movement:
Allegro

The fourth movement, in sonata form, is the climax of the symphony. It brings the victory of C major over C minor, of optimism and exultation over struggle and uncertainty. For greater power and brilliance, Beethoven enlarged the orchestra in the finale to include three trombones, a piccolo, and a contrabassoon. Brass instruments are especially prominent and give a marchlike character to much of the movement.

The exposition is rich in melodic ideas; even the bridge has a theme of its own, and there is also a distinctive closing theme. The triumphant opening theme begins with the three tones of the C major triad, brilliantly proclaimed by the trumpets.

Section A′
3:15

Bridge
4:27

Expositoin

First theme
0:00

Bridge
0:33

A bridge theme, similar in mood to the opening theme, is announced by the horns and continued by the violins.

Second theme
0:58

Triplets lend a joyous quality to the second theme, which contrasts loud and soft phrases.

Closing theme
1:25

Two powerful chords and a brief pause announce the closing theme of the exposition. The closing theme develops from a motive consisting of a descending scale segment followed by repeated notes. The three repeated notes followed by a long note recall the basic motive of the first movement.

Development
1:50

Quotation of scherzo theme
3:30
Recapitulation
4:09
Coda
6:40

The closing theme is introduced by the strings and woodwinds and then forcefully repeated by the entire orchestra.

The development focuses mainly on the second theme and its triplet rhythm. A huge climax at the end of the development is followed by one of the most marvelous surprises in all music. Beethoven dramatically quotes the whispered repeated-note theme (short-short-short-long) of the preceding scherzo movement. This ominous quotation is like a sudden recollection of past anxiety, and it creates a connection between the last two movements. Leading into the powerful recapitulation of the fourth movement, it prepares for the renewal of victory over uncertainty.

During the long coda of the finale, earlier themes are heard in altered and quickened versions. Several times, the music keeps going even though the listener thinks it's coming to an end. Over and over, Beethoven affirms the tonic key and resolves the frenzied tensions built up during the symphony. Such control over tension is an essential element of Beethoven's genius.

The Classical Period: Summary

IMPORTANT TERMS

Exposition, p. 162
Bridge (transition), p. 162
Development, p. 162
Motive, p. 162
Recapitulation, p. 162
Coda, p. 162
Countermelody, p. 166
Da capo, p. 168
Cadenza, p. 172

FEATURED GENRES

Serenade, p. 168
Symphony, p. 171
Concerto, p. 172
Chamber music, p. 173
String quartet, p. 173

FEATURED FORMS

Sonata form, p. 161
Theme and variations, p. 165
Minuet and trio, p. 168
Scherzo, p. 168
Rondo, p. 169
Sonata-rondo, p. 170

MAJOR COMPOSERS

Three composers, all of whom were active in Vienna at some time during their lives, dominate the classical era:
Joseph Haydn (1732–1809)
Wolfgang Amadeus Mozart (1756–1791)
Ludwig van Beethoven (1770–1827)

Music in Society

- Composers strove to write music that would appeal simultaneously to amateurs and learned connoisseurs.
- The growing middle class, who had greater access to education, financial stability, and leisure time than ever before, fueled a demand for public concerts.
- Composers increasingly broke from the patronage system to seek their fortune as freelance musicians.
- The aristocracy and middle class considered training in music an important educational skill.
- Music making in the home became increasingly important.

Important Style Features

Mood and Emotional Expression
- Classical music features fluctuations of mood within a movement.
- Changes in mood may occur gradually or suddenly, but are always firmly controlled by the composer and typically fall within a tastefully acceptable emotional range.
- Music was expected to be immediately appealing, pleasing, natural-sounding, and tasteful.

Rhythm
- Numerous rhythmic patterns provide variety and contrast.
- Unexpected pauses, syncopations, and frequent changes between long notes and shorter notes also provide variety and contrast.
- Rhythmic changes occur suddenly or gradually.

Dynamics
- Dynamics change gradually or suddenly, enabling the expression of highly varied emotional nuances within one movement.

Tone Color
- The characteristic sound of an orchestra with four families of instruments (strings, woodwinds, brass, and percussion) of approximately twenty-five to sixty players gradually became the standard.
- Wind and brass instruments were used in the orchestra to provide contrasts of timbre.
- The most important form of classical chamber music was the string quartet, written for two violins, viola, and cello.

Melody and Harmony
- Melodies are tuneful and easily remembered after one or two hearings.
- Phrases often occur in pairs, with the first phrase ending with an incomplete cadence and the second phrase ending more conclusively.
- Classical melodies may be broken into fragments or motives that undergo development to explore different moods.
- Harmonies are based on major and minor scales.
- Dissonance is used to provide contrast, suspense, or excitement.

Texture
- Texture is predominantly homophonic.
- Fluctuations of texture occur to provide contrasts; a piece may shift gradually or suddenly from one texture to another.

Performance Practice

- During the classical era, the use of the characteristic baroque basso continuo was gradually abandoned.
- The piano, able to create subtle dynamic changes through varied finger pressure on the keys, became favored over the harpsichord.
- An increase in the number of amateur musicians, unable to improvise an accompaniment at the keyboard from a figured bass, led to simpler accompaniments written out by the composer.
- Audiences were keenly aware of differences in musical style, and they expected music to be composed for specific performers to capitalize on their musical strengths.
- Regarding cadenzas in concertos for solo instrument by Mozart, performers must choose between using one composed by Mozart (if one exists), using one by another composer, or creating one.

Beyond the Classroom: Attending an Orchestra Concert

Haydn, Mozart, Beethoven, and their contemporaries established and developed the symphony by composing numerous symphonies that are still performed today, but later eras adapted the model to fit their own aesthetic vision, producing a symphonic repertoire that today is vast and richly diverse. On any given evening, thousands of people around the world can be found at concerts featuring symphony orchestras, many of which have their own unique and distinctive histories extending back more than a century.

When you attend an orchestra concert, check to see if a program is available. Usually the program specifies the name of the orchestra, its conductor, and any featured soloists, as well as the specific repertoire programmed for that evening. Some programs even list the specific instrumentation for each selection. Pay close attention to what you hear at any moment, and ask yourself the following questions:

- Does the program include a symphony, a concerto, or some other type of orchestral work? Does a work contain separate movements?
- Does the program include classical composers other than the "big three"?
- What is the specific orchestration of each selection? Pay particular attention to see if the number and kind of instruments change between different compositions.
- Are there any sections in which one instrument within the orchestra plays a memorable melody or is featured in some special way?
- Is a soloist featured on the program, and if so, who is performing and on which instrument? If a concerto is on the program, do the program notes indicate which cadenza is being used?
- In a piano concerto, is the work played on a modern piano or on a replica of an early piano (fortepiano)?

■ The romantic orchestra was larger and more varied in tone color than the classical orchestra. *The Orchestra of the Opéra* (c. 1870), by the French painter Edgar Degas (1834–1917).

PART V

The prevailing qualities of my music are passionate expressiveness, inner fire, rhythmic drive, and unexpectedness.

—Hector Berlioz

The Romantic Period

LEARNING OBJECTIVES

- Describe the characteristics of romantic music considering individuality of style, expressive aims and subjects, nationalism, program music, tone color, harmony, range of dynamics and pitch, and form

- Explain how the composer's role in society changed during the nineteenth century

- Analyze the relationship between words and music in Schubert's song Erlkönig (The Erlking)

- Compare and contrast piano pieces by Schumann, Chopin, and Liszt

- Define program music and compare and contrast orchestral works by Berlioz, Tchaikovsky, and Smetana

- Discuss the relationship between music and drama in scenes from operas by Puccini and Wagner

TIME LINE

Romantic Period (1820–1900)

| 1820–1850 | 1850–1900 |

Historical and Cultural Events

1823 Monroe Doctrine

1830 Revolutions in France, Belgium, Poland

1837–1901 Queen Victoria reigns in England

1848 Revolutions in Europe

1848 Marx and Engels, *The Communist Manifesto*

1859 Darwin, *Origin of Species*

1861–1865 American Civil War

1870 Franco-Prussian War

1876 Bell invents telephone

1898 Spanish-American War

Arts and Letters

1819 Keats, *Ode to a Nightingale*

1822 Delacroix, *Dante and Virgil in Hell*

1830 Delacroix, *Liberty Leading the People*

1831 Hugo, *The Hunchback of Notre Dame*

1835 Friedrich, *The Evening Star*

1837 Dickens, *Oliver Twist*

1840 Turner, *The Slave Ship*

1844 Dumas, *The Three Musketeers*

1845 Poe, *The Raven*

1857 Millet, *The Gleaners*

1866 Dostoevsky, *Crime and Punishment*

1870 Degas, *The Orchestra of the Opéra*

1874 Monet, *Impression, Sunrise*

1877 Cézanne, *Still Life with Apples*

1877 Tolstoy, *Anna Karenina*

1884 Twain, *The Adventures of Huckleberry Finn*

1889 van Gogh, *The Starry Night*

1893 Munch, *The Scream*

Music

1815 Franz Schubert, *Erlkönig*

1830 Berlioz, *Symphonie fantastique*

1831 Chopin, Nocturne in E♭ Major, Op. 9, No. 2

1831 Chopin, Étude in C Minor, Op. 10, No. 12 (*Revolutionary*)

1835 Robert Schumann, *Carnaval*

1842 Chopin, Polonaise in A♭ Major, Op. 53

1844 Mendelssohn, Violin Concerto in E Minor, Op. 64

1851 Liszt, *Transcendental* Étude in F Minor

1851 Verdi, *Rigoletto*

1856 Wagner, *Die Walküre*

1868 Brahms, *German Requiem*

1870 Tchaikovsky, *Romeo and Juliet*

1874 Smetana, *The Moldau*

1893 Dvořák, Symphony No. 9 in E Minor (From the *New World*)

1896 Puccini, *La Bohème*

Romanticism
(1820–1900)

The early nineteenth century brought the flowering of romanticism, a cultural movement that stressed emotion, imagination, and individuality. In part, romanticism was a rebellion against the neoclassicism of the eighteenth century and the age of reason. Romantic writers broke away from time-honored conventions and emphasized freedom of expression. Romantic painters used bolder, more brilliant colors and preferred dynamic motion to gracefully balanced poses.

But romanticism was too diverse and complex to be defined by any single formula. It aimed to broaden horizons and encompass the totality of human experience. The romantic movement was international in scope and influenced all of the arts.

Emotional subjectivity was a basic quality of romanticism in art. "All good poetry is the spontaneous overflow of powerful feelings," wrote William Wordsworth, the English romantic poet. And "spontaneous overflow" made much romantic literature autobiographical; authors projected their personalities in their work. Walt Whitman, the American poet, expressed this

Romantic artists often depicted scenes of extreme violence and suffering. In *The Raft of the Medusa* (1819), the French painter Théodore Géricault conveyed the epic tragedy of a contemporary shipwreck. The ship captain—appointed only because of his noble birth—saved himself and other officers, while abandoning many other survivors to their horrible fate on a primitive raft.

Emotional subjectivity was
a basic quality of romanticism. A portrait of the Polish
composer and pianist Frédéric
Chopin by Eugène Delacroix.

The *Gleaners* (1857) by Jean-
François Millet. The industrial
revolution caused vast social
and economic changes and
awakened interest in the poor.
The French painter Millet
portrayed the labor of peasant
women picking up leftover
grain in the fields.

subjective attitude beautifully when he began a poem, "I celebrate myself, and sing myself."

In exploring their inner lives, the romantics were especially drawn to the realm of fantasy: the unconscious, the irrational, the world of dreams. Romantic fiction includes tales of horror and the supernatural, such as *The Cask of Amontillado,* by Edgar Allan Poe; and *Frankenstein,* by Mary Wollstonecraft Shelley. The writer Thomas De Quincey vividly describes his drug-induced dreams in *Confessions of an English Opium-Eater:* "I was buried, for a thousand years, in stone coffins, with mummies and sphinxes. I was kissed, with cancerous kisses, by crocodiles." The visual arts also depict nightmarish visions. In an etching called *The Sleep of Reason Breeds Monsters,* the Spanish painter Francisco Goya shows batlike

monsters surrounding a sleeping figure. The realm of the unknown and the exotic also interested the French artist Eugène Delacroix, who often depicted violent scenes in far-off lands.

The romantic fascination with fantasy was paired with enthusiasm for the Middle Ages, that time of chivalry and romance. Whereas neoclassicists had thought of the medieval period as the "dark ages," the romantics cherished it. They were inspired by medieval folk ballads and by tales of fantasy and adventure. Romantic novels set in the Middle Ages include *Ivanhoe* (1819), by Walter Scott; and *The Hunchback of Notre Dame* (1831), by the French writer Victor Hugo. Gothic cathedrals, which had long gone unappreciated, now seemed picturesque and mysterious. A "gothic revival" in architecture resulted in the construction of

buildings such as the houses of Parliament in London (1836–1852) and Trinity Church in New York (1839–1846).

Of all the inspirations for romantic art, none was more important than nature. The physical world was seen as a source of consolation and a mirror of the human heart. Wordsworth, for example, thought of nature as "the nurse,/the guide, the guardian of my heart, and soul." One of his poems begins:

There was a time when meadow, grove, and stream,
The earth, and every common sight,
    To me did seem
    Apparelled in celestial light,
The glory and the freshness of a dream.

The romantic sensitivity to nature is revealed in landscape painting, which

Man and Woman Contemplating the Moon (1818–1824) by the German painter Caspar David Friedrich. The romantics were particularly drawn to the realms of fantasy, the unconscious, the irrational, and the world of dreams.

Stour Valley and Dedham Church (c. 1815), by John Constable. Of all the inspirations for romantic art, none was more important than nature.

Slave Ship (Slavers Throwing Overboard the Dead and Dying, Typhoon Coming On) (1840) by the English painter J. M. W. Turner. In Turner's seascapes, the sweep of waves expresses not only the power of nature but also human passion.

attained new importance. Artists like John Constable and J. M. W. Turner in England were masters at conveying movement in nature: rippling brooks, drifting clouds, stormy seas. In Turner's seascapes, the sweep of waves expresses not only the grandeur of nature but human passion as well.

Romanticism coincided with the industrial revolution, which caused vast social and economic changes. Many writers and painters recorded the new social realities of their time. The novels of Charles Dickens and the paintings of Honoré Daumier reflect an interest in the working class and the poor.

Subjectivity, fantasy, and enthusiasm for nature and the Middle Ages are only a few aspects of romanticism in literature and painting. We now focus on romanticism in music.

1 Romanticism in Music (1820–1900)

The romantic period in music extended from about 1820 to 1900. Among the most significant romantic musicians were Franz Schubert, Robert Schumann, Frédéric Chopin, Franz Liszt, Felix Mendelssohn, Hector Berlioz, Peter Ilyich Tchaikovsky, Bedřich Smetana, Antonín Dvořák, Johannes Brahms, Giuseppe Verdi, Giacomo Puccini, and Richard Wagner. The length of this list—and some important composers have been omitted from it—testifies to the richness and variety of romantic music and to its continuing impact on today's concert and operatic repertoire.

Composers of the romantic period continued to use the musical forms of the preceding classical era. The emotional intensity associated with romanticism was already present in the work of Mozart and particularly in that of Beethoven, who greatly influenced composers after him. The romantic preference for expressive, songlike melody also grew out of the classical style.

Nonetheless, there are many differences between romantic and classical music. Romantic works tend to have greater ranges of tone color, dynamics, and pitch. Also, the romantic harmonic vocabulary is broader, with more emphasis on colorful, unstable chords. Romantic music is linked more closely to the other arts, particularly to literature. New forms developed, and in all forms there was greater tension and less emphasis on balance and resolution. But romantic music is so diverse that generalizations are apt to mislead. Some romantic composers, such as Mendelssohn and Brahms, created works that were deeply rooted in classical tradition; other composers, such as Berlioz, Liszt, and Wagner, were more revolutionary.

Characteristics of Romantic Music

Individuality of Style Romantic music puts unprecedented emphasis on self-expression and individuality of style. There is "not a bar which I have not truly felt and which is not an echo of my innermost feelings," wrote Tchaikovsky of his Fourth Symphony. A "new world of music" was the goal of the young Chopin. Many romantics created music that sounds unique and reflects their personalities. As Robert Schumann observed, "Chopin will soon be unable to write anything without people crying out at the seventh or eighth bar, 'That is indeed by him.'" And today, with some listening experience, a music lover can tell within a few minutes—sometimes within a few seconds—whether a piece is by Schumann or Chopin, Tchaikovsky or Brahms.

Expressive Aims and Subjects The romantics explored a universe of feeling that included flamboyance and intimacy, unpredictability and melancholy, rapture and longing. Countless songs and operas glorify romantic love; often, the lovers are unhappy and face overwhelming obstacles. Fascination with the fantastic and diabolical is expressed in music like the *Dream of a Witches' Sabbath* from Berlioz's *Symphonie fantastique* (*Fantastic Symphony*). All aspects of nature attracted romantic musicians. In different sections of Part V we study music that depicts shepherds' pipes and distant thunder (Berlioz's *Fantastic Symphony*), a wild horseback ride on a stormy night (Schubert's *Erlkönig*, or *Erlking*), and the flow of a river (Smetana's *Moldau*). Romantic composers also dealt with subjects drawn from the Middle Ages and from Shakespeare's plays.

Nationalism and Exoticism Nationalism was an important political movement that influenced nineteenth-century music. Musical **nationalism** was expressed when romantic composers deliberately created music with a specific national identity, using the folksongs, dances, legends, and history of their homelands. This national flavor of romantic music—whether Polish, Russian, Bohemian (Czech), or German—contrasts with the more universal character of classical music.

Fascination with national identity also led composers to draw on colorful materials from foreign lands, a trend known as musical **exoticism.** For instance, some composers wrote melodies in an Asian style or used rhythms and instruments associated with distant lands. The French composer Georges Bizet wrote *Carmen,* an opera set in Spain; the Italian Giacomo Puccini evoked Japan in his opera *Madame Butterfly*; and the Russian Rimsky-Korsakov suggested an Arabian atmosphere in his orchestral work *Scheherazade.* Musical exoticism was in keeping with the romantics' attraction to things remote, picturesque, and mysterious.

Program Music The nineteenth century was the great age of **program music,** instrumental music associated with a story, poem, idea, or scene. The nonmusical element is usually specified by a title or by explanatory comments called a **program.** A programmatic instrumental piece can represent the emotions, characters, and events of a particular story, or it can evoke the sounds and motion of nature. For example, in Tchaikovsky's *Romeo and Juliet,* an orchestral work inspired by Shakespeare's play, agitated music depicts the feud between the rival families, a tender melody conveys young love, and a funeral-march rhythm suggests the lovers' tragic fate. And in *The Moldau,* an orchestral work glorifying the main river of Bohemia, Smetana uses musical effects that call to mind a flowing stream, a hunting scene, a peasant wedding, and the crash of waves.

Program music in some form or another has existed for centuries, but it became particularly prominent in the romantic period, when music was closely associated with literature. Many composers—Berlioz, Schumann, Liszt, and Wagner, for example—were prolific authors as well. Artists in all fields were intoxicated by the concept of a "union of the arts." Poets wanted their poetry to be musical, and musicians wanted their music to be poetic.

Expressive Tone Color Romantic composers reveled in rich and sensuous sound, using tone color to obtain a variety of moods and atmosphere. Never before had timbre been so important.

In both symphonic and operatic works, the romantic orchestra was larger and more varied in tone color than the classical orchestra. Toward the end of the romantic era, an orchestra might include close to one hundred musicians. (There were twenty to sixty players in the classical ensemble.) The constant expansion of the orchestra reflected composers' changing needs as well as the growing size of concert halls and opera houses. The brass, woodwind, and percussion sections of the orchestra took on a more active role. Romantic composers increased the power of the brass section to something spectacular, calling for trombones, tubas, and more horns and trumpets. In 1824, Beethoven had broken precedent by asking for nine brasses in the Ninth Symphony; in 1894, the Austrian composer Gustav Mahler demanded twenty-five brass instruments for his Second Symphony. The addition of valves had made it easier for horns and trumpets to cope with intricate melodies.

The woodwind section took on new tone colors as the contrabassoon, bass clarinet, English horn, and piccolo became regular members of the orchestra. Improvements in the construction of instruments allowed woodwind players to perform more flexibly and accurately. Orchestral sounds became more brilliant and sensuously appealing through increased use of cymbals, the triangle, and the harp.

New sounds were drawn from all instruments of the nineteenth-century orchestra. Flutists were required to play in the breathy low register, and violinists were asked to strike the strings with the wood of their bows. Such demands compelled performers to attain a higher level of technical virtuosity.

Composers sought new ways of blending and combining tone colors to achieve the most poignant and intense sound. In 1844, Hector Berlioz's *Treatise on Modern Instrumentation and Orchestration* signaled the recognition of orchestration as an art in itself.

The piano, the favorite instrument of the romantic age, was vastly improved during the 1820s and 1830s. A cast-iron frame was introduced to hold the strings under greater tension, and the hammers were covered with felt. Thus the piano's tone became more "singing." Its range was also extended. With a stronger instrument, the pianist could produce more sound. And use of the damper ("loud") pedal allowed a sonorous blend of tones from all registers of the piano.

Colorful Harmony

In addition to exploiting new tone colors, the romantics explored new chords and novel ways of using familiar chords. Seeking greater emotional intensity, composers emphasized rich, colorful, and complex harmonies.

There was more prominent exploitation of **chromatic harmony,** which uses chords containing tones not found in the prevailing major or minor scale. Such chord tones come from the chromatic scale (which has twelve tones), rather than from the major or minor scales (which have seven different tones). Chromatic chords add color and motion to romantic music. Dissonant, or unstable, chords were also used more freely than during the classical era. By deliberately delaying the resolution of dissonance to a consonant, or stable, chord, romantic composers created feelings of yearning, tension, and mystery.

A romantic piece tends to have a wide variety of keys and rapid modulations, or changes from one key to another. Because of the nature and frequency of these key shifts, the tonic key is somewhat less clear than in classical works. The feeling of tonal gravity tends to be less strong. By the end of the romantic period, even more emphasis was given to harmonic instability and less to stability and resolution.

Expanded Range of Dynamics, Pitch, and Tempo

Romantic music also calls for a wide range of dynamics. It includes sharp contrasts between faint whispers and sonorities of unprecedented power. The classical dynamic extremes of *ff* and *pp* didn't meet the needs of romantics, who sometimes demanded *ffff* and *pppp*. Seeking more and more expressiveness, nineteenth-century composers used frequent crescendos and decrescendos, as well as sudden dynamic changes.

The range of pitch was expanded too, as composers reached for extremely high or low sounds. In search of increased brilliance and depth of sound, the romantics exploited instruments like the piccolo and contrabassoon, as well as the expanded keyboard of the piano.

Changes of mood in romantic music are often underlined by accelerandos, ritardandos, and subtle variations of pace: there are many more fluctuations in tempo than there are in classical music. To intensify the expression of the music, romantic performers made use of **rubato,** the slight holding back or pressing forward of tempo.

Form: Miniature and Monumental

The nineteenth century was very much an age of contradictions. Romantic composers characteristically expressed themselves both in musical miniatures and in monumental compositions. On one hand are piano pieces by Chopin and songs by Schubert that last but a few minutes. Such short forms were meant to be heard in the intimate surroundings of a home; they met the needs of the growing number of people who owned pianos. The romantic genius for creating an intense mood through a melody, a few chords, or an unusual tone color found a perfect outlet in these miniatures. On the other hand, there are gigantic works by Berlioz and Wagner that call for a huge number of performers, last for several hours, and were designed for large opera houses or concert halls.

Romantic composers continued to write symphonies, sonatas, string quartets, concertos, operas, and choral works, but their individual movements tended to be longer than Haydn's and Mozart's. For example, a typical nineteenth-century symphony might last about forty-five minutes, as opposed to twenty-five minutes for an eighteenth-century symphony. And as the romantic period drew to a close, compositions tended to become even more extended, more richly orchestrated, and more complex in harmony.

New techniques were used to unify such long works. The same theme or themes might occur in several different movements of a symphony. Here composers followed the pioneering example of Beethoven's Fifth Symphony, in which a theme from the scherzo is quoted within the finale. When a melody returns in a later movement or section of a romantic work, its character may be transformed by changes in dynamics, orchestration, or rhythm—a technique known as ***thematic transformation.*** A striking use of thematic transformation occurs in Berlioz's *Symphonie fantastique* (*Fantastic Symphony,* 1830), in which a lyrical melody from the opening movement becomes a grotesque dance tune in the finale.

Different movements or sections of a romantic work also can be linked through transitional passages; one movement of a symphony or concerto may lead directly into the next. Here, again, Beethoven was the pioneer. And nineteenth-century operas are unified by melodic ideas that reappear in different acts or scenes, some of which may be tied together by connecting passages.

In dealing with an age that so prized individuality, generalizations are especially difficult. The great diversity found in romantic music can best be appreciated, perhaps, by approaching each piece as its composer did—with an open mind and heart.

2 Romantic Composers and Their Public

The composer's role in society changed radically during Beethoven's lifetime (1770–1827). In earlier periods, part of a musician's job had been the composition of works for a specific occasion and audience. Thus Bach wrote cantatas for weekly church services in Leipzig, and Haydn composed symphonies for concerts in the palaces of the Esterházy family. But Beethoven, as we have seen, was one of the first great composers to work as a freelance musician outside the system of aristocratic or church patronage.

The image of Beethoven as a "free artist" inspired romantic musicians, who often composed to meet an inner need rather than fulfill a commission. Romantic composers were interested not only in pleasing their contemporaries but also in being judged favorably by posterity. The young Berlioz wrote to his father, "I want to leave on this earth some trace of my existence." It became common for romantics to create extended works with no immediate prospects for performance. For example, Wagner wrote *Das Rheingold* (*The Rhine Gold*), a two and a half hour opera, and then had to wait fifteen years before seeing its premiere.

Sometimes the romantic composer was a "free artist" by necessity rather than choice. Because of the French Revolution and the Napoleonic wars (1789–1814), many aristocrats could no longer afford to maintain private opera houses, orchestras, and

Romantic composers wrote primarily for a middle-class audience. In this picture by Moritz von Schwind, Franz Schubert is shown at the piano accompanying the singer Johann Michael Vogl.

"composers in residence." Musicians lost their jobs when many of the tiny princely states of Germany were abolished as political units and merged with neighboring territories. (In Bonn, Germany, the court and its orchestra were disbanded; Beethoven could not have returned to his position there even if he had wanted to.) Many composers who would have had modest but secure incomes in the past had to fight for their livelihood and sell their wares in the marketplace.

Romantic composers wrote primarily for a middle-class audience whose size and prosperity had increased because of the industrial revolution. During the nineteenth century, cities expanded dramatically, and a sizable number of people wanted to hear and play music.

The needs of this urban middle class led to the formation of many orchestras and opera groups during the romantic era. Public concerts had developed during the eighteenth century, but not until the nineteenth century did regular subscription concerts become common. The London Philharmonic Society was founded in 1813, the Paris Société des Concerts du Conservatoire was founded in 1828, and the Vienna Philharmonische Konzerte and the New York Philharmonic were founded in 1842.

The first half of the nineteenth century also witnessed the founding of music conservatories throughout Europe. In the United States, conservatories were founded in Chicago, Cleveland, Boston, Oberlin (Ohio), and Philadelphia during the 1860s. More young men and women than ever before studied to be professional musicians. At first women were accepted only as students of performance, but by the late 1800s they could study musical composition as well.

The nineteenth-century public was captivated by virtuosity. Among the musical heroes of the 1830s were the pianist Franz Liszt and the violinist Niccolò Paganini (1782–1840), who toured Europe and astonished audiences with their feats. Never before had instrumental virtuosity been so acclaimed. After one concert by Liszt in Budapest,

The needs of the urban middle class led to the formation of many orchestras during the romantic era. This engraving shows Louis Jullien conducting an orchestra and four military bands at Covent Garden Theater in London in 1846.

Hungarian nobles presented him with a jeweled sword, and a crowd of thousands formed a torchlight parade to escort him to his dwelling. Following Liszt's example, performers such as pianist Clara Wieck Schumann and violinist Joseph Joachim began to give solo recitals in addition to their customary appearances with orchestras.

Private music making also increased during the romantic era. The piano became a fixture in every middle-class home, and there was great demand for songs and solo piano pieces. Operas and orchestral works were transcribed, or arranged, so that they could be played on a piano in the home.

Romantic composers came from the social class that was their main audience. Berlioz was the son of a doctor; Schumann was the son of a bookseller; Mendelssohn was the son of a banker. This was a new situation. In earlier periods, music, like cabinet-making, had been a craft passed from one generation to another. Bach, Mozart, and Beethoven were all children of musicians. But the romantics often had to do a great deal of persuading before their parents permitted them to undertake a musical career. Berlioz wrote to his reluctant father in 1824: "I am voluntarily driven toward a magnificent career (no other term can be applied to the career of an artist) and I am not in the least headed toward damnation. . . . This is the way I think, the way I am, and nothing in the world will change me."

Middle-class parents had reason for concern when their children wanted to be musicians. Few romantic composers were able to support themselves through composition alone. Only a very successful opera composer like Verdi could become wealthy by selling music to opera houses and publishers. Most composers were forced to work in several areas at once. Some were touring virtuosos like Paganini and Liszt. Many taught; Chopin charged high fees for giving piano lessons to rich young women in Paris. Music criticism was a source of income for Berlioz and Schumann. (And Berlioz bitterly resented having to waste time reviewing compositions by nonentities.) Some of the finest conductors of the romantic period were composers, among them Mendelssohn and Mahler. Only a few fortunates, such as Tchaikovsky and Wagner, had wealthy patrons to support them while they created.

3 The Art Song

One of the most distinctive forms in romantic music is the ***art song,*** a composition for solo voice and piano. Here, the accompaniment is an integral part of the composer's concept, and it serves as an interpretive partner to the voice. Although they are now performed in concert halls, romantic songs were written to be sung and enjoyed at home.

Poetry and music are intimately fused in the art song. It is no accident that this form flowered with the emergence of a rich body of romantic poetry in the early nineteenth century. Many of the finest song composers—Schubert, Schumann, and Brahms, for example—were German or Austrian and set poems in their native language. Among the poets favored by these composers were Johann Wolfgang von Goethe (1749–1832) and Heinrich Heine (1797–1856). The German word *Lied* (*song*) is commonly used for a song with German text. (*Lied* is pronounced *leet*; its plural, *Lieder,* is pronounced *leader.*)

Yearning—inspired by a lost love, nature, a legend, or other times and places—haunted the imagination of romantic poets. Thus art songs are filled with the despair of unrequited love; the beauty of flowers, trees, and brooks; and the supernatural happenings of folktales. There are also songs of joy, wit, and humor. But by and large, romantic song was a reaching out of the soul.

Song composers would interpret a poem, translating its mood, atmosphere, and imagery into music. They created a vocal melody that was musically satisfying and perfectly molded to the text. Important words were emphasized by stressed tones or melodic climaxes.

The voice shares the interpretive task with the piano. Emotions and images in the text take on an added dimension from the keyboard commentary. Arpeggios in the piano might suggest the splashing of oars or the motion of a mill wheel. Chords in a low register might depict darkness or a lover's torment. The mood is often set by a brief piano introduction and summed up at the end by a piano section called a ***postlude.***

The Song Cycle

Romantic art songs are sometimes grouped in a set, or ***song cycle.*** A cycle may be unified by a story line that runs through the poems, or by musical ideas linking the songs. Among the great romantic song cycles are *Winterreise* (*Winter's Journey,* 1827) by Schubert, and *Dichterliebe* (*Poet's Love,* 1840) by Schumann.

In many of their art songs, romantic composers achieved a perfect union of music and poetry. They created an intensely personal world with a tremendous variety of moods. These miniatures contain some of the most haunting melodies and harmonies in all music.

4 Franz Schubert

The career of Franz Schubert (1797–1828), the earliest master of the romantic art song, was unlike that of any great composer before him. He never held an official position and was neither a conductor nor a virtuoso. His income came entirely from musical composition. "I have come into the world for no other purpose but to compose," he told a friend. The full measure of his genius was recognized only years after his tragically early death.

Franz Schubert did not mingle with the aristocracy, preferring instead the company of poets, painters, and other musicians.

Schubert was born in Vienna, the son of a schoolmaster. Even as a child, he had astounding musical gifts. "If I wanted to instruct him in anything new," recalled his amazed teacher, "he knew it already." At eleven, he became a choirboy in the court chapel and won a scholarship to the Imperial Seminary.

Schubert managed to compose an extraordinary number of masterpieces in his late teens while teaching at his father's school, a job he hated. His love of poetry led him to the art song; he composed his first great song, *Gretchen am Spinnrade* (*Gretchen at the Spinning Wheel*), when he was seventeen. The next year he composed 143 songs, including *The Erlking*. When he was nineteen, his productivity rose to a peak: he composed 179 works, including two symphonies, an opera, and a mass.

At twenty-one, he gave up teaching school to devote himself entirely to music. He associated with a group of Viennese poets and artists who led a bohemian existence. Often he lived with friends because he did not have money to rent a room of his own. Working incredibly fast, from seven in the morning until early afternoon, he turned out one piece after another. He spent his afternoons in cafés, and many of his evenings at "Schubertiads," parties where only his music was played. Most of his works were composed for performances in the homes of Vienna's cultivated middle class. Unlike Beethoven, Schubert did not mingle with the aristocracy. The publication and performance of his songs brought him some recognition, but his two most important symphonies—the *Unfinished* and the *Great* C Major—were not performed in public during his lifetime.

Schubert died in 1828, at age thirty-one. He was thought of mainly as a fine song composer, until the *Unfinished* Symphony was performed almost forty years later. Then the world began to recognize Schubert's comprehensive greatness.

Schubert's Music

Along with more than 600 songs, Schubert composed symphonies, string quartets, chamber music for piano and strings, piano sonatas, short piano pieces for two and four hands, masses, and operatic compositions. The songs embrace an enormous variety of moods and types. Their melodies range from simple, folklike tunes to complex lines that suggest impassioned speech, and their piano accompaniments are equally rich and evocative. Schubert's imaginative harmonies and dissonances provide some of the most poetic moments in music.

The spirit of song permeates Schubert's instrumental music too. His longer works often include variation movements based on his own songs; his famous *Trout* Quintet in A Major (1819) is an example. Many of the symphonies and chamber works have long, lyrical melodies, and some—especially the *Unfinished* Symphony (1822) and the *Great* C Major Symphony (1825–1826)—are comparable in power and intensity to those of his idol, Beethoven. The *Unfinished* was written six years before his death; no one knows why it has only two movements rather than the usual four. The *Great* C Major Symphony was discovered ten years after Schubert's death by Robert Schumann.

Erlkönig (*The Erlking*; 1815)

Schubert's song *Erlkönig* (*The Erlking*) is one of the earliest and finest examples of musical romanticism. It is a musical setting of a narrative ballad of the supernatural by Goethe. A friend of Schubert's tells how he saw the eighteen-year-old composer reading

Goethe's poem. "He paced up and down several times with the book; suddenly he sat down, and in no time at all (just as quickly as he could write) there was the glorious ballad finished on the paper." Goethe's ballad, in dialogue almost throughout, tells of a father riding on horseback through a storm with his sick child in his arms. The delirious boy has visions of the legendary Erlking, the king of the elves, who symbolizes death.

Schubert uses a through-composed setting to capture the mounting excitement of the poem. The piano part, with its rapid octaves and menacing bass motive, conveys the tension of the wild ride.

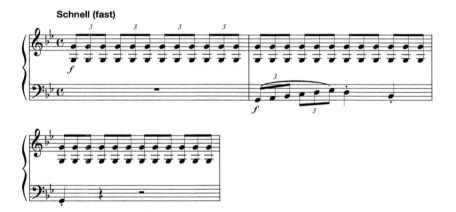

The piano's relentless triplet rhythm unifies the episodes of the song and suggests the horse's gallop.

By imaginatively varying the music, Schubert makes one singer sound like several characters in a miniature drama. The terrified boy sings in a high register in minor. Three times during the poem, he cries out, "My father, my father." Each time, the boy sings a musical outcry that is intensified through dissonant harmonies.

Mein Va - ter, mein Va - ter,

To convey mounting fear, Schubert pitches the boy's outcry higher and higher each time. The reassuring father sings in a low register that contrasts with the high-pitched outcries of his child. The Erlking, who tries to entice the boy, has coy melodies in major keys.

Du lie - bes Kind, komm, geh mit mir! gar scho - ne Spie - le   spiel' ich mit dir;

The deeply moving climax of *The Erlking* comes when father and son arrive home and the galloping accompaniment gradually comes to a halt. In a bleak, heartbreaking recitative that allows every word to make its impact, the narrator tells us, "In his arms the child was dead!"

Vocal Music Guide

SCHUBERT, *Erlkönig*

0:00
Piano introduction,
rapid octaves,
f, bass motive,
minor key.

Narrator

Wer reitet so spät durch Nacht und Wind?	Who rides so late through the night and the wind?
Es ist der Vater mit seinem Kind;	It is the father with his child;
Er hat den Knaben wohl in dem Arm,	he holds the boy close in his arms,
Er fasst ihn sicher, er hält ihn warm.	he clasps him securely, he holds him warmly.

0:55
Low register.

Father

"Mein Sohn, was birgst du so bang dein Gesicht?"	"My son, why do you hide your face so anxiously?"

1:04
Higher register

Son

"Siehst, Vater, du den Erlkönig nicht?	"Father, don't you see the Erlking?
Den Erlenkönig mit Kron' und Schweif?"	The Erlking with his crown and his train?"

1:20
Low register

Father

"Mein Sohn, es ist ein Nebelstreif."	"My son, it is a streak of mist."

1:29
Coaxing tune,
pp, higher
register, major.

Erlking

"Du liebes Kind, komm, geh mit mir!	"Dear child, come, go with me!
Gar schöne Spiele spiel' ich mit dir,	I'll play the prettiest games with you.
Manch bunte Blumen sind an dem Strand,	Many colored flowers grow along the shore;
Meine Mutter hat manch gülden Gewand."	My mother has many golden garments."

1:51
Outcry, *f*, minor.

Son

"Mein Vater, mein Vater, und hörest du nicht,	"My father, my father, and don't you hear
Was Erlenkönig mir leise verspricht?"	the Erlking whispering promises to me?"

2:03
Low register.

Father

"Sei ruhig, bleibe ruhig, mein Kind:	"Be quiet, stay quiet, my child;
In dürren Blättern säuselt der Wind."	the wind is rustling in the dead leaves."

2:14
Playful tune,
pp, major.

Erlking

"Willst, feiner Knabe, du mit mir gehn?	"My handsome boy, will you come with me?
Meine Töchter sollen dich warten schön;	My daughters shall wait upon you;
Meine Töchter führen den nächtlichen Reihn	my daughters lead off in the dance every night,
Und wiegen und tanzen und singen dich ein."	and cradle and dance and sing you to sleep."

		Son	
2:30 Outcry, *f*, higher than before, minor.	*"Mein Vater, mein Vater, und siehst du nicht dort Erlkönigs Töchter am düstern Ort?"*		"My father, my father, and don't you see there the Erlking's daughters in the shadows?"

Father

| 2:44 Lower register. | *"Mein Sohn, mein Sohn, ich seh' es genau: Es scheinen die alten Weiden so grau."* | "My son, my son, I see it clearly; the old willows look so gray." |

Erlking

| 3:01 | *"Ich liebe dich, mich reizt deine schöne Gestalt; Und bist du nicht willig, so brauch' ich Gewalt."* | "I love you, your beautiful figure delights me! And if you are not willing, then I shall use force!" |

Son

| 3:12 Outcry, *f*, highest yet. | *"Mein Vater, mein Vater, jetzt fasst er mich an! Erlkönig hat mir ein Leids getan!"* | "My father, my father, now he is taking hold of me! The Erlking has hurt me!" |

Narrator

| 3:26 | *Dem Vater grauset's, er reitet geschwind, Er hält in Armen das ächzende Kind, Erreicht den Hof mit Mühe und Not;* | The father shudders, he rides swiftly on; he holds in his arms the groaning child, he reaches the courtyard weary and anxious: |

| Piano stops. Recitative. | *In seinen Armen das Kind war tot.* | in his arms the child was dead. |

5 Robert Schumann

Robert Schumann (1810–1856) in many ways embodied musical romanticism. His works are intensely autobiographical and usually have descriptive titles, texts, or programs. He expressed his essentially lyrical nature in startlingly original piano pieces and songs. As a gifted writer and critic, he also discovered and made famous some of the leading composers of his day.

Schumann was born in Zwickau, Germany. He studied law at Leipzig University, but he rarely attended lectures and devoted his time instead to literature and music. At twenty, he decided to become a piano virtuoso, but this goal became impossible when he developed serious problems with his right hand. In search of a cure, he used a mechanical gadget designed to stretch and strengthen the fingers. But neither this device nor various medical treatments alleviated his condition. "Don't worry about my finger," he wrote to his mother. "I can compose without it." Indeed, in his twenties he composed many piano works that remain a basic part of the repertoire, although at the time they were often considered too unconventional and personal. During his twenties, too, he founded and edited the influential *New Journal of*

Robert Schumann's works are intensely autobiographical and are usually linked with descriptive titles, texts, or programs.

Music, which contained his appreciative reviews of "radical" young composers such as Chopin and Berlioz.

While studying piano, Schumann met his teacher's daughter and prize pupil, Clara Wieck. Schumann was eighteen, and Clara was a nine-year-old prodigy. The two were engaged when Clara was seventeen, despite bitter opposition from her father. The couple fought bitter court battles against Wieck before they could be married. Their marriage was a happy one. Clara, herself a composer, was the ideal interpreter of her husband's piano works and introduced many of them to the public.

Schumann held some musical positions but was temperamentally ill-suited for them. During his later years his mental and physical health deteriorated. In 1854 he tried to drown himself and was committed to an asylum, where he died two years later.

Schumann's Music

During the first ten years of his creative life, Schumann published only piano pieces, and his musical style seemed to grow out of piano improvisation. His short pieces often express a single mood through a sensitive melody; dance rhythms, syncopations, and dotted rhythms are also important.

In 1840, the year of his marriage, Schumann composed many art songs, which also reveal his gift for melody. Both the songs and the short piano pieces are usually organized into sets or cycles, whose titles—*Carnaval* (*Carnival*), *Kinderscenen* (*Scenes of Childhood*), *Nachtstücke* (*Night Pieces*), *Dichterliebe* (*Poet's Love*), *Fantasiestücke* (*Fantasy Pieces*)—provide insight into his imagination. Schumann thought of music in emotional, literary, and autobiographical terms; his work is full of extramusical references.

After 1840, possibly as a result of Clara's influence, he turned to symphonies and chamber music. His symphonies are romantic in their emphasis on lyrical second themes, use of thematic transformation, and connections between movements.

Carnaval (*Carnival;* 1834–1835)

Carnaval is a cycle of twenty-one brief pieces with descriptive titles evoking a festive masked ball, with its varied characters, moods, and activities. This "musical picture gallery," as Schumann called it, includes sketches of fellow musicians, young women in the composer's life, stock characters from *commedia dell'arte* (Italian improvised theater), and self-portraits representing the introverted and outgoing sides of his own personality.

Schumann used the four-note group A-E flat-C-B or the three-note group A flat-C-B to open most of the pieces in *Carnaval,* creating musical links between them. However, these links are quite concealed because the same notes are presented in ever-changing rhythms, melodic shapes, and harmonies.

We now focus on two pieces from this best-known of Schumann's extended piano works. The two successive pieces *Estrella* and *Reconnaissance* (Nos. 13 and 14) illustrate the contrasting moods within *Carnaval.* The first of these is in minor, and the second is in major. Each opens with the same three-note group, A flat–C–B (see the letters at the beginning of the music examples).

Estrella

Estrella, marked *con affecto* (*with feeling*), is a sketch of Schumann's fiancée Ernestine von Fricken. The composer thought of Estrella as "the kind of name one would put

Selection available on:
Connect Music
Mp3 download card
Mp3 disc

under a portrait to fix it more clearly in one's memory." *Estrella* is in minor and in triple meter; it includes a variety of rhythmic patterns and has a waltzlike accompaniment.

Estrella is in A B A′ (abridged) form. The outer sections, which are consistently forceful, contrast with the middle section, which begins softly. Section B is permeated by syncopations—accents on the second and third beats—a distinctive feature of Schumann's music.

Reconnaissance (Reunion)

Reconnaissance is a lyrical piece, which Schumann described as a "scene of reunion." In A B A′ form, it is longer than *Estrella*. Schumann's style of piano writing is highly original here. In the outer (A) sections, which are in major, the pianist's right hand simultaneously plays two versions of the same melody an octave apart: the higher melody is legato, whereas the lower one is decorated with fast, staccato, repeated notes.

Perhaps these pulsating repeated notes represent the throbbing hearts of the reunited lovers.

The calmer middle section (B) brings a new major key and a shift from homophonic to polyphonic texture. The original melody is presented in the top part and imitated in the bass. Rhythmic excitement is maintained by a syncopated accompaniment in the middle parts.

The concluding A′ section is a shortened and slightly varied version of the opening A section.

Together, *Estrella* and *Reconnaissance* reveal different facets of Schumann's musical personality.

6 Frédéric Chopin

Frédéric Chopin (1810–1849) was the only great composer who wrote almost exclusively for the piano. The son of a Polish mother and a French father, he was brought up in Warsaw and graduated from the Warsaw Conservatory.

At twenty-one he arrived in Paris, then the center of romanticism and the artistic capital of Europe. In Paris he met such writers as Victor Hugo, Balzac, and Heine. The painter Delacroix was a close friend of Chopin, as were Liszt and Berlioz. His playing soon gained him access to aristocratic salons. He was a shy, reserved man who preferred salons to concert halls, and it was for such intimate gatherings that he conceived short pieces such as the nocturnes, preludes, and waltzes. He earned a good living by teaching piano to the daughters of the rich, and lived in luxury.

Chopin had a well-known love affair with Aurore Dudevant, a novelist whose pen name was George Sand. A frail man, he thrived on her care and composed many of his greatest works during the years they lived together. After they separated, his health declined rapidly and he composed very little. He died of tuberculosis at thirty-nine.

Chopin was a shy, reserved man who disliked crowds and preferred to play in salons rather than in public concert halls. Photograph of Chopin by L. A. Bisson, Paris, 1849.

Chopin's Music

By the age of eighteen, Chopin had evolved an utterly personal and original style. Most of his pieces are exquisite miniatures; they evoke an infinite variety of moods and are always elegant, graceful, and melodic. Unlike Schumann, Chopin did not attach literary programs or titles to his pieces. The mazurkas and the polonaises—stylized dances—capture a Polish spirit without actually using folk tunes.

No composer has made the piano sound as beautiful as Chopin. His unique melodic gift creates the illusion that the piano is singing. He uses delicate and graceful ornamental tones and exploits the pedal sensitively. His colorful treatment of harmony was highly original and influenced later composers.

Nocturne in E Flat Major, Op. 9, No. 2 (1830–1831)

Chopin composed his popular Nocturne in E Flat Major, Op. 9, No. 2, when he was about twenty. A *nocturne,* or *night piece,* is a slow, lyrical, intimate composition for piano. Like much of Chopin's music, this nocturne is tinged with melancholy.

Nocturne in E Flat Major opens with a legato melody containing graceful upward leaps, which become increasingly wide as the line unfolds. This melody is heard again three times during the piece. With each repetition, it is varied by ever-more elaborate decorative tones and trills. The nocturne also includes a subordinate melody, which is played with rubato—slight fluctuations of tempo.

A sonorous foundation for the melodic line is provided by the widely spaced notes in the accompaniment, connected by the damper ("loud") pedal. The waltzlike accompaniment gently emphasizes the $\frac{12}{8}$ meter, 12 beats to the measure subdivided into four groups of 3 beats each.

The nocturne is reflective in mood until it suddenly becomes passionate near the end. The new concluding melody begins softly but then ascends to a high register and is played forcefully in octaves. After a brilliant trill-like passage, the excitement subsides; the nocturne ends calmly.

Listening Outline

CHOPIN, Nocturne in E Flat Major, Op. 9, No. 2

Andante, ¹²⁄₈ meter
Piano
(Duration, 4:05)

0:00   **1. a.** Main melody, dolce, espressivo, waltzlike accompaniment.

0:25   **b.** Main melody, **p**, embellished with decorative notes and trills.

0:51   **2. a.** Subordinate melody, **p**, played with rubato;

crescendo to

1:18   **b.** Main melody, with more elaborate decorative notes and trills; chromatic descent leads to cadence.

1:44   **c.** Subordinate melody, **p**, played with rubato; crescendo to

2:11   **d.** Main melody with more elaborate decorative notes and trills; chromatic descent leads to cadence.

2:39   **3. a.** Concluding melody, **_p_**, then **_pp_**.

3:10   **b.** Concluding melody varied, crescendo with ascent to high register, melody played forcefully in octaves, **_ff_**; high trill-like figure, decrescendo and descent to gentle, rocking close, **_pp_**, then **_ppp_**.

Étude in C Minor, Op. 10, No. 12 (*Revolutionary*; 1831?)

The Russian takeover of Warsaw in 1831 may have inspired Chopin to compose the blazing and furious *Revolutionary* Étude in C Minor, Op. 10, No. 12. An **_étude_** is a study piece designed to help a performer master specific technical difficulties. The *Revolutionary* Étude, for example, develops speed and endurance in the pianist's left hand, which must play rapid passages throughout. Chopin's études reach beyond mere exercises in technique to become masterpieces of music, exciting to hear as well as to master.

The *Revolutionary* Étude, in A A'—coda form, begins with a dramatic outburst. High, dissonant chords and downward rushing passages lead to the main melody, marked *appassionato* (*impassioned*), which is played in octaves by the right hand. Tension mounts because of the melody's dotted rhythms and its tempestuous accompaniment. After a climax at the end of section A', the coda momentarily relaxes the tension. Then a torrential passage sweeps down the keyboard to come to rest in powerful closing chords.

Listening Outline

CHOPIN, Étude in C Minor, Op. 10, No. 12 (*Revolutionary*)

Allegro con fuoco (allegro with fire), duple meter (²⁄₂)
Piano
(Duration, 2:31)

A

0:00   **1. a.** High accented chords, **_f_**, answered by downward rushing passages; low running notes introduce
0:15   **b.** Passionate main melody in octaves, **_f_**, dotted rhythm, minor,

decrescendo to

0:32   **c.** Repetition of main melody, **_p_**, with different continuation, syncopated chords, crescendo to cadence in major.

0:46   **d.** Lyrical melody in dotted rhythm, minor, crescendo and downward running notes; very high descending phrases lead to return of

A′

1:07   **2. a.** High accented chords, **_f_**, answered by downward rushing passages; low running notes introduce

1:22   **b.** Passionate main melody intensified, **_f_**, decrescendo; low running notes introduce

1:40   **c.** Repetition of intensified main melody leading to

1:47   **d.** Majestic downward phrases in major, **_ff_**, decrescendo, **_p_**, return to minor, low running notes rise and fall, ritardando to

Coda

2:10   **e.** Gentle upward phrase repeated with ritardando. Sudden **_ff_**, downward rushing passage, powerful closing chords, **_fff_**.

Polonaise in A Flat Major, Op. 53 (1842)

The **_polonaise,_** a piece in triple meter, originated as a stately processional dance for the Polish nobility. Chopin's heroic polonaises evoke the ancient splendor of the Polish people.

His Polonaise in A Flat Major is majestic and powerful, with moments of lyrical contrast. It may be outlined as follows: introduction—A B A′—coda. Its main theme makes a grand entrance.

Introduction
0:00
Section A
0:28

The majesty of this theme is enhanced by intervals of thirds in the right hand and by the resonant, wide-ranging accompaniment. After the main theme is repeated twice with an even richer texture, Chopin offers the contrasting middle section (B). This is a marchlike melody accompanied by relentlessly repeated rapid octaves in the left hand. This section tests a pianist's strength and endurance. Powerful crescendos bring mounting excitement. Then Chopin gradually relaxes the mood to prepare for the final return of the heroic main theme (A′).

Section B
2:48

Section A′
5:17

Polonaise in A Flat Major
available in Connect Music

7 Franz Liszt

Franz Liszt (1811–1886) was handsome, magnetic, an incredible showman, irresistible to women, and a pacesetter in musical history. During the 1840s, he performed superhuman feats at the piano, overwhelming the European public and impressing musicians as much as the concertgoing public.

Chopin wished he could play his own piano études the way Liszt played them. Robert Schumann wrote that Liszt "enmeshed every member of the audience with his art and did with them as he willed." Brahms later said, "Whoever has not heard Liszt cannot speak of piano playing."

Liszt was born in Hungary. His father was an administrator for the same Esterházy family that Haydn had served. As a boy of eleven, Liszt studied in Vienna, where he met Schubert and Beethoven. During his teens and twenties, he lived in Paris, a city where romanticism flourished and a mecca for virtuosos. When he was nineteen and already acclaimed as a brilliant pianist, Liszt was awed by the great violinist Paganini, who drove audiences into a frenzy and was half suspected of being in league with the devil. Young Liszt was determined to become the Paganini of the piano. He withdrew from the concert stage for a few years, practiced from eight to twelve hours a day, and emerged as probably the greatest pianist of his time.

To display his own incomparable piano mastery, Liszt composed his *Transcendental* Études and made piano transcriptions of Paganini's violin pieces. "My piano," he wrote, "is my very self. . . . A man's ten fingers have the power to reproduce the harmonies which are created by hundreds of performers." Once, after an orchestral performance of a movement from Berlioz's *Fantastic Symphony,* Liszt played his own piano arrangement and made a more powerful effect than the entire orchestra.

Franz Liszt—handsome, long-haired, magnetic—performed superhuman feats at the piano and overwhelmed the European musical public.

He toured Europe tirelessly between 1839 and 1847, playing mainly his own piano music and receiving unprecedented public adulation.

But Liszt also wanted recognition as a serious composer. At thirty-six, he abandoned his career as a traveling virtuoso to become court conductor in Weimar, where he composed many orchestral pieces (developing a new and influential form of program music) and conducted works by such contemporaries as Berlioz, Schumann, and Wagner. Unselfish and generous, he taught hundreds of gifted pianists free of charge and provided musical and financial support crucial to Wagner's success. He also wrote music criticism and books on Chopin and Gypsy music. His literary efforts were aided by two aristocratic women writers: Countess Marie d'Agoult and, later, the Russian Princess Carolyne Sayn-Wittgenstein. (Marie d'Agoult left her husband to live with Liszt; she and Liszt had three children, one of whom, Cosima, later left her own husband to marry Richard Wagner.)

Liszt went to Rome to pursue religious studies in 1861, and, in 1865 he took minor holy orders, becoming Abbé Liszt. Contemporaries were stunned by the seeming incongruity: a notorious Don Juan and diabolical virtuoso had become a churchman. In Rome, he composed oratorios and masses.

During his last years, Liszt traveled between Rome, Weimar, and Budapest, where he was president of the new Academy of Music. Now he began to write curious, experimental piano pieces that foreshadowed some features of twentieth-century music. Though these late works went unappreciated, Liszt had become a living legend. The grand duke of Weimar said, "Liszt *was* what a prince *ought* to be."

Liszt's Music

Liszt's music is controversial. Some consider it vulgar and bombastic; others revel in its extroverted romantic rhetoric. Yet few would deny Liszt's originality, his influence, or his importance as the creator of the symphonic poem.

Liszt found new ways to exploit the piano; his melodies are sometimes surrounded by arpeggios that create the impression of three hands playing; and in the *Hungarian Rhapsodies,* which influenced a generation of nationalist composers, he makes the piano sound at times like an entire Gypsy band. His piano works contain daring leaps, rapid octaves and runs, and an unprecedented range of dynamics. Before the age of recordings and frequent concerts, Liszt's transcriptions made it possible for people to play operas and symphonies on their own pianos.

Breaking away from classical sonata form and the standard four-movement symphony, Liszt created the **symphonic poem,** or **tone poem,** a one-movement orchestral composition based to some extent on literary or pictorial ideas (see Section 9). Among his favorite inspirations were the works of Goethe (on which he based his *Faust* Symphony, 1854) and Dante (which inspired the *Dante* Symphony, 1856). Many of his compositions are concerned with the devil or death and bear titles like *Mephisto Waltz, Totentanz* (*Dance of Death*), or *Funérailles* (*Funeral Ceremony*). Continual changes of tempo and mood and alternations between diabolical fury and semireligious meditation contribute to a feeling of improvisation; but in his symphonic poems and other orchestral works, contrasting moods are often unified through thematic transformations of a single, recurring musical idea.

Liszt's music influenced many composers, including Wagner, who admitted to him: "When I compose and orchestrate, I always think only of you." As a stupendous performer, innovative composer, and charismatic personality, Liszt typified the romantic movement.

Transcendental Étude No. 10 in F Minor (1851)

0:00
0:42
1:14

As dazzling, passionate, and poetic as Liszt himself, the *Transcendental* Étude No. 10 in F Minor is one of the finest virtuoso pieces of the romantic era. Liszt had written an early, simpler version of this piece in 1824, when he was only thirteen, and included it in a group of twelve studies. Fifteen years later, at the peak of his career as a virtuoso, he published a revised version that demanded transcendent, almost superhuman technical skill from the pianist. (Schumann was so overwhelmed by Liszt's études that he described them as "studies in storm and dread meant to be played by, at most, ten or twelve players in the world.") In 1851, after retiring from the concert stage, Liszt dedicated a third and final version—which we study—to his piano teacher Carl Czerny (1791–1857) "as a token of esteem, gratitude, and friendship."

The étude taxes the player with left-hand passages that require rapid skips and changes of hand position. Though written in A B A′—coda form, it almost seems like an improvisation, owing to its frequent alternations between brilliant virtuoso passages and more melodic ideas. Section A contains three themes. The first, in minor, is fragmentary and syncopated.

0:00

0:42

The second, in major, is more lyrical and in a high register, with dotted rhythms, and with rapid notes in the accompaniment.

1:14

The third, which has a processional character, is a transformation of the second. A melody that was introduced in major in a high register is now presented in minor, in a low register set against higher arpeggios.

1:26
2:04
4:05

Transcendental Étude available in Connect Music

The brief section B develops and transforms the syncopated main theme. All three themes return in section A′, which is introduced by a decrescendo and ritardando. The étude ends with a furious coda based on a speeded-up transformation of the main theme.

8 Felix Mendelssohn

Felix Mendelssohn (1809–1847), a romantic whose music was rooted in classical tradition, was born in Hamburg, Germany, to a wealthy and distinguished Jewish family. (He was, however, raised as a Protestant.) By the age of nine, he was a brilliant pianist; by thirteen, he had written symphonies, concertos, sonatas, and vocal works of astounding quality. As a teenager, he performed his works at home with a private orchestra for the intellectual and artistic elite of Berlin, where the Mendelssohns had settled.

In 1829, at twenty, he conducted Bach's *St. Matthew Passion* in its first performance since the composer's death. This historic concert rekindled interest in Bach's music and earned Mendelssohn an international reputation. He often performed as a pianist, an organist, and a conductor in Germany and in England, where his music was especially popular.

He often visited and played for Queen Victoria and the high point of his career was the triumphant premiere of his oratorio *Elijah* in Birmingham, England, in 1846.

When only twenty-six, he became conductor of the Leipzig Gewandhaus Orchestra, and he founded the Leipzig Conservatory at age thirty-three.

Mendelssohn's personal life was more conventional than that of many romantics. He was happily married and had four children. But constant travel and exhausting work sapped Mendelssohn's strength, and he died, after a stroke, at thirty-eight.

Mendelssohn's Music

Besides his musical achievements, Felix Mendelssohn was a talented painter, a fine writer, and a brilliant conversationalist in four languages.

Mendelssohn's music radiates the elegance and balance of his personality. It evokes a variety of moods but avoids emotional extremes and typically conveys an elfin quality through rapid movement, lightness, and transparent orchestral texture.

He wrote an enormous amount of music in all the forms of his day except opera. Today, only a few of his works are in the concert repertoire, but these are very popular. They include the Violin Concerto—which we study—the *Midsummer Night's Dream* and *Hebrides* overtures, the *Italian* and *Scotch* symphonies (1833, 1842), the oratorio *Elijah,* and a number of chamber works.

Concerto for Violin and Orchestra in E Minor, Op. 64 (1844)

Mendelssohn's Violin Concerto in E Minor, Op. 64, was inspired by his friendship with the concertmaster of his orchestra, the famous violinist Ferdinand David. "I should like to make a violin concerto for you next winter," Mendelssohn wrote. "One in E minor runs in my head and its beginning gives me no rest." With David as soloist, the Violin Concerto met with great success at its premiere in 1845. Ever since, its unique fusion of lyricism and virtuosity has made it one of the best-loved concertos.

The concerto's three movements are played without pause, in a characteristic linking technique used by romantic composers. Mendelssohn's love of balance is reflected in the cooperation and interplay between soloist and orchestra. Themes pass from one to another, producing a beautiful contrast of tone color and expression. At one moment, the violinist plays a melody while the orchestra discreetly accompanies; at another, the woodwinds present thematic fragments while the soloist has dazzling running passages.

First Movement:
Allegro molto appassionato (very impassioned allegro)

Though Mendelssohn is usually considered a conservative composer, a "classical romantic," his opening movement departs from classical concerto form. Traditionally, the opening movement of a concerto began with an extended section for orchestra. But Mendelssohn's first movement begins with the soloist, who presents the main theme. This ardent, expansive melody is heard high above a murmuring string accompaniment. The orchestra then expands the violin's theme and introduces a new, flowing melody that begins the bridge section of this sonata-form movement. Toward the end of the bridge, the excitement is gradually relaxed to prepare for the second theme, a tranquil woodwind melody the soloist accompanies with a single sustained tone. This unusual combination of instruments produces a delicate, intimate sound. Following this, the violin reclaims the spotlight and sings the tranquil theme while the woodwinds support it.

The cadenza has a new function in this movement. In classical concertos, the cadenza was improvised by the soloist and played near the end of the movement. Here, the composer has written it out and placed it at the end of the development section as a transition to the recapitulation. Mendelssohn wanted the cadenza to be an integral part of the movement, not merely something tacked on to display the soloist's virtuosity. Listen for the magical moment when the violinist's rapid arpeggios are joined by the orchestra softly playing the first theme of the recapitulation.

Listening Outline

MENDELSSOHN, Concerto for Violin and Orchestra in E Minor

First Movement: Allegro molto appassionato
Sonata form, duple meter (²⁄₂), E minor
Solo violin, 2 flutes, 2 oboes, 2 clarinets, 2 bassoons, 2 French horns, 2 trumpets, timpani, 1st violins, 2d violins, violas, cellos, double basses
(Duration, 12:01)

Exposition

First theme

0:00   **1. a.** Strings, ***p***, introduce solo violin. Main melody in minor, high register, legato.

0:29   **b.** Running notes in solo violin. Crescendo, climbing phrases.
0:53   **c.** Orchestra, ***ff***, main melody. Increased rhythmic motion leads to cadence.

Bridge

1:22   **2. a.** Violins, flowing bridge theme. Solo violin repeats bridge theme an octave higher.

1:35   **b.** Solo violin phrases sweep downward and upward through wide range. Flute joins. Crescendo. Running passage rises and falls. Decrescendo, mood calms.

Second theme

2:34   **3. a.** Clarinets and flutes, ***pp***, calm melody in major. Solo violin accompanies with sustained tone.

2:49   **b.** Solo violin, ***pp***, calm theme expanded. Woodwinds, then strings accompany.

3:53   **4. a.** Main melody in solo violin, major. Brilliant running passages, pizzicato accompaniment. Crescendo.

4:40   **b.** Climactic orchestral trills alternate with solo violin, opening of main melody. Decrescendo.

Development

5:00	**1. a.** Solo violin, *p*, flowing bridge theme. Violins, *f*.
5:13	**b.** Running passage in solo violin and fragments of main melody in orchestra.
5:38	**2.** Solo violin, *p*, main melody varied. Decrescendo. Violin melody slowly descends. Orchestral crescendo to *ff*.

Cadenza

6:27	**3.** Unaccompanied solo violin, broken chords. Ascents to high tones, trills, fragment of main melody. Rapid broken chords lead into

Recapitulation

First theme

8:01	**1.** Main melody in orchestra, *p*. Broken chords continue in solo violin. Crescendo.

Bridge

8:18	**2. a.** Orchestra, *ff*, bridge theme.
	b. Solo violin, *mf*, bridge theme carried downward. Decrescendo.

Second theme

8:48	**3. a.** Woodwinds, *pp*, calm melody in major. Solo violin accompanies with sustained tone.
9:02	**b.** Solo violin, *pp*, calm theme expanded. Woodwinds, then strings accompany.
10:09	**4. a.** Brilliant running passages in solo violin. Pizzicato accompaniment. Crescendo.
10:55	**b.** Climactic orchestral trills alternate with solo violin, opening of main melody. Decrescendo.

Coda

11:14	**5.** Solo violin, bridge theme. Tempo becomes faster. Crescendo. Brilliant running passages. Full orchestra, *ff*.

Second Movement: Andante

A single bassoon tone links the brilliant opening movement with the hushed introduction to the slow second movement. The C major andante is a songlike, intimate piece in A B A′ form. Its opening section (A) features a warm, expansive melody in the solo violin's high register; a string accompaniment gently emphasizes the $\frac{6}{8}$ meter (1–2–3–4–5–6). The middle section (B) becomes more agitated, and the accompaniment is rhythmically more active. The orchestra plays a more important role as it engages in dialogue with the soloist. Mendelssohn requires the solo violinist to play a melody and a trembling accompaniment figure at the same time. The soloist also presents the melody in full-sounding octaves. The transition to the concluding A′ section is very smooth because the trembling accompaniment figure is maintained. The andante ends quietly with a tender epilogue for solo violin and woodwinds.

Third Movement:
Allegretto non troppo (transitional section);
Allegro molto vivace (very lively allegro)

A pensive transitional section for solo violin and strings connects the andante with the concluding movement of the concerto. The very rapid finale, in sonata form, creates the lightness, joy, and brilliance so typical of Mendelssohn's art. Forceful chords in the woodwinds and upward solo figures usher in the playful and mostly staccato opening theme of the exposition; it is presented by the solo violin and high woodwinds.

Performance Perspectives

Hilary Hahn, Violinist, Playing the First Movement of Mendelssohn's Violin Concerto in E Minor, Op. 64

Hilary Hahn is one of the most prominent concert violinists of our time. In 1999, when she was nineteen, *Time* magazine called her "America's best" young classical musician.

As with most concert artists, Hahn's extraordinary musical talent was recognized at a very early age. When not quite four, she began studying violin, and at age ten she was accepted at the Curtis Institute of Music in Philadelphia. At sixteen, she signed a recording contract, made her debut at Carnegie Hall with the Philadelphia Orchestra, and completed the requirements for her bachelor of music degree. However, she chose to delay her graduation from Curtis for three years: "I loved the school, so I stayed as long as I could. There were a lot of classes that interested me that I hadn't taken yet; for extra electives, I enrolled in poetry and fiction-writing workshops and several literature classes, in addition to continuing with German."

For Hahn, "communicating music to people is something that I feel very lucky to be able to do." She writes her own liner notes for her recordings and maintains an online journal (on her Web site, HilaryHahn.com) of her experiences in cities where she performs. To expand children's musical horizons, Hahn often plays in grade schools. "I always play solo Bach, a slow and a fast movement. The music casts a spell. They really like it."

Hahn enjoys music in a wide range of styles, from blues and world music to hip-hop and classical. Her prize-winning recordings include works by Mendelssohn, Bach, Beethoven, and Bernstein, and she performs on the sound track of the M. Night Shyamalan film *The Village,* as well as on an album by Austin alt-rockers . . . *And You Will Know Us by the Trail of Dead.*

Hahn learned the Mendelssohn Violin Concerto when she was eleven and performed excerpts with the Curtis Orchestra

the following year. (Her performance of the first movement of the concerto is included in the recordings.) "Not long after, I performed the entire concerto with a chamber orchestra in Florida, and since then the Mendelssohn concerto has been a staple of my repertoire." For Hahn, the first movement of the concerto is full of "lyricism, fire, drama, and contrast."

Hahn observes that performing a concerto requires close cooperation with the conductor and members of the orchestra. "Sometimes the conductor and I will disagree about something and meet in the middle. There's a system of give-and-take, opinions, and compromise—though as a musician, you try to never be compromised or compromise someone else's interpretation. Musicians inevitably interact with each other, so we have to be aware of what the others are doing. For example, if I share a solo line with the flute, I will pay attention to how the flutist plays the line so that it sounds like a duet. The conductor coordinates some of that, but in a concerto, the minutiae are really decided by the musicians, by listening to each other and reacting to the musical ideas that we hear."

For Hahn, playing before a live audience is very different from recording in a studio. "The audience influences performing to a large extent because the presence of people affects the way the concert hall sounds. The energy in the hall is hard to describe, but there is a different feeling when you know people are there to absorb the music (both acoustically and psychologically). It's quite energizing and inspiring. In recording, you have a limited time and an empty hall—any tiny noise can ruin a take, so no audience is allowed in the studio—and you have to get it right, so that situation takes a different approach. I try to keep the feeling as similar as possible, though, by imagining an audience listening in the hall, or in their car, or to their stereo."

A dazzling series of running passages and a long upward scale lead directly into the second theme, which is also a carefree one. With great effect, it combines a loud, marchlike phrase by the full orchestra with a softer motive from the opening theme.

In the development, the woodwinds softly present the marchlike phrase while the soloist plays brilliant running passages. A highlight of the development comes when the violinist presents a new legato melody that the strings lightly accompany with fragments of the opening theme.

Then there is a reversal of roles: the strings sing the lyrical melody while the soloist gracefully presents the fragment of the opening theme.

At the beginning of the recapitulation, the two themes are combined once again. The French horn and lower strings play the warm legato melody while the soloist brings back the sparkling first theme. After a return of the second theme, the movement builds to an exciting climax in the coda, which is fuller in sound than anything that has come before.

9 Program Music

Romantic composers were particularly attracted to program music—instrumental music associated with a story, poem, idea, or scene. Programmatic works such as Berlioz's *Fantastic Symphony,* Tchaikovsky's *Romeo and Juliet,* and Smetana's *Moldau* depict emotions, characters, and events, or the sounds and motions of nature. Such nonmusical ideas are usually specified by the title or by the composer's explanatory comments (the program).

Program music draws on the capacity of music to suggest and evoke. Music can, of course, imitate certain sounds—birdsongs, thunder, bells, wind. But "sound effects" are only part of the descriptive resources of music. A composer can also exploit the correspondence between musical rhythm and objects in motion. A continuous flow of rapid notes, for example, can evoke waves or a stream. Most important is the ability of music to create mood, emotion, and atmosphere. An agitated theme may represent conflict; a lyrical melody may symbolize love. However, music alone makes no definite reference to ideas, emotions, and objects. Music cannot identify anything. It is the title or a verbal explanation that lets us fully grasp a composer's source of inspiration.

The aim of most program music is expression more than mere description. Beethoven, for example, referred to his *Pastoral* Symphony (Symphony No. 6) as "an expression of feeling rather than painting." Even the most "realistic" episodes in program music can also serve a purely musical function; and one can generally appreciate a descriptive piece as pure music, without knowing its title or program. (We can enjoy the lyrical theme of Tchaikovsky's *Romeo and Juliet,* for example, without associating it with young love.) The forms used for program music are similar to those used for nonprogram music, or **absolute music.** A programmatic work can be heard simply as an example of rondo, fugue, sonata form, or theme and variations. But our pleasure may be greater when we can relate music to literary or pictorial ideas, and romantic composers were well aware of this. Occasionally, they even added titles or programs to finished works. Both musicians and audiences in the romantic period liked to read stories into all music, whether intended by the composer or not.

Most romantic program music was written for piano or for orchestra. The main forms of orchestral program music are the program symphony, the concert overture, the symphonic poem (tone poem), and incidental music.

A **program symphony** is a composition in several movements—as its name implies, a symphony with a program. Usually, each movement has a descriptive title. For example, Berlioz's *Fantastic Symphony* has five movements: (1) *Reveries, Passions,* (2) *A Ball,* (3) *Scene in the Country,* (4) *March to the Scaffold,* and (5) *Dream of a Witches' Sabbath.* (This work is discussed in Section 10.)

A **concert overture** has one movement, usually in sonata form. The romantic concert overture was modeled after the opera overture, a one-movement composition that establishes the mood of an opera. But the concert overture is *not* intended to usher in a stage work; it is an independent composition. Well-known concert overtures include Mendelssohn's *Hebrides* Overture and Tchaikovsky's *Overture 1812* and *Romeo and Juliet* Overture, which is studied in Section 13.

A symphonic poem, or **tone poem,** is also in one movement. Symphonic poems take many traditional forms—sonata form, rondo, or theme and variations—as well as irregular forms. This flexibility of form separates the symphonic poem from the concert overture, which is usually in sonata form. Franz Liszt developed the symphonic poem in the late 1840s and 1850s, and it became the most important type of program music after 1860. Well-known tone poems include *Les Préludes* (1854) and *Hamlet* (1858), by Liszt; *Danse macabre* (1874), by Camille Saint-Saëns (1835–1921); and *The Sorcerer's Apprentice* (1897), by Paul Dukas (1865–1935). A leading composer of tone poems at the end of the nineteenth century was Richard Strauss (1864–1949). His tone poems—characterized by brilliant orchestration—include *Don Juan* (1889), *Till Eulenspiegel's Merry Pranks* (1895), and *Also sprach Zarasthustra* (So Spoke Zoroaster; 1896), which was used in the film *2001: A Space Odyssey.* During the late nineteenth century, symphonic poems became an important means of expression for nationalism in music. In Section 11, we consider a nationalistic tone poem, Smetana's *Moldau,* depicting the longest river of Bohemia (a region that became part of the modern Czech Republic) as it winds through the countryside.

Incidental music is music to be performed before and during a play. It is "incidental" to the staged drama, but it sets the mood for certain scenes. Interludes, background music, marches, and dances are all incidental music (as are today's movie scores). Mendelssohn's incidental music for *A Midsummer Night's Dream* includes his famous *Wedding March.*

10 Hector Berlioz

The French composer Hector Berlioz was a daring creator of new orchestral sounds and one of the first great orchestra conductors.

Hector Berlioz (1803–1869), one of the first French romantic composers and a daring creator of new orchestral sounds, was born in a small town near Grenoble. His father, a physician, sent him to Paris to study medicine, but Berlioz was "filled with horror" by the dissecting room and shocked his parents by abandoning medicine to pursue a career in music. He studied at the Paris Conservatory, haunted the opera house, and composed.

When he was twenty-three, Berlioz was overwhelmed by the works of Shakespeare and also fell madly in love with a Shakespearean actress, Harriet Smithson, to whom he wrote such wild, impassioned letters that she thought he was a lunatic and refused to see him. To depict his "endless and unquenchable passion," Berlioz wrote the *Symphonie fantastique* (*Fantastic Symphony*) in 1830, which startled Parisians by its sensationally autobiographical program, its amazingly novel orchestration, and its vivid depiction of the weird and diabolical.

In 1830, too, Berlioz won the Prix de Rome (Rome Prize), subsidizing two years' study in Rome. When he returned to Paris, Berlioz met and married Harriet Smithson—after she had attended a performance of the *Fantastic Symphony* and realized that it depicted her. (They separated, however, after only a few years.)

Berlioz's unconventional music irritated the opera and concert establishment. To get a hearing for his works, he had to arrange concerts at his own expense—an enormous undertaking that drained him financially, physically, and emotionally. Although he had a following of about 1,200 who faithfully bought tickets to his concerts, this was not enough support for a composer of difficult, monumental works requiring hundreds of performers. Berlioz turned to musical journalism, becoming a brilliant and witty music critic who tried to convince the Parisian public that music was not merely entertainment but dramatic emotional expression.

Outside France, Berlioz's stock was higher. After 1840, he was in demand throughout Europe, conducting his own and others' music. As one of the first great conductors, he influenced a whole generation of musicians. But his last years were bitter. He was repeatedly passed over for important positions and honors and composed very little during the six years before his death at sixty-five.

Berlioz's Music

"The prevailing qualities of my music," wrote Berlioz, "are passionate expressiveness, inner fire, rhythmic drive, and unexpectedness." Above all, Berlioz's music sounds unique. It includes abrupt contrasts, fluctuating dynamics, and many changes in tempo.

As an orchestrator, Berlioz was extraordinarily imaginative and innovative. At a time when the average orchestra had about sixty players, he often assembled hundreds of musicians to achieve new power, tone colors, and timbres. His melodies are often long, irregular, and asymmetrical, taking unexpected turns. Most of his works are for orchestra, or orchestra with chorus and vocal soloists; all are dramatic and programmatic. He invented new forms: his "dramatic symphony" *Romeo and Juliet* (1839) is for orchestra, chorus, and vocal soloists; and his "dramatic legend" *The Damnation of*

Faust (1846) combines opera and oratorio. He also wrote three operas and a grandiose, monumental Requiem (1837).

He knew he was a pioneer. He wrote of the Requiem, "I have seen one man listening in terror, shaken to the depths of his soul, while his next neighbor could not catch an idea, though trying with all his might to do so."

Symphonie fantastique (Fantastic Symphony; 1830)

The astonishing *Symphonie fantastique (Fantastic Symphony)*, a five-movement program symphony (we study its fourth and fifth movements), is a romantic manifesto. Both the symphony and Berlioz's program reflect the twenty-six-year-old composer's unrequited passion for the actress Harriet Smithson:

> A young musician of extraordinary sensibility and abundant imagination, in the depths of despair because of hopeless love, has poisoned himself with opium. The drug is too feeble to kill him but plunges him into a heavy sleep accompanied by weird visions. His sensations, emotions, and memories, as they pass through his affected mind, are transformed into musical images and ideas. The beloved one herself becomes to him a melody, a recurrent theme (*idée fixe*) which haunts him continually.

A single melody, which Berlioz called the **idée fixe,** or *fixed idea,* is used to represent the beloved. When introduced in the first movement—*Reveries, Passions*—it sounds, in Berlioz's description, "passionate but at the same time noble and shy."

It appears in all five movements and unifies the contrasting episodes of the symphony. This recurrence of the same theme in every movement of a symphony was a striking novelty in Berlioz's day. The theme changes in character during the work. For example, in the second movement—*A Ball*—it is transformed into a waltz, and in the third movement—*Scene in the Country*—it is played against an agitated countermelody.

Another innovation in the symphony is its use of a very large and colorful orchestra: piccolo, 2 flutes, 2 oboes, English horn, 2 clarinets, 4 bassoons, 4 French horns, 2 cornets, 2 trumpets, 3 trombones, 2 tubas, 4 timpani, bass drum, snare drum, cymbals, bells, 2 harps, and strings. (Beethoven, for one, had not used the English horn, tuba, bells, cornet, or harp in his symphonies.) Berlioz saves the heaviest orchestration for the last two movements, where he depicts the fantastic and diabolical. Though the macabre and supernatural had long been dealt with in opera (for example, in Mozart's *Don Giovanni*), this is its first expression in an important symphony.

Fourth Movement: *March to the Scaffold* Allegretto non troppo

> He dreams that he has murdered his beloved, that he has been condemned to death and is being led to the scaffold. The procession moves forward to the sounds of a march that is now somber and fierce, now brilliant and solemn, in which the muffled

sounds of heavy steps give way without transition to the noisiest outbursts. At the end, the *idée fixe* returns for a moment, like a last thought of love interrupted by the death blow.

"The *March to the Scaffold* is fifty times more frightening than I expected," Berlioz gleefully observed after the first rehearsals of the *Fantastic Symphony*. It is not until this fiendish fourth movement that all the brass and percussion instruments enter the action. Berlioz creates a menacing atmosphere with the opening orchestral sound, a unique combination of muted French horns, timpani tuned a third apart, and basses playing pizzicato chords.

Two contrasting themes alternate within *March to the Scaffold*. The first theme, described as "somber and fierce" in Berlioz's program, is introduced by cellos and basses and moves down the scale for two octaves. This scalewise melody appears both in minor and in major and is combined with countermelodies. It is also inverted, moving upward rather than downward. The second theme, described as "brilliant and solemn" in the program, is a syncopated march tune blared by the brasses and woodwinds. At the end of the march a solo clarinet begins to play the *idée fixe* but is savagely interrupted by a very loud chord representing the fall of the guillotine's blade. The following string pizzicato may well have been intended to suggest the bouncing of the severed head.

Listening Outline

BERLIOZ, *Symphonie fantastique*

Fourth Movement: *March to the Scaffold*
Allegretto non troppo
2 flutes, 2 oboes, 2 clarinets, 4 bassoons, 2 trumpets, 2 cornets, 4 French horns, 3 trombones, 2 tubas, timpani, bass drum, snare drum, cymbals, 1st violins, 2d violins, violas, cellos, double basses
(Duration 4:48)

0:00   **1.** Timpani, pizzicato basses, ***pp***; syncopations in muted French horns, ***p***, crescendo to ***ff*** chord.

0:27   **2. a.** Basses and cellos alone, ***ff***, downward scalewise melody, minor, decrescendo.

0:41   **b.** Downward melody repeated with countermelody in high bassoons.
0:54   **c.** High violins, ***f***, downward melody, major, accompanied by staccato lower strings. Sudden ***ff***. Melody repeated by violins, ***f***.
1:19   **d.** Staccato bassoons, ***p***, together with pizzicato strings, minor, decrescendo to ***pp***, quick crescendo to

1:39   **3.** Brasses and woodwinds, ***f***, syncopated march tune, major. March tune repeated.

2:04 **4. a.** Very loud brass and woodwind fanfare introduces

2:11 **b.** Splintered downward melody, pizzicato and bowed strings, staccato winds, minor. Pizzicato violins and timpani, crescendo to

2:22 **c.** Brasses, woodwinds, *f*, syncopated march tune, major, active string accompaniment. March tune repeated.

2:46 **d.** Very loud brass and woodwind fanfare introduces

2:54 **e.** Splintered downward melody, pizzicato and bowed strings, staccato winds, minor.

3:02 **f.** Brasses, *mf*, shortened downward melody repeated on higher pitches, active string accompaniment, crescendo.

3:16 **5. a.** Whole orchestra, downward melody, *ff*, timpani, cymbals, minor, decrescendo to *pp*.

3:27 **b.** Sudden *ff*, whole orchestra, upward scalewise melody, major, timpani, cymbals.

Staccato strings alone, orchestral punctuation, *ff*, excited dotted rhythm in strings, repeated figure in brasses and woodwinds; downward staccato strings, *ff*, lead to

4:01 **c.** Wind and string chords alternate, *f*, decrescendo to *pp*. Sudden *ff*, full orchestra.

4:14 **d.** Solo clarinet, *idée fixe*,

interrupted by

4:24 **e.** Short orchestral chord, *ff* (fall of guillotine blade), and string pizzicato (bouncing of severed head), powerful timpani roll, *ff*, brasses and woodwinds *f*, repeated major chord, strings, *ff*, cymbals, ending chord by full orchestra, *ff*.

Dream of a Witches' Sabbath
available in Connect Music

Fifth Movement: *Dream of a Witches' Sabbath*
Larghetto; Allegro

He sees himself at a witches' sabbath in the midst of a hideous crowd of ghouls, sorcerers, and monsters of every description, united for his funeral. Strange noises, groans, shrieks of laughter, distant cries, which other cries seem to answer. The melody of the loved one is heard, but it has lost its character of nobleness and timidity; it is no more than a dance tune, ignoble, trivial, and grotesque. It is she who comes to the sabbath! . . . A howl of joy greets her arrival. . . . She participates in the diabolical orgy. . . . The funeral knell, burlesque of the *Dies irae*. Witches' dance. The dance and the *Dies irae* combined.

0:00 *Dream of a Witches' Sabbath* is the most "fantastic" movement of the symphony; it depicts a series of grotesque events. Its slow, hushed introduction (larghetto) immediately draws the listener into the realm of the macabre and supernatural, evoking "strange noises, groans, shrieks of laughter" and "distant cries." Eerie tremolos in high muted strings and menacing low tones of cellos and basses begin a succession of fragmentary ideas in starkly contrasting tone colors, registers, and dynamics. In the exploratory spirit of his romantic age, Berlioz dared to create sounds that are weird rather than conventionally pleasing.

1:39

In the allegro section, the beloved is revealed to be a witch. Her theme, the once "noble and timid" *idée fixe,* is transformed into a dance tune that is "trivial and grotesque." Played shrilly by a high-pitched clarinet, the tune moves in quick notes decorated by trills.

3:22

A "funeral knell" of sonorous bells lends an awesome atmosphere to the next part of the movement. Tubas and bassoons intone a solemn low melody in long, even notes.

This melody is the medieval chant *Dies irae (Day of wrath),* traditionally sung in the mass for the dead. Berlioz quotes it here as a symbol of eternal damnation. Soon the chant melody is shifted up to a high register and played by woodwinds and pizzicato strings in a quick dancelike rhythm.

3:54

Thus Berlioz dared to parody a sacred chant by transforming it into a trivial tune, as he had just done moments earlier with the *idée fixe.*

5:14

Berlioz conveys the frenzy of a witches' dance in a fuguelike section. The fugue subject (the witches' dance) is introduced by the lower strings and then imitated by other instruments.

7:52   A crescendo builds to a powerful climax in which the rapid witches' dance, played in the strings, is set against the slower-moving *Dies irae,* proclaimed by the brasses and woodwinds. This musical nightmare ends in an orgy of orchestral power.

11 Nationalism in Nineteenth-Century Music

During the nineteenth century, Europeans felt strongly that their homelands merited loyalty and self-sacrifice. These nationalistic feelings were awakened during the upheavals of the French Revolution and the Napoleonic wars (1789–1814), when French armies invaded much of Europe. In many countries, military resistance to Napoleon aroused the citizens' sense of national identity. Common bonds of language, culture, and history were strengthened as battles now were fought by soldiers drawn from the general population—not by mercenaries, as in the past. These patriotic feelings were intensified by romanticism, which glorified love for one's national heritage.

As a revolutionary political movement, nationalism led to the unification of lands— such as Germany and Italy—that had previously been divided into tiny states. It spurred revolts in countries under foreign rule, such as Poland and Bohemia (later part of the Czech Republic).

Nationalism was a potent cultural movement as well, particularly regarding language. In lands dominated by foreign powers, the national language was used increasingly in textbooks, newspapers, and official documents. For example, Bohemia saw a revival of the Czech language, which before 1800 had lost ground to the German spoken by its Austrian rulers. By the 1830s and 1840s, important textbooks on astronomy and chemistry were written in Czech, and there were many collections of Czech folk poetry. In every land, the "national spirit" was felt to reside in the "folk," the peasantry. The national past became a subject of intense historical investigation, and there was new enthusiasm for folksongs, dances, legends, and fairytales.

Nationalism influenced romantic music, as composers deliberately gave their works a distinctive national identity. They used folksongs and dances and created original melodies with a folk flavor. Nationalist composers wrote operas and program music inspired by the history, legends, and landscapes of their native lands. Their works bear titles like *Russian Easter* Overture (Rimsky-Korsakov), *Finlandia* (Sibelius), and *Slavonic Dances* (Dvořák). But a genuine feeling of national style does not come merely through the use of folksongs or patriotic subjects. A piece of music will *sound* French, Russian, or Italian when its rhythm, tone color, texture, and melody spring from national tradition. There were regional traits in music before the romantic period, but never had differences of national style been emphasized so strongly or so consciously.

In these revolutionary times, musical compositions could symbolize nationalist yearnings and sometimes stirred audiences to violent political demonstrations. The Italian opera composer Giuseppe Verdi deliberately chose librettos that fanned public hatred for the Austrian overlords; censors constantly pressured him to change scenes that might be interpreted as anti-Austrian or antimonarchical. A twentieth-century parallel occurred when the Nazis banned performances of Smetana's symphonic poem *The Moldau* in Prague, the composer's home city.

The strongest impact of nationalism was felt in lands whose own musical heritage had been dominated by the music of Italy, France, Germany, or Austria. During the romantic period, Poland, Russia, Bohemia, the Scandinavian countries, and Spain produced important composers whose music had a national flavor. Early in the nineteenth century, Chopin transformed his native Polish dances into great art. After about 1860, groups or "schools" of composers consciously declared their musical independence and established national styles. Among the leading musical nationalists were Mussorgsky, Rimsky-Korsakov, and Borodin from Russia; Smetana and Dvořák from Bohemia; Edvard Grieg (1843–1907) from Norway; Jean Sibelius (1865–1957) from Finland; and Isaac Albéniz (1860–1909) from Spain.

An important national school is the Russian, which created highly distinctive music. The opera *A Life for the Tsar,* by Mikhail Glinka (1804–1857), laid the groundwork for a national style, and in the 1860s five young men—now known as the *Russian Five*—formed a true national school. They were Mily Balakirev (1837–1910), César Cui (1835–1918), Alexander Borodin (1833–1887), Nikolai Rimsky-Korsakov (1844–1908), and Modest Mussorgsky (1839–1881). Remarkably, all but Balakirev began as amateurs, and most of them held nonmusical jobs. Mussorgsky was the most original of the Russian five, and his opera *Boris Godunov* is a masterpiece of musical nationalism.

The Moldau (1874), by Bedřich Smetana

Bedřich Smetana (1824–1884) was the founder of Czech national music. His works are steeped in the folk music and legends of his native Bohemia. But he grew up when Bohemia was under Austrian domination, and in this repressive atmosphere, his musical nationalism could make little headway. He emigrated to Sweden in 1856.

In 1862, when Austria had made some liberal concessions, Smetana returned to Prague. He was active as a composer, pianist, conductor, and teacher and wrote the *Bartered Bride,* his most famous opera. At age fifty, he became completely deaf, but some of his finest works followed, including *Má Vlast* (*My Country;* 1874–1879), a cycle of six symphonic poems. His last years were blighted by syphilis, and he died in an insane asylum at age sixty.

"Today I took an excursion to the St. John Rapids where I sailed in a boat through huge waves. . . . The view of the landscape was both beautiful and grand." Smetana's trip inspired his famous symphonic poem *The Moldau,* which depicts Bohemia's main river as it flows through the countryside. This orchestral work, part of the cycle *Má Vlast* (*My Country*), is both a romantic representation of nature and a display of Czech nationalism. *The Moldau* was written in three weeks shortly after Smetana became deaf, but its fresh, optimistic mood gives no hint of the composer's anguish and despair.

Smetana wrote the following program to preface his score:

> The composition depicts the course of the river, beginning from its two small sources, one cold the other warm, the joining of both streams into one, then the flow of the Moldau through forests and across meadows, through the countryside where merry feasts are celebrated; water nymphs dance in the moonlight; on nearby rocks can be seen the outline of ruined castles, proudly soaring into the sky. The Moldau swirls through the St. John Rapids and flows in a broad stream toward Prague. It passes Vyšehrad [where an ancient royal castle once stood], and finally the river disappears in the distance as it flows majestically into the Elbe.

The Moldau falls into contrasting musical sections that represent different scenes and episodes described in the program. Hunting along the riverbank is suggested by horn fanfares; a peasant wedding by a rustic polka, the Bohemian dance; and a moonlit night by shimmering woodwinds and a serene melody in high muted strings. An expansive folklike theme that recurs several times symbolizes the river. Smetana unifies the symphonic poem with running notes evoking the movement of water, sometimes rippling, sometimes turbulent.

Listening Outline

SMETANA, *The Moldau*

Allegro commodo non agitato (unhurried allegro, not agitated), sextuple meter (§), E minor
Piccolo, 2 flutes, 2 oboes, 2 clarinets, 2 bassoons, 4 French horns, 2 trumpets, 3 trombones, tuba, timpani, bass drum, triangle, cymbals, harp, 1st violins, 2d violins, violas, cellos, double basses
(Duration, 11:35)

Two springs

0:00   **1. a.** Flutes, *p*, running notes. Harp, pizzicato violins.

Clarinets, *p*, join, running notes.
b. Lower strings, *p*, running notes lead to

The river

1:10   **2.** Violins, songlike river theme, minor key. Running-note accompaniment in strings.

1:39   River theme extended.

Forest hunt

3:00   **3. a.** French horns and trumpets, *f*, hunting calls. Strings, running notes. Crescendo to *ff*.
b. Decrescendo to *ppp*.

Peasant wedding

3:57   **4. a.** Strings, *p*, polka.

Crescendo to *f*, triangle strokes.
b. Decrescendo to *ppp*, melody descends.

Moonlight: dance of water nymphs

5:19   **5. a.** Woodwinds, *pp*, sustained tones. Flutes, *p*, running notes lead to
5:42   **b.** High muted violins, *pp*, serene legato melody, flutes and harp accompany, *p*.
6:58   **c.** Brasses, *pp*. Gentle staccato chords join accompaniment to violin melody.
7:36   **d.** Crescendo. Woodwinds, running notes lead to

The river

7:59   **6.** Violins, river theme. Running-note accompaniment in strings.

The rapids

8:40   **7. a.** Full orchestra, ***ff***. Brasses, timpani roll, piccolo, cymbal crashes.

   b. Strings, ***pp***. Quick crescendo.

The river at its widest point

9:53   **8.** Full orchestra, ***ff***, river theme in major key. Faster tempo.

Vyšehrad, the ancient castle

10:21   **9. a.** Brasses and woodwinds, ***ff***, hymnlike melody. Cymbal crashes.

   b. Decrescendo. Violins, ***ppp***. Full orchestra, ***ff***, closing chords.

12 Antonin Dvořák

Antonin Dvořák (1841–1904) followed Smetana as the leading composer of Czech national music. He infused his symphonies and chamber music with the spirit of Bohemian folksong and dance.

Dvořák's father was a poor innkeeper and butcher in a small town near Prague. After working in his father's butcher shop, Dvořák left home at the age of sixteen to study music in Prague. For years he earned a meager living by playing in an opera orchestra under Smetana's direction. He was little known as a composer until his works came to the attention of the German master Brahms, who recommended Dvořák to his own publisher: "I took much pleasure in the works of Dvořák of Prague. If you play them through, you will enjoy them as much as I have done. Decidedly he is a very talented man."

From this time on—Dvořák was then about thirty-six—his fame spread rapidly. He was invited several times to England, where the melodiousness of his symphonies, chamber music, Slavonic dances, and choral works appealed to the English love for folk music and the countryside. Although Dvořák rarely quoted actual folk tunes, his works breathe a folk quality and express a cheerful and direct personality.

In 1892, Dvořák went to New York, where he was to spend almost three years as director of the National Conservatory of Music. He received a salary of $15,000, about twenty times what he was earning as a professor at the Prague Conservatory. In addition to his urban impressions, Dvořák learned about the American heartland by spending a summer in Spillville, Iowa, where there was a colony of Czechs.

Dvořák encouraged American composers to write nationalistic music. He had become interested in Native American melodies and African American spirituals, which were sung for him by Henry T. Burleigh, a black composer and baritone who studied at the National Conservatory of Music. Dvořák told a reporter from the New York *Herald* that in the spirituals he had "found a secure basis for a new national musical school. America can have her own music, a fine music growing up from her own soil and having its own character—the natural voice of a free and great nation."

In 1895 Dvořák returned to his homeland and rejoined the faculty of the Prague Conservatory, becoming its director six years later.

Symphony No. 9 in E Minor (*From the New World*; 1893)

Dvořák wrote his *New World* Symphony, Symphony No. 9 in E Minor, during his first year in the United States. One of the best-known of all symphonies, it glorifies the

American and the Czech folk spirit. Its popular character grows out of Dvořák's use of syncopations, **pentatonic** (five-note) **scales,** and modal scales often found in folk music. Colorful orchestration and melodious thematic material add to the attractiveness of the *New World* Symphony. Its four contrasting movements are unified through quotation of thematic material: themes from the first movement are recalled in the second and third movements, and the finale brings back themes from all three preceding movements. Dvořák said that the second and third movements were inspired by *The Song of Hiawatha* (1855), a poem by Henry Wadsworth Longfellow featuring a Native American hero.

First Movement:
Adagio (slow introduction); Allegro molto

The slow introduction to the first movement builds great tension and contains an ominous low motive foreshadowing the opening theme of the energetic allegro that follows. In the exposition of this sonata-form movement, there are three distinctive themes. The first begins in minor with a syncopated arpeggio motive that dominates the entire symphony. The dancelike second theme, also in minor, is gentler than the first and narrower in range. Dvořák shifts to a major key for the third theme, a gracious melody that was probably inspired by the spiritual *Swing Low, Sweet Chariot.* (In the Listening Outline this is called the *Swing Low theme.*) Between these themes come beautiful bridge passages that rise to a climax and then calm down to usher in new melodic material. In his development, Dvořák concentrates on the first and third themes, which he varies and combines. The recapitulation of all three themes is followed by a coda, which brings the first movement to a climactic close.

Listening Outline

DVOŘÁK, Symphony No. 9 in E Minor (*From the New World*)

First Movement: Adagio (slow introduction); Allegro molto
Sonata form, duple meter (²⁄₄), E minor
Piccolo, 2 flutes, 2 oboes, 2 clarinets, 2 bassoons, 4 French horns, 2 trumpets, 3 trombones, timpani, 1st violins, 2d violins, violas, cellos, double basses
(Duration, 9:07)

Adagio (slow introduction)

0:00   **1. a.** Cellos, ***pp***, downward phrases. French horns.

0:32   **b.** Flute, ***p***, downward phrases.

0:55   **2. a.** Strings, ***ff***, alternate with timpani, woodwinds, horns, ***ff***.
          b. Cellos and basses, ***pp***.
          c. High woodwinds alternate with low strings, bass motive.
          d. Full orchestra, crescendo, timpani roll, violin tremolo, ***pp***.

Allegro molto

Exposition

First theme

1:53   **1. a.** Horns, arpeggio motive. Woodwinds, *p*, playful rhythm, minor key.

   b. Oboes, arpeggio motive. Woodwinds, playful rhythm.
   c. Strings, *ff*, arpeggio motive developed. Crescendo.

Bridge

2:25   **2.** Brasses, *ff*, arpeggio motive. Strings, playful rhythm developed. Decrescendo.

Second theme

2:57   **3. a.** Flute and oboe, *p*, dancelike tune.

   b. Violins, *ppp*, dancelike tune developed, crescendo to *f*. Decrescendo.

Third theme

4:03   **4. a.** Flute, *p*, *Swing Low* theme, major.

   b. Violins, *Swing Low* theme. Crescendo to *ff*, full orchestra.

Development

4:32   **1.** Strings, decrescendo.

4:45   **2. a.** Horn, *p*, *Swing Low* motive, piccolo. Crescendo.
   b. Trumpets, *f*, *Swing Low* motive. Trombones, *f*, arpeggio motive. Horns, *ff*. Strings, *ff*.
   c. Trombones, *ff*, arpeggio motive. High violins, *ff*. Rhythm quickens.

5:52   **3.** Oboes, *p*, arpeggio motive, flute. Crescendo.

Recapitulation

First theme

6:08   **1. a.** Horns, *mf*, arpeggio motive. Woodwinds, *p*, playful rhythm, minor.
   b. Oboes, arpeggio motive. Woodwinds, *p*, playful rhythm.
   c. Strings, *ff*, arpeggio motive developed. Decrescendo.

Second theme

6:48   **2. a.** Flute, *p*, dancelike tune.
   b. Woodwinds, *p*, dancelike tune. Strings, dancelike tune developed, crescendo to *ff*.
   Decrescendo.

Third theme

7:50   **3. a.** Flute, *p*, *Swing Low* theme, major.
   b. Violins, *Swing Low* theme. Crescendo.

Coda

8:18   **1.** Full orchestra, *fff*. *Swing Low* and arpeggio motives, minor.

   2. Repeated chords, *ff*, at end.

13 Peter Ilyich Tchaikovsky

Peter Ilyich Tchaikovsky was the most famous Russian composer of the nineteenth century.

Peter Ilyich Tchaikovsky (1840–1893), the most famous Russian composer, started his career as a government clerk and began to study music theory at the relatively late age of twenty-one. His progress in music was rapid, however. After graduating from the St. Petersburg Conservatory, he became professor of harmony at the new Moscow Conservatory, and composed furiously: a symphony, an opera, a tone poem, and by the age of thirty, his first great orchestral work, *Romeo and Juliet.*

The year 1877 was dramatic for Tchaikovsky. He married, disastrously and apparently only to conceal his homosexuality; attempted suicide two weeks later; and had a nervous collapse. (He separated from his wife and never saw her again.) But in 1877 he also acquired a wealthy benefactress, Nadezhda von Meck, with whom he had a curious but intimate friendship—they corresponded but did not meet. She gave him an annuity that allowed him to quit his conservatory position and devote himself to composition. Fourteen years later, Tchaikovsky was deeply hurt when she abruptly cut off the annuity and stopped writing to him.

During these years, Tchaikovsky achieved success conducting his own works throughout Europe (and, in 1891, in the United States). Yet success did not bring spiritual peace. In 1893, nine days after conducting the premiere of his Symphony No. 6 (*Pathétique*), which ends unconventionally with a slow, despairing finale, he died at the age of fifty-three.

Tchaikovsky's Music

Tchaikovsky thought of himself as "*Russian* in the fullest sense of the word," but his style was influenced by French, Italian, and German music as well as Russian folksong. His works are much more in the western tradition than those of his contemporaries, the Russian five. He fused national and international elements to produce intensely subjective and passionate music.

Among his most popular orchestral compositions are the Fourth, Fifth, and Sixth (*Pathétique*) Symphonies (1877, 1888, and 1893); Piano Concerto No. 1 in B Flat Minor (1875); the Violin Concerto (1878); and the overture-fantasy *Romeo and Juliet* (1869), which we study. He wrote some of his best music for ballet: *Swan Lake* (1876), *Sleeping Beauty* (1889), and *The Nutcracker* (1892). The spirit of ballet permeates much of Tchaikovsky's music. He also wrote eight operas and the orchestral showpieces *Marche slave* and *Overture 1812.*

Romeo and Juliet, Overture-Fantasy (1869)

Overture-Fantasy from *Romeo and Juliet* available in Connect Music

Romantic composers felt an artistic kinship with Shakespeare because of his passionate poetry, dramatic contrasts, and profound knowledge of the human heart. Shakespeare's plays inspired some of the finest nineteenth-century compositions. Among these were *Macbeth* and *Othello,* set as operas by Verdi; and *A Midsummer Night's Dream,* depicted in incidental music by Mendelssohn. *Romeo and Juliet* inspired both a "dramatic symphony" by Berlioz and a concert overture by Tchaikovsky.

Tchaikovsky composed *Romeo and Juliet* at twenty-nine, near the beginning of his musical career. Although it is now one of the best-loved works, *Romeo and Juliet* was a dismal failure at its premiere in 1870. "After the concert we dined. . . . No one said a single word to me about the overture the whole evening. And yet I yearned so for appreciation and kindness." Tchaikovsky decided to revise the overture. He composed a new theme to represent Friar Laurence, adopting a suggestion made by his friend Balakirev. Despite this, the work remained unappreciated. Only about twenty years later, after further revisions, did it achieve worldwide popularity.

Like Shakespeare's play, Tchaikovsky's *Romeo and Juliet* glorifies a romantic love powerful enough to triumph over death. Tchaikovsky captures the essential emotions of Shakespeare's play without defining the characters or the exact course of events. Highly contrasted themes are used to express the conflict between family hatred and youthful love. Tchaikovsky also depicts the gentle and philosophical Friar Laurence, intermediary between the lovers and the harsh outside world.

Romeo and Juliet is a concert overture consisting of a slow introduction followed by a fast movement in sonata form. (Tchaikovsky's title—Overture-Fantasy—implies that he treated the musical material in a free and imaginative way.) We can enjoy *Romeo and Juliet* as an exciting orchestral piece without knowing the play. However, a new dimension is added to our listening experience when we associate the music with the drama.

Tchaikovsky opens the overture with the Friar Laurence theme, a solemn, hymnlike melody.

First theme
5:16

As the slow introduction unfolds, brooding strings set an atmosphere of impending tragedy. The clash of swords and the anger of the feud between the Montagues and the Capulets are suggested by the violent first theme of the allegro.

Bridge
6:38

Syncopations, rushing strings, and massive sounds create enormous excitement. The exposition continues with a bridge section that brings a sudden **pp**, a calmer mood, and a slower rhythm.

Second theme
7:28

The second theme of the exposition, a tender love theme, is expressively scored for English horn and muted violas.

Pulsating Melody
7:48

It is followed by a gently pulsating melody in the muted violins.

Development
10:32

Recapitulation
12:35

Pulsating Melody
12:57

Love theme
13:34

Coda
6:24

The development section focuses mainly on the feud theme and the Friar Laurence theme. In the recapitulation, the gently pulsating melody precedes the love theme, which now has a new exultant character as Tchaikovsky envelops the listener in opulent sound. There are long crescendos as the melody is led higher and higher to ever-more passionate orchestral climaxes.

In the coda, Tchaikovsky transforms the love theme into a song of mourning, while timpani softly beat the rhythm of a funeral march.

Then, a new hymn and a tender reminiscence of the love theme suggest that Romeo and Juliet are reunited in death.

14 Johannes Brahms

Johannes Brahms (1833–1897) was a romantic who breathed new life into classical forms. He was born in Hamburg, Germany, where his father made a precarious living as a bass player. At thirteen, Brahms led a double life: during the day he studied piano, music theory, and composition; at night he played dance music in cafés.

On his first concert tour, when he was twenty, Brahms met Robert Schumann and Schumann's wife Clara, who were to shape the course of Brahms's artistic and personal life. The Schumanns listened enthusiastically to Brahms's music, and Robert published an article hailing young Brahms as a musical messiah.

Brahms was a romantic who breathed new life into classical forms.

As Brahms was preparing new works for an eager publisher, Robert Schumann had a nervous collapse and tried to drown himself. When Robert Schumann was committed to an asylum, leaving Clara with seven children to support, Brahms came to live in the Schumann home. He stayed for two years, helping to care for the children when Clara was on tour and becoming increasingly involved with Clara, who was fourteen years older than he. It is not known what passed between them (they destroyed many of their letters). They remained lifelong friends, and Brahms never married.

Brahms desperately wanted to become conductor of the Philharmonic Orchestra in Hamburg. When he was passed over for the post in 1862, he left Hamburg for Vienna, where he spent the rest of his life. He conducted a Viennese musical society and introduced many forgotten works of Bach, Handel, and Mozart. He had a wide knowledge of older music (which made him extremely critical of his own work), edited baroque and classical compositions, and collected music manuscripts.

Brahms always lived frugally, though he earned a good income from publishers and from playing and conducting his works. He hid a shy, sensitive nature behind a mask of sarcasm and rudeness; yet he could be extremely generous to talented young musicians (Dvořák was one).

When Clara Schumann lay dying in 1896, his grief found expression in the haunting *Four Serious Songs*. Not long after, it was discovered that he had cancer. On March 7, 1897, he dragged himself to hear a performance of his Fourth Symphony; the audience and orchestra gave him a tremendous ovation. Less than a month later, at the age of sixty-four, he died.

Brahms's Music

Brahms created masterpieces in all the traditional forms (except opera): four symphonies; two concertos for piano, one for violin, and one for violin and cello; piano pieces; over 200 songs; some magnificent choral music, such as the *German Requiem*; and numerous chamber pieces. His work is personal in style, but rooted in the music of Haydn, Mozart, and Beethoven. Brahms reinterprets classical forms while using the harmonic and instrumental resources of his own time.

Brahms's music has a range of moods, but particularly an autumnal feeling and a lyrical warmth. Lyricism pervades even the rich polyphonic textures he was so fond of, and he was always able to make them sound natural and spontaneous. One scholar has observed, "It is possible to sing every Brahms movement from beginning to end as though it were a single, uninterrupted melody."

His music is rhythmically exciting, with contrasting patterns and syncopations. (The use of "2 against 3"—one instrument playing two even notes to a beat while another plays three—is one of his trademarks.) His music also has a special quality of sound: rich, dark tone colors and, in the orchestral works, a blending of the instrumental choirs that favor mellow instruments like the viola, clarinet, and French horn.

All of his music radiates the security and solidity of a complete master. He justified Schumann's prediction of greatness for the "young eagle."

Symphony No. 3 in F Major, Op. 90

Shortly after completing his Third Symphony during the summer of 1883, Brahms was visited in Vienna by the younger composer Antonin Dvořák, whose *New World* Symphony was studied in Section 12. "At my request to hear something of his new symphony," Dvořák reported later, Brahms "was immediately forthcoming" and played two movements on the piano. Dvořák's reaction was ecstatic: "What magnificent melodies are to be found! It is full of love, and it makes one's heart melt."

The briefest of Brahms's symphonies, the Third Symphony, is characterized by thematic connections among its four movements and pervasive contrasts between major and minor. At the very end of the last movement, for example, the impassioned opening of the symphony, which combines F major and F minor harmonies, is gently recalled in F major. We focus on the third movement, a short interlude between the slow movement and the climactic finale.

Third Movement:
Poco Allegretto

Instead of using a rapid scherzo, standard in nineteenth-century symphonies, Brahms created a unique kind of third movement that is moderate in tempo (poco allegretto) and intensely lyrical in character. Brahms enhanced the intimate mood of the poco allegretto by reducing the size of its orchestra, which does not include the trumpets, trombones, contrabassoon, and timpani heard in the outer movements. Though romantic in style, the poco allegretto reflects Brahms's strong feeling for musical tradition: it has the triple meter, ternary form, and relaxed middle section typical of third movements in classical symphonies.

The poco allegretto contains one of Brahms's most haunting melodies. (In 1999, this melody was used by Carlos Santana and Dave Matthews in their song *Love of My Life,* from the album *Supernatural*.) The melody's yearning mood is created by its minor key and by its three-note dotted-rhythmic motive (long-short-long) that rises on the upbeat and falls on the downbeat.

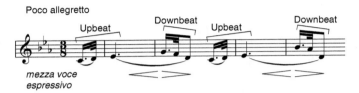

In the poco allegretto, Brahms creates variety by presenting the main melody in different tone colors and in successively higher octaves. In the opening section (A), the melody is introduced by the cellos, playing expressively (*espressivo*) and softly in an intimate "half voice" (*mezza voce*). Then it is heard in the violins, and—after an interlude—in the flute. When the opening section returns (A'), Brahms reorchestrates the main melody, which now is presented first by the French horn, then by the oboe, and finally by the high violins, as the climax of the movement.

The middle section (B) brings a shift from minor to major, from yearning to graciousness. Section B opens with a lilting waltzlike melody in the winds, accompanied by a staccato syncopated figure in the cellos. Later, Brahms creates a contrast of mood and tone color by introducing a new expressive melody in the strings alone. A hushed transition smoothly links the middle section (B) to the concluding A' section. Brahms prepares beautifully for the return of the main melody with an upward sequence in the woodwinds of the melody's initial dotted-rhythm motive (long-short-long). After the reorchestrated repetition of the opening section (A'), we hear a coda in which the dotted-rhythm motive flowers into an eloquent phrase that epitomizes the movement's intense lyricism.

Listening Outline

BRAHMS, Symphony No. 3 in F Major

Third Movement: Poco allegretto
A B A' Coda form, triple meter ($\frac{3}{8}$), C minor
2 flutes, 2 oboes, 2 clarinets, 2 bassoons, 2 French horns, 1st violins, 2d violins, violas, cellos, double basses
(Duration, 5:45)

A (minor)

0:00   **1. a.** Cellos, ***p***, yearning main melody in minor, middle register, strings and pizzicato basses accompany; ends with incomplete cadence.

0:25   **b.** Violins, ***p***, repeat main melody an octave higher, string accompaniment more animated; ends with complete cadence.

0:49   **c.** Cellos, ***p***, new flowing idea in major, imitated in violins,

Cellos

dolce

downward sequence in violins, quick rising arpeggios in cellos and clarinets introduce

1:19   **d.** Flute, oboe, ***mp***, main melody in minor, at even higher octave, accompanied by strings, winds, and pizzicato basses; complete cadence, winds, soft sustained chord introduces

B (Major)

1:45   **2. a.** Flutes and clarinets, ***p***, lilting waltzlike melody in major, cellos accompany with syncopated staccato figure.

Winds

p *dolce*

Cellos

1:59   **b.** Winds, ***p***, repeat waltzlike melody, violins and cellos accompany with syncopated staccato arpeggios.

2:13   **c.** Strings alone, ***pp***, new expressive legato melody, crescendo to ***f***, decrescendo to ***p***.

Violins

pp   *espressivo*   *crescendo*

2:32   **d.** Winds, soft waltzlike melody, accompanied by syncopated staccato arpeggios in violins and cellos.

2:46   **e.** Strings alone, ***p***, expressive legato melody, decrescendo to ***pp***, woodwinds, ***p***, upward sequence of opening dotted-rhythm motive from main melody, sustained chord.

Woodwinds

p

A′ (Minor)

3:23   **3. a.** French horn, ***p***, main melody in minor, middle register, strings and pizzicato basses accompany, ends with incomplete cadence.

3:50   **b.** Oboe, ***p***, repeats main melody an octave higher, strings accompany, ends with complete cadence.

4:12   **c.** High bassoon, ***p***, flowing idea in major, imitated in clarinet, downward sequence in winds; clarinets and bassoons alone, quick rising arpeggios in strings and flute introduce

4:43   **d.** Violins, ***mp***, main melody in minor at even higher octave, accompanied by strings, winds, pizzicato basses; complete cadence.

Coda

5:08   **4. a.** Winds, soft sustained chords.

5:17   **b.** Strings and winds, **_pp_**, repeat soft chords, eloquent rising and falling phrase in dotted rhythm, cadence;

soft sustained wind chord, pizzicato strings close movement.

15 Giuseppe Verdi

Giuseppe Verdi was one of the greatest opera composers and an ardent Italian nationalist.

Giuseppe Verdi (1813–1901), the most popular of all opera composers, was born in a tiny Italian village. He began studying music in a nearby town, Busseto, where he was taken into the home of a wealthy patron who later also supported Verdi's education in Milan. When he completed his studies, he became municipal music director in Busseto and was able to marry his patron's daughter. Three years later he returned to Milan with the score of his first opera, *Oberto* (1839).

Oberto was produced at La Scala (Milan's opera house), had a modest success, and brought Verdi a contract for more operas. Then disaster struck: his wife and their two children died. Verdi managed to complete his next opera, but it was a failure and, in despair, he vowed to compose no more.

He changed his mind after reading a libretto about the ancient Jews exiled from their homeland. Verdi was an ardent nationalist who yearned for a free and unified Italy and saw the Jews as a symbol of the oppressed Italians. He quickly composed *Nabucco* (*Nebuchadnezzar,* king of Babylon, 1842), which was an enormous success. From then on, Verdi and his operas symbolized Italian independence. (The cry *Viva Verdi* also stood for the patriotic slogan, "*Vittorio Emmanuele, Re D'Italia*"—*Victor Emmanuel, king of Italy.*)

In his late thirties, Verdi composed *Rigoletto* (1851), *Il Trovatore* (1853), and *La Traviata* (1853). Although the public loved them, critics were often scandalized by their subject matter. *Rigoletto* seemed to condone rape and suicide, and *La Traviata* apparently glorified free love and made a heroine out of a kept woman. But Verdi was fiercely independent and himself lived openly with his second wife for ten years before marrying her.

After these successes had made him wealthy, Verdi bought an estate at Busseto. In 1861 he was elected deputy to the first Italian parliament to convene after Italy had become a nation. In his later years he wrote *Aïda* (1871), *Otello* (1887), and—at the age of seventy-nine—his final opera *Falstaff* (1893).

Verdi's Music

Verdi composed not for the musical elite, but for a mass public whose main entertainment was opera. He wanted subjects that were "original, interesting . . . and passionate; passions above all!" Almost all of his mature works are serious and end unhappily. The operas move quickly and involve extremes of hatred, love, jealousy, and fear. His powerful music underlines the dramatic situations.

Expressive vocal melody is the soul of a Verdi opera. There are many duets, trios, and quartets; and the chorus plays an important role. Verdi's style became less conventional as he grew older. His later works have greater musical continuity, less difference between aria and recitative, more imaginative orchestration, and richer accompaniments. His last three operas—*Aïda, Otello* and *Falstaff*—are perhaps his greatest. *Falstaff,* his final work, is a comic masterwork with a carefree fugue to the words *All the world's a joke!*

Rigoletto (1851)

Verdi dared to create an operatic hero out of a hunchbacked court jester—Rigoletto—whose only redeeming quality is an intense love for his daughter, Gilda. Rigoletto's master, the licentious Duke of Mantua, has won Gilda's love while posing as a poor student. When the Duke seduces the innocent girl, Rigoletto plots his death. Gilda loves the Duke even after learning about his dissolute character, and she ultimately sacrifices her own life to save his. Vice triumphs in this powerful drama.

Act III:
La donna è mobile (Woman is Fickle)

La donna è mobile available in Connect Music

Act III of *Rigoletto* contains one of the most famous and popular pieces in opera, the Duke's aria *La donna è mobile.* The scene is an inn where the Duke has come to meet Maddalena, the voluptuous sister of Sparafucile, a cutthroat whom Rigoletto has hired to kill the Duke. *La donna è mobile* (*Woman is fickle*) perfectly expresses the Duke's pleasure-loving personality. Even before the premiere of *Rigoletto,* which was to take place in Venice, Verdi knew this aria would be a hit. Afraid that his catchy tune would leak out during rehearsals and be sung by every Venetian gondolier, he waited until the last possible moment before giving the manuscript to the tenor who was to sing it.

0:00
Aria.
Orchestra introduces
Duke's melody.

La donna è mobile	Woman is fickle
Qual piuma al vento,	Like a feather in the wind,
Muta d'accento	She changes her words
E di pensiero.	And her thoughts.
Sempre un amabile	Always a lovable
Leggiadro viso,	And lovely face,
In pianto o in riso,	Weeping or laughing,
È menzognero.	Is lying.
La donna è mobile, ecc.	Woman is fickle, etc.

1:00
Orchestra.
Duke's melody
repeated with
different words

È sempre misero	The man's always wretched
Chi a lei s'affida,	Who believes in her,
Chi le confida	Who recklessly entrusts
Mal cauto il core!	His heart to her!
Pur mai non sentesi	And yet one who never
Felice appieno	Drinks love on that breast
Chi su quel seno	Never feels
Non liba amore!	Entirely happy!
La donna è mobile, ecc.	Woman is fickle, etc.

16 Giacomo Puccini

Giacomo Puccini.

Giacomo Puccini (1858–1924), who created some of the best-loved operas, came from a long line of composers and church organists. During his student years at the Milan Conservatory, he lived a hand-to-mouth existence. The success of his first opera, shortly after his graduation, brought him commissions and an annual income from Italy's leading music publisher. In 1893, he became well known throughout Italy for his opera *Manon Lescaut;* after 1896, he was wealthy and world-famous from the enormous success of *La Bohème. Tosca* (1900) and *Madame Butterfly* (1904) were also very popular. He died before completing his last opera, *Turandot,* which was completed by a friend.

Puccini's marvelous sense of theater has given his operas lasting appeal. His melodies have short, remembered phrases and are intensely emotional. He used the orchestra to reinforce the vocal melody and to suggest mood. To achieve unity and continuity, he minimized the difference between aria and recitative and used the same material in different acts. Puccini was very much concerned with the literary and dramatic qualities of his librettos; he spent as much time polishing them as composing the music and often demanded endless changes from the librettists. Some of his operas, notably *Tosca,* reflect an artistic trend of the 1890s known as *verismo—realism,* or the quality of being "true to life." But they also feature exoticism: *Madame Butterfly* is set in Japan and *Turandot* in China, and both have melodic and rhythmic elements derived from the music of those countries.

La Bohème (1896)

La Bohème (*Bohemian Life*) takes place in the Latin Quarter of Paris around 1830. Its hero is Rodolfo, a young poet who shares a garret with Marcello, a painter; Colline, a philosopher; and Schaunard, a musician. Mimi, the heroine, is a poor, tubercular seamstress who lives in the same building. The simple, touching plot has been aptly summarized as "boy meets girl, boy loses girl, boy and girl are reunited as girl dies of consumption in boy's arms and curtain falls." Everyone can relate to the characters

Angela Gheorghiu as Mimi and Roberto Alagna as Rodolfo in a performance of *La Bohème* at the Norwegian National Opera.

and emotions of this enchanting opera. Though there are many realistic touches in this picture of bohemian life, it is seen through a romantic haze.

Act I:
Scene between Rodolfo and Mimi through Rodolfo's aria *Che gelida manina (How cold your little hand is)*

virtual fieldtrip

La Bohème

Mimi and Rodolfo meet and fall in love toward the end of Act I, which takes place on a cold Christmas eve. Her candle has blown out, and she knocks on his door asking for a light. At Rodolfo's insistence, Mimi enters, but she suddenly has a coughing fit and faints in his arms.

She revives after Rodolfo sprinkles water on her face. She then leaves, her candle alight, but she returns immediately, for she has lost her key. They must search for the key in the dark—a gust of wind has extinguished their candles. When their hands touch, Rodolfo sings the aria *Che gelida manina (How cold your little hand is!)*.

Puccini's sensuous melody casts a glow over the entire scene. His music has an improvisatory quality, with many fluctuations of tempo that reflect changes of mood and dramatic action. In the musical dialogue between Mimi and Rodolfo, Puccini easily alternates between speechlike and melodic phrases. When Mimi enters, the orchestra murmurs a touching phrase—Mimi's theme—that suggests her fragility and tenderness. Mimi's coughing fit is evoked by agitated music and her fainting by a poignant oboe solo. When Mimi returns to get her key, she introduces a new melody in a faster tempo.

Each of the two arias begins simply, almost conversationally. Then the melody grows warmer until it reaches a climax in a broad, passionate phrase. The climactic phrase of Rodolfo's aria, sung to the words *Talor dal mio forziere (My hoard of treasure is robbed by two thieves: a pair of beautiful eyes)*, is the love theme of the whole opera. Mimi's emotional high point is reached when she dreams about the end of winter (*ma quando vien la sgelo*), when "the first kiss of April" is hers. Returning to reality at the end of her aria, she sings in conversational repeated tones.

The mood changes momentarily as Rodolfo goes to the window and has a brief exchange with his friends in the courtyard—an example of Puccini's theatrical timing, for he provides a moment of relaxation before the lovers join in the closing duet. First, Rodolfo sings alone; then both voices unite beautifully in a declaration of love.

Vocal Music Guide

PUCCINI, *La Bohème*

Excerpt from Act I

0:00		
Flute melody.	(Rodolfo closes the door, sets his light on the table, and tries to write. But he tears up the paper and throws the pen down.)	

		Rodolfo	
	Non sono in vena.	I'm not in the mood.
	(A timid knock at the door.)	
Speechlike.	*Chi è la?*	Who's there?

| | | **Mimi** | |
| | *Scusi.* | Excuse me. |

| | | **Rodolfo** | |
| | *Una donna!* | A woman! |

		Mimi	
Mimi's theme,	*Di grazia, me si è spento*	I'm sorry . . . my light
pp, in orchestra.	*Il lume.*	Has gone out.

		Rodolfo	
	(opens the door)	
	Ecco.	Here.

		Mimi	
	(in the doorway, with a candlestick and a key)	
	Vorrebbe . . . ?	Would you . . . ?

| | | **Rodolfo** | |
| | *S'accomodi un momento.* | Come in for a moment. |

| | | **Mimi** | |
| | *Non occorre.* | There's no need. |

		Rodolfo	
	La prego, entri.	Please . . . come in.
	(Mimi enters, has a fit of coughing.)	

| | | **Rodolfo** | |
| | *Si sente male?* | You're not well? |

| | | **Mimi** | |
| | *No . . . nulla.* | No . . . it's nothing. |

| | | **Rodolfo** | |
| | *Impallidisce!* | You're pale! |

| | | **Mimi** | |
| | *È il respir . . . quelle scale . . .* | I'm out of breath . . . the stairs . . . |

1:06		
Oboe.	(She faints, and Rodolfo is just in time to support her and help her to a chair. The key and the candlestick fall from her hands.)	

	Rodolfo	
Pizzicato violins.	*Ed ora come faccio?*	Now what shall I do?
	(He gets some water and sprinkles her face.)	
	Così.	So.
	Che viso d'ammalata!	How ill she looks!
	(Mimi comes to.)	
1:30		
Staccato muted strings.	*Si sente meglio?*	Are you better now?
	Mimi	
	Sì.	Yes.
	Rodolfo	
	Qui c'è tanto freddo.	It's so cold here.
	Segga vicino al fuoco.	Come and sit by the fire.
	(He helps her to a chair by the stove.)	
	Aspetti . . . un po' di vino.	Wait . . . some wine.
	Mimi	
	Grazie.	Thank you.
	Rodolfo	
	A lei.	Here.
	Mimi	
	Poco, poco.	Just a little.
	Rodolfo	
	Così.	There.
	Mimi	
	Grazie.	Thank you.
	Rodolfo	
	(Che bella bambina!)	(What a lovely creature!)
	Mimi	
	(rising)	
	Ora permetta	Now, please,
	Che accenda il lume.	Relight my candle.
	È tutto passato.	I'm better now.
	Rodolfo	
	Tanta fretta.	Such a hurry!
	Mimi	
	Sì.	Yes.
	(Rodolfo lights her candle for her.)	
	Mimi	
	Grazie. Buona sera.	Thank you. Good evening.
	Rodolfo	
	Buona sera.	Good evening.
	(Mimi goes out, then reappears at the door.)	
2:23	**Mimi**	
A little faster.	*Oh! sventata, sventata,*	Oh! foolish me! . . .

Tuneful vocal
melody.

La chiave della stanza   Where have I left
Dove l'ho lasciata?   The key to my room?

Rodolfo

Non stia sull'uscio: Don't stand in the door:
Il lume vacilla ai vento.   The wind makes your light flicker.
    (Her candle goes out.)

Mimi

Oh Dio! Torni ad accenderlo.   Heavens! Will you relight it?
(Rodolfo rushes to her with his light, but when he reaches the door, his candle
goes out, too. The room is dark.)

Rodolfo

Oh Dio! Anche il mio s'è spento.   Heavens! Now mine's out, too.

Mimi

Ah! E la chiave ove sarà?   Ah! And where can my key be?

Rodolfo

Buio pesto!   Pitch-dark!

Mimi

Disgraziata!   Unlucky me!

Rodolfo

Ove sarà?   Where can it be?

Mimi

Importuna è la vicina . . .   You've a bothersome neighbor . . .

Rodolfo

Ma le pare!   Not at all.

Mimi

Importuna è la vicina . . .   You've a bothersome neighbor . . .

Rodolfo

Cosa dice, ma le pare!   What do you mean? Not at all!

Mimi

Cerchi.   Search.

Rodolfo

Cerco.   I'm searching.
    (They both grope on the floor for the key.)

Mimi

Ove sarà?   Where can it be?

Rodolfo
(finds the key, pockets it)
Ah!   Ah!

Mimi

L'ha trovata?   Did you find it?

Rodolfo

No.   No.

Mimi

Mi parve . . .   I thought . . .

Rodolfo

In verità!	Truthfully!

Mimi

Cerca?	Are you hunting?

Rodolfo

Cerco.	I'm hunting for it.

3:40
Orchestra alone, tempo slows.

(Guided by her voice, Rodolfo pretends to search as he draws closer to her. Then his hand meets hers, and he holds it.)

Mimi
(surprised)

Ah!	Ah!

(They rise. Rodolfo continues to hold Mimi's hand.)

4:01
Rodolfo's aria.

Rodolfo

Che gelida manina,	How cold your little hand is!
Se la lasci riscaldar.	Let me warm it for you.

Harp.

Cercar che giova? Al buio	What's the use of searching?
Non si trova. Ma per fortuna	We'll never find it in the dark.
È una notte di luna,	But luckily there's a moon,
E qui la luna l'abbiamo vicina.	And she's our neighbor here.
Aspetti, signorina,	Just wait, my dear young lady,
Le dirò con due parole chi son,	And meanwhile I'll tell you
Chi son, e che faccio, come vivo.	In a word who and what I am.
Vuole?	Shall I?

(Mimi is silent.)

Chi son? Chi son? Son un poeta.	Who am I? I'm a poet.
Che cosa faccio? Scrivo.	My business? Writing.
E come vivo? Vivo.	How do I live? I live.
In povertà mia lieta	In my happy poverty
Scialo da gran signore	I squander like a prince
Rime ed inni d'amore.	My poems and songs of love.
Per sogni e per chimere	In hopes and dreams
E per castelli in aria	And castles in air,
L'anima ho milionaria.	I'm a millionaire in spirit.

6:22
Love theme.

Talor dal mio forziere	My hoard of treasure
Ruban tutti i gioielli	Is stolen by two thieves:
Due ladri: gli occhi belli.	A pair of beautiful eyes.

	V'entrar con voi pur ora	They came in now with you
	Ed i miei sogni usati,	And all my lovely dreams,
	Ed i bei sogni miei	My dreams of the past,
	Tosto si dileguar!	Were soon stolen away.
	Ma il furto non m'accora	But the theft doesn't upset me,
	Poichè, poichè v'ha preso stanza	Since the empty place was filled
	La speranza.	With hope.
	Or che mi conoscete	Now that you know me,
	Parlate voi, deh! parlate.	It's your turn to speak.
	Chi siete? Vi piaccia dir?	Who are you? Will you tell me?

8:23

Mimi's aria.

Mimi

Sì.	Yes.
Mi chiamano Mimì,	They call me Mimi,
Ma il mio nome è Lucia.	But my real name is Lucia.

Andante lento

Mi chia-ma-no Mi-mì, ma il mio no-me e Lu-ci-a. _____

La storia mia è breve.	My story is brief.
A tela o a seta	I embroider silk and satin
Ricamo in casa e fuori.	At home or outside.
Son tranquilla e lieta,	I'm tranquil and happy,
Ed è mio svago	And my pastime
Far gigli e rose.	Is making lilies and roses.
Mi piaccion quelle cose	I love all things
Che han si dolce malia,	That have a gentle magic,
Che parlano d'amor, di primavere,	That talk of love, of spring,
Che parlano di sogni e di chimere,	That talk of dreams and fancies—
Quelle cose che han nome poesia . . .	The things called poetry . . .
Lei m'intende?	Do you understand me?

Rodolfo

Sì.	Yes.

10:13

Mimi

Mi chiamano Mimì—	They call me Mimi—
Il perchè non so.	I don't know why.
Sola, mi fo il pranzo	I live all by myself
Da me stessa.	And I eat all alone.
Non vado sempre a messa,	I don't often go to church,
Ma prego assai il Signor.	But I like to pray.
Vivo sola, soletta,	I stay all alone
Là in una bianca cameretta;	In my tiny white room,
Guardo sui tetti e in cielo.	I look at the roofs and the sky.
Ma quando vien lo sgelo	But when the thaw comes
Il primo sole è mio,	The first sunshine is mine,
Il primo bacio	The first kiss
Dell'aprile è mio!	Of April is mine!
Il primo sole è mio!	The first sunshine is mine!
Germoglia in un vaso una rosa.	A rose blossoms in my vase,
Foglia a foglia l'aspiro.	I breathe in its perfume,
Così gentil è il profumo d'un fior.	Petal by petal. So lovely,

Ma i fior ch'io faccio, ahimè,	So sweet is the flower's perfume.
I fior ch'io faccio,	But the flowers I make,
Ahimè non hanno odore.	Alas, have no scent.
Altro di me non le saprei narrare.	What else can I say?
Sono la sua vicina	I'm your neighbor,
Che la vien fuori d'ora a importunare.	Disturbing you at this impossible hour.

13:02

Friends in the courtyard.

Schaunard
(from below)

Eh! Rodolfo!	Hey! Rodolfo!

Colline

Rodolfo!	Rodolfo!

Marcello

Olà! Non senti?	Hey! Can't you hear?
Lumaca!	You snail!

Colline

Poetucolo!	You fake!

Schaunard

Accidenti al pigro!	To hell with that lazy one!

(Rodolfo, impatient, goes to the window to answer. When the window is opened, the moonlight comes in, lighting up the room.)

Rodolfo

Scrivo ancora tre righe a volo.	I've a few more words to write.

Mimi

Chi son?	Who are they?

Rodolfo

Amici.	Friends.

Schaunard

Sentirai le tue.	You'll hear about this.

Marcello

Che te ne fai lì solo?	What are you doing there alone?

Rodolfo

Non son solo. Siamo in due.	I'm not alone. There's two of us.
Andate da Momus, tenete il posto.	Go to Momus and get a table.
Ci saremo tosto.	We'll be there soon.

Marcello, Schaunard, Colline

Momus, Momus, Momus,	Momus, Momus, Momus.
Zitti e discreti audiamocene via.	Quietly, discreetly, we're off.
Momus, Momus, Momus.	Momus, Momus, Momus.
Trovò la poesia.	He's found his poem at last.

(Turning, Rodolfo sees Mimi wrapped in a halo of moonlight. He contemplates her, in ecstasy.)

13:40

Duet.

Rodolfo

O soave fanciulla, o dolce viso	Oh! lovely girl, oh! sweet face
Di mite circonfuso alba lunar,	Bathed in the soft moonlight.
In te, ravviso il sogno	I see in you the dream
Ch'io vorrei sempre sognar!	I'd dream forever!

14:18
Voices unite,
love theme.

Fremon già nell'anima	Already I taste in spirit
Le dolcezze estreme,	The heights of tenderness!
Amor nel bacio freme!	Love trembles in our kiss!

Mimi

Ah, tu sol comandi, amore. . . .	Ah! Love, you rule alone. . . .
Oh! come dolci scendono	How sweet his praises
Le sue lusinghe al core. . . .	Enter my heart. . . .
Tu sol comandi, amore!	Love, you alone rule!

(Rodolfo kisses her.)

Mimi

| No, per pietà! | No, please! |

Rodolfo

| Sei mia! | You're mine! |

Mimi

| V'aspettan gli amici. . . . | Your friends are waiting. |

Rodolfo

| Già mi mandi via? | You send me away already? |

Mimi

| Vorrei dir . . . ma non oso. | I daren't say what I'd like . . . |

Rodolfo

| Di'. | Tell me. |

Mimi

| Se venissi con voi? | If I came with you? |

Rodolfo

Che? Mimì!	What? Mimi!
Sarebbe così dolce restar qui.	It would be so fine to stay here.
C'è freddo fuori.	Outside it's cold.

Mimi

| Vi starò vicina! | I'd be near you! |

Rodolfo

| E al ritorno? | And when we come back? |

Mimi

| Curioso! | Who knows? |

Rodolfo

16:15
Melody from
Rodolfo's aria.

| Dammi il braccio, o mia piccina . . . | Give me your arm, my little one . . . |

Mimi

| Obbedisco, signor! | Your servant, sir . . . |

Rodolfo

| Che m'ami . . . di' . . . | Tell me you love me! |

Mimi

| Io t'amo. | I love you. |

	Rodolfo
Amor!	My love!
	Mimi
Amor!	My love!
	Rodolfo and Mimi
Amor!	Beloved!

Performance Perspectives

Luciano Pavarotti, Tenor, Singing the Part of Rodolfo in Puccini's *La Bohème*

The operatic tenor Luciano Pavarotti (1935–2007) was probably the world's best-known classical performer during the late twentieth century. He appeared frequently not only on operatic and concert stages, but in stadiums, on television, and in movies. In June 1993, more than 500,000 fans attended his performance in New York's Central Park and millions more watched on television. In July 1994, he participated in the second of several "Three Tenors" concerts—together with Placido Domingo and José Carreras—in Dodger Stadium, Los Angeles; it was seen on television by an estimated billion people in 107 countries.

Pavarotti was born in Modena, Italy, in 1935. As a boy, he listened avidly to recordings of tenors brought home by his father, an amateur singer. At nineteen Pavarotti began serious vocal study, and at twenty-five he won a singing competition that led to his operatic debut as Rodolfo in Puccini's *La Bohème.* Pavarotti later recalled the thrill of "singing for the first time with a full orchestra. All those years of studying and thinking of yourself as a singer—there is always an orchestra there, in your mind. But the first time it is *really* there—it is an experience, impossible to describe to someone who hasn't dreamed for years of becoming an opera singer." From then on his career rose rapidly: he made his debut at Milan's La Scala—Italy's most important opera house—in 1965, and his debut at New York's Metropolitan Opera in 1968.

Pavarotti wrote insightfully on his approach to Rodolfo's aria *Che gelida manina* from Puccini's *La Bohème* (included in the video clip found on the CD-ROM accompanying this book). "For me the most difficult notes for the tenor in *La Bohème* are in Act I when Rodolfo sings to Mimi, '*Che gelida manina.*' . . . Those quiet low notes must have a big rich sound—a steady, pure sound that floods the opera house. They may be soft notes, but they must have behind them all your power as a singer. They must have the same amount of support from your diaphragm that you give the big notes."

Pavarotti was inspired by the great conductors with whom he worked: they revealed deeper aspects of the drama, and they influenced him to try new approaches "to passages I had sung many times in a different way." When the conductor Carlos Kleiber directed a performance of *La Bohème* at La Scala, "difficult places in the score that had caused me problems before, I found myself singing without effort. As an example, it is traditional to transpose '*Che gelida manina*' down a half tone to spare the tenor the difficult high C at the end. Although few people were aware of it, most of the great tenors of the past had done this. But Kleiber made me sing the aria in the original key. Somehow I soared up to the high C with no strain. It may seem like superstition, but I am sure that was due to the inspiration of working with him and the way he conducted." No one did more than Pavarotti to introduce listeners to the magic of opera.

17 Richard Wagner

Few composers have had so powerful an impact on their time as Richard Wagner (1813–1883). His operas and artistic philosophy influenced not only musicians, but also poets, painters, and playwrights. Such was his preeminence that an opera house of his own design was built in Bayreuth, Germany, solely for performances of his music dramas.

Wagner was born in Leipzig into a theatrical family. His boyhood dream was to be a poet and playwright, but at fifteen he was overwhelmed by Beethoven's music and he decided to become a composer. He taught himself by studying scores and had almost three years of formal training in music theory, but he never mastered an instrument. As a student at Leipzig University, he dueled, drank, and gambled. A similar pattern persisted throughout his life; Wagner shamelessly lived off other people and accumulated enormous debts that he never repaid.

Richard Wagner's operas and artistic philosophy had a powerful impact on musicians, poets, painters, and playwrights.

During his early twenties, Wagner conducted in small German theaters and wrote several operas. In 1839 he decided to try his luck in Paris, then the center of grand opera. He and his wife Minna spent two miserable years there, during which he was unable to get an opera performed and was reduced to musical hackwork. Wagner returned to Germany in 1842 to supervise the production of his opera *Rienzi* in Dresden. The work was immensely successful, and Wagner was appointed conductor of the Dresden Opera. Wagner spent six years at this post, becoming famous both as an opera composer and as a conductor.

When the revolutions of 1848 were sweeping across Europe, Wagner's life in Dresden had become difficult because of accumulated debts. Hoping that a new society would wipe out his debts and produce conditions favorable to his art, he participated in the insurrection and then had to flee to Switzerland. For several years Wagner did no composing; instead he worked out theories of art in several essays and completed the librettos to *Der Ring des Nibelungen* (*The Ring of the Nibelung*), a set of four operas based on Nordic myth, which would occupy him for twenty-five years. He interrupted his work on the music for *The Ring* to compose *Tristan and Isolde* (1857–1859).

Wagner had several bad years after finishing *Tristan*. His opera *Tannhäuser* was a failure at the Paris Opera; *Tristan* was abandoned by the Vienna Opera; and he was hounded by creditors. In 1864, however, he was rescued by King Ludwig of Bavaria, an eighteen-year-old fanatical Wagnerian who put all the resources of the Munich Opera at Wagner's disposal. At this time, Wagner fell in love with Cosima von Bülow, who was Liszt's daughter and the wife of Hans von Bülow, Wagner's close friend and favorite conductor. Cosima gave birth to two of Wagner's children while still married to von Bülow. Shortly after Wagner's first wife died, he married Cosima.

In Wagner, towering musical genius was allied with selfishness, ruthlessness, rabid German nationalism, and absolute self-conviction. He forged an audience for his complex music dramas from a public accustomed to conventional opera. The performance of the *Ring* cycle in 1876 was perhaps the single most important musical event of the century. Though some critics still found his music too dissonant, heavily orchestrated, and long-winded, Wagner was generally acclaimed the greatest composer of his time. A year after completing *Parsifal* (1877–1882), his last opera, he died in Venice, at age sixty-nine.

Wagner's Music

For Wagner, an opera house was a temple in which the spectator was to be overwhelmed by music and drama. He wrote his own librettos, which he based on medieval Germanic legends and myths. His characters are usually larger than life—heroes, gods, demigods. He called his works *music dramas* rather than operas, but today many people find Wagner's music more exciting than his rather static drama.

Within each act, there is a continuous musical flow (Wagner called this "unending melody") instead of traditional arias, recitatives, and ensembles; and there are no breaks where applause can interrupt. His vocal line, which he conceived as "speech song," is inspired by the rhythms and pitch of the German text. Wagner revolutionized opera by shifting the focus from voice to orchestra and treating the orchestra symphonically. His expanded and colorful orchestration expresses the drama and constantly develops, transforms, and intertwines musical ideas. (And the orchestral sound is so full that only very powerful voices can cut through it.) In the orchestra—and sometimes in the vocal parts—he uses brief, recurrent musical ideas called *leit motifs,* or *leading motives*. A **leitmotif** is a short musical idea associated with a person, an object, or a thought in the drama.

The tension of Wagner's music is heightened by chromatic and dissonant harmonies. Wagner's chromatic harmony ultimately led to the breakdown of tonality and to the new musical language of the twentieth century.

Die Walküre (The Valkyrie; 1856)

Die Walküre (*The Valkyrie*) is the second and most widely performed of the four music dramas in Wagner's gigantic cycle *Der Ring des Nibelungen* (*The Ring of the Nibelung*). Despite its gods, giants, dwarfs, and magic fire, the *Ring* is really about Wagner's view of nineteenth-century society. He uses Nordic mythology to warn that society destroys itself through lust for money and power. It is fitting that Wagner first sketched the plot of the *Ring* in 1848, the year that brought Marx's *Communist Manifesto* and revolutions throughout Europe.

Jeannine Altmeyer as Sieglinde and Peter Hoffmann as Siegmund in the love scene from Act I of *Die Walküre.*

Act I:
Love scene (conclusion)

Wagner builds the first act of *Die Walküre* to an overwhelming climax in the passionate love scene that concludes it. To grasp this scene fully, it's helpful to know what has happened earlier in the *Ring*.

A Nibelung dwarf, Alberich, has stolen gold belonging to the Rhine maidens, mermaids in the Rhine River. From this gold, the dwarf fashions a ring that can bestow immense power on anyone who wears it and is willing to renounce love. The dwarf, in turn, is robbed of his prize by Wotan, king of the gods. (*Wednesday* comes from *Wotan's day*.) Soon Wotan himself is forced to give up the ring; he then lives in fear that Alberich will get it back and use it to destroy him. Hoping to protect himself, he surrounds his castle, Valhalla, with a bodyguard of heroes. His daughters, goddesses called *Valkyries,* swoop over battlefields on horseback and bear away the dead bodies of the bravest warriors. The Valkyrie of the opera's title is Brünnhilde, Wotan's favorite daughter.

Seeking to create a hero who can help him regain the ring, Wotan takes a human wife and fathers the Volsung twins—a son, Siegmund; and a daughter, Sieglinde. The twins know their father as Wälse, unaware that he is the god Wotan. They are separated as children when a hostile clan kidnaps Sieglinde and kills their mother. Siegmund becomes an outlaw and Sieglinde is eventually forced to marry the warrior-chief Hunding, whom she hates. During the wedding feast in Hunding's home, Wotan appears, disguised as an old man dressed in gray. He thrusts a magic sword into the tree around which the house is built, and proclaims that the weapon belongs to the one who can draw it out. Hunding and his followers try but are unable to withdraw the sword.

The first act of *Die Walküre* begins as Siegmund, weaponless and pursued by enemies, unwittingly takes refuge in the house of Hunding, who is away hunting. Sieglinde and Siegmund almost immediately fall in love, unaware that they are brother and sister. Hunding returns and soon realizes that the stranger—who identifies himself as *Wehwalt* (*Woeful*)—is an enemy of his clan. He says that Siegmund is his guest for the night, but the next day they must do battle. Sieglinde gives her husband a sleeping potion and tells Siegmund that her shame and misery will be avenged by the hero who can withdraw the sword from the tree. As they embrace passionately, the door of the hut suddenly opens, allowing the moonlight of a beautiful spring night to shine on them.

The following excerpt occurs at the end of the love scene, when Siegmund and Sieglinde gradually become aware of their amazing resemblance to each other and finally realize that they are brother and sister. Since her beloved no longer wants to be called *Wehwalt*, Sieglinde renames him *Siegmund* (*Victor*). With a powerful effort, Siegmund withdraws the sword from the tree and the lovers rapturously embrace. (The offspring of this unlawful union will be Siegfried, the human hero of the *Ring* cycle. In the mythology and folklore of many lands, heroes are often born of incestuous love.)

In the excerpt we study, Wagner creates a continuous musical flow that depicts the surging passions of the lovers through frequent changes of tempo, dynamics, and orchestral color. Typically, the vocal lines range from speechlike to highly melodic and closely reflect the inflections and meaning of the text. For example, the word *Notung* (*Needy*)—the name of the sword—is powerfully emphasized when it is sung to the downward leap of an octave.

Several leitmotifs are heard, sometimes together. In this excerpt, the leitmotif *Valhalla*—Wotan's castle—is first presented when Sieglinde looks at Siegmund and later the leitmotif returns when she recalls how their father (Wotan disguised as the old man) gazed at her during her marriage feast. The very important *sword* leitmotif is barely noticeable when it first appears, as Sieglinde refers to the fire in Siegmund's eyes. It is presented **pp**, in combination with the leitmotif *Volsung* (the people to which Siegmund and Sieglinde belong). Later, the sword motif is very prominent when it is proclaimed by the brasses as Siegmund draws the sword out of the tree and as the lovers embrace during the orchestral conclusion of the act. Other leitmotifs heard in our excerpt are *love* and *spring*.

Vocal Music Guide

WAGNER, *Die Walküre*

Act I, Love Scene, Conclusion

(Sieglinde pushes Siegmund's hair back from his brow and looks at him with astonishment.)

Sieglinde

0:00

Wie dir die Stirn so offen steht, der Adern Geäst in den Schläfen sich schlingt! Mir zagt es vor der Wonne, die mich entzückt!

Look how your forehead broadens out, and the network of veins winds into your temples. I tremble with the delight that enchants me.

0:19

Valhalla, French horns, *p.*

Ein Wunder will mich gemahnen: den heut zuerst ich erschaut, mein Auge sah dich schon!

It brings something strange to my mind: though I first saw you today, I've set eyes on you before.

Siegmund

0:45

Ein Minnetraum gemahnt auch mich: in heissem Sehnen sah ich dich schon!

A dream of love comes to my mind as well: burning with longing I have seen you before.

Sieglinde

1:04

Im Bach erblickt' ich mein eigen Bild und jetzt gewahr ich es wieder: wie einst dem Teich es enttaucht, bietest mein Bild mir nun du!

In the stream I've seen my own likeness; and now I see it again. As once it appeared in the water so now you show me my likeness.

Siegmund

1:28

Love, voice.

Du bist das Bild, das ich in mir barg.

You are the likeness that I hid in myself.

Sieglinde

Love, French horn, *p.*

O still! Lass mich der Stimme lauschen: mich dünkt, ihren Klang hört' ich als Kind.

Hush! let me listen to your voice. Its sound, I fancy, I heard as a child,

2:00

Doch nein! Ich hörte sie neulich, als meiner Stimme Schall mir widerhallte der Wald.

but no! I heard it recently— when the echo of my voice sounded back through the forest.

Siegmund

O lieblichste Laute, denen ich lausche!

O loveliest sound for me to hear!

2:24

Volsung, low strings, **pp**, together with *Sword*, bass trumpet, **pp**.

2:34

Valhalla. French horns, **pp**, then strings, **pp**.

Pause.

Sieglinde

Deines Auges Glut erglänzte mir schon:	The fire in your eyes has blazed at me before:

2:34

so blickte der Greis grüssend auf mich, als der Traurigen Trost er gab.	So the old man gazed at me in greeting when to my sadness he brought comfort.
An dem Blick erkannt' ihn sein Kind. schon wollt' ich beim Namen ihn nennen!	By his look his child recognized him, I even wanted to call him by name.

3:04

Wehwalt heisst du fürwahr?	Are you really called Woeful?

Siegmund

Nicht heiss ich so, seit du mich liebst: nun walt ich der hehrsten Wonnen!	I am not called that since you love me: Now I am full of purest rapture.

Sieglinde

3:23

Und Friedmund darfst du froh dich nicht nennen?	And "Peaceful" may you not, being happy, be named?

Siegmund

Nenne mich du, wie du liebst, dass ich heisse: den Namen nehm ich von dir!	Name me what you love to call me. I take my name from you.

Sieglinde

3:42

Doch nanntest du Wolfe den Vater?	But did you name Wolf as your father?

Siegmund

Ein Wolf war er feigen Füchsen! Doch dem so stolz strahlte das Auge, wie, Herrliche, hehr dir es strahlt, der war: Wälse genannt.	A Wolf he was to craven foxes! But he whose proud eyes shone as grandly as yours, you marvel, his name was "Volsa."

Sieglinde

4:03

War Wälse dein Vater, und bist du ein Wälsung, stiess er für dich sein Schwert in den Stamm, so lass mich dich heissen, wie ich dich liebe: Siegmund: so nenn ich dich!	If "Volsa" was your father and you are a "Volsung," it was for you he thrust his sword into the tree— so let me call you by the name I love: Siegmund (Victor)—so I name you.

Siegmund

4:27

Siegmund heiss ich und Siegmund bin ich! Bezeug es dies Schwert, das zaglos ich halte!	Siegmund I am called and Siegmund I am, let this sword, which I fearlessly hold, bear witness.

4:42

Wälse verhiess mir, in höchster Not fänd' ich es einst: ich fass es nun! Heiligster Minne höchste Not,	Volsa promised me that in deepest distress I should one day find it. Now I grasp it. Holiest love's deepest distress,

	sehnender Liebe sehrende Not	yearning love's scorching desire,
	brennt mir hell in der Brust,	burn bright in my breast,
	drängt zu Tat und Tod:	urge me to deeds and death.
5:20 Voice, downward octave leaps.	Notung! Notung! so nenn ich dich,	"Needy," "Needy," I name you,
	Schwert.	sword.
	Notung, Notung! neidlicher Stahl!	"Needy," "Needy," precious blade,
	Zeig deiner Schärfe schneidenden Zahn:	show your sharpness and cutting edge:
	heraus aus der Scheide zu mir!	come from your scabbard to me!

5:50

Sword,
the trumpets, *ff*.

(With a powerful effort, Siegmund pulls the sword from the tree, showing it to astonished and delighted Sieglinde.)

6:07

Volsung,
trumpets, *pp*.

Siegmund, den Wälsung, siehst du, Weib!	You see Siegmund, the Volsung, woman!
Als Brautgabe bringt er dies Schwert:	As wedding gift he brings this sword;
so freit er sich	so he weds
die seligste Frau;	the fairest of women;
dem Feindeshaus entführt er dich so.	he takes you away from the enemy's house.
Fern von hier folge mir nun,	Now follow me far from here,

6:41

Spring, voice.

fort in des Lenzes lachendes Haus:	out into springtime's smiling house.

dort schützt dich Notung, das Schwert,	For protection you'll have "Needy" the sword,
wenn Siegmund dir liebend erlag!	even if Siegmund expires with love.

Sieglinde

7:10

Bist du Siegmund, den ich hier sehe,	Are you Siegmund whom I see here?
Sieglinde bin ich, die dich ersehnt:	I am Sieglinde who longed for you:
die eig'ne Schwester	your own sister
gewannst du zu eins mit dem Schwert!	you have won and the sword as well.

Siegmund

Braut und Schwester bist du dem Bruder,	Wife and sister you'll be to your brother.
so blühe denn Wälsungen-Blut!	So let the Volsung blood increase!

7:39

Sword,
brasses, *ff*.
Passionate
orchestral
conclusion.

(He draws her to him with passionate fervor.)

The Romantic Period: Summary

IMPORTANT TERMS

FEATURED GENRES

Music in Society

- A large and growing urban middle class wanted to hear and play music; this trend resulted in the formation of numerous orchestras, opera companies, and music societies.
- Subscription concerts became common.
- The nineteenth-century musical public was captivated by virtuoso performers.
- Numerous music conservatories were founded in Europe and the United States.
- Women assumed greater roles as performers, composers, and patrons in professional music making.
- Music making in the home took on great importance.
- The piano became a regular fixture in middle-class and upper-class homes, used both for entertainment and for educating children, particularly girls.

Important Style Features

Mood and Emotional Expression

- Music of the romantic era is closely related to the other arts, particularly literature.
- Art forms, including music, exhibited extreme interest in subjects related to nature, death, the fantastic, the macabre, and the diabolical.
- Unprecedented emphasis was placed on self-expression and the development of a uniquely personal musical style.
- Music explored a universe of feeling that included flamboyance and intimacy, unpredictability and melancholy, rapture and longing, the mysterious and the remote.
- Some composers wrote music evoking a specific national identity ("nationalism") or an exotic location ("exoticism").

Rhythm

- Rhythm is extremely diverse.
- Tempos are flexible and may change frequently.
- Tempo rubato permitted greater expressivity and freedom in performance.

Dynamics

- Dynamic changes can be sudden or gradual.
- Extremely wide dynamic ranges, from very soft to very loud, add considerably to emotional excitement and intensity.

Tone Color

- Romantic music exhibits a wide range of expressive tone color and sensuous sound.
- The addition of new instruments and the increased size of the orchestra led to new and varied timbres.
- Woodwinds, brass, and percussion instruments played prominent roles in orchestral and operatic works. Composers experimented with timbre through unusual combinations of instruments or by having instruments play in unusual ways.

Melody and Harmony

- Melodies are often long, complex, and highly expressive.
- Recurring melodies and thematic transformation unify longer works.
- Prominent use of chromatic harmony based on pitches that lie outside the prevailing major or minor scale results in harmonies that are rich, colorful, and complex.
- Dissonance is used more freely; resolutions are often delayed to create feelings of yearning, tension, and mystery.
- A wide range of keys and frequent modulations sometimes obscure the sense of an overall tonic or home key.

Texture

- Texture is generally homophonic, but fluctuations of texture may occur to provide contrasts.
- A piece may shift gradually or suddenly from one texture to another.

Form

- Forms are rooted in the classical tradition, but now are more expansive and treated freely.
- New forms and genres were developed, such as the symphonic poem.
- Symphonies are typically longer than those of the classical era.
- Less emphasis is placed on balance, proportion, and resolution of tension than in the classical era.
- Works can be very brief (e.g., Chopin's *Minute* Waltz, Op. 64, No. 1) or long and monumental (e.g. Wagner's four-evening opera cycle *Der Ring des Nibelungen*).

Romantic Performance Practice

- Philharmonic societies appeared, and concert halls grew in size and number.
- Larger concert halls required a greater number of performers to fill the space with sound. Orchestras grew to one hundred or more musicians, reflecting the desire for greater varieties of orchestral timbres and bigger sounds to fill large concert halls.
- Significant technological advances resulted in instruments that could be played louder, higher, lower, and faster than ever before. Performers capitalized on these advances to satisfy audiences who lavished praise on virtuoso performances.
- Cadenzas in concertos were usually written out rather than improvised.

FEATURED COMPOSERS

The romantic period in music lasted from about 1820 to 1900. The long list of important romantic-period composers whose music is still heard today testifies to the richness and variety of this music.

Franz Schubert (1797–1828)
Robert Schumann (1810–1856)
Frédéric Chopin (1810–1849)
Franz Liszt (1811–1886)
Felix Mendelssohn (1809–1847)
Hector Berlioz (1803–1869)
Bedřich Smetana (1824–1884)
Antonín Dvořák (1841–1904)
Peter Ilyich Tchaikovsky (1840–1893)
Johannes Brahms (1833–1897)
Giuseppe Verdi (1813–1901)
Giacomo Puccini (1858–1924)
Richard Wagner (1813–1883)

Beyond the Classroom: Attending a Chamber Music Concert

Watching a small number of musicians in an intimate setting where one can see the interaction of performers as they gesture and glance at one another reveals energy and excitement during the performance that are almost palpable. Some chamber music concerts are held in large concert halls where this give-and-take between the musicians is lost, owing to the distance between the performers and the audience; but in a smaller setting, the audience feels as if it were one with the musicians.

Students often are stunned by the intensity of focus at these concerts. Playing chamber music is difficult, but fun too. It demands extraordinary coordination among the players and great individual concentration. The slightest mistake is glaringly apparent. The audience is intently focused on the players because everything is revealed by the intimacy of the event.

Before attending a chamber music concert, do some research on the composers and the selections on the program. If possible, listen to a recording of the selections beforehand. Doing so will increase your enjoyment of the live event. Unlike popular music that is instantly appealing on one hearing, chamber music unfolds its glories through repeated listening.

When attending a chamber music concert, ask yourself the following questions:

- Who composed the selections that you are hearing? When were the works composed? Might you be able to predetermine some of the stylistic features of the music by considering the composer and the composition date?
- How many movements are within each selection? Can you recognize any familiar forms, such as sonata form, theme and variations, minuet and trio, or rondo?
- How many musicians are performing, and what instruments do they play?
- Listen carefully to the interaction between the performers. Does one player have most of the melodic interest, or is this shared by the ensemble?
- Does one musician in the group, such as the first violinist in a string quartet, function as a kind of conductor?
- Do you notice instances of great technical virtuosity by one or more of the players?
- If you are listening to chamber music composed during the twentieth century, are the musicians asked to provide any unusual sound effects with their instruments or by some other means?

■ Music was a favorite subject of cubist artists of the early twentieth century. In Pablo Picasso's *Three Musicians* (1921), two comic characters from Italian popular theater, Pierrot and Harlequin, are combined with a monklike figure in a two-dimensional space. A year before Picasso painted *Three Musicians,* he designed the costumes for *Pulcinella* (1920), a ballet with music by Igor Stravinsky.

PART VI

We find ourselves confronted with a new logic of music that would have appeared unthinkable to the masters of the past. This new logic has opened our eyes to riches whose existence we never suspected.

— Igor Stravinsky

LEARNING OBJECTIVES

- Summarize the new approaches to tone color, consonance and dissonance, tonality, rhythm, and melody in works by composers such as Stravinsky, Schoenberg, Berg, Webern, and Bartok during the first half of the twentieth century

- Describe the new ways in which music has reached listeners during the twentieth and twenty-first centuries

- Compare and contrast impressionism, primitivism, expressionism, and neoclassicism in music

- Explain how American composers created music that was recognizably American

- Identify the major developments and characteristics of music since 1945

- Discuss the roots of jazz

- Enumerate the features of blues and 12-bar blues form

- Describe the elements and substyles of jazz

- Examine the innovations and new directions in jazz since 1950

- List and describe the elements of a musical

- Examine the sources of the musical and trace its development up to the present

- Discuss the functions and styles of music for film

- Discuss the roots of rock and trace its development

- Examine the characteristics of rock

The Twentieth Century and Beyond

TIME LINE

Twentieth Century and Beyond (1900–2013)

1900–1945	1946–2013

Historical and Cultural Events

1900 Freud, *Interpretation of Dreams*
1905 Einstein, special theory of relativity
1914–1918 First World War
1917 Russian Revolution begins
1929 Great Depression begins
1929–1953 Stalin dictator of Soviet Union
1933 Franklin D. Roosevelt inaugurated
1933 Hitler appointed chancellor of Germany
1939–1945 Second World War
1945 Atomic bomb destroys Hiroshima

1950–1953 Korean War
1953 Crick and Watson discover the structure of DNA
1955–1975 Vietnam War
1959 Fidel Castro becomes premier of Cuba
1963 President Kennedy assassinated
1969 American astronauts land on the moon
1974 President Nixon resigns
1981 Ronald Reagan inaugurated
1990 Reunification of Germany

1991 Dissolution of the Soviet Union
1994 Mandela elected president of South Africa
2001 Terrorist attacks in United States on September 11
2003 War in Iraq begins
2004 Tsunami in Asia
2005 New Orleans flooded
2007 Worldwide recession
2009 Barack Obama inaugurated
2012 Barack Obama reelected

Arts and Letters

1907 Picasso, *Les Demoiselles d'Avignon*
1913 Kirchner, *Street, Berlin*
1914 Kandinsky, *Panels for Edward R. Campbell*
1915 Kafka, *The Metamorphosis*
1922 Eliot, *The Waste Land*
1922 Joyce, *Ulysses*
1929 Faulkner, *The Sound and The Fury*
1932 Picasso, *Girl before a Mirror*
1940–1941 Lawrence, *The Migration Series*
1942 Camus, *The Stranger*

1946 Sartre, *Existentialism and Humanism*
1948 Mailer, *The Naked and the Dead*
1950 Pollock, *One*
1951 Salinger, *Catcher in the Rye*
1955 Baldwin, *Notes of a Native Son*
1962 Warhol, *Campbell's Soup Cans*
1964 Riley, *Hesitate*
1967 Frankenthaler, *Flood*
1974 Solzhenitsyn, *The Gulag Archipelago*

1988 Morrison, *Beloved*
1990 Hockney, *Thrusting Rocks*
1996 Larson, *Rent*
2002 Kiefer, *The Sky Palace*
2002 Parks, *Topdog/Underdog*
2003 Gehry, Walt Disney Concert Hall
2005 Rowling, *Harry Potter and the Half-Blood Prince*
2007 Richter, *4900 Colors*
2012 Morrison, *Home*

Music

1894 Debussy, *Prelude to the Afternoon of a Faun*
1911–1913 Webern, *Five Pieces for Orchestra*
1912 Schoenberg, *Pierrot lunaire*
1913 Stravinsky, *The Rite of Spring*
1917–1922 Berg, *Wozzeck*
1924 Gershwin, *Rhapsody in Blue*
1926 Bessie Smith, *Lost Your Head Blues*
1927 Armstrong, *Hotter Than That*
1930 Stravinsky, *Symphony of Psalms*
1931 Still, *Afro-American Symphony*
1941 Ginastera, *Estancia* Suite
1942 Ellington, *C-Jam Blues*
1943 Bartók, Concerto for Orchestra
1943–1944 Copland, *Appalachian Spring*
1945 Parker, *KoKo*

1946 Benjamin Britten, *Young Person's Guide to the Orchestra*
1946–1948 Cage, *Sonatas and Interludes*
1947 Schoenberg, *A Survivor from Warsaw*
1957 Bernstein, *West Side Story*
1958 Varèse, *Poème électronique*
1960 Penderecki, *Threnody: To the Victims of Hiroshima*
1961 Carter, Double Concerto
1967 The Beatles, *Sgt. Pepper's Lonely Hearts Club Band*
1970 Crumb, *Ancient Voices of Children*

1976 Philip Glass, *Einstein on the Beach*
1985 Zwilich, *Concerto Grosso 1985*
1986 Adams, *Short Ride in a Fast Machine*
1996 Walker, *Lilacs*
1997 Carter, *Shard*
2004 Reich, *You Are (Variations)*
2005 Adams, *Dr. Atomic*
2007 Glass, *Appomattox*
2008 Zwilich, Symphony No. 5
2008 Carter, *Interventions for Piano and Orchestra*
2009 Adams, *City Noir*
2013 Whitacre, *Sainte-Chapelle*

Twentieth-Century Developments

Extremes of violence and progress marked the twentieth century. During the first half of the century, two world wars—in 1914–1918 and 1939–1945—unleashed new weapons of unprecedented destructive force. Between the wars, dictatorships and a global depression caused massive hardship. The second half of the century saw the breakup of colonial empires, an extended cold war between the United States and the Soviet Union (a nation that later dissolved), and armed conflicts around the world. At the same time, rapid economic growth propelled prosperity for many. The principle of equal rights gained ground after protracted struggles by women, African Americans, and others.

Extraordinarily accelerated developments in technology and science transformed politics and society. The Wright brothers made the first powered flight in 1903; sixty-six years later, humans walked on the moon. A flood of new technologies including sound recordings, movies, radio, satellites, computers, and the Internet triggered a continuous revolution in communications. Albert Einstein reshaped our understanding of the universe with his theory of relativity, Sigmund Freud probed the unconscious, and Francis Crick and James Watson discovered the structure of DNA, the basic material of heredity.

Rapid changes and radical breaks with earlier traditions characterized the arts. Shock as a goal was a twentieth-century phenomenon.

In the decade before World War I, Isadora Duncan's modern dance clashed with conventions of classical ballet; Pablo Picasso's cubist paintings distorted figures and objects, showing them from several angles at one time; and Wassily Kandinsky's abstract paintings no longer tried to represent the visual world at all.

In the arts, as in other aspects of life, there was an increased emphasis on pluralism and diversity. Contradictory styles and tendencies coexisted, as conservative and avant-garde works appeared at the same time. Moreover, individual artists, such as Picasso and the composer Igor Stravinsky, often

In *Dance* (1909), by Henri Matisse, there is little sense of perspective or realistic detail. The five dancers are flattened to silhouettes, and colors are mainly limited to large areas of green, blue, and flesh tones.

In the cubist painting *Violin and Grapes* by Pablo Picasso, the violin is flattened into fragmented planes.

Girl Before a Mirror (1932) by Pablo Picasso. The young girl on the left looks at an older, troubled reflection of herself. Here, Picasso reinterprets a traditional theme: a woman seeing a death's-head in her mirror. Twentieth-century composers such as Stravinsky have also reinterpreted earlier musical forms and styles.

alternated between radical and more traditional styles.

Summarizing such an incredibly diverse cultural landscape is difficult, yet any overview must include the following developments:

1. The United States powerfully shaped world culture and entertainment, as well as politics and economics. Cities like Paris and Vienna that had so dominated nineteenth-century and early twentieth-century culture were supplanted by New York and Hollywood.

2. Nonwestern cultures and thought had wide and profound effects on all the arts. Examples include the impact of African sculpture on Picasso, of Japanese design on the architect Frank Lloyd Wright, and of Indian philosophy on the composer John Cage.

3. New technologies stimulated many artists. Sculptors used such materials as plastic, fluorescent lights, and television monitors; architects called for reinforced concrete and steel girders; and musicians exploited audiotape, electric guitars, and computers.

4. Artists explored the varieties of human sexuality with extraordinary frankness.

5. The concerns of women, African Americans, and other minorities were more powerfully represented in the arts than ever before.

6. Many artists expressed alienation, antirationality, nihilism, and dehumanization in their works, partly in reaction against catastrophic wars and massacres. The antihero became a prominent feature of novels, plays, and musical compositions.

7. Since the 1960s, many painters, architects, writers, and musicians have rejected the seriousness of modernism in favor of more pluralistic approaches. "Postmodern" artists have combined different styles, blurred the boundaries between elite and popular culture, and used preexisting images and texts from history, advertising, and the media. The pop artist Andy Warhol, for example, painted multiple Campbell's soup cans and heads of Marilyn Monroe.

Panel for Edwin R. Campbell, No. 3 (left) and *Panel for Edwin R. Campbell, No. 1* (right), by Wassily Kandinsky (1914). Kandinsky stated that his abstract paintings were a "graphic representation of a mood and not of objects."

Street, Berlin (1913) by Ernst Ludwig Kirchner. German expressionist painters used deliberate distortion and violent colors to communicate the tension and anguish of the human psyche. Expressionist composers include Arnold Schoenberg, Alban Berg, and Anton Webern.

Panel 58, "In the North the African American had more educational opportunities," from *The Migration Series* (1940–1941) by the history painter Jacob Lawrence. In his depictions of black experiences in the United States, Lawrence was influenced by the Harlem Renaissance, a cultural movement of the 1920s and 1930s that included African American writers, artists, and musicians. An important musical voice of this movement was William Grant Still, who often made use of spirituals, ragtime, and blues.

1 Musical Styles: 1900–1945

In music, as in the other arts, the early twentieth century was a time of revolt. The years following 1900 saw more fundamental changes in the language of music than any time since the beginning of the baroque era. There were entirely new approaches to the organization of pitch and rhythm and a vast expansion in the vocabulary of sounds, especially percussive sounds. Some compositions broke with tradition so sharply that they were met with violent hostility. The most famous riot in music history occurred in Paris on May 29, 1913, at the premiere of Igor Stravinsky's ballet *Le Sacre du printemps* (*The Rite of Spring*). Police had to be called in as hecklers booed, laughed, made animal noises, and actually fought with those in the audience who wanted to hear Stravinsky's evocation of primitive rites. One music critic complained that *The Rite of Spring* produced a "sensation of acute and almost cruel dissonance" and that "from the first measure to the last, whatever note one expects is never the one that comes." Another wrote, "To say that much of it is hideous in sound is a mild description. . . . It has no relation to music at all as most of us understand the word."

Today, we are amused by the initial failure of some music critics to understand this composition, now recognized as a masterpiece. Chords, rhythms, and percussive sounds that were baffling in 1913 are now commonly heard in jazz, rock, and music for movies and television. But the hostile critics of the early 1900s were right in seeing that a great transformation in musical language was taking place.

From the late 1600s to about 1900, musical structure was governed by certain general principles. As different as the works of Bach, Beethoven, and Brahms may be, they share fundamental techniques of organizing pitches around a central tone. Since 1900, however, no single system has governed the organization of pitch in all musical compositions. Each piece is more likely to have its own unique system of pitch relationships.

In the past, composers depended on the listener's awareness—conscious or unconscious—of the general principles underlying the interrelationship of tones and chords. For example, they relied on the listener's expectation that a dominant chord would normally be followed by a tonic chord. By substituting another chord for the expected one, the composer could create a feeling of suspense, drama, or surprise. Twentieth-century music relies less on preestablished relationships and expectations. Listeners are guided primarily by musical cues within an individual composition. This new approach to the organization of sound makes twentieth-century music fascinating. When we listen openly, with no assumptions about how tones "should" relate, modern music is an adventure.

1900–1945: An Age of Musical Diversity

The range of musical styles during the first half of the twentieth century was vast. The stylistic diversity in the works of Claude Debussy, Igor Stravinsky, Arnold Schoenberg, Alban Berg, Anton Webern, Béla Bartók, Dmitri Shostakovich, Amy Beach, Charles Ives, George Gershwin, William Grant Still, Aaron Copland, and Alberto Ginastera—to name only composers studied here—is a continuation and intensification of the diversity we've seen in romantic music. During the twentieth century, differences among styles were so great that it seems as though composers used different musical languages, not merely different dialects of the same musical language. Radical changes of style occur even within the works of individual composers.

This great variety of musical styles reflected the diversity of life during the early twentieth century. More people were free to choose where to live, how to earn a living, and how to spend their time. The automobile, airplane, telephone, phonograph, movies, and radio all made the world more accessible and expanded the range of experiences.

Through the work of scholars and performers, a wider range of music became available. Composers drew inspiration from an enormous variety of sources, including folk and popular music; the music of Asia, Africa, and Latin America; and European art music from the Middle Ages through the nineteenth century.

Elements of folk and popular music were often incorporated within personal styles. Composers were especially attracted to unconventional rhythms, sounds, and melodic patterns that deviated from the common practice of western music. Folk music was studied more systematically than before, partly because scholars could now record the actual sounds of peasant songs. One of the greatest twentieth-century composers, Béla Bartók, was also a leading scholar of the peasant music of his native Hungary and other parts of eastern Europe. "Studies of folk music in the countryside," he wrote, "are as necessary to me as fresh air is to other people." Bartók's imagination was fired by Hungarian, Bulgarian, and Romanian folksongs, and he believed that peasant music provided "the ideal starting point for a musical renaissance." Other composers stimulated by folklore were Stravinsky, who drew on the folksongs of his native Russia; and Charles Ives, who used American revival hymns, ragtime, and patriotic songs.

During the early twentieth century, non-European music had a deep influence on the music of the west. Western composers and painters were more receptive and sympathetic to Asian and African cultures than they had been earlier. For example, in 1862, Hector Berlioz could say that "the Chinese sing like dogs howling, like a cat screeching when it has swallowed a toad." But in 1889, Debussy was delighted by the Javanese music he heard at the Paris International Exhibition. "If we listen without European prejudice to the charm of their percussion," he wrote later, "we must confess that our percussion is like primitive noises at a country fair." Echoes of the gamelan (Indonesian orchestra) can be heard in the bell-like sounds and five-tone melodic patterns of Debussy's piano piece *Pagodes* (*Pagodas,* 1903). Another French composer influenced by Asian culture was Olivier Messiaen (1908–1992); Messiaen's novel rhythmic procedures grew out of his study of Indian music.

American jazz was another non-European influence on twentieth-century composers. Musicians were fascinated by its syncopated rhythms and improvisational quality, as well as by the unique tone colors of jazz bands. Unlike a string-dominated symphony orchestra, a jazz band emphasizes woodwinds, brasses, and percussion.

Jazz elements were used in works as early as Debussy's *Golliwogg's Cake-Walk* (from the suite *Children's Corner,* 1908) and Stravinsky's *Ragtime* (from *The Soldier's Tale,* 1918). But the peak of jazz influence came during the 1920s and 1930s, with works such as the ballet *Le Création du monde* (*The Creation of the World,* 1923) by Darius Milhaud, the Piano Concerto (1926) by Aaron Copland, and the *Afro-American Symphony* (1931) by William Grant Still. For Americans, jazz idioms represented a kind of musical nationalism, a search for an "American sound." For European composers, the incorporation of jazz rhythms and tone colors represented a kind of musical exoticism. During the 1920s and 1930s, popular composers such as George Gershwin (1898–1937) used jazz and popular elements within "classical" forms. Gershwin's *Rhapsody in Blue* (1924) and his opera *Porgy and Bess* (1934–1935) are well known.

Modern composers can also draw inspiration from a wider historical range of music. During the twentieth century, music from remote times was unearthed by scholars and then published, performed, and recorded. There was a rediscovery of earlier masters such as Perotin and Machaut from the medieval period, Josquin Desprez and Gesualdo from the Renaissance, and Purcell and Vivaldi from the baroque. Some important modern composers have been music historians, like Anton Webern; or experts in the performance of "old" music, like Paul Hindemith.

Music from the past is a fruitful source of forms, rhythms, tone colors, textures, and compositional techniques. Baroque dances like the gavotte and gigue and forms like the passacaglia and concerto grosso are being used again. The long-forgotten harpsichord has been put to new use in compositions such as the Sonata for Flute, Oboe, Cello, and Harpsichord (1952) by the American composer Elliott Carter (1908–2012). In the *Classical Symphony* (1917) by the Russian composer Sergei Prokofiev (1891–1953), a classical orchestra is used, and the texture is light and transparent like much late eighteenth-century music. Occasionally twentieth-century composers used themes of earlier composers, as Benjamin Britten did in *The Young Person's Guide to the Orchestra,* which is based on a theme by Henry Purcell (about 1659–1695).

Modern compositions may be inspired by older music, but this does not mean that they simply imitate past styles. Instead, a traditional form might be used with harmonies, rhythms, melodies, and tone colors that would have been inconceivable before the twentieth century.

Modern composers were also influenced by the music of the immediate past. Nineteenth-century composers such as Wagner, Brahms, Mahler, Richard Strauss, and Mussorgsky were musical points of departure for composers of the early twentieth century. Wagner's music, in particular, was as potent an influence as Beethoven's was for romantic musicians. Composers took Wagner's style as a point of departure, or else they reacted violently against all he stood for.

Characteristics of Twentieth-Century Music

Having reviewed some of the sources of inspiration for twentieth-century music, let's now examine some of its characteristics.

Tone Color During the twentieth century, tone color became a more important element of music than it ever was before. It often had a major role, creating variety, continuity, and mood. In Webern's Orchestral Piece, Op. 10, No. 3 (1913), for example, the use of eerie, bell-like sounds at the beginning and end is vital to the form. If this composition were altered in tone color—say, by being played on a piano—it would lose much. An orchestral work from an earlier period, like Beethoven's Fifth Symphony, suffers less in a piano arrangement.

In modern music, noiselike and percussive sounds are often used, and instruments are played at the very top or bottom of their ranges. Uncommon playing techniques have become normal. For example, the ***glissando,*** a rapid slide up or down a scale, is more widely used. Woodwind and brass players are often asked to produce a fluttery sound by rapidly rolling their tongues while they play. And string players frequently strike the strings with the stick of the bow, rather than draw the bow across the strings.

Percussion instruments have become prominent and numerous, reflecting the twentieth-century interest in unusual rhythms and tone colors. Instruments that became standard during the 1900s include the xylophone, celesta, and wood block, to name a few. Composers occasionally call for noisemakers—typewriters, sirens, automobile brake drums. A piano is often used to add a percussive edge to the sound of an orchestra. Modern composers often draw hard, drumlike sounds from the piano, in contrast to the romantics, who wanted the instrument to "sing." In addition to expanding the percussion section of the orchestra, early twentieth-century composers wrote works for unconventional performing groups in which percussion plays a major role. Well-known examples are Stravinsky's *Les Noces* (*The Wedding,* 1914–1923), for vocal soloists, chorus, four pianos, and percussion; Bartók's Music for Strings, Percussion, and Celesta (1936); and Edgard Varèse's *Ionisation* (1931), which was one of the first works for percussion ensemble.

Modern orchestral and chamber works often sound transparent; individual tone colors are heard clearly. To bring out the individuality of different melodic lines that are played simultaneously, a composer will often assign each line to a different timbre. In general, there is less emphasis on blended sound than there was during the romantic period. Many twentieth-century works are written for nonstandard chamber groups made up of instruments with sharply contrasting tone colors. Stravinsky's *L'Histoire du soldat* (*The Soldier's Tale*, 1918), for example, is scored for violin, double bass, clarinet, bassoon, cornet, trombone, and percussion. Even orchestral works often sound as though they are scored for a group of soloists.

Harmony

Consonance and Dissonance The twentieth century brought fundamental changes in the way chords are treated. Up to about 1900, chords were divided into two opposing types: consonant and dissonant. A consonant chord was stable; it functioned as a point of rest or arrival. A dissonant chord was unstable; its tension demanded onward motion, or resolution to a stable, consonant chord. Traditionally, only the triad, a three-tone chord, could be consonant. All others were considered dissonant. In the nineteenth century, composers came to use ever-more dissonant chords, and they treated dissonances with increasing freedom. By the early twentieth century, the traditional distinction between consonance and dissonance was abandoned in much music. A combination of tones that earlier would have been used to generate instability and expectation might now be treated as a stable chord, a point of arrival. In Stravinsky's words, dissonance "is no longer tied down to its former function" but has become an entity in itself. Thus "it frequently happens that dissonance neither prepares nor anticipates anything. Dissonance is thus no more an agent of disorder than consonance is a guarantee of security."

This "emancipation of dissonance" does not prevent composers from differentiating between chords of greater or lesser tension. Relatively mild-sounding chords may be goals of motion, and harsher chords are used for transitional sounds. But no longer is there a general principle that determines whether a chord is stable or not. It is now entirely up to the composer's discretion. "We find ourself confronted with a new logic of music that would have appeared unthinkable to the masters of the past," wrote Stravinsky. "This new logic has opened our eyes to riches whose existence we never suspected."

New Chord Structures Before 1900, there were general principles governing chord construction: certain combinations of tones were considered chords, and others were not. At the core of traditional harmony is the triad. A triad might be made up of alternate tones of a major scale, such as the first (*do*), third (*mi*), and fifth (*sol*). Within a triad, there are two intervals of a third:

Although the triad often appears in twentieth-century music, it is no longer so fundamental.

Some twentieth-century composers create fresh harmonies by placing one traditional chord against another. Such a combination of two chords heard at the same time is called a ***polychord***.

Copland, *Appalachian Spring*

E major chord
A major chord

A polychord can be heard either as a single block of sound or as two distinct layers, depending on whether the two combined chords contrast in tone color and register.

Another development in twentieth-century music was the use of chordal structures *not* based on triads. One used commonly is the **fourth chord,** in which the tones are a fourth apart, instead of a third. (From *do* to *fa,* or from *re* to *sol,* is an interval of a fourth.)

Ives, *The Cage*

Harmonic resources were also extended through the **tone cluster,** a chord made up of tones only a half step or a whole step apart. A tone cluster can be produced on a piano by striking a group of adjacent keys with the fist or forearm.

Ives, *The Majority*

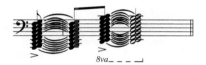

Alternatives to the Traditional Tonal System In addition to creating new chord structures, twentieth-century composers explored alternatives to the traditional tonal system. This system of tonal gravity, known as *tonality* or *key,* governed the organization of pitch from the 1600s to about 1900. By the late nineteenth century, the gravitational pull of a central tonality had been weakened by rapid and frequent key shifts. After 1900, some composers continued to use the traditional system, but others modified it greatly and still others discarded it entirely.

Before looking at new approaches to pitch organization, recall the basic principles of the traditional tonal system. As we saw in Part I ("Elements"), *tonality,* or *key,* refers to the use of a central tone, scale, and chord within a composition. The central tone, called the *tonic* or *keynote* (*do*), is the composition's resting point. The tonic major or minor scale and the tonic triad are built on this tone. Because the tonic triad is stable and restful, compositions almost always ended with it. Next in importance to the tonic triad is the *dominant chord,* which is built on the fifth tone (*sol*) of the tonic scale. There is a special gravitational pull from the dominant chord toward the tonic chord, and the motion from dominant to tonic is the essential chord progression of the tonal system. This cadence provides a strong sense of conclusion, and traditionally it was used to round off melodies, sections, and entire pieces. In summary, the tonal system is based on a central tone, a major or minor scale, and a triad; and there is a special relationship between the tonic and dominant chords.

After 1900, this system was modified in many different ways. The new techniques of pitch organization are so varied as to resist easy generalization. Some compositions have a central tone but are missing other traditional elements, such as the tonic triad, the central major or minor scale, or the dominant-tonic relationship.

To create fresh sounds, composers used scales other than major or minor. For example, they breathed new life into the church modes—scales that had been used widely before 1600 as well as in folksongs of every period. Other scales were borrowed from the musical tradition of lands outside western Europe, and still others were invented by composers.

Twentieth-century compositions are often organized around a central chord other than the triad. Thus, the basic chord may well be one that was considered a dissonance earlier. In some works, the traditional relationship between dominant and tonic triads is replaced by other chord relationships. Melodies, sections, or entire pieces are rounded off not by the usual dominant-tonic cadence, but by other chord progressions.

Another twentieth-century approach to pitch organization is the use of two or more keys at one time: *polytonality*. When only two different keys are used at once—as is most common—the technique is called **bitonality**. A famous bitonal passage occurs in Stravinsky's ballet *Petrushka*, when one clarinet plays in C major and another plays in F sharp major:

In general, the greater the contrast of tone color, register, and rhythm between the different layers of sound, the more we can hear the different keys.

A further departure from tradition is **atonality**, the absence of tonality or key. Atonality was foreshadowed in nineteenth-century works such as Wagner's *Tristan and Isolde*, in which the pull of a central key is weakened by frequent modulations and by liberal use of all twelve tones in the chromatic scale. Arnold Schoenberg wrote the first significant atonal pieces around 1908. He avoided traditional chord progressions in these works and used all twelve tones without regard to their traditional relationship to major or minor scales. But atonality is not a specific technique of composition; each atonal work is structured according to its own needs. (Though the word *atonality* is imprecise and negative, no other term has yet come into general use.)

Before long, Schoenberg felt the need for a more systematic approach to atonal composition, and during the early 1920s he developed the *twelve-tone system,* a new technique of pitch organization. This system gives equal prominence to each of the twelve chromatic tones, rather than singling out one pitch, as the tonal system does. For about twenty years, only Schoenberg and a few disciples used the twelve-tone system, but during the 1950s it came to be used by composers all over the world.

Rhythm The new techniques of organizing pitch were accompanied by new ways of organizing rhythm. The rhythmic vocabulary of music was expanded, with increased emphasis on irregularity and unpredictability. Rhythm is one of the most striking elements of twentieth-century music; it is used to generate power, drive, and excitement.

In the twentieth century, new rhythmic procedures were drawn from many sources, including jazz, folk music from all over the world, and European art music from the Middle Ages through the nineteenth century. The syncopations and complex rhythmic combinations of jazz fired the imagination of Stravinsky and Copland. Béla Bartók used the "free and varied rhythmic structures" of east European peasant music. And irregular phrase structures in Brahms's music inspired rhythmic innovations in Schoenberg's works.

Rapidly changing meters are characteristic of twentieth-century music, whereas baroque, classical, or romantic music maintains a single meter throughout a movement or section. Before the twentieth century, beats were organized into regularly recurring groups; the accented beat came at equal time intervals. Rhythmic irregularities such as syncopations or accents on weak beats were heard against a pervasive meter. But in many twentieth-century compositions, beats are grouped irregularly, and the accented beat comes at unequal time intervals. In some modern music the meter changes with almost every bar, so that we might count *1–2–3, 1–2–3–4–5, 1–2–3–4–5, 1–2–3, 1–2–3–4, 1–2–3–4–5, 1–2–3–4–5–6, 1–2–3–4–5, 1–2, 1–2–3–4–5–6:*

Stravinsky, *Ritual of Abduction from The Rite of Spring*

Count this again quickly and experience some of the rhythmic excitement of twentieth-century music, which often has a rapid and vigorous beat with jolting accents at unexpected times.

The rhythmic resources of twentieth-century music were also expanded through unconventional meters. Along with traditional meters such as duple and triple, modern composers use meters with five or seven beats to the measure. The pulses within a measure of any length may be grouped in irregular, asymmetrical ways. For example, eight quick pulses in a measure may be subdivided 3 + 3 + 2, or **1**–2–3–**4**–5–6–**7**–8, **1**–2–3–**4**–5–6–**7**–8. This meter, common in east European folk music, is used by Bartók in one of his *Six Dances in Bulgarian Rhythm:*

Twentieth-century music often has two or more contrasting, independent rhythms at the same time; this is called **polyrhythm.** Each part of the musical texture goes its own rhythmic way, often creating accents that are out of phase with accents in the other parts. Different meters are used at the same time. For example, one instrument may play in duple meter (*1–2, 1–2*) while another plays in triple meter (*1–2–3, 1–2–3*). Although polyrhythm occasionally occurs in classical and romantic music, it became more common and more complex after 1900. The polyrhythms of jazz strongly influenced composers in the 1920s and 1930s.

Rhythmic repetition of a group of pitches is a unifying technique widely used in twentieth-century music. Many modern compositions contain an **ostinato,** a motive or phrase that is repeated persistently at the same pitch throughout a section. The ostinato may occur in the melody or in the accompaniment. (The accompaniment for the example from Bartók's *Six Dances* has an eight-note ostinato: **1**–2–3–**4**–5–6–**7**–8.) Ostinatos can be found in music from various periods and cultures. In twentieth-century music, they usually serve to stabilize particular groups of pitches.

Melody   The new techniques of pitch and rhythmic organization that we've surveyed had a strong impact on twentieth-century melody. Melody is no longer necessarily tied to traditional chords or to major and minor keys. It may be based on a wide variety of scales, or it may freely use all twelve chromatic tones and have no tonal center. Melody often contains wide leaps that are difficult to sing. Rhythmic irregularity and changing meters tend to make twentieth-century melodies unpredictable. They often consist of a series of phrases that are irregular in length. In general, twentieth-century music relies less than classical and romantic music on melodies that are easy to sing and remember. Melody is as rich and varied as twentieth-century music itself; neither can be classified easily.

2 Music and Musicians in Society since 1900

The twentieth and early twenty-first centuries have seen dramatic changes in how music reaches its listeners. To experience music before the 1890s—that is, before phonographs and recordings first became commercially available—you had to listen to live performers, or sing or play an instrument yourself. Since 1900, recordings, radio, film, television, the Internet, cell phones, and portable digital music players have brought a wider variety of music to more people than ever before.

Early recordings were relatively poor in sound quality and limited to about three minutes per side of a 78-rpm record. During the later twentieth century such technological advances as long-playing records, audiotape, multichannel recording, and compact discs brought higher-fidelity sound reproduction and increased the potential playing time per recording to about seventy-five minutes. In the twenty-first century, you can carry an entire music library in your pocket: digital devices such as the iPod and MP3 players have the capacity for hundreds of hours of music.

Radio broadcasts of live and recorded music began to reach a large audience during the 1920s and 1930s. Very popular in the mid-1930s were live performances by the Benny Goodman band broadcast on NBC's *Let's Dance.* In 1937, the National Broadcasting Company established the NBC Symphony Orchestra, directed by Arturo Toscanini (1867–1957), which was heard weekly over the radio until 1954. In addition, regular radio broadcasts of the Saturday matinee performances of the Metropolitan Opera in New York made opera available to millions of people nationwide. In 2006, the Metropolitan Opera initiated the series Met Live in HD, live opera performances transmitted in high-definition video to movie theaters in the United States and in more than sixty countries worldwide.

The first pairing of music and film took place in Paris in 1895, when short silent movies were accompanied by a pianist. In the late 1920s, films with synchronized sound tracks began to be screened. Since then, film music has been composed in a variety of styles. Most movie music functions as a discreet background to the events onscreen, but some, such as John Williams's score for *Star Wars* (1977), is enjoyed apart from the film, on recordings and in concert halls.

With the advent of commercial television in the early 1950s, broadcast music performances could be seen as well as heard. Christmas eve, 1951, brought the premiere of the first opera created for television, *Amahl and the Night Visitors,* by the Italian American composer Gian-Carlo Menotti (1911–2007). Other television highlights included Leonard Bernstein (1918–1990) conducting the New York Philharmonic orchestra. Public television brought a wide range of music to home viewers, including *Live from Lincoln Center* and *Live from the Met.* The 1980s saw the development of MTV, a cable television network broadcasting rock videos. An innovator in the use of rock video was the singer Michael Jackson (1958–2009), whose *Thriller* (1983) was one of the most widely viewed videos ever made.

Owing to advances in communication, transportation, and technology during the twentieth century, leading musicians come not only from Europe—as in the past—but from almost everywhere in the world. The music world also has become more inclusive, as women and African Americans have become prominent as composers, soloists, and music educators.

Like all people, musicians were affected by the political, economic, and social upheavals of the twentieth century. Adolf Hitler's rise to power in Germany in 1933 had an especially dramatic impact on musicians. Avant-garde, socialist, Jewish, and anti-Nazi musicians were abruptly ousted from their jobs, and their works were no longer performed. Dictatorship, persecution, and the onset of World War II led to the largest migration of artists and intellectuals in history. Many composers, including Stravinsky, Bartók, Schoenberg, and Hindemith, left Europe for the United States. Such distinguished immigrants made enormous contributions to American musical culture. Schoenberg and Hindemith are examples of émigrés who taught in universities and helped train young American composers. Since the early twentieth century, American music has been performed worldwide. By 1918, ragtime and jazz were often heard in Paris, played by African American musicians. Leading composer Igor Stravinsky said that "I know little about American music except that of the music hall, but I consider that unrivaled. It is veritable art and I can never get enough of it to satisfy me." American musical theater and popular song also swept the world. In 1937, Italian composers in Rome elected the American composer George Gershwin—famous for his musicals, popular songs, and orchestral work *Rhapsody in Blue*—to be included as an honorary member of the prestigious Academy of Santa Cecilia. Music in America is explored further in Section 12.

3 Impressionism and Symbolism

Many different musical styles coexisted around the beginning of the twentieth century. Among the most important was impressionism, best represented by the music of the French composer Claude Debussy (1862–1918). We look closely at musical impressionism in Section 4; but first, two related, though slightly earlier, artistic movements in France demand our attention: impressionist painting and symbolist poetry.

French Impressionist Painting

In 1874, a group of French painters including Claude Monet (1840–1926), Auguste Renoir (1841–1919), and Camille Pissarro (1830–1903) had an exhibition in Paris. One painting by Monet titled *Impression: Sunrise*—a misty scene of boats in port—particularly annoyed an art critic, who wrote, "Wallpaper in its embryonic state is more finished than that seascape." Using Monet's title, the critic mockingly called the entire show "the exhibition of the impressionists." The term *impressionist* stuck, but it eventually lost its derisive implication.

Today most of us appreciate impressionist paintings, which colorfully depict the joys of life and the beauties of nature. But during the 1870s, they were seen as formless collections of tiny colored patches—which they are when viewed closely. From a distance, however, the brushstrokes blend and merge into recognizable forms and shimmering colors. Impressionist painters were concerned primarily with effects of light, color, and atmosphere—with impermanence, change, and fluidity. Monet created a series of twenty paintings (1892–1894) showing Rouen Cathedral at different times of the day, from dawn to dusk. In this series, the cathedral's stone facade is desolidified and looks like colored mist. Many impressionist painters preferred to work in the open air rather than in a studio. They were fascinated by outdoor scenes from contemporary life, picnics in the woods, and crowds on Parisian boulevards. But most of all, the impressionists were obsessed with water. Using light pastel colors, they depicted the ripples and waves of the ocean and sailboats on the river Seine.

Impression: Sunrise (1874) by Claude Monet. At an exhibition in Paris in 1874, this painting annoyed a critic who saw it as a formless collection of tiny colored patches. Using Monet's own title, he mockingly called the entire show the "exhibition of the impressionists." Like the impressionist painters, the French composer Claude Debussy was a master at evoking a fleeting mood and misty atmosphere.

French Symbolist Poetry

As impressionist painters broke from traditional depictions of reality, writers called *symbolists* rebelled against the conventions of French poetry. Like the painters, poets such as Stéphane Mallarmé (1842–1898), Paul Verlaine (1844–1896), and Arthur Rimbaud (1854–1891) emphasized fluidity, suggestion, and the purely musical, or sonorous, effects of words. "To *name* an object," insisted Mallarmé, "is to suppress three-quarters of the enjoyment of a poem, which is made up of gradually guessing; the dream is to *suggest* it."

Claude Debussy was a close friend of many symbolist poets, especially Mallarmé, whose poem *L'Après-midi d'un faune* (*The Afternoon of a Faun*) inspired Debussy's most famous orchestral work. Many poems by Verlaine became texts for Debussy's songs. (And, more personally, Verlaine's mother-in-law was Debussy's first piano teacher.) Impressionist painting and symbolist poetry were an impetus for many developments during the twentieth century. Section 4 describes their effect on music.

4 Claude Debussy

The French impressionist composer Claude Debussy (1862–1918) linked the romantic era with the twentieth century. From the early age of ten until he was twenty-two, he studied at the Paris Conservatory, where his teachers regarded him as a talented rebel. In 1884, he won the prestigious Prix de Rome, which subsidized three years of study in Rome. But he left Italy after only two years because he lacked musical inspiration away from his beloved Paris.

Influences on Debussy's work included several visits to Russia, where he worked as a pianist for Tchaikovsky's patroness, Nadezhda von Meck, and formed a lifelong interest

The impressionist Claude Debussy was a master at evoking a fleeting mood and misty atmosphere.

in Russian music. He was also influenced by the Asian music performed at the Paris International Exposition of 1889, and by the ideas and music of Richard Wagner, which were having a profound effect in France and both attracted and repelled him.

For years, Debussy led an unsettled life, earning a small income by teaching piano. His friends were mostly writers, like Stéphane Mallarmé, whose literary gatherings he attended regularly. He was little known to the musical public and not completely sure of himself, though he composed important work, including his String Quartet (1893) and the tone poem *Prelude to the Afternoon of a Faun* (1894). But his opera *Pelléas et Mélisande* (1902) marked a turning point in his career. Although the critics were sharply divided over it, the opera soon caught on, and Debussy was recognized as the most important living French composer.

Debussy led a life filled with financial and emotional crises, constantly borrowing money (he had a craving for luxuries) and having tempestuous love affairs. He was not gifted as a conductor and hated appearing in public, but to maintain his high standard of living he undertook concert tours and presented his music throughout Europe. He died in Paris in 1918.

Debussy's Music

Like the impressionist painters and symbolist poets, Debussy evoked fleeting moods and misty atmosphere, as the titles of his works suggest: *Reflets dans l'eau* (*Reflections in the Water*), *Nuages* (*Clouds*), and *Les Sons et les parfums tournent dans l'air du soir* (*Sounds and Perfumes Swirl in the Evening Air*).

Debussy was often inspired by literary and pictorial ideas, and his music sounds free and spontaneous, almost improvised. His stress on tone color, atmosphere, and fluidity is characteristic of ***impressionism*** in music.

Tone color truly gets unprecedented attention in Debussy's works. They have a sensuous, beautiful sound and subtle but crucial changes of timbre. The entire orchestra seldom plays together to produce massive sound. Instead, there are brief but frequent solos. Woodwinds are prominent; strings and brasses are often muted.

In his music for piano—which includes some of the finest piano works of the twentieth century—he creates hazy sonorities and uses a rich variety of bell and gonglike sounds.

Debussy's treatment of harmony was a revolutionary aspect of musical impressionism. He tends to use a chord more for its special color and sensuous quality than for its function in a standard harmonic progression. He uses successions of dissonant chords that do not resolve. (As a young man, Debussy was once asked which harmonic rules he followed; he replied, simply, "My pleasure.") He freely shifts a dissonant chord up or down the scale; the resulting parallel chords characterize his style:

Debussy, *La Cathédrale engloutie* (*The Sunken Cathedral*)

molto diminuendo

Debussy's harmonic vocabulary is large. Along with traditional three- and four-note chords, he uses five-note chords with a lush, rich sound. Chord progressions that were highly unorthodox when Debussy wrote them soon came to seem mild and natural.

"One must drown the sense of tonality," Debussy wrote. Although he never actually abandoned tonality, Debussy weakened it by avoiding chord progressions that would strongly affirm a key and by using scales in which the main tone is not emphasized. He turned to the medieval church modes and the **pentatonic,** or five-tone, scales heard in Javanese music. A pentatonic scale is produced by five successive black keys of the piano—for example, F♯–G♯–A♯–C♯–D♯.

Debussy's most unusual and tonally vague scale is the **whole-tone scale,** made up of six different notes each a whole step away from the next (C–D–E–F♯–G♯–A♯–C).

Unlike major or minor, the whole-tone scale has no special pull from *ti* to *do* because its tones are all the same distance apart. And because no single tone stands out, the whole-tone scale creates a blurred, indistinct effect.

Debussy, *Voiles* **(Sails)**

The pulse in Debussy's music is sometimes as vague as the tonality. This rhythmic flexibility reflects the fluid, unaccented quality of the French language, and in fact he set French to music very sensitively. He composed fifty-nine art songs, many of which are set to symbolist poems. His only opera, *Pelléas et Mélisande,* is an almost word-for-word setting of a symbolist play by Maurice Maeterlinck. It is the essence of musical impressionism: nebulous, mysterious, dreamlike, with a discreet, understated orchestral accompaniment.

Although not large, Debussy's output is remarkably varied. In addition to his opera and art songs, it includes works for piano, orchestra, and chamber ensembles. Echoes of his music can be heard in the works of many composers during the first two decades of the twentieth century; but no other important musician can so fairly be described as an impressionist. Even the composer most similar to him, his younger French contemporary Maurice Ravel (1875–1937), wrote music with greater clarity of form. Debussy's style was both a final expression of romanticism and the beginning of a new era.

Prélude à l'Après-midi d'un faune (*Prelude to the Afternoon of a Faun;* 1894)

"The music of this Prelude," wrote Debussy of his *Prelude to the Afternoon of a Faun,* "is a very free illustration of the beautiful poem by Stéphane Mallarmé, *The Afternoon of a Faun.*" This poem evokes the dreams and erotic fantasies of a pagan forest creature who is half man, half goat. While playing a "long solo" on his flute, the intoxicated faun tries to recall whether he actually carried off two beautiful nymphs or only dreamed of doing so. Exhausted by the effort, he falls back to sleep in the sunshine.

Debussy intended his music to suggest "the successive scenes through which pass the desires and dreams of the faun in the heat of this afternoon." The subtle, sensuous timbres of this miniature tone poem were new in Debussy's day. Woodwind solos, muted horn calls, and harp glissandos create a rich variety of delicate sounds. The dynamics are usually subdued, and only rarely does the entire orchestra—from which trombones, trumpets, and timpani are excluded—play at one time. The music often swells sensuously and then subsides in voluptuous exhaustion.

The prelude begins with an unaccompanied flute melody; its vague pulse and tonality make it dreamlike and improvisatory. This flute melody is heard again and again, faster, slower, and against a variety of lush chords. Though the form of the prelude may be thought of as A B A', one section blends with the next. It has a continuous ebb and flow. The fluidity and weightlessness typical of impressionism are found in this music. We are never tempted to beat time to its subtle rhythms. The prelude ends magically with the main melody, played by muted horns, seeming to come from far off. The bell-like tones of antique cymbals finally evaporate into silence. With all its new sounds and musical techniques, the piece has aptly been described as a "quiet revolution" in the history of music.

Listening Outline

DEBUSSY, *Prélude à l'Après-midi d'un faune*

At a very moderate tempo, A B A' form, E major
3 flutes, 2 oboes, 1 English horn, 2 clarinets, 2 bassoons, 4 French horns, 2 harps, antique cymbals, 1st violins, 2d violins, violas, cellos, double basses
(Duration, 9:40)

A

0:00   **1. a.** Solo flute, *p*, main melody.

Harp glissando; soft horn calls. Short pause. Harp glissando; soft horn calls.

0:43   **b.** Flute, *p*, main melody; tremolo strings in background. Oboe, *p*, continues melody. Orchestra swells to *f*. Solo clarinet fades into

1:35   **c.** Flute, *p*, main melody varied and expanded; harp and muted strings accompany. Flute melody comes to quiet close.

2:48   **2. a.** Clarinet; harp and cellos in background.

3:16   **b.** New oboe melody.

Violins take up melody, crescendo and accelerando to climax. Excitement subsides. Ritardando. Clarinet, *p*, leads into

B

4:33   **3. a.** Woodwinds, *p*, legato melody in long notes. Crescendo.

5:16   **b.** Strings repeat melody; harps and pulsating woodwinds in background, crescendo. Decrescendo. Horns, *p*, solo violin, *p*, clarinet, oboe.

A'

6:21   **4. a.** Harp accompanies flute, p, main melody in longer notes. Oboe, staccato woodwinds.

6:56   **b.** Harp accompanies oboe, p, main melody in longer notes. English horn, harp glissando.

7:39   **5. a.** Antique cymbals, bell-like tones. Flutes, p, main melody. Solo violins, pp, in high register.

8:16   **b.** Flute and solo cello, main melody; harp in background.

8:45   **c.** Oboe, p, brings melody to close. Harps, p.

9:10   **d.** Muted horns and violins, ppp, beginning of main melody sounding far off. Flute, antique cymbals, and harp; delicate tones fade into silence.

5 Neoclassicism

From about 1920 to 1950, the music of many composers, including Igor Stravinsky and Paul Hindemith (1895–1963), reflected an artistic movement known as **_neoclassicism._** Neoclassicism is marked by emotional restraint, balance, and clarity; neoclassical compositions use musical forms and stylistic features of earlier periods, particularly of the eighteenth century. Stravinsky summed it up: "I attempted to build a new music on eighteenth-century classicism." Neoclassical music is not merely a revival of old forms and styles; it uses earlier techniques to organize twentieth-century harmonies and rhythms.

"Back to Bach" was the slogan of this movement, which reacted against romanticism and impressionism. (Because many neoclassical compositions were modeled after Bach's music, the term _neobaroque_ might have been more appropriate.) Neoclassical composers turned away from program music and the gigantic orchestras favored at the turn of the century. They preferred absolute (nonprogrammatic) music for chamber groups. This preference for smaller performing groups partly reflected economic necessity: during the post–World War I period, economic conditions were so bad in parts of Europe that there was little money to hire large orchestras. Favoring clear polyphonic textures, composers wrote fugues, concerti grossi, and baroque dance suites. Most neoclassical music was tonal and used major and minor scales. Still, neoclassicism was more an attitude than a style. Schoenberg wrote minuets and gigues using his twelve-tone system. And though neoclassical composers referred to many past styles, their works sound completely modern. They play on the delightful tension between our expectations about old forms and styles and the novel harmonies and rhythms.

Neoclassicism was an important trend in other arts too. The poet T. S. Eliot often quoted and alluded to earlier writers. Picasso, who designed sets for Stravinsky's first neoclassical work, _Pulcinella_ (1920), went through a phase during which he created paintings that show the influence of ancient Greek art. Picasso described the neoclassical attitude by saying that artists "must pick out what is good for us where we find it. When I am shown a portfolio of old drawings, for instance, I have no qualms about taking anything I want from them."

6 Igor Stravinsky

Even during his lifetime, Igor Stravinsky (1882–1971) was a legendary figure. His once revolutionary works had already become modern classics and he influenced three generations of composers and other artists. Cultural giants like Picasso and T. S. Eliot were his

Igor Stravinsky in a sketch by Picasso.

friends. President John F. Kennedy honored him at a White House dinner in his eightieth year.

Stravinsky, who was born in Russia, near St. Petersburg, grew up in a musical atmosphere, and studied with Nikolai Rimsky-Korsakov. He had his first important opportunity in 1909, when the great impresario Sergei Diaghilev heard his music. Diaghilev was the director of the Russian Ballet, an extremely influential troupe which employed great painters as well as dancers, choreographers, and composers. Diaghilev first asked Stravinsky to orchestrate some piano pieces by Chopin as ballet music and then, in 1910, commissioned an original ballet, *The Firebird,* which was immensely successful. A year later (1911), Stravinsky's second ballet, *Petrushka,* was performed, and Stravinsky was hailed as a modern master. His orchestral colors delighted sophisticated Parisians. When his third ballet, *The Rite of Spring,* had its premiere in Paris in 1913, a riot erupted in the audience—spectators were shocked and outraged by its pagan primitive, harsh dissonance, percussiveness, and pounding rhythms. But it too was recognized as a masterpiece and influenced composers all over the world.

During World War I, Stravinsky sought refuge in Switzerland. After the armistice, he moved to France, his home until the onset of World War II, when he came to the United States. In the 1920s and 1930s, he was an international celebrity, constantly touring in Europe and the United States; and his compositions—which had originally been inspired by Russian folk music—became cooler and more objective. During his years in the United States (he lived outside Los Angeles), his young musical assistant Robert Craft familiarized him with the works of Schoenberg, Berg, and Webern. In the 1950s, Stravinsky astonished his followers by adopting Schoenberg's twelve-tone system. Unlike Schoenberg and Bartók, Stravinsky got well-paying commissions for his work and was an astute businessman. He also loved order and discipline and said that he composed "every day, regularly, like a man with banking hours." In his seventies and eighties, he was still touring, conducting his rich and intense late works. He also, for the first time in fifty years, returned to Russia and bared his soul to a group of Soviet composers: "The smell of the Russian earth is different. . . . A man has one birthplace, one fatherland, one country."

Stravinsky's Music

Stravinsky's extensive output includes compositions of almost every kind, for voices, instruments, and the stage; and his innovations in rhythm, harmony, and tone color had an enormous influence.

Stravinsky's development shows dramatic changes of style. His three early ballets— *The Firebird* (1910), *Petrushka* (1911), and *The Rite of Spring* (1913)—call for very large orchestras and draw on Russian folklore and folk tunes. During World War I, he wrote for chamber groups using unconventional combinations of instruments and incorporating ragtime rhythms and popular dances (an example is *The Soldier's Tale,* 1918). From about 1920 to 1951 (his "neoclassical" period), he was inspired largely by eighteenth-century music. His ballet *Pulcinella* (1920) was based partly on the music of Giovanni Battista Pergolesi (1710–1736), his opera *The Rake's Progress* (1951) was modeled on Mozart. Stravinsky's neoclassical works emphasize restraint, balance, and wit, and are far removed from the violence of *The Rite of Spring.* But his shift to the twelve-tone system in the 1950s was an even more dramatic change of approach because until then all of his music had a clear tonal center. Inspired by Anton Webern (1883–1945), Stravinsky now wrote brief works in which melodic lines were "atomized" into short fragments in continually changing tone colors and registers.

Despite such stylistic changes, all of his music has an unmistakable "Stravinsky sound." Tone colors are dry and clear, and the beat is strong. His music abounds in changing and irregular meters; sometimes several meters are heard at once. Ostinatos, or repeated rhythmic patterns, frequently unify sections of a piece. His treatment of musical form is also unique: rather than connecting themes with bridge passages, he makes abrupt shifts, but his music nevertheless sounds unified and continuous. The effectiveness of his rhythms, chords, and melodies often depends largely on his orchestration, in which highly contrasting tone colors are frequently combined.

Stravinsky's music has rich, novel harmonies—he makes even conventional chords sound unique through spacing, doubling, and the orchestration of their tones.

Stravinsky drew on a wide range of styles, from Russian folksongs to baroque melodies, from Renaissance madrigals to tango rhythms. He sometimes used existing music to create original compositions, but more often the music is entirely his own while vaguely suggesting a past style.

Le Sacre du printemps (The Rite of Spring, 1913)

Few compositions have had so powerful an impact on twentieth-century music as *Le Sacre du printemps* (*The Rite of Spring*), Stravinsky's third ballet score for the Russian Ballet. Its harsh dissonances, percussive orchestration, rapidly changing meters, violent offbeat accents, and ostinatos fired the imagination of many composers. The idea for *The Rite of Spring* came to Stravinsky as a "fleeting vision," while he was completing *The Firebird* in St. Petersburg in 1910. "I saw in imagination a solemn pagan rite: wise elders, seated in a circle, watching a young girl dance herself to death. They were sacrificing her to propitiate the god of spring." Later in life, Stravinsky remarked that the "most wonderful event" of every year of his childhood was the "violent Russian spring that seemed to begin in an hour and was like the whole earth cracking."

Stravinsky's interest in so-called primitive or preliterate culture was shared by many artists and scholars in the early 1900s. In 1907, Picasso's violent and path-breaking painting *Les Demoiselles d'Avignon* reflected the influence of African sculpture. In 1913—the same year as *The Rite of Spring*—Freud published *Totem and Taboo,* a study of "resemblances between the psychic lives of savages and neurotics." But *primitivism*— the deliberate evocation of primitive power through insistent rhythms and percussive sounds—did not have a lasting impact on early twentieth-century music. Stravinsky never again wrote anything like *The Rite of Spring;* and few primitivistic compositions have entered the repertoire.

The Rite of Spring has two large parts, which are subdivided into sections that move at various speeds. These subsections follow each other without pause. The titles of the dances suggest their primitive subject matter. Part I, *The Adoration of the Earth,* consists of (1) *Introduction;* (2) *Omens of Spring: Dances of the Youths and Maidens;* (3) *Ritual of Abduction;* (4) *Spring Rounds;* (5) *Games of the Rival Tribes;* (6) *Procession of the Wise Elder;* (7) *Adoration of the Earth;* (8) *Dance of the Earth.* Part II, *The Sacrifice,* consists of (1) *Introduction;* (2) *Mysterious Circles of the Young Girls;* (3) *Glorification of the Chosen Maiden;* (4) *Evocation of the Ancestors;* (5) *Ritual of the Ancestors;* (6) *Sacrificial Dance.* Each of the two large parts begins with a slow introduction and ends with a frenzied, climactic dance.

The Rite of Spring is written for an enormous orchestra including eight horns, four tubas, and a very important percussion section made up of five timpani, bass drum, tambourine, tam-tam, triangle, antique cymbals, and a guiro (a notched gourd scraped with a stick). The melodies of *The Rite of Spring* are folklike. Like ancient Russian folk tunes, they have narrow ranges, and they are made up of fragments that are repeated with slight changes in rhythm and pitch. Many individual chords are repeated, and

Les Demoiselles d'Avignon (1907) by Picasso reflects the influence of African sculpture.

each change of harmony produces a great impact. This melodic and harmonic repetition gives the music a ritualistic, hypnotic quality. Rhythm is a vital structural element in *The Rite of Spring;* it has a life of its own, almost independent of melody and harmony. Today, *The Rite of Spring* is performed more frequently as a concert piece than as a ballet.

We now take a closer look at four sections of *The Rite of Spring: Introduction, Omens of Spring—Dances of the Youths and Maidens,* and *Ritual of Abduction,* which open Part I; and *Sacrificial Dance,* which concludes Part II.

Part I:
Introduction

For Stravinsky, the *Introduction* to Part I represented "the awakening of nature, the scratching, gnawing, wiggling of birds and beasts." It begins with the strangely penetrating sound of a solo bassoon straining at the top of its register. As though improvising, the bassoon repeats a fragment of a Lithuanian folk tune in irregular ways.

Soon other woodwind instruments join the bassoon with repeated fragments of their own. The impression of improvisation is strengthened by the absence of a clearly defined pulse or meter. Dissonant, unconventional chord structures are used. Toward the end of the *Introduction,* different layers of sounds—coming mostly from woodwinds and brasses—are piled on top of each other, and the music builds to a piercing climax. But suddenly, all sound is cut off; only the solo bassoon forlornly repeats its opening melody. Then the violins, playing pizzicato, introduce a repeated four-note "ticking" figure. This figure later serves as an ostinato in *Omens of Spring—Dances of the Youths and Maidens,* which immediately follows the *Introduction.*

Part I:
Omens of Spring—Dances of the Youths and Maidens

Sounding almost like drums, the strings pound out a dissonant chord. There are unexpected and irregular accents whose violence is heightened by jabbing sounds from the eight horns. This is the way the passage might be counted (with a rapid pulse): 1–2–3–**4,** 1–2–3–4, 1–**2**–3–**4,** 1–2–3–4, 1–**2**–3–4, **1**–**2**–3–4, **1**–2–3–4, 1–2–3–4. The unchanging dissonant harmony is a polychord that combines two different traditional chords. Successive melodic fragments soon join the pounding chord and other repeated figures. The melodic fragments, played by brass and woodwind instruments, are narrow in range and are repeated over and over with slight variations. The rhythmic activity is ceaseless and exciting, and gradually more and more instruments are added.

It's interesting to contrast Stravinsky's musical techniques in *Dances of the Youths and Maidens* with those of a classical movement in sonata form. A classical movement grows out of conflicts between different keys; this section of *The Rite of Spring* is based almost entirely on repetition of a few chords. Themes in a classical movement are developed through different keys, varied, and broken into fragments that take on new emotional meanings. In *Dances of the Youths and Maidens,* Stravinsky simply repeats melodic fragments with relatively slight variation. To create movement and growth, he relies instead on variations of rhythm and tone color—a technique that can be traced back to nineteenth-century Russian musical tradition.

Part I:
Ritual of Abduction

The frenzied *Ritual of Abduction* grows out of the preceding section and is marked by violent strokes on the timpani and bass drum. Enormous tension is generated by powerful accents and rapid changes of meter (see the music example on page 302). This section of *The Rite of Spring* closes with high trills in the strings and flutes.

Listening Outline

STRAVINSKY, *Le Sacre du printemps*

Part I: *Introduction, Omens of Spring—Dances of the Youths and Maidens, Ritual of Abduction*

2 piccolos, 3 flutes, alto flute, 4 oboes, English horn, E flat clarinet, 3 clarinets, 2 bass clarinets, 4 bassoons, 2 contrabassoons, 8 French horns, small trumpet in D, 4 trumpets, 3 trombones, 3 tubas, timpani, bass drum, triangle, antique cymbals, 1st violins, 2d violins, violas, cellos, double basses
(Duration, 7:24)

Introduction

0:00   **1. a.** High solo bassoon, repeated folksong fragment in changing meters, joined by French horn, *mp*, then clarinets and bass clarinets, *p*.

0:43   **b.** English horn, new melodic fragment; high bassoon; English horn, melodic fragment, bassoons accompany in faster rhythm.

1:12   **c.** Pizzicato strings, oboe, repeated notes introduce high clarinet melody.

1:24   **d.** Oboe phrase, *f*, high flutes accompany; English horn phrase, *mf*, bass clarinets accompany; flutes and English horn move in even rhythm; violin trill joins.

1:53   **e.** Pizzicato cello pulsations, rhythmic activity quickens, rapid shifts between large and small wind groups; clarinet, repeated descending phrase.

2:18   **f.** Oboe with rapid alto flute accompaniment; piercing high clarinet, *ff*, joins; music builds to *ff* climax, different layers of woodwind and brass sound piled on each other.

2:52   **2. a.** Sudden *p*, solo high bassoon, opening fragment; clarinet trill, joined by

3:03   **b.** Pizzicato violins, "ticking" ostinato figure.

Low held tone in bass clarinet; high chord in violins; pizzicato violins, "ticking" ostinato figure.

Omens of Spring—Dances of the Youths and Maidens

3:22   **3. a.** Sudden *f*, strings, repeated dissonant polychord with punctuations in French horns, irregular accents, moderate tempo, duple meter.

3:29   **b.** English horn, *mf*, "ticking" ostinato figure.

3:39   **c.** Strings, *f*, repeated dissonant polychord with punctuations in French horns; piccolos, trumpets, oboes join.

3:49   **d.** Pizzicato basses and cellos introduce loud, rapid interjections in high trumpet and piccolos;

3:54   **e.** Strings, *f*, repeated dissonant polychord with punctuations in French horns.

4:02   **f.** Bassoons join with melodic fragment played staccato, string pulsations; trombone joins;

Bassoons repeat staccato melodic fragment; oboes, flute, and trombone imitate;

4:28   **g.** Sudden break in pulse, French horns, *f*, sustained tone, timpani strokes, tubas, *ff*, low sustained tone;

4:33   **h.** High "ticking" ostinato figure descends to English horn, *mf*, trills in winds and strings; loud "ticking" ostinato in violins and trumpet.

4:49   **i.** French horn, *mp*, joins with legato melody; flute answers;

Horn

descending figure in oboes and trumpet.

5:07   **j.** Legato melody in alto flute; legato melody in high flutes, pizzicato strings accompany.

5:20   **k.** Trumpets join with repeated-note melody; triangle joins.

Trumpets

5:34   **l.** Sudden *p*, strings and syncopated accents introduce piccolo, high legato melodic fragment; full orchestra, melodic figures repeated with long crescendo to

Ritual of Abduction

6:10   **4. a.** Sustained brass chord, violent strokes on timpani and bass drum; high trumpet, rapid-note fanfare, very fast tempo, changing meters.

6:23   **b.** Horn calls, *f*, alternate with piccolo and flutes, rapid-note fanfare; timpani, bass drum join; crescendo to

6:43   **c.** High woodwinds and brasses, *ff*, staccato passage in changing meters; horn calls; full orchestra, *ff*.

6:59   **d.** Timpani accents punctuate staccato phrases with changing meters in trumpets and high winds; timpani accents punctuate repeated rapid figure in strings.

7:18   **e.** Trill in violins, *ff*, accented chords; trill in flutes, *p*.

Part II: *Sacrificial Dance*

Section A
0:00

Sacrificial Dance is the overwhelming climax of the work. It consists of sections that can be outlined as follows: A B A′ C A″ (very brief) C A‴. In the opening section (A), explosive, percussive chords fight brutal blows on the timpani. The time signature changes with almost every bar: $\frac{3}{16}$ $\frac{2}{16}$ $\frac{3}{16}$ $\frac{2}{8}$ $\frac{2}{16}$ $\frac{3}{16}$. The rapid pulse and irregular, jolting accents create intense excitement.

Section B
0:27

The second section (B) begins with a sudden drop in dynamic level as a single chord is repeated obsessively. Brief silences between these repeated chords urge the listener to supply accents.

Section C
2:17

Sacrificial Dance available in Connect Music

Section C features brasses and percussive sounds from five timpani, a tam-tam (gong), and a bass drum. *Sacrificial Dance* glorifies the power of rhythm, as does the entire *Rite of Spring*.

7 Expressionism

Much music of the twentieth century reflects an artistic movement called *expressionism,* which stressed intense, subjective emotion. It was largely centered in Germany and Austria from 1905 to 1925. Expressionist painters, writers, and composers explored

The Scream (1893), by the Norwegian expressionist Edvard Munch. Expressionist painters reacted against French impressionism; they often used jarring colors and grotesquely distorted shapes to explore the subconscious.

inner feelings rather than depicting outward appearances. They used deliberate distortion to assault and shock their audience, to communicate the tensions and anguish of the human psyche. Expressionism grew out of the same intellectual climate as Freud's studies of hysteria and the unconscious. German expressionist painting was in part a reaction against the pleasant subjects, delicate pastel colors, and shimmering surfaces of French impressionism.

The expressionists rejected conventional prettiness. Their works may seem "ugly" in their preoccupation with madness and death. Expressionist painters such as Ernst Ludwig Kirchner, Emil Nolde, Edvard Munch, and Oskar Kokoschka often use jarring colors and grotesquely distorted shapes. Expressionist art tends to be fragmentary; the scenes of an expressionist play may be episodic and discontinuous. Expressionism is also an art concerned with social protest. It movingly conveyed the anguish felt by the poor and oppressed. Many expressionists opposed World War I and used art to depict their horror of bloodshed.

There was close communication among expressionist writers, painters, and musicians. Many were creative in more than one art form. The painter Wassily Kandinsky wrote essays, poetry, and plays; the composer Schoenberg painted and even participated in the shows of expressionist artists.

Twentieth-century musical expressionism grows out of the emotional turbulence in the works of romantics like Wagner and Mahler. Immediate precedents for expressionism are the operas *Salome* (1905) and *Elektra* (1908) by Richard Strauss, in which extremely chromatic and dissonant music depicts perversion and murder. In Sections 8, 9, and 10, we study four expressionistic compositions: *Pierrot lunaire,* Op. 21 (*Moonstruck Pierrot,* 1912), and *A Survivor from Warsaw,* Op. 46 (1947), by Schoenberg; the opera *Wozzeck* (1917–1922), by Alban Berg; and Five Pieces for Orchestra, Op. 10 (1911– 1913), by Anton Webern. These works all stress harsh dissonance and fragmentation, and exploit extreme registers and unusual instrumental effects. All four avoid tonality and traditional chord progressions. Both *A Survivor from Warsaw* and *Wozzeck* depict a nightmarish world and express a profound empathy with the poor and tormented.

8 Arnold Schoenberg

Arnold Schoenberg (1874–1951), who was born in Vienna, was an almost entirely self-taught musician. He acquired his profound knowledge of music by studying scores, playing in amateur chamber groups, and going to concerts. After he lost his job as a bank clerk at age twenty-one, he devoted himself to music, earning a poor living conducting a choir of industrial workers and orchestrating popular operettas. Performances of his own early works met with hostility from the conservative Viennese public. In 1904, Schoenberg began to teach music theory and composition in Vienna, and he inspired love and loyalty in his students, two of whom—Alban Berg and Anton Webern—themselves became leading composers.

Around 1908 Schoenberg took the revolutionary step of abandoning the traditional tonal system. He was a man possessed ("I have a mission," he said; "I am but the loudspeaker of an idea."). His productivity between 1908 and 1915 was incredible.

Arnold Schoenberg developed the twelve-tone system, which offered the composer a new way of organizing pitch in a composition.

For the next eight years, however, he searched for a way to organize his musical discoveries and published nothing. Then, in 1921, he told a student, "I have made a discovery which will ensure the supremacy of German music for the next hundred years." From 1923 to 1925 Schoenberg published compositions using his new twelve-tone system. Although his music did not find a large audience, many important musicians respected it. At the age of fifty-one, he received an appointment at the Prussian Academy of Arts in Berlin.

After the Nazis seized power in Germany, Schoenberg, who was Jewish, was dismissed from his post. The same year, 1933, he and his family came to the United States, where he joined the music faculty at the University of California in Los Angeles. Schoenberg felt neglected in America: his music was rarely performed and he was financially unsuccessful. But after his death, the twelve-tone system was used increasingly by composers throughout the world. It remains an important influence to this day.

Schoenberg's Music

"I claim the distinction of having written a truly new music which, based upon tradition as it is, is destined to become tradition." This assertion by Schoenberg contains a great deal of truth: his musical language was indeed new, but it had evolved from the past and was eventually widely adopted.

His early works, like the string sextet *Verklärte Nacht* (*Transfigured Night,* 1899), show many features of the late romantic style. Some of them—such as the immense cantata *Gurrelieder* (*Songs of Gurre,* 1901)—use very large orchestras; dissonances and angular melodies create a feeling of subjectivity; chromatic harmony is prominent; and the central tonality is weakened as the music moves through remote keys. But from 1903 to 1907, he departed further from romanticism, and in the *Chamber Symphony,* Op. 9 (1906), he uses whole-tone scales and fourth chords.

Atonality Around 1908, Schoenberg began to write atonal music. *Atonality*—the absence of key—evolved from his earlier use of chromatic harmony and the chromatic scale. But in his atonal works, all twelve tones are used without regard for their traditional relationship to major or minor scales. Dissonances are "emancipated" from the necessity of resolving to consonances. *Atonality* does not imply a single system of composition: each atonal work has its own means of achieving unity, and a piece usually grows out of a few short motives transformed in many different ways.

Schoenberg's atonal compositions include Five Pieces for Orchestra, Op. 16 (1909); and *Pierrot lunaire,* Op. 21 (*Moonstruck Pierrot,* 1912). They are characterized by jagged melodies, novel instrumental effects, extreme contrasts of dynamics and register, and irregular phrases. *Pierrot lunaire* and other works by Schoenberg call for an unusual style of vocal performance—**Sprechstimme,** literally *speech-voice*—halfway between speaking and singing. Schoenberg's atonal style was soon adopted by his students Berg and Webern. Their early atonal works, like Schoenberg's, tended to be very short. Without a musical system like tonality, extended compositions were possible only when there was a long text to serve as an organizing force.

The Twelve-Tone System   In the early 1920s, Schoenberg developed a more systematic method of organizing atonal music; he called it the "method of composing with twelve tones." He partly applied this new technique in Five Piano Pieces, Op. 23, and Serenade, Op. 24, and then fully elaborated it in Suite for Piano, Op. 25 (all composed from 1920 to 1923). The twelve-tone system enabled Schoenberg to write more extended compositions, such as the monumental Variations for Orchestra (1928) and the unfinished opera *Moses und Aron* (*Moses and Aaron;* 1930–1932). From 1933 to 1951, in the United States, he used the twelve-tone system in many rich and varied works.

The ***twelve-tone system*** is a twentieth-century alternative to tonality, a new way of organizing pitch in a composition. It is a systematized form of atonality that gives equal importance to each of the twelve chromatic tones. In a twelve-tone composition, the ordering or unifying idea is called a ***tone row, set,*** or ***series.**** The composer creates a unique tone row for each piece (the choice of rows is practically limitless because there are 479,001,600 possible arrangements of the twelve tones), and the row is the source of every melody and chord in it. No pitch occurs more than once within a row. This prevents any tone from receiving too much emphasis.

A composition is built by manipulating the tone row, which may be presented in four basic forms: forward (original form), backward (retrograde), upside down (inversion), and backward and upside down (retrograde inversion). (See the illustrations below that show the row used in Suite for Piano, Op. 25.) Any of the four forms of a row may be shifted to any pitch level—that is, it may begin on any of the twelve tones while keeping the original pattern of intervals. Thus there are forty-eight (twelve times four) possible versions of a row.

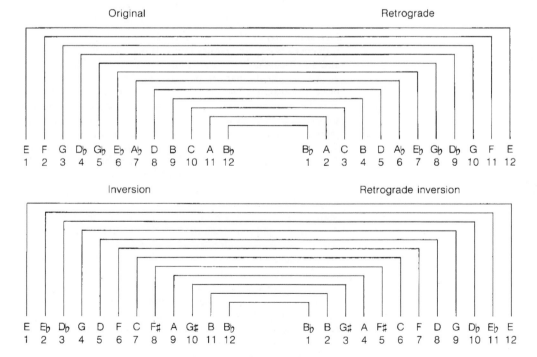

Each tone of a row may also be placed in any register; this enhances the flexibility of the system and may partially explain why so many twelve-tone melodies have very

---

*Because of its systematic use of a *series* of tones, the twelve-tone method is also referred to as *serial technique.*

wide leaps. Finally, the tones of a row may be presented one after another (as on a melodic line) or simultaneously (as chords). Here is the row from the Suite for Piano treated in two different ways.

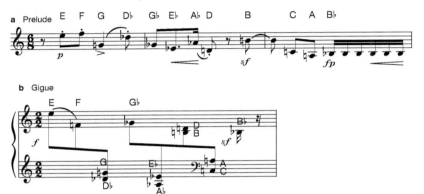

Two treatments of the tone row in Schoenberg's Suite for Piano, Op. 25.

We now study two works by Schoenberg: the "freely" atonal *Pierrot Lunaire*, Op. 21 (*Moonstruck Pierrot*; 1912); and the twelve-tone cantata *A Survivor from Warsaw*, Op. 46 (1947), composed almost thirty-five years later.

Pierrot Lunaire, Op. 21 (*Moonstruck Pierrot*; 1912)

Like Stravinsky's *The Rite of Spring*, composed around the same time, Schoenberg's *Pierrot lunaire*, or *Moonstruck Pierrot*, is a revolutionary masterpiece that profoundly influenced twentieth-century music. It is a cycle of twenty-one songs for female voice and an ensemble of five musicians who play eight instruments: piano, cello, violin-viola, flute-piccolo, clarinet–bass clarinet. The instrumental ensemble varies with each piece. For example, *The Sick Moon* (No. 7) uses only the flute; *Prayer to Pierrot* (No. 9) uses the piano and clarinet; and *O Ancient Scent* (No. 21) uses all eight instruments. A song cycle accompanied by a chamber music ensemble—rather than by piano alone—represented a departure from convention. Another novelty was the pervasive use of *Sprechstimme*, the technique of half speaking, half singing developed by Schoenberg. The rhythms and pitches of the words are precisely notated, but the voice touches the notated pitch only momentarily and then departs from it.

Pierrot lunaire is based on weird poems written in 1884 by the Belgian poet Albert Giraud and later translated into German by Schoenberg's friend Otto Erich Hartleben. Many of the poems deal with the puppet Pierrot, a tragic clown character derived from the centuries-old *commedia dell'arte* (Italian improvised theater). Pierrot, who represented the isolated modern artist, was a favorite subject for artists, writers, and musicians of the late nineteenth century and the early twentieth century.

The cycle divides into three groups of seven songs that evoke a surrealistic night vision. In the first group, Pierrot, a poet, drunk on moonlight, becomes increasingly deranged. The second group is a nightmare filled with images of death and martyrdom. In the third group, Pierrot seeks refuge from the nightmare through clowning, sentimentality, and nostalgia. *Pierrot lunaire* is expressionist in its weird text, eerie *Sprechstimme*, unique instrumental effects, and atonal musical language. We focus on the opening piece of the cycle, *Mondestrunken* (*Moondrunk*).

Mondestrunken (*Moondrunk*)

Scored for voice, piano, flute, violin, and cello, *Mondestrunken* (*Moondrunk*) begins the fantastic nocturnal journey. Its text depicts moonlight as a sacramental "wine we drink through the eyes." The poet (Pierrot) becomes intoxicated as moonlight floods the still horizon with desires that are "horrible and sweet." Like the other poems in *Pierrot lunaire, Mondestrunken* is a rondeau—a verse form—of thirteen lines in which lines 1–2 reappear as lines 7–8 and line 1 repeats as line 13.

Mondestrunken is mostly soft and light in texture. It opens with a high seven-note motive that hypnotically repeats in the piano and evokes a feeling of moonlight.

The pervasive varied recurrence of this ostinato motive in different instruments unifies the piece. Schoenberg's music parallels the changing images of the text. The wine that "the moon pours down in torrents," for example, is depicted by a descending sequence of the motive in the piano and flute.

The poet's intoxication from "the holy drink" is suggested by a sudden *forte,* thick piano chords, and the first appearance of the cello. *Mondestrunken* rounds off with a final appearance of the motive at a slower tempo in the piano and flute.

Vocal Music Guide

SCHOENBERG, *Pierrot lunaire (Moonstruck Pierrot)*

No. 1, *Mondestrunken (Moondrunk)*

Piano, **pp**, high repeated motive.

Flute	*Den Wein, den man mit Augen trinkt,*	The wine that with eyes is drunk,
	Giesst Nachts der Mond in Wogen nieder,	at night the moon pours down in waves,
	Und eine Springflut überschwemmt	and a spring-flood overflows
	Den stillen Horizont.	the silent horizon.
Long flute melody, high piano		
	Gelüste, schauerlich und süss.	Desires shuddering and sweet
	Durchschwimmen ohne Zahl die Fluten!	swim countless through the floods!
	Den Wein, den man mit Augen trinkt,	The wine that with eyes is drunk
Piano, flute, motive descends	*Giesst Nachts der Mond in Woge nieder.*	at night the moon pours down in waves.
Sudden *f,* cello enters.	*Der Dichter, die den Andacht treibt*	The poet, whom devotion inspires

High violin.

Berauscht sich an dem heiligen Tranke,
Gen Himmel wendet er verzückt
Das Haupt und taumelnd saugt und schlürft er
Den Wein, den man mit Augen trinkt.

made drunk by the sacred drink,

toward heaven he turns
his entranced head and, reeling, sucks and slurps
the wine that with eyes is drunk.

Piano motive, flute imitates.

A Survivor from Warsaw, Op. 46 (1947)

A Survivor from Warsaw, a dramatic cantata for narrator, male chorus, and orchestra, deals with a single episode in the murder of 6 million Jews by the Nazis during World War II. Schoenberg wrote the text himself, basing it partly on a direct report by one of the few survivors of the Warsaw ghetto. Over 400,000 Jews from this ghetto died in extermination camps or of starvation; many others perished during a heroic revolt against the Nazis in 1943.

The narrator's text is spoken in English, except for some terrifying Nazi commands, which are shouted in German. The narrator's part is a kind of *Sprechstimme,* the novel speech-singing developed by Schoenberg. The rhythms of the spoken words are precisely notated, but their pitch fluctuations are indicated only approximately.

I can-not re-mem-ber ev-'ry-thing,   I must have been un - con-scious most of the time;

Besides English and German, the text includes Hebrew. These were the three languages of Schoenberg's life: German, his native tongue; English, his adopted language in the United States; and Hebrew, the language of the faith to which he returned. The six-minute cantata builds to an overwhelming conclusion when the male chorus sings in unison the Hebrew words of the prayer *Shema Yisroel* (*Hear, O Israel*). For centuries this has been the prayer of Jewish martyrs in their last agonized moments.

A Survivor from Warsaw is a twelve-tone composition written in 1947, when Schoenberg was seventy-two. The music vividly sets off every detail in the text.

A Survivor from Warsaw opens with a brief orchestral introduction that captures the nightmarish atmosphere that prevailed as Nazi soldiers awakened the Warsaw Jews for transport to death camps. We hear a weirdly shrill reveille in the trumpet and fragmentary sounds in the military drum and high xylophone.

During the narrator's opening lines, Schoenberg already prepares for the concluding Hebrew prayer. As the narrator speaks of "the old prayer they had neglected for so many years," a French horn softly intones the beginning of the melody that is later proclaimed by the chorus.

French horn

An especially vivid musical description comes when the narrator tells how the Nazis counted their victims: "They began again, first slowly: One, two, three, four, became faster and faster. . . ." The music itself becomes faster and louder, building to the powerful entrance of the chorus.

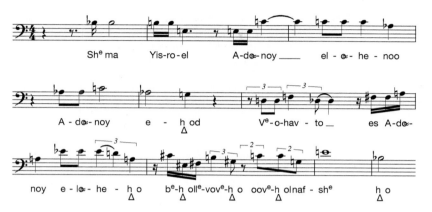

Sh^e ma   Yis-ro-el   A-do-noy _____ el-o-he-noo

A-do-noy   e-hod   V^e-o-hav-to _ es A-do-

noy   e-lo-he-ho   b^e-holl^e-vov^e-h o oov^e-h olnaf-sh^e   ho

The sung Hebrew contrasts dramatically with the spoken English and German that comes before, and it is the first extended melody in the work.

Vocal Music Guide

SCHOENBERG, *A Survivor from Warsaw*

Orchestral introduction

French horn, ***pp***.

I cannot remember everything. I must have been unconscious most of the time; I remember only the grandiose moment when they all started to sing, as if prearranged, the old prayer they had neglected for so many years—the forgotten creed!

But I have no recollection how I got underground to live in the sewers of Warsaw so long a time.

The day began as usual. Reveille when it still was dark—get out whether you slept or whether worries kept you awake the whole night: you had been separated from your children, from your wife, from your parents, you don't know what happened to them; how could you sleep?

They shouted again: "Get out! The sergeant will be furious!" They came out; some very slow, the old ones, the sick men, some with nervous agility. They fear the sergeant. They hurry as much as they can. In vain! Much too much noise, much too much commotion and not fast enough!

The Feldwebel shouts: "Achtung! Still gestanden! Na wird's mal, oder soll ich mit dem Gewehrkolben nachhelfen? Na jut; wenn Ihr's durchaus haben wollt!" ("Attention! Stand still! How about it, or should I help you along with the butt of my rifle? Oh well, if you really want to have it!")

The sergeant and his subordinates hit everyone: young or old, strong or sick, guilty or innocent—it was painful to hear the groaning and moaning.

I heard it though I had been hit very hard, so hard that I could not help falling down. We all on the ground who could not stand up were then beaten over the head.

I must have been unconscious. The next thing I knew was a soldier saying, "They are all dead!" Whereupon the sergeant ordered to do away with us.

There I lay aside half conscious. It had become very still—fear and pain—Then I heard the sergeant shouting: "Abzählen!" ("Count off!")

They started slowly, and irregularly: One, two, three, four, "Achtung." The sergeant shouted again: "Rascher! Nochmals von vorn anfangen! In einer Minute will ich wissen wieviele ich zur Gaskammer abliefere! Abzählen!" ("Faster! Once more, start from the beginning! In one minute I want to know how many I am going to send off to the gas chamber! Count off!")

They began again, first slowly: one, two, three, four, became faster and faster, so fast that it finally sounded like a stampede of wild horses, and all of a sudden, in the middle of it, they began singing the Shema Yisroel.

Shema Yisroel Adonoy elohenoo Adonoy eḥod. Veohavto es Adonoy eloheḥö eḥol levoveḥo ooveḥol nafsheḥo ooveḥol meodeḥo. Vehoyoo haddevoreem hoelleh asher onoḥee metsavveḥo hayyom al levoveḥo. Veshinnantom levoneḥo vedibbarto bom beshivteḥo beveteḥo oovelehteḥö addereḥ ooveshoḥbeḥo oovekoomeḥo. ("Hear, O Israel, the Lord our God, the Lord is One! And thou shalt love the Lord thy God with all thy heart, and with all thy soul, and with all thy might. And these words, which I command thee this day, shall be in thy heart. And thou shalt teach them diligently unto thy children, and speak of them when thou sittest in thy house, and when thou goest on the way, and when thou liest down, and when thou risest up." [Deuteronomy 6:4–9])

9 Alban Berg

Alban Berg (1885–1935), a student of Schoenberg, wrote music that is a unique synthesis of traditional and twentieth-century elements. Berg, who was born in Vienna, first attracted international attention in 1925, when his opera *Wozzeck* premiered in Berlin. Though its atonality baffled many critics, *Wozzeck* made such a powerful impression on the public that it was soon performed throughout Europe and in the United States. Perhaps because of chronic ill health, Berg did not perform or conduct, and he composed relatively few works. These include *Chamber Concerto,* for piano, violin, and thirteen winds (1925); *Lyric Suite,* for string quartet (1926); the opera *Lulu* (1929–1935, orchestration not completed); and the Violin Concerto (1935).

Wozzeck (1917–1922)

Wozzeck is the tragic story of a soldier who is driven to murder and madness by a hostile society. An antihero obsessed by strange visions, Wozzeck is persecuted by his sadistic captain, used as a guinea pig by a half-demented doctor, and betrayed by the woman with whom he lives, Marie. Wozzeck stabs Marie to death and drowns while trying to wash her blood from his hands.

Berg's musical imagination was fired in 1914 when he saw *Woyzeck,* a play by the German dramatist and revolutionary Georg Büchner (1813–1837). Though written in the early 1830s, the play is amazingly modern in its starkly realistic dialogue and disconnected scenes. Berg adapted the play into an opera while in the Austrian army in World War I. His own traumatic army experiences may well have deepened his sympathy for Wozzeck.

The opera's nightmarish atmosphere makes it a musical counterpart of expressionist painting and literature. Berg conveys the tensions and torments of the unconscious through harsh dissonances and grotesque distortions. The range of emotions and styles in the music is tremendous. Though most of *Wozzeck* is freely atonal—it does not use the twelve-tone system—major and minor keys occasionally add contrast. The vocal line includes speaking, shrieking, *Sprechstimme,* distorted folksongs, and melodies

The concluding scene of *Wozzeck* in a production by the Berlin State Opera.

with wide leaps that are difficult to sing. The gigantic orchestra closely parallels the dialogue and stage action. Descriptive effects include vivid orchestral depictions of the moon rising, frogs croaking, and water engulfing the drowning Wozzeck. Berg's music rapidly shifts between very high and very low registers, between *ffff* and *pppp*.

Wozzeck has three acts, each with five scenes. Connecting the scenes are short orchestral interludes that comment musically on the preceding action and serve as preparation for what is to come. As in Wagner's music dramas, there is a continuous musical flow within each act, and characters are associated with specific musical ideas. A novel feature of *Wozzeck* is that the music for each scene is a self-contained composition with a particular form (passacaglia, sonata form, etc.) or of a definite type (military march, lullaby). The five scenes of the last act—we study scenes 4 and 5—are organized as (1) variations on a theme, (2) variations on a single tone, (3) variations on a rhythmic pattern, (4) variations on a chord, and (5) variations on continuous running notes. But Berg did not intend for the listener to concentrate on or even be aware of these unifying techniques. He wanted the audience to be caught up in the opera's dramatic flow.

In Act II, Wozzeck has been driven to desperation by Marie's infidelity and by a savage beating from the man who has slept with her. Near the beginning of Act III, Wozzeck stabs Marie to death as they walk along a forest path near a pond.

Act III: Scenes 4 and 5

Scene 4: A path near a pond Wozzeck returns to the scene of the crime to dispose of his knife. Berg's orchestra vividly evokes the dark forest scene as a background to Wozzeck's anguished shrieks. Rising harp tones suggest the blood-red moon coming up through the clouds. Wozzeck goes mad and drowns in the pond while trying to wash the blood from his hands. Soft chromatic slides depict the engulfing water as the Captain and the Doctor, Wozzeck's tormentors, indifferently comment that someone is drowning. As Wozzeck drowns, the slides become slower and narrower in range.

The long orchestral interlude that follows is a deeply moving expression of grief for Wozzeck's tragic fate. It recalls the musical themes associated with his life. Berg described it as "a confession of the author stepping outside the dramatic events of the theater and appealing to the public as representing mankind." For this outpouring of compassion, Berg returns to tonality (the interlude is in D minor) and the musical language of late romanticism.

Scene 5: A street before Marie's door Children are playing in front of Marie's house; bright sunshine brings a glaring contrast to the darkness of the preceding scenes. One of the children cruelly tells Wozzeck's son: "Hey! Your mother is dead." The boy rides off on his hobby horse with the other children to see the body. The orchestra is

virtual fieldtrip

Wozzeck

Scenes 4 and 5 available in Connect Music

reduced in size to produce delicate sounds that match the children's high voices, and a continuous rhythm symbolizes their utter indifference.

The opera does not end with a conclusive chord. It simply breaks off as though to suggest that the tragedy could begin again.

Vocal Music Guide

BERG, *Wozzeck,* Act III, scenes 4 and 5

Scene 4

0:00 Winds, *p*, repeated chord.	(Forest path by the pond. Moonlit night as before. Wozzeck staggers on hastily, and then stops as he searches for something.)	

Wozzeck

Spoken (*Sprechstimme*).	*Das Messer? Wo ist das Messer? Ich hab's dagelassen . . . Näher, noch näher. Mir graut's! Da regt sich was. Still! Alles still und tot . . .*	The knife! Where's the knife? I left it somewhere here . . . Somewhere . . . It's terrifying! Something's moving Silence . . . Everything's silent and dead!
Shouted.	*Mörder! Mörder! Ha! Da ruft's. Nein, ich selbst.*	Murder! Murder! Someone called . . . No, it was me

(Still searching, he staggers forward a few more steps,
and comes on the corpse.)

	Marie! Marie! Was hast du für eine rote Schnur um den Hals? Hast Dir das rote Halsband verdient, wie die Ohrringlein, mit Deiner Sünde! Was hängen Dir die schwarzen Haare so wild? Mörder! Mörder! Sie werden nach mir suchen . . . Das Messer verrät mich!	Marie! Marie! What is that red cord round your neck? Did you earn this red necklace, like those gold earrings? A reward for your sins? Why is your lovely dark hair so unruly? Murder! Murder! They'll be looking for me that knife will betray me (*seeks it feverishly*)
	Da, da ist's. So! Da hinunter. Es taucht ins dunkle Wasser wie ein Stein.	Ah, here it is! (At the pond) Into the water! (Throws the knife in) It sinks into the dark water like a stone.

1:55   (The moon comes up blood-red through the clouds.)

Rising harp tones, *pp*.	*Aber der Mond verrät mich . . . der Mond ist blutig. Will denn die ganze Welt es ausplaudern?!—Das Messer, es liegt zu weit vorn, sie finden's beim Baden oder wenn sie nach Muscheln tauchen. Ich find's nicht . . . Aber ich muss mich waschen. Ich bin blutig. Da ein Fleck . . . und noch einer. Weh! Weh! Ich wasche mich mit Blut! Das Wasser is Blut . . . Blut . . .*	But the moon betrays me The moon is bloody. Will the whole world be talking about it? The knife It's too near the shore, they'll find it while swimming Or when they look for mussels. (Wades in) I can't find it I must wash myself. I'm all bloody There's a spot here . . . and here! Woe! Woe! I'm washing myself in blood! The water is blood . . . blood . . . (He drowns.)
3:03 Water music. Upward orchestral slides, *pp*. Rhythm gradually slows.		

(After a short time the Doctor enters, followed by the Captain.)

Captain

Spoken.

Halt!   Stop!

Doctor
(Stands still)

Hören Sie? Dort!   Do you hear? Over there!

Captain
(Stands still)

Jesus! Das war ein Ton.   Jesus! I heard a sound.

Doctor
(Pointing to the pond.)

Ja, dort!   Yes, over there.

Captain

*Es ist das Wasser im Teich. Das Wasser   It's the water in the pond. The water
ruft. Es ist schon lange Niemand   calls out. It's a long time since anyone
ertrunken. Kommen Sie, Doktor! Es ist   drowned here. Come away, Doctor! It's
nicht gut zu hören.*   not good to hear it.
(He tries to drag the Doctor off.)

Doctor
(Stands still and listens.)

*Das stöhnt . . . als stürbe ein Mensch.   It groans . . . It sounds like a dying man . . .
Da ertrinkt Jemand!*   Someone's drowning there.

3:59   **Captain**

Celesta.

*Unheimlich! Der Mond rot und die   It's eerie . . .The moon is red and the
Nebel grau. Hören Sie? . . . Jetzt   mist is . . . gray. Did you hear?
wieder das Ächzen.*   It's groaning again.

Doctor

Stiller, . . . jetzt ganz still.   It's fainter. . . . and now quite silent.

Captain

Kommen Sie! Kommen Sie schnell.   Come away! Hurry!
(Drags the Doctor off with him.)

4:40

Extended
orchestral
interlude.

Scene 5   (Street before Marie's door. Bright morning. Sunshine. Children are playing and
shouting. Marie's child is riding a hobbyhorse.)

Children

8:29

*Ringel, Ringel, Rosenkranz, Ringel   Ring around the rosie
reih'n! Ringel, Ringel, Rosenkranz,   Ring around the rosie
Rin . . .*
(They stop, and other children come rushing on.)

One of them

Du Käthe! . . . Die Marie . . .   Hey, Katie! You know about Marie?

Second Child

Was is?   What?

First Child

Weisst' es nit? Sie sind schon Alle'naus.

I don't know, they've all gone there.

Third Child
(To Marie's child.)

Du! Dein Mutter ist tot!

Hey, you! Your mother's dead.

Marie's Child
(Still riding his horse.)

Hopp, hopp! Hopp, hopp! Hopp, hopp!   Hop, hop! Hop, hop! Hop, hop!

Second Child

Wo is sie denn?

So where is she?

First Child

Draus' leigt sie, am Weg, neben dem Teich.

She's over there, by the pond, lying on the path.

Third Child

Kommt, anschaun!

Come, let's have a look!

(All the children run off.)

Marie's Child
(Continues to ride.)

Hopp, hopp! Hopp, hopp! Hopp, hopp!   Hop, hop! Hop, hop! Hop, hop!

Music breaks off.

(He hesitates for a moment, then rides off after the other children.)

10 Anton Webern

Anton Webern (1883–1945) was neglected during his lifetime, though his music influenced composers throughout the world during the 1950s and 1960s. He was born in Vienna; studied piano, cello, and music theory as a young man; and earned a doctorate in music from the University of Vienna. While at the university, he studied composition privately with Schoenberg. His career was solid but unspectacular. He made a modest living conducting various orchestras and choruses. The rare performances of his own works were usually met with ridicule. He was a shy man, devoted to his family, and a Christian mystic who loved to commune with nature. Although his life seems ordinary enough, his death was a bizarre tragedy. Toward the end of World War II, he was shot by mistake by an American soldier.

Webern's Music

Poetic lyricism pervades Webern's music, which is amazingly original in its brevity, quietness, and concentration. Most of his works are miniatures lasting only two or three minutes and virtually all of his mature output can be played in less than three and a half hours—rarely has a composer achieved such worldwide influence on the basis of so little music. About half of Webern's music is for solo voice or chorus; the rest is for chamber orchestra or small chamber groups. He wrote atonal works at about the same time as Schoenberg (starting in 1908–1909) and adopted the twelve-tone system soon after Schoenberg developed it. He also exploited Schoenberg's idea of a "melody built of tone colors." Webern's melodic lines are "atomized" into two- or three-note fragments which may at first seem isolated but add up to a unified whole. He forces us to focus on the tone color, dynamic level, and register of each note. His textures are delicate and transparent; usually not more than a few solo instruments play at once. In his twelve-tone works, there is often strict polyphonic imitation.

Composers in the 1950s and 1960s were fascinated by Webern's techniques and often imitated his deceptively "cool" sound. Works that appealed to very few during Webern's lifetime became a source of inspiration after his death.

Five Pieces for Orchestra, Op. 10 (1911–1913)

Webern's unique style is fully revealed in his early, atonal *Five Pieces for Orchestra, Op. 10,* composed before he adopted the twelve-tone system. These five "expressions of musical lyricism," as Webern called them, are among the shortest orchestral compositions ever written. The fourth piece is only 6⅓ measures long and lasts less than thirty seconds. Webern's chamber orchestra of eighteen soloists includes unconventional instruments such as the mandolin, guitar, cowbells, and harmonium (a small organ with metal reeds). Each piece (we consider the third) is scored for a different number and combination of instruments.

Melodic fragments are whispered by ever-changing solo instruments and framed by poetic silences. Tone-color melodies replace "tunes" in this music. There are few notes, but each is crucial. The tempo continually fluctuates. Brasses and strings are usually muted.

Third Piece:
Very slow and extremely calm

With its bell sounds coming as though from far off, the third piece has a feeling of solitude and eerie stillness. The dynamics never rise above *pp*. The sustained bell-like sounds—produced by mandolin, celesta, guitar, harp, glockenspiel, cowbells, chimes, and harmonium—are heard both at the beginning and at the end. This creates a vague A B A' effect. Melodic fragments in ever-changing solo instruments are set apart from one another by brief moments of near silence.

Listening Outline

WEBERN, Third Piece from Five Pieces for Orchestra

Clarinet, muted French horn, muted trombone, harmonium, mandolin, guitar, celesta, harp, bass drum, snare drum, chimes, cowbells, violin, muted viola, muted cello
Very slow and extremely calm
(Duration, 1:28)

0:00	**1. a.**	Pulsating bell-like sounds, *ppp*.
	b.	Violin, *pp*, pulsating bell-like sounds, *ppp*.
	c.	Muted horn, *pp*, chimes, *ppp*.
0:38	**2.**	Quicker notes in clarinet. Muted viola.
0:47	**3. a.**	Pulsating bell-like sounds, *ppp*.
	b.	Muted trombone, *ppp*; pulsating bell-like sounds, *ppp*. Snare drum roll, extremely soft.

11 Béla Bartók

Béla Bartók (1881–1945), whose music is infused with the spirit of east European folksong, was born in Hungary. His mother gave him his first lessons on the piano, an instrument that was important to his career. For twenty-seven years (1907–1934), Bartók taught piano at his alma mater, the Budapest Academy of Music, and gave recitals throughout Europe. During the early 1900s, Bartók was influenced by the Hungarian nationalist movement, and he spent most of his free time in tiny villages recording peasant folksongs. He became a leading authority on peasant music, and his own music was profoundly affected by it.

Béla Bartók.

Though he was neglected in Hungary until the Budapest premiere of his ballet *The Wooden Prince* in 1917, Bartók was recognized early as an important composer abroad and had a successful career during the 1920s and 1930s. But he was vehemently anti-Nazi, and in 1940, he emigrated from Hungary to the United States, where he was to spend the last five years of his life. This was a bleak period for him; he had little money, he was in poor health, and he felt isolated and neglected.

In 1943, while in a hospital in New York, he received an unexpected commission for the Concerto for Orchestra, now his best-known work. The success of its first performance resulted in several other commissions. Tragically, Bartók had only a year to live and could write just two more compositions, his Sonata for Solo Violin (1944) and Third Piano Concerto (1945). Soon after his death in New York in 1945, Bartók became one of the most popular twentieth-century composers.

Bartók's Music

"I do not reject any influence," wrote Bartók, "provided this source be pure, fresh and healthy." But he emphasized that the "Hungarian influence is the strongest." He evolved a completely individual style that fused folk elements, classical forms, and twentieth-century sounds. He did arrange many folk tunes (often giving them highly dissonant accompaniments), but in most of his works he does not quote folk melodies—he uses original themes that have a folk flavor.

Bartók's genius found its most characteristic expression in instrumental music. He wrote many works for piano solo, six string quartets (which are among the finest since Beethoven's) and other chamber music, three piano concertos, two violin concertos, and several compositions for orchestra. His music embraces a wide range of emotions and is deeply expressive; and he revitalized and reinterpreted traditional forms such as the rondo, fugue, and sonata form.

Bartók always organized his works around a tonal center; but within this framework, he often used harsh dissonances, polychords, and tone clusters (though some of his late works have a more traditional and less dissonant vocabulary). Rhythmically, his music is characterized by a powerful beat, unexpected accents, and changing meters. He was imaginative in his use of tone colors, particularly of percussion instruments. In works such as Music for Strings, Percussion, and Celesta (1936), he drew unusual

Caught up in the nationalist movement that swept Hungary, Bartók spent most of his free time in tiny villages recording folk songs on a cylinder phonograph.

sounds from the xylophone and timpani. Like many twentieth-century composers, he also drew percussive, drumlike sounds from the piano.

Concerto for Orchestra (1943)

The commission that led to Bartók's Concerto for Orchestra was offered to him in 1943, while he was hospitalized in New York City. Serge Koussevitzky, the conductor of the Boston Symphony Orchestra, offered him $1,000 for a new work. While recuperating at Saranac Lake, New York, Bartók was able to work "practically day and night" on his new composition. He finished it in six weeks. Concerto for Orchestra was an enormous success at its premiere in Boston in 1944 and has since become Bartók's most popular work.

"The general mood of the work," wrote Bartók, "represents, apart from the jesting second movement, a gradual transition from the sternness of the first movement and the lugubrious death-song of the third, to the life-assertion of the last one." Bartók explained that the unusual title reflects the work's "tendency to treat the single orchestral instruments in a *concertant* or soloistic manner."

Indeed, Concerto for Orchestra is a showpiece for an orchestra of virtuosos. It is romantic in spirit because of its emotional intensity, memorable themes, and vivid contrasts of mood. Though its melodies were created by Bartók, they have a distinct folk flavor. The concerto is an example of Bartók's mellow "late" style, which is characterized by more frequent use of traditional chords. In all five movements, time-honored procedures like A B A form, sonata form, and fugue are fused with twentieth-century rhythms and tone colors. We focus on the second movement.

Second Movement: *Game of Pairs*
Allegretto scherzando

The jesting second movement, *Game of Pairs,* which is in A B A′ form, is a "game" involving different pairs of woodwind and brass instruments. The melodic lines of each pair are in parallel motion and are separated by a distinctive pitch interval.

In the opening section (A), pairs of bassoons, oboes, clarinets, flutes, and muted trumpets play a chain of five melodies consecutively. The contrasting middle section

(B) is a hymnlike melody played softly by brass instruments. When the opening section returns (A'), it has a more active accompaniment. The incisive sound of a side drum (without snares) is prominent throughout the movement. It plays syncopated solos at the beginning and the end, as well as in the hymnlike middle section.

Listening Outline

BARTÓK, Concerto for Orchestra

Second Movement: *Game of Pairs* (Allegretto scherzando)
A B A' form, duple meter ($\frac{2}{4}$)
2 flutes, 2 oboes, 2 clarinets, 3 bassoons, 4 French horns, 2 trumpets, 2 trombones, tuba, timpani, side drum, 2 harps, 1st violins, 2d violins, violas, cellos, double basses
(Duration, 6:40)

A

0:00   **1.** Solo side drum (without snares), *mf*.

0:12   **2.** Two bassoons, *p*, accompanied by pizzicato strings.

0:36   **3. a.** Two oboes, *p*, in higher register. Pizzicato strings accompany.
        b. Low strings, pizzicato, while oboes sustain tones.

1:05   **4. a.** Two clarinets.
        b. Low strings, accented notes.

1:27   **5. a.** Two flutes, *mf*, in higher register.
        b. Low strings, pizzicato, while flutes sustain tones.

2:14   **6.** Two muted trumpets, *p*. Muted string tremolos, *pp*, in background.

B

3:02   **1. a.** Brasses, *mf*, hymnlike legato melody. Side drum accompanies.
        b. French horns, *p*, conclude hymnlike melody and sustain chord.

        2. Oboe, flute, and clarinet, *p*, lead to

A'

4:09   **1.** Two bassoons, *p*, opening melody. Staccato third bassoon in background.

4:33   **2. a.** Two oboes, *p*, in higher register. Clarinets and strings in background.
        b. Low strings, pizzicato, while oboes sustain tones.

4:50   **3. a.** Two clarinets. Flutes and strings in background.
        b. Low strings, accented notes.

5:19   **4. a.** Two flutes, *mf*, in higher register. Woodwinds and strings in background.
        b. Low strings, pizzicato, while flutes sustain tones.

5:44   **5.** Two muted trumpets, *mf*. Harp glissandos and muted string tremolos in background.

6:20   **6.** Woodwinds, *p*, repeated chord; solo side drum, decrescendo, ends *Game of Pairs*.

12 Music in America

America's musical traditions are extraordinarily rich and diverse owing to the country's multiethnic character. Our society includes Native Americans, who arrived thousands of years ago, as well as Americans whose ancestors came from Europe, Africa, Latin America, or Asia over the last four hundred years. Since the early seventeenth century, Americans have sung, played, and listened to psalms, hymns, popular songs, folk and patriotic tunes, dances, marches, and instrumental music.

This section provides a brief overview of the American musical landscape and a background for later sections of Part VI.

Colonial America

Singing psalms was a central social activity in the Protestant churches of colonial America. The very first book printed in the English-speaking colonies was the *Bay Psalm Book*. It appeared in 1640, only twenty years after the Mayflower had brought 102 Pilgrims to present-day Plymouth, Massachusetts. Translated from the original Hebrew into English verse, psalms were sung to tunes familiar to congregants who had come from England.

More than a century later came the first publication of original choral music by an American-born composer, *The New-England Psalm-Singer* (1770) by William Billings (1746–1800). This collection included "Chester," a song that became a popular patriotic anthem during the American Revolution. Billings wrote both the words and music:

Let tyrants shake their iron rod
And Slav'ry clank her galling chains,
We fear them not, we trust in God,
New England's God forever reigns.

Billings earned a meager living in Boston tanning animal hides. He also taught in the "singing schools" founded by Protestant ministers who hoped to improve the level of singing in their churches by encouraging their congregants to learn to read music.

Music in Nineteenth-Century America

The nineteenth century witnessed a population explosion in America: from 5 million people in 1800 to more than 76 million in 1900, giving rise to an expansion and diversification of musical activity.

Up to the early twentieth century, bands were the favorite instrumental organizations in America. By 1860 there were more than 3,000 bands including 60,000 musicians. Virtually every village had its band and bandstand; bands performed at picnics, parades, political rallies, dances, and carnivals. The leading American composer and conductor of band music was John Philip Sousa (1854–1932), nicknamed the "march king." His best-known marches include *The Stars and Stripes Forever, The Washington Post,* and *Semper Fidelis.* From 1892 to 1931 the famous fifty-person Sousa Band toured across America, and during the early 1900s it performed in Europe as well.

During the nineteenth century, symphony orchestras were founded in New York (1842), Cincinnati (1872), Boston (1881), and Chicago (1890). The transcontinental railroad facilitated concert tours by orchestras during the last three decades of the century. Between 1864 and 1888, the Theodore Thomas Orchestra, conducted by the German-born American Theodore Thomas (1835–1905), performed in several

John Philip Sousa and the Sousa Band in 1893.

thousand concerts, introducing many American audiences to symphonic music. Orchestral music was played not only in concert halls but also in venues such as restaurants, dance halls, beer halls, and theaters. Orchestra and band concert programs often mixed "classical" music with popular dances, marches, and songs.

In nineteenth-century America, as in Europe, there was a great demand for songs to be performed in private homes with pianos. The most popular songwriter of the mid-1800s was Stephen Foster (1826–1864), whose works include the well-known *Oh! Susanna, Jeanie with the Light Brown Hair,* and *Beautiful Dreamer.* Foster was the first American composer to earn a living from writing songs. However he often earned little from published songs due to competing publishers who pirated them. Sadly, Foster died in poverty at the age of thirty-seven.

Also popular in nineteenth-century America were Italian operas, often performed with English texts rather than the original Italian. Music from operas was heard not only in opera houses but also in homes, streets, and public ceremonies. At President Abraham Lincoln's inauguration in 1861, a band played music from the opera *Rigoletto,* by the Italian composer Giuseppe Verdi (studied in Part V, Section 15). Italian operas were enjoyed nationwide by music lovers coming from a cross-section of social and economic groups. In New Orleans, four opera companies presented nine different operas during the spring of 1836.

Nationalism in American Music

During the 1800s nationalism began to influence American music. A leading American nationalist composer was Louis Moreau Gottschalk (1829–1869), who also was famous as a concert pianist. Born in New Orleans, he went to Paris to study piano at age thirteen. Three years later, in 1845, he gave a piano recital attended by Frédéric Chopin, who predicted that Gottschalk would become the "king of pianists." Gottschalk captivated the European public with his piano pieces including *Bamboula: African-American Dance* (1848), which drew upon African American, Cuban, and Puerto Rican melodies and rhythms.

In 1853, Gottschalk returned to the United States, where he performed both in large cities and small towns. During the American Civil War, he played his composition

Union, in which *The Star-Spangled Banner* was followed by *Yankee-Doodle* and *Hail Columbia* played simultaneously in perfect harmony.

The Czech-composer Antonín Dvořák's three-year stay in the United States from 1892 to 1895 strongly influenced American musical nationalism. Considered the leading composer in the United States, he was Director of the National Conservatory in New York, and treated as a celebrity. In newspaper interviews and articles, he suggested that the foundation for "the future music of this country" should be African American and Native Indian melodies, Some American composers began to draw inspiration from these sources and from Dvořák's *New World* Symphony (1893) discussed in Part V, Section 12. Other composers influenced by Dvořák chose to define their national identity through other kinds of folk music. Amy Beach (1867–1944), from Boston, wrote her *Gaelic* Symphony (1896) after hearing Dvořák's *New World* Symphony. Identifying with her Anglo-Saxon ancestors, Beach incorporated Irish folksongs in her *Gaelic* Symphony. We study Beach's song *The Year's at the Spring* later in Part VI.

Around 1900 New York–born Edward MacDowell (1860–1908) was considered the outstanding American composer. Among his teachers was Teresa Carreño, the celebrated Venezuelan concert pianist.

Between the ages of fifteen and twenty-eight, MacDowell lived in Europe, where he continued his music studies and composed, taught, and performed his works for piano. In 1884 he married Marian Nevins, an American who was one of his piano students. Four years later the young couple returned to the United States, first living in Boston and then moving to New York in 1896 when MacDowell became professor of music at Columbia University.

Although MacDowell did not consider himself a musical nationalist, his piano pieces *New England Idylls* (1902) evoke an American landscape. His compositions using folk material include the *Indian Suite,* for orchestra (1896), and *Woodland Sketches* (1896), a set of piano pieces in which the drumming of Native American music is suggested.

The MacDowell Colony, founded in 1907 by Marian MacDowell on their farm in Peterborough, New Hampshire, has served as a creative retreat for several thousand composers, writers, and artists up to the present day.

Music in America after 1900

In the early twentieth century the United States became a potent force in music as American jazz and popular music swept the world. During the first half of the twentieth century many composers sought to achieve an "American sound." At the beginning of the century Charles Ives (1874–1954) used a variety of popular music in his works, including ragtime, barn dances, and revival hymns. During the 1920, 1930s, and 1940s, American composers George Gershwin, William Grant Still, and Aaron Copland found inspiration in jazz, blues, spirituals, and cowboy songs. Copland (1900–1990) wrote that in the 1920s his aim was "to write a work that was recognizably American. . . . Jazz offered American composers a native product from which to explore rhythm."

America's involvement in World War I (1914–1918) and II (1939–1945) gave rise to compositions evoking patriotic feelings. After April 1917, when the United States entered the First World War, many composers wrote war songs that raised people's spirits, the most famous of which was George M. Cohan's *Over There.*

America's entrance into the First World War even affected operatic repertoire. The Metropolitan Opera in New York did not perform German operas during its 1917–1918 season. After the United States entered World War II in December 1941, many composers wrote works based on American history; the best-known of such compositions is Aaron Copland's *A Lincoln Portrait* (1942).

Since the 1950s, America's classical composers have influenced musicians worldwide. Techniques of producing electronic music, the minimalist musical styles of

Philip Glass and John Adams, and the chance music of John Cage have had a major impact. We explore some of the diversity of American music in the following sections.

Colleges and universities in the United States have played an unusually vital role in our musical culture. Not only do they train and employ leading composers, performers, and scholars; they offer music appreciation courses that have expanded the horizons and interests of countless students. Since the 1950s, many universities and music schools have sponsored performing groups specializing in contemporary music and have housed most of the electronic music studios in the United States. In this way, American institutions of higher learning have become modern-day patrons of music, much as the church and nobility were in earlier times.

13 Amy Beach

Amy Beach (1867–1944), the first American woman to achieve international recognition as a composer of large-scale works, was born in the small town of West Henniker, New Hampshire; her maiden name was Amy Marcy Cheney. Both her parents came from distinguished New England families, and her mother was a talented pianist and singer. A child prodigy, Amy hummed forty tunes accurately at one year of age, sang an improvised alto part to her mother's soprano at two, and composed and played her first piano pieces at four.

When she was eight, her family moved to Boston, the home of several leading American composers of the time, including John Knowles Paine (1839–1906), Harvard's first professor of music; and George Whitefield Chadwick (1854–1931), who became director of the New England Conservatory of Music. Unlike these and other talented American musicians of the late 1800s, Beach never studied in Europe. Her piano teachers were the finest in Boston, but she was almost completely self-taught as a composer. When she was sixteen, one of her compositions was published, and she made a highly praised debut as a soloist with orchestra.

Amy Beach.

At eighteen, Amy Cheney married Dr. Henry Beach, a prominent surgeon she first met when he treated her injured finger. A widower, twenty-five years older than she, Dr. Beach was an amateur pianist, singer, and poet. He shared the view prevalent in his time that a husband should be the sole support of his wife. So before the marriage, Amy had to agree to limit the number of her public appearances, to donate her performance fees to charity, and *not* to teach piano. However, Dr. Beach encouraged his wife to compose, and during the twenty-five years of their childless marriage, her works— all of which were published—became widely known. "My compositions gave me a larger field," she later recalled. "From Boston I could reach out to the world. The orders for special compositions kept coming."

In 1910, Amy Beach's husband died as the result of a serious fall, and she felt the need to leave the United States. In 1911, at age forty-four, she sailed to Germany, where performances of her *Gaelic* Symphony and Piano Concerto won critical acclaim. Shortly after World War I broke out in July 1914, she returned to the United States, where she devoted her summers to composing and the rest of the year to concert tours and radio broadcasts.

Most of Beach's compositions are in a late romantic style, influenced by Brahms and Wagner, while displaying her own individuality. After her death in 1944, her works were neglected, but since the 1970s they have been heard increasingly in concerts and recordings. Beach composed in a variety of genres: along with the *Gaelic Symphony* (1896)—partly based on Irish-Gaelic folksongs—and the *Piano Concerto* (1899), she wrote music for piano, chorus, and chamber groups. Beach's chamber music includes a *Quartet for Strings in One Movement* (1929), which is composed in a new, modernist style and uses three Eskimo melodies. Her most widely performed works are her 120 songs for voice and piano, one of which, *The Year's at the Spring*, we study here.

The Year's at the Spring (1900)

Amy Beach once said, "I like to sit out of doors. I want to be in the midst of nature when I write." Beach's love of nature is reflected in her best-known song, *The Year's at the Spring*. Its text—an eight-line poem from the play *Pippa Passes*, by Robert Browning (1812–1889)—expresses the happiness of a young girl during a spring morning. About a minute in length, the song conveys joy and excitement through its very rapid tempo (allegro di molto), major key, rising melodic line, and almost continuous rapid, repeated triplets in the right hand of the piano accompaniment.

This use of triplets in the accompaniment recalls the rapid triplets in the piano part of Schubert's song *Erlkönig* (*The Erlking*), studied in Part V, Section 4. But the minor key and tragic text of *Erlkönig* make its tension-filled triplets sound very different from the joyful triplets of Beach's song.

The Year's at the Spring has the form A A'. Part A is very brief and sets the opening four lines of the poem with a melody that gradually ascends five notes up the scale to the words *dew-pearled*. Part A' is twice as long as A and brings a crescendo to the song's climax. A' begins with a return to the opening music and words (lines 1–2) of A, but then takes a new musical path for lines 5–8. The melody of A' gradually climbs an entire octave up the scale to the song's highest and longest note on the word *right* in the concluding line *All's right with the world!*

Vocal Music Guide

BEACH, *The Year's at the Spring*

A

Rising vocal melody, triplet piano accompaniment.

The year's at the spring,
And day's at the morn;
Mornings at seven;
The hill-side's dew-pearled;

A'

Vocal melody
gradually ascends
an octave, crescendo.

Climax on *right*.

The year's at the spring,
And day's at the morn;
The lark's on the wing;
The snail's on the thorn;
God's in His heaven;
All's right with the world!

14 Charles Ives

The American composer
Charles Ives knew that his unconventional music would not
be popular, and he became
a businessman so that his
family would not "starve on
his dissonances."

The American composer Charles Ives (1874–1954) wrote startlingly original music that was far ahead of its time. He was born in Danbury, Connecticut, the son of a bandmaster who loved to experiment with unusual sounds ("Pa taught me what I know," he later recalled), and he studied composition at Yale University. But when he graduated, he entered the insurance business, having decided that he could keep his music "stronger, cleaner, bigger, and freer" if he did not try to make a living out of it. (He also said that he did not want to raise a family that might "starve on his dissonances.") Eventually he founded a successful insurance agency and became very wealthy.

Ives composed furiously after business hours, on weekends, and on holidays, in isolation from the music world. He was completely unknown, none of his major works was publicly performed, and his scores accumulated in the barn of his Connecticut farm.

World War I dampened his creative urge, and in 1918 he had a heart attack from which he never completely recovered. He composed almost nothing after 1921 but instead began to make his compositions known to the public.

From 1920 to 1922, Ives privately printed his monumental *Concord* Sonata (1909–1915) for piano and his collection *114 Songs*. At first, they aroused little more than ridicule, but gradually a few young composers and performers recognized that Ives was enormously original. In 1939, the *Concord* Sonata received an ovation at its first complete New York performance. By the 1940s, many considered Ives the first great composer from the United States. In 1947 he won a Pulitzer Prize for his Third Symphony (1904–1911), written some forty years earlier.

Ives's Music

Though experimental, Ives's compositions are deeply rooted in the folk and popular music he knew as a boy: revival hymns, ragtime, village bands, church choirs, patriotic songs, and barn dances. He was inspired by "unconventional" features of the American tradition: the village fiddler playing slightly out of tune, the cornetist a fraction ahead of the rest of the band, the church organist accidentally holding one chord while the choir sings another. His polyrhythms, polytonality, and tone clusters grew out of the music he knew.

One boyhood experience in particular seems to have had an important influence on Ives. Two bands playing different music passed each other as they marched by him in different directions. Their dissonant clash fascinated the young boy. In later works Ives simultaneously presents musical events that seem unrelated: two bands play in different keys; consonant chords are set against dissonant chords; conflicting meters and rhythmic patterns are intertwined. To evoke memories, he often quotes snatches of familiar tunes, develops them and integrates them within his music. Even the titles of his works evoke Ives's New England heritage—for example, the movements of the *Concord* Sonata are *Emerson, Hawthorne, The Alcotts,* and *Thoreau.* We study one movement from a set of orchestral pieces titled *Three Places in New England.*

Ives's music shows a wide range of emotions, styles, and techniques. It includes mild-sounding consonant chords and earsplitting dissonances. Ives scorned those who couldn't take dissonance. "Beauty in music," he wrote, "is too often confused with something that lets the ears lie back in an easy chair." Much of his music is extraordinarily difficult to perform. His large and varied output includes five symphonies and other orchestral music; works for piano, chorus, and chamber ensembles; and more than 200 songs.

Putnam's Camp, Redding, Connecticut available in Connect Music

Putnam's Camp, Redding, Connecticut (1912), from *Three Places in New England* (1908?–1914)

Putnam's Camp, Redding, Connecticut (1912), is part of *Three Places in New England,* a set of three pieces for orchestra evoking American history, life, and landscape. Though completed around 1914, *Three Places in New England* was not performed until 1930. Today it is one of Ives's most popular works and is considered a landmark in American music.

The daring and brilliant second movement, *Putnam's Camp,* is a child's impression of a Fourth of July picnic. Ives recaptures his boyhood memory of two marching bands clashing dissonantly as they play different tunes. His quotations of snatches of marches and patriotic songs contribute to the piece's popular flavor. Like much of his music, *Putnam's Camp* shifts abruptly between conventional harmonies and harsh "modern" dissonances.

Ives prefaced his score with a literary program for the movement. "Near Redding Center, Conn., is a small park preserved as a Revolutionary Memorial; for here General Israel Putnam's soldiers had their winter quarters in 1778–1779." One Fourth of July, "a child went there on a picnic held under the auspices of the First Church and the Village Cornet Band." The child wanders "away from the rest of the children past the camp ground into the woods. As he rests on the hillside of laurel and hickories, the tunes of the band and the songs of the children grow fainter." He falls asleep and dreams of "a tall woman standing . . . the Goddess of Liberty . . . pleading with the soldiers not to forget their 'cause.' . . . But they march out of the camp with fife and drum to a popular tune of the day. Suddenly a new national note is heard. Putnam is coming over the hills from the center—the soldiers turn back and cheer. The little boy awakes, he hears the children's songs and runs down past the monument to 'listen to the band' and join in the games and dances."

Putnam's Camp is in three sections (A B A') that parallel the composer's descriptive program. The first section, which is marked *quick step time,* captures the gaiety and confusion of a picnic. After a raucous, highly dissonant introduction, the strings play the main theme, a vigorous march that begins with conventional harmonies.

Introduction
0:00

Main theme
0:10

0:59

Such abrupt shifts between harsh dissonances and mild consonances are typical of Ives and are heard throughout *Putnam's Camp*. The piano, woodwinds, and brasses begin to compete for the listener's attention, and soon it sounds as though two bands are playing against each other. The mood becomes even more comic when a parody of the opening phrase of *Yankee Doodle* is quickly played by trumpet, flute, and violins.

A sentimental violin melody probably represents the child, whose falling asleep is suggested when the music becomes softer and slows to a halt.

2:08
3:03

The middle section (B) represents the child's dream. The goddess of liberty pleading with the soldiers is suggested by the impression of two bands playing in different tempos. One band begins with a sad oboe melody accompanied by strings, the other with a march rhythm in the piano and snare drum. A quotation of *The British Grenadiers,* a favorite tune of the Revolutionary army, represents the army marching out of the camp.

4:06

In the riotous concluding section (A′), Ives creates deliberate melodic and rhythmic confusion as the main march theme is combined with *The British Grenadiers* and other fragments.

15 George Gershwin

George Gershwin wrote jazz-flavored orchestral works and an opera as well as popular songs and musical comedies.

Popular songs and musical comedies as well as jazz-flavored orchestral works and opera won worldwide fame for the American composer George Gershwin (1898–1937). His parents were Russian-Jewish immigrants, and he grew up on the lower east side of Manhattan. As a boy, he taught himself to play hit tunes on a neighbor's piano. When he was thirteen, he began studying with a teacher who recognized his talent and introduced him to piano works ranging from Bach to Liszt and Debussy.

At fifteen, he left school to become a pianist, demonstrating new songs in the salesrooms of a music publisher. Three years later he started his own career as a songwriter, and in 1919 (at the age of twenty) he wrote *La, La, Lucille,* his first complete Broadway musical. In 1920, his song *Swanee* was a tremendous hit; during the 1920s and 1930s he wrote one brilliant musical after another—including *Lady, Be Good* (1924), *Funny Face* (1927), and *Of Thee I Sing* (1931)—usually with his brother Ira as a lyricist.

Gershwin was not only a creator of the golden age of American musical theater but also a successful composer of music for the concert hall, beginning with the triumphant premiere of *Rhapsody in Blue* in 1924. He gave the first performance of his Concerto in F at Carnegie Hall in 1925 and traveled to Europe in the 1920s (meeting Berg in Vienna and Ravel and Stravinsky in Paris). Part of his symphonic poem *An American in Paris* (1928) was composed on one of those visits. His most extended work is the opera *Porgy and Bess* (1935), which deals with the lives of poor black people in Charleston, South Carolina. It has been performed all over the world.

Gershwin was outgoing, a sportsman, an art collector and amateur painter, and irresistible to women. He was also wealthy from royalties, concert fees, and his weekly radio show.

During the last year of his life, he lived in Hollywood, where he wrote the music for several movies (and played tennis with Arnold Schoenberg in his spare time). He died of a brain tumor at the age of thirty-eight.

Rhapsody in Blue (1924)

Rhapsody in Blue available in Connect Music

Rhapsody in Blue, Gershwin's most famous composition, is a one-movement work for piano and orchestra. The title reflects its free, rhapsodic form and blues flavor (see pages 359–360 for a description of blues). But it is not true jazz, though it employs jazzlike rhythms and melodies and the orchestration suggests the distinctive sounds of jazz. There are three main sections and a coda; the extended piano solos in the main sections reflect Gershwin's own dazzling pianism and his genius as an improviser.

Rhapsody in Blue opens with a now-famous clarinet solo that starts from a low trill, climbs the scale, and then slides up to a high "wailing" tone. The blueslike opening theme, which grows out of the clarinet slide, is marked by the syncopations so typical of Gershwin's style.

It is followed by a repeated-note theme, presented by French horns, which reappears many times.

The opening section continues with an extended piano solo, a return of the blues theme, and a marchlike trumpet theme.

A new jazzlike theme, introduced in the low register, begins the lively second section, marked *con moto.*

The moderately slow third section is based on a lyrical, romantic melody first presented by the violins. This memorable tune is combined with a countermelody played by the French horns.

Andante moderato con espressione

Rhapsody in Blue concludes with a rapid coda, which is ushered in by an accelerated transformation of the romantic melody.

16 William Grant Still

The flowering of African American culture during the years 1917 to 1935—sometimes called the "Harlem Renaissance"—found musical expression in the works of the composer William Grant Still (1895–1978). His *Afro-American Symphony* (1931), which we study, was the first composition by a black composer to be performed by a major American symphony orchestra.

The flowering of African American culture during the years 1917–1935 found musical expression in the works of William Grant Still.

Still was born in Woodville, Mississippi, but grew up in Little Rock, Arkansas, where he began to study violin. At the age of sixteen, Still enrolled at Wilberforce University (Ohio) as a premedical student; but he devoted himself to musical activities, such as playing violin in the university string quartet, and decided to abandon medicine for music. He left college before graduating to enter the world of popular music as an arranger and performer. Still worked for the composer and publisher W. C. Handy in Memphis and arranged Handy's *St. Louis Blues* for military band (1916). In 1917, he enrolled at Oberlin College Conservatory to continue his formal music training, but he soon left to serve in the navy in World War I.

After his navy service and a brief return to studies at Oberlin College, Still moved to New York, where he lived a double life as a popular musician and as a composer of concert works. He made band arrangements and played in the orchestras of such all-black musical shows as *Shuffle Along* (1921). He also studied privately with two important composers in opposing musical camps: the conservative George Whitefield Chadwick and the modernist Edgard Varèse. After composing a few highly dissonant works under Varèse's influence, Still turned away from avant-garde styles and wrote compositions with a uniquely African American flavor that were performed to critical acclaim in New York.

A turning point in Still's career came in 1931, with the highly successful premiere of his *Afro-American Symphony* by the Rochester Philharmonic. Within the next two decades, this symphony was performed by thirty-eight orchestras in the United States and Europe. In 1934, Still was awarded a Guggenheim Fellowship, and the next year he moved to Los Angeles, where he wrote film scores, concert works, and operas. Still was the first African American to conduct a major symphony orchestra—the

Los Angeles Philharmonic, in 1936. He was also the first to have an opera performed by a major opera company—*Troubled Island,* about the Haitian slave rebellion, in 1949. In 1981, three years after Still's death, his opera *A Bayou Legend,* written in 1941, was broadcast on national television.

Afro-American Symphony (1931)

The *Afro-American Symphony,* Still's best-known work, was composed in 1930, shortly after the onset of the Great Depression. "It was not until the Depression struck," he later observed, "that I was jobless long enough to let the symphony take shape. In 1930, I rented a room in a quiet building not far from my home in New York, and began to work." Still devised his own blues theme and explained that he "wanted to demonstrate that the blues, so often considered a lowly expression, could be elevated to the highest musical level." The blues theme is introduced in the first movement and then reappears in various transformations in the three later movements as a unifying thread. Still also gave an African American character to the symphony by using a tenor banjo as part of the orchestra and by inventing themes that recall spirituals and jazz tunes. Each of the symphony's four movements has a subtitle and is prefaced by lines from a poem by the African American poet Paul Laurence Dunbar (1872–1906). We focus on the third movement.

Third Movement: Animato

Still gave this joyful, scherzo-like movement the subtitle *Humor* and prefaced it with the following quotation from Dunbar's poem: "An' we'll shout ouah hallelujahs/On dat mighty reck'nin' day." After a brief introduction, Still presents two melodies that reappear in varied guises within the movement. The lively, syncopated opening melody is made up of short motives, each ending with a repeated note and pause. Still called this the *hallelujah* melody, perhaps because its opening four notes fit the word "hallelujah." The *hallelujah* melody is accompanied by a syncopated countermelody that recalls Gershwin's song *I Got Rhythm.* (It is not certain whether one composer influenced the other.) The movement's jubilant second melody, more fully orchestrated than the first, is reminiscent of a spiritual. This theme includes two "blue" notes, the lowered third and seventh of the scale. The movement falls into three sections (1, 2, 3 in the listening outline), of which the last is an abridged return of the first. Varied orchestral colors and lively countermelodies contribute to the movement's high spirits.

Listening Outline

STILL, *Afro-American Symphony*

Third Movement: Animato
Quadruple meter ($\frac{4}{4}$), A flat major
Piccolo, 2 flutes, 2 oboes, English horn, 2 clarinets, bass clarinet, 4 French horns, 3 trumpets, 3 trombones, tuba, timpani, small cymbal, large suspended cymbal, tenor banjo, 1st violins, 2d violins, violas, cellos, double basses
(Duration, 3:03)

1. a. Timpani roll, syncopated motive in French horns, *f*, syncopated motive in brasses, cymbal crash, introduce

0:15   **b.** Syncopated hallelujah melody in major, violins, *f*, off-beat accompaniment in banjo and French horns, *mf*,

0:24   **c.** Syncopated countermelody in high wooodwinds introduces

0:31   **d.** Full orchestra, *f*, second melody.

0:49   **e.** Suddenly softer, hallelujah melody in oboe, then flutes, running notes in bass clarinet.

1:04   **f.** Sudden *ff*, trombones and French horns in unison, minor; suddenly softer, violins lead upward, violins, *f*, cymbals, answered by brasses, dotted rhythm, decrescendo to

1:34   **2. a.** Staccato flutes, *mp*, *hallelujah* melody varied, continuation in oboes,

legato flutes, English horn, violins, *p*, descend.

1:59   **b.** Muted trumpets answered by French horns, *p*, new variation of *hallelujah* melody,

2:07   **c.** Sudden *f*, trombones and tuba in unison, minor, full orchestra, cymbal crashes.

2:19   **3. a.** Violins, *mf*, *hallelujah* melody, with high flute and piccolo countermelody, banjo accompanies, oboes and flutes, *hallelujah* melody embellished.

2:35   **b.** Violins, *mf*, second melody, sudden *f*, low strings and woodwinds in unison, minor.

2:57   **c.** Full orchestra, *ff*, jubilant variant of *hallelujah* melody,

quick brass countermelody, rising strings, cymbal crash, and staccato ending chord.

17 Aaron Copland

Aaron Copland (1900–1990), a leading American composer, was born in Brooklyn. His parents (like Gershwin's) were Russian-Jewish immigrants. "No one ever talked music to me or took me to a concert," he recalled; but he discovered music on his own and at the age of fifteen decided to become a composer. He was drawn to "modern" music although his first teacher discouraged it; and in 1921 he went to France to study with

Aaron Copland drew on American folklore for his ballets *Billy the Kid, Rodeo,* and *Appalachian Spring.*

Nadia Boulanger (1887–1979), an extraordinary woman who taught several generations of American composers and was sympathetic to contemporary musical trends.

Copland's music went through several phases. When he returned to New York, he wanted to write works that would be "American in character." For Copland in 1925, *American* meant jazz. An example is his *Music for the Theater* (1925), a piece for orchestra, with elements of blues and ragtime. This "jazz period" lasted only a few years. During the early 1930s he composed serious, highly dissonant, sophisticated works (such as the highly regarded *Piano Variations,* 1930) that convey starkness, power, percussiveness, and intense concentration.

In the late 1930s, Copland modified his style again, writing more accessible works for a larger audience. These were the depression years, when many composers rejected the idea of writing for an elite audience. Copland now drew on American folklore—as in his ballets *Billy the Kid* (1938), *Rodeo* (1942), and *Appalachian Spring* (1944)—and on jazz, revival hymns, cowboy songs, and other folk tunes. His scores for films and his patriotic works (such as *A Lincoln Portrait,* 1942) also reached a mass public, and his name became synonymous with American music.

Copland accomplished the difficult feat of writing simple yet highly professional music. His textures clear; his slow-moving harmonies—often almost motionless—seem to evoke the openness of the American landscape; and though strongly tonal, his works embody twentieth-century techniques such as polychords, polyrhythm, changing meters, and percussive orchestration. He also used serial technique (that is manipulation of a tone row or series) in such works as *Connotations* for orchestra (1962).

Aside from his numerous compositions, Copland made many other contributions to American music by directing composers' groups, organizing concerts, lecturing, writing books and articles, teaching, and conducting.

A scene from the original production of *Appalachian Spring*. © Jack Vartoogian

Appalachian Spring (1943–1944)

Appalachian Spring originated as a ballet score for Martha Graham, the great modern dancer and choreographer. It took Copland about a year (1943–1944) to finish the music. While composing *Appalachian Spring,* he thought, "How foolhardy it is to be spending all this time writing a thirty-five-minute score for a modern-dance company, knowing how short-lived most ballets *and* their scores are." But in 1945 Copland arranged parts of the ballet as a suite for full orchestra (originally, the ballet used only thirteen instrumentalists) that won important prizes and brought his name to a large public. Today, *Appalachian Spring* is widely performed both as a ballet and as a concert piece.

The ballet concerns a "pioneer celebration in spring around a newly built farmhouse in the Pennsylvania hills" in the early 1800s. Its characters include a bride and groom, a neighbor, and a revivalist preacher with his followers. The rhythms and melodies are American-sounding and suggest barn dances, fiddle tunes, and revival hymns.

But Copland uses only one actual folk tune in the score—a Shaker melody titled *Simple Gifts.* (The Shakers were a religious sect established in America around the time of the Revolution. They expressed religious fervor through shaking, leaping, dancing, and singing.) *Appalachian Spring* is bright and transparent, has a clear tonality, and is basically tender and calm in mood. The score's rhythmic excitement comes from delightful syncopations and rapid changes of meter. As in many twentieth-century works, the orchestra includes a piano and a large percussion section.

The ballet suite has eight sections, including a duo for the bride and groom, a fast dance for the revivalist preacher and his followers with "suggestions of square dances and country fiddlers," and a finale in which the couple are left "quiet and strong in their new house." We focus on Section 7, which originally accompanied "Scenes of daily activity for the Bride and her Farmer-husband."

Section 7:
Theme and Variations on *Simple Gifts*

Section 7 is a theme and five variations on the Shaker tune *Simple Gifts*. The melody's folklike simplicity reflects the Shaker text, which opens as follows:

'Tis the gift to be simple, 'tis the gift to be free,
'Tis the gift to come down where we ought to be.

In each variation, Copland brings the tune back unadorned, creating variety and contrast through changes of tempo, tone color, dynamics, register, accompaniment, and key. Variation 2 sounds thoughtful and lyrical, as the tune is played more slowly, in a lower register, with polyphonic imitations. Variation 3 brings a brilliant contrast, as *Simple Gifts* is presented faster and staccato by trumpets and trombones. In each of the last two variations, Copland uses only part of the tune: its second part in the pastoral variation 4, and its first part in the majestic closing variation.

Listening Outline

COPLAND, *Appalachian Spring*

Section 7: Theme and Variations on *Simple Gifts*
Theme and variations, duple meter (²⁄₄), A flat major
2 flutes, 2 oboes, 2 clarinets, 2 bassoons, 2 French horns, 2 trumpets, 2 trombones, timpani, triangle, glockenspiel, harp, piano, 1st violins, 2d violins, violas, cellos, double basses
(Duration, 3:09)

Theme

0:00   Clarinet, *p*, *Simple Gifts,* legato.

Variation 1

0:33   Oboe, *mp* , and bassoon, *mp*, *Simple Gifts,* slightly faster, in higher register.

Variation 2

1:00   High harp, piano, glockenspiel, *p*, introduce *Simple Gifts,* violas and trombone, *mf*, played half as fast, in lower register. *Simple Gifts* imitated in violins, *f*, then in cellos and basses, *f*. Woodwinds, *p*, brief transition to

Variation 3

1:52   Trumpets and trombones, *f*, *Simple Gifts,* twice as fast, staccato.

Variation 4

2:16   Woodwinds, *mf*, second part of *Simple Gifts,* slightly slower than variation 3, gentle and legato.

Variation 5

2:34   Full orchestra, *fff*, first part of *Simple Gifts,* played slowly and majestically, in high register.

18 Alberto Ginastera

The Argentinean Alberto Ginastera (1916–1983) was one of the most prominent Latin American composers of the twentieth century. Ginastera began studying piano when he was seven, graduated from the National Conservatory in Buenos Aires when he was twenty-two, and became a faculty member at that conservatory when he was twenty-five. In 1945 Ginastera went with his family to the United States, where he studied with Aaron Copland at the Berkshire Music Center at Tanglewood. After returning to Argentina in 1947, he taught at several important music schools.

Ginastera's music began to attract international attention in the 1950s. By the 1960s he was so well regarded that three of his operas—*Don Rodrigo* (1964), *Bomarzo* (1967), and *Beatrix Cenci* (1971)—were performed in the United States. From 1963 to 1971, Ginastera directed the Latin American Center for Advanced Musical Studies, which promoted avant-garde musical techniques. In 1971, after divorcing his first wife, Ginastera married the Argentinean cellist Aurora Natola. Ginastera and Aurora left Argentina for Switzerland, where he spent his last twelve years and composed many of his pathbreaking works. In 1973, Ginastera's music reached millions of listeners when a movement from his first piano concerto was adapted into the hit song *Toccata* by the progressive rock group Emerson, Lake, and Palmer.

Ginastera's music employs forceful rhythms, powerful percussion, and dense orchestra textures. His early works are nationalistic and incorporate Argentinean folk material, including popular dances. Starting in the 1950s, with the Piano Sonata (1952), Ginastera adopted Schoenberg's twelve-tone system. Even though his works starting in

The early works of the Argentinean Alberto Ginastera are nationalistic and incorporate popular dances from his homeland.

the 1950s are no longer overtly nationalistic, Ginastera insisted that they have an Argentinean character. "Instead of using folkloristic material," he wrote, "the composer achieves an Argentine atmosphere by using his own thematic and rhythmic elements." After 1957, works such as his three operas and the Cello Concerto No. 2 make use of post-1945 musical techniques like tone clusters, chance music, and microtones.

We study Ginastera's *Estancia* Suite, an early work rooted in Argentinean folk tradition.

Estancia Suite, Op. 8a (1941)

The ballet *Estancia*—Spanish for an Argentine ranch—was commissioned by Lincoln Kirsten, director of the American Ballet Caravan, to be premiered in a planned program of Latin American ballets in New York. However, Kirsten's ballet company was disbanded in 1942, and *Estancia* was not performed as a ballet until much later. But in 1941 Ginastera arranged several of its dances as the *Estancia* Suite for orchestra, which became one of his most popular works.

Ginastera described his ballet *Estancia* as presenting "various aspects of ranch activities during a day, from dawn to dawn." *Estancia* has a distinct national flavor because of its setting on an Argentinean ranch, and its use of musical idioms associated with the gaucho, or horseman of the plain. The plot deals with "a country girl who despises a man from the city. She finally admires him when he proves that he can perform the roughest and most difficult tasks of the country."

The *Estancia* Suite uses a large orchestra and has four movements: (1) *Los trabajadors* (*The Land Workers*), (2) *Danza del Trigo* (*Wheat Dance*), (3) *Los Peones de Hacienda* (*The Cattlemen*), (4) *Danza Final* (*Final Dance*): *Malambo*. The first movement of the suite is rapid, loud, syncopated, and energetic, with violent accents on the bass drum. In contrast, the second movement is calm and lyrical, opening with a flute solo accompanied by soft pizzicato strings and harp that suggest the strumming of the gaucho's guitar. The wild, propulsive third movement features rapid shifts of meter that recall Stravinsky's *The Rite of Spring*. We focus on the climactic fourth movement, *Danza Final* (*Final Dance*): *Malambo*.

Final Dance: Malambo

The *malambo* is a dance for men only performed by the gaucho. Both the *malambo* and the gaucho are traditional symbols of Argentina. In a competitive *malambo*, one dancer tries to outshine the other through the energy and complexity of his steps.

Ginastera's comment that "always in my music there is this violent rhythm" aptly describes the fast tempo, perpetual motion, and percussive sounds of *Final Dance: Malambo*. The orchestra includes a very large percussion section, and the energetic melodies are often syncopated. The meter is $\frac{6}{8}$, and six rapid pulses per measure represent the foot tapping of the dancing gauchos. The form of this brief dance is A A′ (shortened) B. Part B, which is marked *Tempo di malambo*, builds to a climax and introduces a lively *malambo* melody. In this melody, six fast pulses first subdivide into two groups of three pulses and then into three groups of two pulses. A similar rhythm appears in *America* from Leonard Bernstein's *West Side Story*, studied in Section 22, "Music for Stage and Screen."

Listening Outline

GINASTERA, *Estancia* Suite, Op. 8a

Final Dance: Malambo

A A′ B form, Allegro, triple meter ($^6_8$), C major

Piccolo, 2 flutes, 2 oboes, 2 clarinets, 2 bassoons, 4 French horns, 2 trombones, timpani, bass drum, snare drum, tenor drum, cymbals, triangle, tambourine, castanets, gong, xylophone, piano, 1st violins, 2d violins, violas, cellos, double basses

(Duration, 3:24)

A

0:00   **1. a.** Piccolo and flute, ***pp***, high rapid ostinato, pizzicato violins, three-beat pattern; low strings join, crescendo.

0:14   **b.** Violins, ***f***, high syncopated melody, brasses join.

0:25   **c.** Xylophone, two-note melody.

0:32   **d.** Brasses, ***mf***, melody beginning with long note; violins, ***f***, repeat melody.

0:45   **e.** Pizzicato violins, ***mf***, two-note ostinato, crescendo to

A′

1:00   **2. a.** Piccolo and flute, ***f***, high rapid ostinato, pizzicato violins, three-beat pattern, French horns, downward scale, crescendo to

1:11   **b.** Violins, ***f***, high syncopated melody.

1:22   **c.** Xylophone, new melody, bass drum pulses, crescendo to

B Tempo di malambo

1:39   **3. a.** Trumpets, winds, xylophone, ***f***, lively *malambo* melody repeated many times; bass drum.

1:58   **b.** Brasses, ***ff***, fast repeated notes; bass drum.

2:05   **c.** Repeated *malambo* melody, trumpets, winds, xylophone, ***f***, bass drum.

2:23   **d.** Brasses, ***ff***, fast repeated notes, slides; bass drum.

2:30   **e.** Lively *malambo* melody repeats, trumpets, winds, xylophone,

2:46   **f.** Brasses, ***ff***, syncopations; bass drum.

2:56   **g.** Full orchestra, *malambo* melody repeats.

3:09   **h.** High repeated notes, ***ff***, full orchestra, very loud closing chord.

Performance Perspectives

Gustavo Dudamel Conducting the *Final Dance: Malambo* from Ginastera's *Estancia* Suite

Probably the most famous young conductor today is the Venezuelan Gustavo Dudamel, who was named by *Time* magazine as one of the hundred most influential people of 2009. Dudamel began as music director of the Los Angeles Philharmonic on October 3, 2009, with a five-hour free community concert—called *¡Bienvenido Gustavo!*—at the Hollywood Bowl. The first half of the event included jazz, gospel, pop, rock, and Cuban and Latin regional music, played by local youth ensembles joined by established stars; and the second half culminated in a performance of Beethoven's Ninth Symphony.

Dudamel was born in 1981 in the city of Barquisimeto, Venezuela; his father played trombone in salsa bands and his mother taught voice. When he was four, he began to study within a national network known as *El Sistema* (*The System*), which includes about 250 free music schools and hundreds of orchestras for children and youth. After beginning to play violin at age ten, Dudamel progressed so rapidly that two years later he was appointed concertmaster of a youth orchestra, which he sometimes conducted. He began to study conducting in his early teens, and at eighteen he was appointed music director of El Sistema's top ensemble, the Simón Bolívar Youth Orchestra of Venezuela, a position he still holds.

Dudamel's meteoric rise to international fame began when he won the Gustav Mahler Conducting Competition at age twenty-three. Over the next few years, he guest-conducted such leading ensembles as the Vienna, New York, and Israel philharmonic orchestras and made DVDs and CDs with the Simón Bolívar Youth Orchestra.

This huge youth orchestra, which has given concert tours in Europe and the United States, includes 200 musicians between the ages of fifteen and twenty-eight, mostly from poor homes. The aims of the orchestra go beyond making music: "When you have around your life, drugs, crime," says Dudamel, "the best that you can give to a kid is an instrument. Then they can change their lives." He says that his orchestra is a community: "We are a family. . . . I am part of the orchestra. We give our all with every performance." Dudamel describes the role of a conductor as "a bridge between the composer and the orchestra" and hopes his audiences "feel the joy of music."

Dudamel's recording with the Simón Bolívar Youth Orchestra titled *Fiesta* presents mostly music of Latin American composers, including the four dance movements of Ginastera's *Estancia* Suite. Dudamel believes that dance is a key element in Latin American music. "I started to dance when I was really small—a baby. You know, learning to dance is part of our culture—dancing is in our blood. . . . Latin music is all about dance, about rhythm. And we try to put this spice into all of our music."

19 Musical Styles since 1945

Since World War II, we have lived with instant communication—television, computers, and the Internet provide access to a virtually unlimited flow of information. Not only have we been bombarded by an incredible variety of stimuli, but there has also been a constant demand for novelty. New styles in fashion and the visual arts spread rapidly and then disappear.

In music as well, the emphasis has been on novelty and change. Musical innovations since 1945 have been even more far-reaching than those of the first half of the twentieth century. There have been many new directions, and the range of musical styles and systems is wider than ever. As the American composer Milton Babbitt (1916–2011) observed in 1984, "The world of music never before has been so pluralistic, so fragmented."

Particularly since the 1970s, many composers have advocated stylistic pluralism or eclecticism. Their works include sections in a variety of styles ranging from baroque to rock. In 1999, the American composer John Adams (b. 1947) told an interviewer, "We're in a kind of post-style era. Composers of my age and younger, we are not writing in one, highly defined, overarching expression." Adams believes that the contemporary composer can follow the examples of Bach, Mahler, and Stravinsky, and be "somebody who just reached out and grabbed everything" and through musical technique and spiritual vision "turned it into something great."

Today, the Internet provides composers with instant access to a limitless variety of music. The American composer Eric Whitacre (b. 1970) has said, "Today I can go through thirty or forty genres of music just by browsing the web. As a composer I know that all sorts of sounds I hear are making their way into my brain and soul."

Characteristics of Music since 1945

Accurately describing the relatively recent past is difficult. Yet any overview of music since 1945 must include the following major developments:

1. Increased use of the *twelve-tone system*.
2. *Serialism*—use of the techniques of the twelve-tone system to organize rhythm, dynamics, and tone color.
3. *Chance music,* in which a composer chooses pitches, tone colors, and rhythms by random methods, or allows a performer to choose much of the musical material.
4. *Minimalist music,* characterized by a steady pulse, clear tonality, and insistent repetition of short melodic patterns.
5. *Musical quotation,* works containing deliberate quotations from earlier music.
6. *Tonal music and a return to tonality* by some composers.
7. *Electronic music.*
8. *"Liberation of sound"*—greater exploitation of noiselike sounds.
9. *Mixed media.*
10. New concepts of *rhythm* and *form*.

Since 1945, long-playing records, audiotape, compact discs, DVDs, and the Internet have spread these new musical ideas far and wide. In Asia, for example, interest in western music has increased dramatically. Many young musicians from Japan, China, Taiwan, and South Korea study in American music schools and universities, and Asian performers are prominent on the international concert scene.

Increased Use of the Twelve-Tone System A striking development after World War II (1945) was the gradual abandonment of tonality in favor of the twelve-tone system. From the early 1920s—when Schoenberg invented the system—to about 1950, most composers still wrote music with a tonal center. Few were attracted to the new method because it was associated with Schoenberg's expressionist style, which had gone out of fashion. During the 1950s, however, the twelve-tone system was

Flood (1967) by Helen Frankenthaler. Working without a brush, Frankenthaler allows paint to soak and stain an unprimed canvas stretched on the floor. Helen Frankenthaler, 1928–2011, Flood, 1967. Acrylic on canvas, Overall: 124¼ × 140½ in. (315.6 × 356.9 cm). Whitney Museum of American Art, New York; purchased with funds from the Friends of the Whitney Museum of American Art 68.12. © 2013 Estate of Helen Frankenthaler/Artists Rights Society (ARS), NY. Photo: © Culver Pictures/The Art Archive at Art Resource, NY

adopted by many composers, including Stravinsky, who had been the leading composer of tonal music.

What contributed to this dramatic shift? In Europe, the end of the war brought a strong desire for new musical beginnings. During the Nazi years, composers had been denied access to the twelve-tone works of Schoenberg and Webern; when peace came, they were eager to explore unfamiliar musical territory. In the United States, twelve-tone music was now available on long-playing records, and complex scores became easier to study.

But the most important reasons for the shift to the twelve-tone system were the resources of the system itself. Composers discovered that it was a compositional technique rather than a special musical style. Musicians as different as Bach, Mozart, and Chopin had all used the tonal system; a comparable diversity of style was possible within the twelve-tone system. The new method also had the advantage of stimulating unconventional approaches to melody, harmony, and form. As Aaron Copland once expressed it, "I began to hear chords that I wouldn't have heard otherwise. Heretofore I had been thinking tonally, but this was a new way of moving tones about. It freshened up one's technique and one's approach."

Many composers of the 1950s and 1960s chose to write music that was stylistically reminiscent of Anton Webern, Schoenberg's disciple. They created "pointillist" music in which melodic lines are "atomized" into tiny fragments that are heard in widely separated registers and framed by moments of silence. Webern's style answered the needs of the post–World War II generation: his music had a lean, "modern" sound, whereas Schoenberg's was considered too "romantic" and traditional in form. The French composer Pierre Boulez (b. 1925) spoke for many of his generation in 1952 when he unfavorably compared Schoenberg's alliance with the "decadence of the great German romantic tradition" and Webern's reaction "against all inherited rhetoric."

Since 1950, there have been many new styles in the visual arts. Bridget Riley's *Nataraja* (1993) is *op*—or *optical*—art, which exploits visual effects and illusions.

Extensions of the Twelve-Tone System: Serialism During the late 1940s and early 1950s, the techniques of the twelve-tone system came to be used to organize dimensions of music other than pitch, such as rhythm, dynamics, and tone color. Recall that in early twelve-tone music the system was used primarily to order *pitch* relationships. All the pitches of a twelve-tone composition would be derived from a single tone row, or series. After 1950, a series of durations (rhythmic values), dynamic levels, or tone colors also could serve as a unifying idea. A rhythmic or dynamic series might be manipulated like the series of twelve tones. The use of a series, or ordered group of musical elements, to organize several dimensions of a composition is called **serialism.** Proponents of serialism include Milton Babbitt in the United States, Karlheinz Stockhausen (1928–2007) in Germany, and Pierre Boulez in France. Their methods lead to a totally controlled and organized music, but the actual sound—in certain cases—might seem random and chaotic. The complex relationships in the music are often difficult to perceive.

Chance Music The 1950s witnessed not only serialism but an opposite approach known as **chance,** or **aleatory, music** (from Latin *alea,* or *game of chance*). In chance music, composers choose pitches, tone colors, and rhythms by random methods such as throwing coins. They may also ask performers to choose the ordering of the musical material, or even to choose much of the material itself. For example, a composer might write out brief passages of a composition but ask the performer to play them in any desired order. Or a composer might indicate a group of pitches but direct the performer to invent rhythmic patterns.

The most famous and influential creator of chance music was the American John Cage (1912–1992). At the beginning of this book, a reference was made to Cage's silent "composition" titled *4'33"* (1952), which requires the performer *not* to make a sound for 4 minutes and 33 seconds. The "music" is made up of the unintentional sounds that an audience might produce in this time span. "I try to arrange my composing means," Cage once explained, "so that I won't have any knowledge of what might happen. . . . My purpose is to eliminate purpose." For Cage, "The purpose of this purposeless music would be achieved if people learned to listen. Then when they listened they

Chance effects are incorporated into *One (Number 31, 1950)* by the abstract expressionist painter Jackson Pollock. The artist dripped, poured, and flung paint onto an enormous canvas tacked to the floor.

might discover that they preferred the sounds of everyday life to the ones they would presently hear in the musical program. . . . That was all right as far as I was concerned."

Cage's approach is also illustrated by his *Imaginary Landscape* No. 4 (1951), for twelve radios. The score gives precise directions to the performers—two at each radio—for manipulating the dials affecting wavelength and volume. Yet all the indications in the score were chosen by chance means. They show no regard for local station wavelengths or the time of performance. "At the actual performance of *Imaginary Landscape*," reported one member of the audience, "the hour was later than anticipated before the work's turn came on the program, so that the instruments were unable to capture programs diversified enough to present a really interesting result." This is not surprising because Cage had chosen the wavelengths and dynamics by throwing dice.

With Cage's work as an example, serial composers such as Pierre Boulez and Karlheinz Stockhausen introduced elements of chance into their compositions during the mid-1950s. Stockhausen's Piano Piece No. 11 (1956) has nineteen short segments of music printed on a large roll of paper that measures 37 by 21 inches. The segments can be played in any order, and the performer is instructed to begin with the fragment that first catches the eye. The piece is likely to be different each time it is played.

Chance music makes a complete break with traditional values in music. It asserts, in effect, that one sound or ordering of sounds is as meaningful as another. To most listeners, a piece of chance music is more often significant as an idea than as a collection of actual sounds. Some composers may be attracted by the sheer novelty of chance music, by its ability to shock and attract attention. Others are influenced by Asian philosophies such as Zen Buddhism, which stresses the harmony of beauty and nature. Finally, some composers may want to give performers a major part in the creative process.

Minimalist Music The mid-1960s saw the development of an artistic movement called *minimalism,* which was partly a reaction against the complexity of serialism and the randomness of chance music. **Minimalist music** is characterized by steady pulse, clear tonality, and insistent repetition of short melodic patterns. Its dynamic

Untitled (1984) by Donald Judd (1928–1994) is a minimalist sculpture in four identical parts.

level, texture, and harmony tend to stay constant for fairly long stretches of time, creating a trancelike or hypnotic effect. Leading minimalist composers, such as Terry Riley (b. 1935), Steve Reich (b. 1936), Philip Glass (b. 1937), and John Adams (b. 1947), have been profoundly influenced by nonwestern thought; many have studied African, Indian, or Balinese music. Minimalist music grew out of the same intellectual climate as minimalist art, which features simple forms, clarity, and understatement. Indeed, in the 1960s, minimalist musicians were appreciated more by painters and sculptors than by their fellow composers. "I gravitated towards artists because they were always more open than musicians, and I liked looking at what they did," Philip Glass has said.

Minimalist composers have generally tried to bring their music to the widest possible audience. "One mode of feedback I rely on most," writes Steve Reich, "is the popular naive reactions. . . . My work, and that of Glass and Riley, comes as a breath of fresh air to the new music world. . . . This feeling is very healthy. It's a feeling of moving back away from a recondite and isolated position, toward a more mainstream approach." Both Reich and Glass have ensembles that perform their music in auditoriums and rock clubs. A turning point in public acceptance of minimalist music came in 1976, when Reich's *Music for 18 Musicians* received an ovation in Town Hall in New York and—also in New York—Glass's opera *Einstein on the Beach,* which we study, sold out the Metropolitan Opera House. After the early 1970s, minimalist music became progressively richer in harmony, tone color, and texture, as is exemplified in Adams's opera *Nixon in China* (1987).

Musical Quotation   Since the mid-1960s, many composers have written works in which they deliberately make extensive use of quotations from earlier music, usually fairly familiar works of the eighteenth, nineteenth, and twentieth centuries. Like minimalist music, *quotation music* often represents a conscious break with serialism, as well as an attempt to improve communication between composer and listener. The quoted material usually either conveys a symbolic meaning or is varied, transformed, and juxtaposed with other music. For example, in the outer movements of *Concerto Grosso 1985,* which we study, Ellen Taaffe Zwilich juxtaposes parts of a Handel sonata with original passages. In *Sinfonia* (1968), a composition for voices and orchestra by the Italian composer Luciano Berio (1925–2003), the third section is based on the

Marilyn Monroe (1964) by Andy Warhol. Pop artists like Warhol use ordinary subjects from everyday life and the mass media.

scherzo from Mahler's Second Symphony; on this quoted material from Mahler, Berio superimposes fragments of music by Bach, Debussy, Ravel, Berlioz, Schoenberg, and other composers, creating a musical collage. Like Charles Ives early in the twentieth century, composers since the 1960s have often juxtaposed heterogeneous material. The American composer George Crumb (b. 1929) explained that in writing his song cycle *Ancient Voices of Children* (1970), he "was conscious of an urge to fuse various unrelated stylistic elements, . . . a suggestion of Flamenco with a Baroque quotation . . . or a reminiscence of Mahler with a breath of the orient."

Some modern composers will not only quote earlier composers but also imitate earlier styles. In String Quartet No. 3 (1972) by the American composer George Rochberg (1918–2005), there are sections of atonal music and passages in the styles of Beethoven and Mahler.

Tonal Music and a Return to Tonality As in the early twentieth century, many composers since 1945 have written tonal music, as opposed to atonal or twelve-tone music. (It may be helpful to review the discussion of alternatives to the traditional tonal system on pages 287–288.) Such tonal music spans a vast range of styles and compositional methods, and includes works by composers as diverse as Benjamin Britten, Dmitri Shostakovich, Leonard Bernstein (1918–1990), and John Adams. Tonal compositions may include central tones or chords as well as consonant sonorities. Some works are entirely tonal, and others are basically atonal but contain chord progressions that provide a fleeting sensation of tonality.

Starting in the late 1960s, some composers, such as the Americans George Rochberg (1918–2005) and David Del Tredici (b. 1937), returned to tonality after having written atonal or twelve-tone music. These composers are sometimes referred to as "new romantics," to emphasize the emotional intensity of their works.

Tonality could be a fascinating "novel" option for musicians trained in the twelve-tone system. "For me," explained Del Tredici, "tonality was actually a daring discovery. I grew up in a climate in which, for a composer, only dissonance and atonality were acceptable. Right now, tonality is exciting for me."

Electronic Music Since the development of tape studios, synthesizers, and computers in the 1950s and 1960s, composers have had potentially unlimited resources for the production and control of sound. *Electronic music* is as varied as nonelectronic music. Its spectrum includes rock, chance music, and serial compositions.

Electronic instruments let composers control tone color, duration, dynamics, and pitch with unprecedented precision. Composers are no longer limited by human performers. For the first time, they can work *directly* in their own medium—sound. There is no more need for intermediaries, that is, performers. The recording of a composition *is* the composition. Thus, a composer alone is now responsible for putting into music the subtle variations of rhythm, tone color, and dynamics that once rested with the performer.

Many composers have combined electronic sounds with live performers. Some pieces use one or more live performers in conjunction with recorded sounds. The recorded sounds may be electronic pitches or noises, or they may be previously recorded sounds of live performers. In some cases, performers may be involved in a duet with themselves, or a duet with electronically manipulated versions of their own performances. Some composers have created interactive works for performers and computer. In such compositions, the computer is programmed by the composer to respond in musically meaningful ways to the live performance.

There are also works for traditional instruments and digital synthesizers and samplers that are performed "live." In addition, traditional instruments may also be "electrified" through amplification. Composers use "electric" pianos and violins, for instance.

Electronic music is important not only in itself but also for its influence on musical thought in general. Electronic instruments have suggested new sounds and new forms of rhythmic organization. "These limitless electronic media," said Milton Babbitt, have shown us new boundaries and new limits that are not yet understood—the very mysterious limits, for example, of the human capacity to hear, to conceptualize, and to perceive. Very often we will specify something and discover that the ear can't take in what we have specified. . . . The human organism simply cannot respond quickly enough, cannot perceive and differentiate as rapidly and precisely as the synthesizer can produce it and as the loudspeaker can reproduce it.

"Liberation of Sound" Composers today use a wider variety of sounds than ever before, including many that were once considered undesirable noises. Composers have achieved what Edgard Varèse called "the liberation of sound . . . the right to make music with any and all sounds." Electronic music may include environmental sounds, such as thunder, or electronically generated hisses and blips. But composers may also draw novel sounds from voices and nonelectronic instruments. Singers are asked to scream, whisper, laugh, groan, sneeze, cough, whistle, and click their tongues. They may sing phonetic sounds rather than words. Composers may treat their vocal text merely as a collection of sounds and not attempt to make the meaning of the words clear to the audience.

Wind and string players tap, scrape, and rub the bodies of their instruments. A brass or woodwind player may hum while playing, thus creating two pitches at once. A flutist may click the keys of the instrument without producing a tone; a pianist may reach inside the piano to pluck a string and then run a chisel along it, creating a sliding sound. To communicate their intentions to performers, composers may devise new systems of music notation because standard notation makes no provision for many noiselike sounds. Recent music scores contain graphlike diagrams, new note shapes and symbols, and novel ways of arranging notation on the page (see the illustration below). But composers are not the only ones to invent unusual sounds. Often the

Scores for recent music often include notes in new shapes, new symbols, and novel ways of arranging notation on the page. Here is a page from the score *Threnody: To the Victims of Hiroshima* by Krzysztof Penderecki.

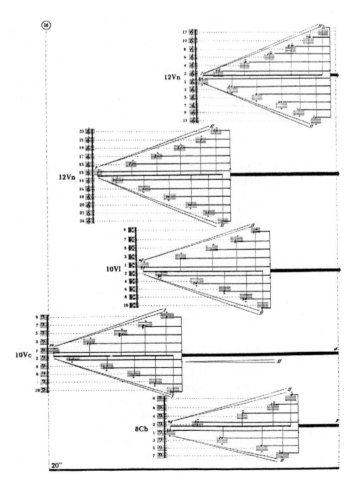

Percussion instruments are imaginatively exploited in much recent music. Shown here is the percussionist EvelynG lennie.

players themselves discover new possibilities for their instruments. Many modern works have been inspired by the discoveries of inventive performers.

The greatest expansion and experimentation have involved percussion instruments. In many recent compositions, percussion instruments outnumber strings, woodwinds, and brasses. Traditional percussion instruments are struck with new types of beaters made of glass, metal, wood, and cloth. Unconventional instruments now widely used include tom-toms, bongos, slapstick, maracas, guiro, and vibraphone.

In the search for novel sounds, increased use has been made of *microtones,* intervals smaller than the half step. Small intervals like quarter tones have long been used in nonwestern music, but they have only recently become an important resource for western composers. Electronic instruments have stimulated this development because they are not restricted to conventional scales and do not force players to unlearn performance habits.

Composers like Krzysztof Penderecki (b. 1933) create sounds bordering on electronic noise through tone clusters—closely spaced tones played together. Clusters are unlike traditional chords in that one usually hears not individual tones but a mass, block, or band of sound. Composers may achieve a sense of growth or change by widening or narrowing such a band, or by making it more or less dense.

The directional aspect of sounds—how they are projected in space—has taken on new importance. Loudspeakers or groups of instruments may be placed at opposite ends of the stage, in the balcony, or at the back and sides of the auditorium. In electronic compositions like Edgard Varèse's *Poème électronique* (1958) and nonelectronic works like Elliott Carter's Double Concerto for harpsichord and piano with two chamber orchestras (1961), sounds are made to travel gradually in space, passing from one loudspeaker or player to another.

Mixed Media Electronic music is often presented together with visual counterparts such as slide projections, films, light shows, gestures, and theatrical action. One such *mixed-media* presentation was Varèse's *Poème électronique,* which combined electronic sounds with images projected on walls. But multimedia works are not confined to electronic music. Chance music and other types of recent music sometimes require performers to function as both actors and sound producers, as in Crumb's *Ancient Voices of Children.* Mixed-media presentations are generally intended to break down the ritual surrounding traditional concerts and to increase communication between composer and audience.

Rhythm and Form Rhythm and form have undergone some of the most striking changes in music since 1945. Earlier in the century, composers often changed

Betty (1988), by Gerhard Richter (b. 1932), is a painting of the artist's daughter. Richter is well known both for abstract works and for realistic paintings inspired by photographs.

meters or used unconventional meters such as $\frac{7}{4}$ and $\frac{5}{8}$. After 1945, some composers abandoned the concepts of beat and meter altogether. This is a natural outcome of electronic music, which needs no beat to keep performers together. In nonelectronic music too, the composer may specify duration in absolute units such as seconds rather than in beats, which are relative units. In some recent music, there may be several different speeds at the same time.

More than ever, each piece of music follows its own laws, and its form grows out of its material. Some composers no longer write music in traditional forms, such as A B A, sonata form, or rondo. Indeed, form may unfold with little or no obvious repetition of material.

20 Music since 1945: Five Representative Pieces

Sonatas and Interludes for Prepared Piano (1946–1948), by John Cage

The American composer John Cage (1912–1992) was the highly influential creator of chance music—as discussed in Section 19—and a major figure in the development of percussion music. He invented the ***prepared piano,*** a grand piano whose sound is altered by objects such as bolts, screws, rubber bands, pieces of felt, paper, and plastic inserted between the strings of some of the keys. "In practice, the preparation takes about three hours," Cage explained. Such preparation results in a wide variety of sounds that resemble those of drums, cymbals, xylophones, tambourines, and gongs. When the pianist's finger strikes a key, sometimes more than one sound is produced.

Cage invented the prepared piano around 1940, when he was asked to write music for a modern dance on an African theme. The dance was to be performed in a small auditorium with enough space for a small grand piano, but not for a group of percussionists. "In effect," Cage wrote, "the prepared piano is a percussion ensemble under the control of a single player."

The large-scale *Sonatas and Interludes* (1946–1948), lasting around sixty-six minutes, is Cage's best-known work for prepared piano and one of his most widely performed and recorded compositions. It includes twenty short pieces—sixteen one-movement sonatas and four interludes—ranging in length from one and a half minutes to five minutes. *Sonatas and Interludes* reflects the composer's study of eastern philosophy. Cage explained that the cycle aims to express the range of stylized emotional states described in Indian aesthetic theory: "the heroic, erotic, wondrous, mirthful, odious, sorrowful, fearful, angry, and their common tendency toward tranquility." We focus on the second sonata of the cycle.

Sonata II

Part A
0:00
Part A repeated
0:24

Part B
0:49
Part B repeated
1:27

Selection available on:
Connect Music
Mp3 download card
Mp3 disc

The two-minute Sonata II, in A A B B form, is characterized by a gradual thickening of texture and increase in rhythmic momentum. Part A moves from a single melodic line—sometimes accompanied by percussive sounds—to a two-voice texture. This part is predominantly soft, in a fairly high register. Short phrases, arranged in question-and-answer pairs, are framed by silences. In two phrases, a melodic fragment immediately repeats.

Part B is almost twice as long as A and has more extended phrases and a richer texture. It begins abruptly with a loud, dense sonority that contrasts with the gentle, lingering sounds and pause ending part A. The concluding phrase of part B is the most climactic and rhythmically active. It begins with a torrent of high running notes and ends with a high trill-like figure and a single accented tone.

Poème électronique (*Electronic Poem;* 1958), by Edgard Varèse

Edgard Varèse (1883–1965), one of the great innovators of twentieth-century music, was born in France but spent most of his life in the United States. As early as 1916, he

The inside of a prepared piano.

dreamed of freeing music from the limitations of traditional instruments and expanding the vocabulary of sounds. During the 1920s and 1930s, Varèse pioneered in the exploration of percussive and noiselike sounds, and he wrote the first important work for percussion ensemble (*Ionisation,* 1931).

But it was the new electronic developments of the 1950s that enabled Varèse to realize his vision of a "liberation of sound." In 1958, at the age of seventy-five, he composed *Poème électronique,* one of the earliest masterpieces of electronic music created in a tape studio. The eight-minute work was designed to be heard within the pavilion of the Philips Radio Corporation at the 1958 Brussels World's Fair. Varèse obtained unique spatial effects by projecting sound from 425 loudspeakers placed all over the interior surfaces of the pavilion. The composer worked in collaboration with the architect Le Corbusier, who selected a series of images—photographs, paintings, and writing—that were projected on the walls as the music was heard. However, Varèse did not make any attempt to synchronize the sounds with the images chosen by Le Corbusier, which included "birds and beasts, fish and reptiles, . . . masks and skeletons, idols, girls clad

Varèse's *Poeme electronique* was first heard within the pavilion of the Philips Radio Corporation, designed by Le Corbusier, at the 1958 Brussels World's Fair.

and unclad, cities in normal appearance and then suddenly askew," as well as atomic mushroom clouds.

Because it was created in a tape studio, *Poème électronique* exists in only a single "performance" whose duration (eight minutes) is fixed on audiotape. Varèse's raw sound material—tones and noises—came from a wide variety of sources, including electronic generators, church bells, sirens, organs, human voices, and machines. The sounds are often electronically processed in such a way that they cannot be precisely identified. In the Listening Outline, the effect of such sounds is conveyed by words placed in quotation marks; for example, "wood blocks" or "chirps." Varèse organized his sounds into an electronic poem that seems weird yet is amazingly logical and compelling.

Poème électronique divides into two main sections, the first lasting two minutes thirty-six seconds and the second five minutes twenty-nine seconds. Each section begins with low bell tolls and ends with sirens. Heard several times during *Poème* is a distinctive group of three rising tones. Human voices and recognizable organ tones appear only during the second section. Varèse once remarked about the female voice heard toward the end: "I wanted it to express tragedy—and inquisition."

Listening Outline

VARÈSE, *Poème électronique (Electronic Poem)*

Tape studio
(Duration, 8:00)

0:00	**1. a.**	Low bell tolls. "Wood blocks." Sirens. Fast taps lead into high, piercing sounds. Two-second pause.
0:43	**b.**	"Bongo" tones and higher grating noises. Short "squawks." Three-tone group stated three times.
1:11	**c.**	Low sustained tones with grating noises. Sirens. Short "squawks." Three-tone group. Two-second pause.
1:40	**d.**	Short "squawks." High "chirps." Variety of "shots," "honks," "machine noises." Sirens. Taps lead to
2:36	**2. a.**	Low bell tolls. Sustained electronic tones. Repeated "bongo" tones. High and sustained electronic tones. Low tone, crescendo. Rhythmic noises lead to
3:41	**b.**	Voice, "Oh-gah." Four-second pause. Voice continues softly.
4:17	**c.**	Suddenly loud. Rhythmic percussive sounds joined by voice. Low "animal noises," scraping, shuffling, hollow vocal sounds. Decrescendo into seven-second pause.
5:47	**d.**	Sustained electronic tones, crescendo and decrescendo. Rhythmic percussive sounds. Higher sustained electronic tones, crescendo. "Airplane rumble," "chimes," jangling.
6:47	**e.**	Female voice. Male chorus. Electronic noises, organ. High taps. Swooping organ sound. Three-note group stated twice. Rumble, sirens, crescendo.

Concerto Grosso 1985 (To Handel's Sonata in D Major for Violin and Continuo, First Movement), by Ellen Taaffe Zwilich

The American composer Ellen Taaffe Zwilich (b. 1939) won the Pulitzer Prize for Music in 1983 for her Symphony No. 1. Zwilich was born in Miami, Florida; her father was an airline pilot. She studied at Florida State University and at the Juilliard School and played for several years as a professional violinist in the American Symphony Orchestra under the direction of Leopold Stokowski. She has composed an impressive series of widely performed instrumental works, including her String Quartet (1974), Symphony No. 2 (1985), Concerto for Piano and Orchestra (1986), Symphony No. 3 (1992), *Millennium Fantasy* for Piano and Orchestra (2000), and Symphony No. 5 (Concerto for Orchestra; 2008), commissioned by the Juilliard School. From 1995 to 1999 she occupied Carnegie Hall's first Composer's Chair, and in 1999 she was named *Musical America*'s Composer of the Year. A professor at her alma mater, Florida State University, she was elected to the American Academy of Arts and Sciences in 2004.

Concerto Grosso 1985 was commissioned by the Washington Friends of Handel to commemorate Handel's three-hundredth birthday. Each of its five movements uses thematic material drawn from the opening movement of Handel's Sonata for Violin and Continuo in D Major. Zwilich has said: "I performed the [Handel] many years ago, and I especially love the opening theme of the first movement. . . . Throughout [*Concerto Grosso 1985*], I found myself using compositional techniques typical of the

Ellen Taaffe Zwilich.

baroque period, including terraced dynamics, repeated phrases . . . techniques I would not normally use, but I felt inspired to do so because of the fact that this piece was based on Handel." Like the concerti grossi of Handel and Bach, Zwilich's *Concerto Grosso 1985* is written for a small orchestra including a harpsichord and gives solo instruments prominent roles. Its five movements are arranged symmetrically: the finale is similar to the opening movement, and the fourth movement parallels the second. The two outer movements include entire passages from the Handel sonata, whereas the three inner movements use no quotations but freely develop the sonata's opening melodic motive. We focus on the first movement, a clear example of "quotation music."

First Movement: Maestoso (majestic)

The maestoso repeatedly alternates quotations from Handel with passages that could have been written only in the twentieth century. Though abrupt, these contrasts somehow add up to a unified whole. Partly, this is because the newly composed sections are often based on a speeded-up variation of Handel's opening four-note motive.

In addition, Zwilich's own music uses compositional techniques associated with the baroque. Long pedal points in the bass give a firm definition of key to melodic lines that use dissonances freely in a twentieth-century manner. And these melodic lines include the repeated rhythmic pattern short-short-long, short-short-long found in music by Bach and Handel.

Listening Outline

ZWILICH, *Concerto Grosso 1985*

First Movement
Maestoso (majestic), quadruple meter ($\frac{4}{4}$), D major
Flute, 2 oboes, bassoon, 2 French horns, harpsichord, 1st violins, 2d violins, violas, cellos, double basses
(Duration, 2:45)

0:00   **1. a.** Orchestra in unison, *f*, single sustained tone presented three times.

        b. Violins, *f*, vigorous phrase, short-short-long rhythm, sustained tone in bass;

       vigorous phrase repeated softly.

0:34   **c.** Handel quotation, strings and harpsichord, *mp*,

       interrupted by

0:55   **2. a.** Vigorous phrase developed in strings and woodwinds; crescendo to f, short string phrases with abrupt pauses.

   b. Handel quotation continued, oboe mf, accompanied by harpsichord and strings.

1:31   **3. a.** Vigorous phrase in violins, f, imitated in flute, f; vigorous phrase in violins, f.

   b. Handel quotation continued, f, trills in strings and woodwinds; harpsichord; melody closes.

2:03   **4. a.** Vigorous phrase in violins, flute, and oboes; crescendo to ff.

2:13   **b.** Woodwinds, high sustained dissonant chords; low strings, fragments of vigorous string phrase, ff. Ends on sustained dissonant chord, f.

Short Ride in a Fast Machine (1986), by John Adams

John Adams (b. 1947) is a leading American composer who has been aptly described as a postminimalist. His music combines the driving pulse, constant repetition, and clear tonality of minimalism with lyrical, expressive melodies and varied orchestral colors. "I grew up in a household where Benny Goodman and Mozart were not separated," Adams once recalled. Indeed, his works reflect the influence of American popular music as well as composers such as Stravinsky and Reich.

A conductor as well as a composer, Adams taught and directed the New Music Ensemble at the San Francisco Conservatory of Music from 1972 to 1982 and was composer in residence with the San Francisco Symphony Orchestra from 1982 to 1985. In 2009, he was appointed creative chair of the Los Angeles Philharmonic to compose works for the orchestra while serving as a member of its planning team. His compositions include *Harmonium* (1980), for chorus and orchestra; the orchestral works *Harmonielehre* (1985), *Short Ride in a Fast Machine* (1986) and *City Noir* (2009); and the operas *Nixon in China* (1987), *The Death of Klinghoffer* (1991), *Dr. Atomic* (2005), dealing with J. Robert Oppenheimer, the physicist known as the father of the atomic bomb, and *A Flowering Tree* (2006), based on a folktale from southern India. In 2003, Adams won the Pulitzer Prize in Music for *On the Transmigration of Souls* (2002), a work for chorus and orchestra commissioned by the New York Philharmonic in commemoration of those who died in the terrorist attacks on the Pentagon and the World Trade Center on September 11, 2001.

Short Ride in a Fast Machine, a four-minute fanfare, is one of the most widely performed orchestral works by a living American composer. The work was commissioned by the Great Woods Festival to celebrate its inaugural concert at Great Woods, Mansfield, Massachusetts. *Short Ride in a Fast Machine* generates enormous excitement because of its rapid tempo, rhythmic drive, and powerful, colorful sonorities. The large orchestra includes two synthesizers and a variety of percussion instruments played by four musicians. These percussion instruments include a sizzle cymbal (a large cymbal with loose rivets placed in a ring of holes) and crotales (small cymbals of definite pitch). *Short Ride in a Fast Machine* is pervaded by steady beats in the wood block, rapid-note ostinatos in synthesizers and clarinets, and repeated orchestral chords that alternate between regular pulsations and irregular rhythms. The climax comes toward the end, when Adams introduces a stirring, fanfare-like melody in the trumpets.

John Adams.

Listening Outline

ADAMS, *Short Ride in a Fast Machine*

Delirando (deliriously)
2 piccolos, 2 flutes, 2 oboes, English horn, 4 clarinets, 3 bassoons, contrabassoon, 4 French horns, 4 trumpets, 3 trombones, tuba, timpani, wood blocks, pedal bass drum, large bass drum, suspended cymbal, sizzle cymbal, large gong (tam-tam), tambourine, triangle, glockenspiel, xylophone, crotales, 2 synthesizers, 1st violins, 2d violins, violas, cellos, double basses
(Duration 4:11)

0:00	**1. a.**	Wood block pulsations followed by ostinatos in clarinets and synthesizer, staccato repeated chords in trumpets, *f*, trombones and French horns join on faster repeated chords; piccolo fragments and snare drum strokes punctuate.
0:32	**b.**	Pulsating brass chords, piccolo fragments, brass chords in irregular rhythms, quick snare drum strokes and suspended cymbal announce
1:01	**c.**	String entrance, chords in irregular rhythms, bass drum strokes, chords rise in pitch, cymbal, bass drum and snare drum strokes, crescendo to *fff*.
1:39	**d.**	Suddenly softer, "walking" figure in cellos and basses below pulsating, rising orchestral chords, irregular rhythms in percussion, brass, and woodwinds, crescendo to *fff*.
2:31	**e.**	Trombones and tubas, *fff*, low downward skip, repeated chords in brasses and woodwinds; bass drum, gong, cymbals, crescendo to *fff*.
2:46	**f.**	Suddenly softer orchestral pulsations, clarinet ostinato.
2:53	**2. a.**	Trumpets, *ff*, extended melody, accompanied by pulsating chords and countermelody in French horns, crescendo to *fff*.
3:49	**b.**	Repeated major chords in trumpets and trombones, *fff*, percussive concluding chord.

Lux Aurumque (Light and Gold; 2000, for a cappella chorus), by Eric Whitacre

Much music conveying a feeling of spirituality has been composed during the late twentieth and early twenty-first centuries. Often written for chorus, this music is set to a wide range of sacred and secular texts originally written in Greek, Hebrew, Latin, Arabic, English, Spanish, Persian, and Sanskrit, among other languages. Though varied in style and technique, such choral works usually include consonant chords and major and minor scales, and are immediately accessible to the listener. Leading representatives of this approach are the Polish composer Henryk Gorecki (1933–2010), the Estonian Arvo Pärt (b. 1935), the Englishman John Tavener (b. 1944) and the American Eric Whitacre (b. 1970), whose *Lux Aurumque* exemplifies this genre. (Whitacre's career and Internet Virtual Choir are discussed in the Performance Perspectives box on p. 356.)

At the beginning of the twenty-first century, Eric Whitacre (b. 1970) emerged as an important composer and conductor of choral music. Born in a small farming town in northern Nevada, he played synthesizers in a rock band in his teens, and dreamed of becoming a pop star. But Whitacre changed direction at age eighteen, when he sang in the University of Nevada chorus and was overwhelmed by the beauty of Mozart's *Requiem.* "In my entire life," Whitacre recalled, "I had seen in black and white and suddenly everything was in shocking Technicolor. The most transformative experience I've ever had." Whitacre began to compose when he was twenty-one, and four years later he enrolled at the Juilliard School, where he earned an MA in music composition and met his future wife, the Grammy award-winning soprano Hila Plitmann.

In 2009 his music became known to millions of listeners though his Internet Virtual Choir project. In 2012 he won a Grammy for *Light & Gold* (2010), his first album as both composer and conductor, which became the number one classical album in the United States. Whitacre's music is frequently performed by choirs in many countries, including the United States, France, England, Switzerland, and Germany. His choral music often alternates consonant chords with sweetly dissonant chords including tone clusters, tones only a half step or a whole step apart. Text and music are sensitively fused in his works. Whitacre says that a choral composer's "first and greatest responsibility is to the poem. I work very hard to understand the meaning of each poem I am setting, and when it comes time to compose the music I simply try to quiet myself enough to hear the notes already hidden below the poet's words."

Lux Aurumque is a brief piece for unaccompanied mixed chorus with a Latin text about light and the soft singing of angels. Whitacre originally wrote the poem in English, using the pen name Edward Esch, but he had it translated into Latin by the American poet Charles Anthony Silvestri. "I love setting Latin," Whitacre has explained, "because of the pure, perfect vowels, and the stoicism and formality it instantly creates. It also allows me to meditate on words, setting them over and over." In *Lux Aurumque* words of the text usually repeat several times in succession.

Lux,	Light,
calida gravisque pura velut auram	warm and heavy as pure gold
et canunt angeli molliter	and the angels sing softly
modo natum	to the newborn baby

A slow tempo, legato performance, and very soft dynamics contribute to the dreamlike mood of *Lux Aurumque*. Its highly varied sounds include a solo soprano voice joining with the chorus, and the chorus singing consonant dyads—two tones sounded simultaneously—as well as mildly dissonant eight-note chords. These eight-note chords, which include tone clusters, result when the individual choral parts—soprano, alto, tenor, and bass—are divided into two. Often a single word begins with a consonance and ends with a dissonance. (See *Lux, calida, pura, canunt,* and *natum* in the Vocal Music Guide.) In his score, Whitacre points out that "if the tight harmonies are carefully tuned and balanced they will shimmer and glow."

Lux Aurumque consists of a main section and a shorter concluding section. The main section is in minor and includes a very brief soprano solo. The concluding section begins in minor with the same music as the main section, an octave lower. *Lux Aurumque* ends with a feeling of peace and resolution as minor gives way to major, and the 1st sopranos softly sustain a single tone while the other voices sing very low eight-note chords.

Vocal Music Guide

WHITACRE, *Lux Aurumque*

Consonance-dissonance, brief pause, minor key.	*Lux*	Light
	Lux	

Soprano solo joins.	Lux	
	Lux	
	calida	warm
	calida	
Sopranos/tenors descending chromatic scale	gravisque	and heavy
	gravisque	
	pura	as pure
High note on pu.	pura	
	velut aurem	as gold
	et canunt	and sing
Basses descend on ca.	et canunt	
Major chord on li.	angeli	angels
Opening music returns one octave lower, minor key.	canunt	sing
	canunt	
	canunt	
	molliter	softly
1st sopranos sustain tone on tum above low chords, major key.	natum	baby
	natum	
	natum	
	modo natum.	newborn baby.

Performance Perspectives

Eric Whitacre Conducting his *Lux Aurumque*, performed by the Virtual Choir

Inspired by the sweet voice of a fan who uploaded a video of herself singing one of his choral works, the American composer Eric Whitacre invited singers to submit videos of themselves performing individual vocal parts of his choral piece *Lux Aurumque* (Light and Gold). He uploaded the sheet music of *Lux Aurumque*, along with a video of himself conducting an imaginary silent choir, and a rehearsal piano track to help singers perform their parts. YouTube videos sent by 185 singers from twelve countries were combined and coordinated to form a Virtual Choir performance of *Lux Aurumque* that has been viewed more than 3.5 million times.

"I was moved to tears when I first saw it," Whitacre has said. "Singing together, and making music together, is a fun-damental human experience. And I love the idea that technology can bring people together from all over the world. People seem to be experiencing an actual connection. I feel a closeness to this choir, almost like a family."

Since its debut in 2009, the Virtual Choir has performed two other compositions by Whitacre, with an increasing number of participating singers: *Sleep* in 2011 with over 2,051 voices from fifty-eight counties and *Water Night* in 2012 with 3,746 voices from seventy-six countries. The success of Whitacre's Virtual Choir project illustrates the Internet's enormous influence on the musical culture of the early twenty-first century.

21 Jazz

About the time Schoenberg and Stravinsky were changing the language of music in Europe, a new musical style called *jazz* was being developed in the United States.* It was created by musicians—predominantly African Americans—performing in the streets, bars, brothels, and dance halls of New Orleans and other southern cities.

Jazz can be described generally as music rooted in improvisation and characterized by syncopated rhythm, a steady beat, and unique tone colors and performance techniques. Although the term *jazz* became current in 1917, the music itself was probably heard as early as 1900. We do not know exactly when jazz started, or how it sounded at first, because this new music existed only in performance, not musical notation. Moreover, very little jazz was captured on recordings before 1923, and none at all before the Original Dixieland Jazz Band recorded in 1917.

Since its beginnings, jazz has developed a rich variety of substyles such as New Orleans style (including Dixieland), swing, bebop, cool, free jazz, and jazz rock. It has produced such outstanding figures as Louis Armstrong, Duke Ellington, Benny Goodman, Charlie Parker, and Miles Davis. Its impact has been enormous and worldwide, affecting not only many kinds of popular music, but the music of such composers as Maurice Ravel, Darius Milhaud, George Gershwin, and Aaron Copland.

The trumpeter, composer, and educator Wynton Marsalis is the first jazz musician to be awarded the Pulitzer Prize (1997).

As both a trumpeter and a singer, Louis "Satchmo" Armstrong had a worldwide impact on jazz.

*Two excellent recorded anthologies of jazz are the *Smithsonian Collection of Classic Jazz* and Ken Burns's *Jazz: The Story of American Music.*

One major source of jazz was the American band tradition.

Jazz in Society

The world of jazz has witnessed many changes since its beginnings at the turn of the century. Geographically, its center has shifted from New Orleans to Chicago, Kansas City, and New York. Today, it is hard to speak of *a* jazz center because jazz, in its many substyles, is heard worldwide, from Los Angeles to Tokyo. Jazz has changed in function too. For a long time, it was basically music for dancing; but since the 1940s, many newer jazz styles have been intended for listening. Now we are as likely to hear jazz in a concert hall or college classroom as in a bar or nightclub. The image of jazz has also changed. Like the blues and rock music, it was originally condemned for its emphasis on sexuality, but it has long since become respected as an American art form.

In recent years, jazz has been sponsored by a number of major American cultural institutions. Both Lincoln Center and Carnegie Hall in New York City have regular jazz series, and a Jazz Masterworks Orchestra has been founded at the Smithsonian National Museum of American History in Washington, D.C. Many colleges and universities now offer courses in jazz as part of the music curriculum.

Roots of Jazz

Early jazz blended elements from many musical cultures, including west African, American, and European. West African influences included an emphasis on improvisation, drumming, percussive sounds, and complex rhythms, as well as a feature known as *call and response*. In much west African vocal music, a soloist's phrases are repeatedly answered by a chorus. Similarly, in jazz, **call and response** occurs when a voice is answered by an instrument, or when one instrument (or group of instruments) is answered by another instrument (or group).

Actually, the call-and-response pattern of jazz was derived more directly from African American church services in which the congregation vocally responds to the preacher's "call." Other American influences on jazz were the rich body of music that blacks developed here—including work songs, spirituals, gospel hymns, and dances like the cakewalk—and the music of white America. Nineteenth-century American and European musical traditions became elements in the background of jazz. In addition to hymns, popular songs, folk tunes, and piano pieces, the American band tradition was a major influence. Many marching band instruments were used in early jazz bands, and band music helped shaped the forms and rhythms of early jazz. Along with band music, the immediate sources of jazz were ragtime and blues.

Ragtime

Maple Leaf Rag

Selection available on:
Connect Music
Mp3 download card
Mp3 disc

Ragtime (1890s to about 1915) is a style of composed piano music developed primarily by black pianists who played in southern and midwestern saloons and dance halls. It is generally in duple meter ($\frac{2}{4}$) and performed at a moderate march tempo. The pianist's right hand plays a highly syncopated melody, while the left hand steadily maintains the beat with an "oom-pah" accompaniment. The "king of ragtime" was Scott Joplin (1868–1917), whose most famous pieces include *Maple Leaf Rag* and *The Entertainer.*

Blues

Blues refers to a form of vocal and instrumental music and to a style of performance. Blues grew out of African American folk music, such as work songs, spirituals, and the field hollers of slaves. Exactly when blues originated is uncertain, but by around the 1890s it was sung in rural areas of the south. The original "country blues," usually performed with guitar accompaniment, was not standardized in form or style.

The poetic and musical form of blues crystallized around 1910 and gained popularity through the publication of *Memphis Blues* (1912) and *St. Louis Blues* (1914), by W. C. Handy (1873–1958). During the 1920s, blues became a national craze among African Americans. Records by such blues singers as Bessie Smith sold in the millions. The 1920s also saw the twelve-bar blues (more on this below) become a musical form widely used by jazz instrumentalists as well as blues singers. Since then, jazz and blues have been intertwined. In the 1930s, the singer-guitarist Robert Johnson (1898–1937) combined the sound of country blues—vocal melody accompanied by acoustic guitar—with the formal structure of blues to create music that has influenced many jazz and rock guitarists up to the present day.

Scott Joplin was the best-known ragtime composer.

From the 1920s to the 1950s, Chicago became a blues center because many African American blues singers and instrumentalists had migrated there from the south in the decades after World War I. The 1940s saw the emergence in Chicago of a new, highly energetic blues style—sometimes called *urban blues*—that derived from earlier blues but used electric guitar and amplification. One of the best-known performers of urban blues was Muddy Waters (1915–1983), who had a distinctive style of moaning and shouting. The continuing impact of the blues is apparent in such popular contemporary styles as rhythm and blues, rock and roll, and soul.

Vocal blues is intensely personal, often containing sexual references and dealing with the pain of betrayal, desertion, and unrequited love. The lyrics consist of several three-line stanzas, each in the same poetic and musical form. The first line is sung and then repeated to roughly the same melodic phrase (a a'); the third line has a different melodic phrase and text (b). Here is stanza 4 of Bessie Smith's *Lost Your Head Blues,* which we study:

a : I'm going to leave baby, ain't going to say goodbye.
a': I'm going to leave baby, ain't going to say goodbye.
b : But I'll write you and tell you the reason why.

A blues stanza is set to a harmonic framework that is usually twelve bars in length. This harmonic pattern, known as **twelve-bar blues,** involves only three basic chords: tonic (I), subdominant (IV), and dominant (V). (The **subdominant** is the triad based on the fourth note—*fa*—of the scale.) The specific ordering of these chords can be outlined as follows: tonic (4 bars)—

subdominant (2 bars)—tonic (2 bars)—dominant (2 bars)—tonic (2 bars). Here is how the three-line stanza is set to this chord progression:

	Line 1 (a)	Line 2 (a′)	Line 3 (b)
Bars	1 2 3 4	5 6 7 8	9 10 11 12
Chords	I	IV I	V I

Each stanza of the text is sung to the same series of chords, although other chords may be inserted between the primary chords of the twelve-bar blues form outlined previously. Singers either repeat the same basic melody for each stanza or improvise new melodies to reflect the changing moods of the lyrics. The music is almost always in quadruple meter ($\frac{4}{4}$), and so each bar contains four beats.

Blues singers and instrumentalists have a special style of performance involving "bent" notes, and vocal scoops and slides. Their melodies—both composed and improvised— contain many "blue" notes, which are produced by slightly lowering or flatting the third, fifth, and seventh tones of a major scale. Blues rhythm is also very flexible. Performers often sing or play "around" the beat, accenting notes either just before or after it.

Jazz instrumentalists imitate the performing style of blues singers and use the harmonic pattern of twelve-bar blues as a basis for improvisation. This twelve-bar pattern is repeated over and over while new melodies are improvised above it. As with the baroque ground bass, the repeated chord progression provides unity while the free flow of improvised melodic lines contributes variety. Music in this twelve-bar form can be happy or sad, fast or slow, and in a wide range of styles. *Lost Your Head Blues* (1926), a vocal blues by Bessie Smith, illustrates twelve-bar blues.

Bessie Smith was one of the most influential blues singers.

Lost Your Head Blues (1926), by Bessie Smith

Bessie Smith (1894–1937), known as the "empress of the blues," was the most famous blues singer of the 1920s. Her *Lost Your Head Blues* is a well-known example of blues form and performance style. The lyrics express the feelings of a woman who plans to leave her man because she's "been treated wrong." Each of the poem's five stanzas is set to the twelve-bar blues pattern. Typically, a cornet response follows each line that is sung.

Lost Your Head Blues begins with a four-bar introduction by the accompanying cornet (Joe Smith) and piano (Fletcher Henderson). Bessie Smith then sings a melody that she'll repeat—with extensive variations of pitch and rhythm—in each stanza. Her "blue" notes, microtonal shadings, and slides between pitches are essential to the effect of the song. Notice the eloquent slides up to *I* in her singing of *I was with you baby,* as well as the ornamental quiver on *down* when she sings the words *throw'd your good gal down.* There are many syncopated rhythms because words are often sung just before or after the beat. Bessie Smith's vocal melody is highly sensitive to the words. For example, the long high notes at the beginning of the last stanza ("*Days* are lonesome, *nights* are long") produce a wonderful climax. Throughout the song, Bessie Smith's vocal inflections are perfectly matched by the cornet's improvised responses and echoes.

Vocal Music Guide

SMITH, *Lost Your Head Blues*

Cornet and piano introduction.	
	I was with you baby when you did not have a dime. I was with you baby when you did not have a dime. Now since you got plenty money you have throw'd your good gal down.
	Once ain't for always, two ain't for twice. Once ain't for always, two ain't for twice. When you get a good gal you better treat her nice.
	When you were lonesome I tried to treat you kind. When you were lonesome I tried to treat you kind. But since you've got money, it's done changed your mind.
	I'm going to leave baby, ain't going to say goodbye. I'm going to leave baby, ain't going to say goodbye. But I'll write you and tell you the reason why.
Long high notes on *Days* and *nights*	Days are lonesome, nights are long. Days are lonesome, nights are so long. I'm a good old gal, but I've just been treated wrong.

Performance Perspectives

Bessie Smith Singing *Lost Your Head Blues*

Since Bessie Smith's death in 1937, her recordings not only have delighted listeners worldwide but have had a powerful impact on several generations of singers. The rock star Janis Joplin (1943–1970) said of her: "No one ever hit me so hard. Bessie made me want to sing."

Bessie Smith was born in 1894 to poor African American parents in a one-room shack in Chattanooga, Tennessee. She began her professional career at eighteen, when she joined an entertainment troupe that included Gertrude "Ma" Rainey, a leading blues singer. Over the next decade Smith gradually achieved stardom as she performed in theaters, tents, dance halls, and cabarets, primarily before black audiences in the south and northeast.

A turning point in Bessie Smith's career came in 1923, when her first commercial 78-rpm record—*Down Hearted Blues*—sold 780,000 copies in less than six months. Her powerful voice, emotional intensity, clear diction, and expressive "bent" notes won for her the uncontested title "empress of the blues." She became the highest-paid African American performer and in 1925 was able to buy her own bright yellow railroad car to transport her troupe of about forty, along with equipment and a large tent. She continued to record blues—including about two dozen of her own compositions—with leading jazz musicians such as Louis Armstrong.

The story of Bessie Smith illustrates how the advent of recording technology changed the position of the performer in

musical life. Up until the twentieth century, performers had an impact only on those who heard them in person. Unlike composers, whose notated compositions could be enjoyed by later generations, performers created for the moment, their work surviving only in written descriptions or visual representations. This situation changed dramatically with the invention of recording. Beginning with phonograph records, and later through radio, film, television, compact discs, and digital media, artists like Bessie Smith found a much wider audience and exerted lasting influence.

Many singers have described the impact of Bessie Smith's recordings. The gospel singer Mahalia Jackson (1911–1972), for example, recalled how, as a youngster in New Orleans, she would imitate Bessie Smith: "I'd play that record over and over again, and Bessie's voice would come out so full and round. . . . I'd make my mouth do the same thing."

In 1989 Bessie Smith was inducted into the Rock and Roll Hall of Fame in Cleveland; and in 2001 a play featuring the songs she made famous, *The Devil's Music: The Life and Blues of Bessie Smith,* was performed in New York City. Thanks to her recordings, the epitaph on her tombstone has proved prophetic. "The greatest blues singer in the world will never stop singing."

Bessie Smith's performance of *Lost Your Head Blues* is included in the recordings.

Elements of Jazz

Tone Color Jazz is generally played by a small group (or *combo*) of three to eight players, or by a "big band" of ten to fifteen. The backbone of a jazz ensemble is its **rhythm section,** usually made up of piano, plucked double bass, percussion, and—sometimes—banjo or guitar, which maintains the beat, adds rhythmic interest, and provides supporting harmonies. In a sense, the function of the rhythm section in jazz is comparable to the supporting role of the basso continuo in baroque music.

The main solo instruments of jazz include the cornet, trumpet, saxophone (soprano, alto, tenor, baritone), piano, clarinet, vibraphone, and trombone. Jazz emphasizes brasses, woodwinds, and percussion rather than the bowed strings that dominate symphonic music. Brass players produce a wide variety of tone colors by using different mutes and muting techniques. A jazz performance usually involves both solo and

The rhythm section of a jazz ensemble usually includes piano, bass, and percussion. Pictured here is the Wayne Shorter Quartet.

ensemble sections. For example, a full ensemble might be followed by a trumpet solo and then by a clarinet solo or a duet for saxophone and trumpet.

The distinctive sounds of jazz are easy to recognize but hard to describe. These sounds result from the specific tones that are chosen, and from the particular way these tones are performed within the melody or accompaniment. For example, melodic tones are often attacked more aggressively in jazz than in other musical styles. Jazz performers sometimes "bend" tones to heighten expressivity or use a distinctive type of vibrato. Transitions between consecutive tones often include a variety of other pitch inflections often referred to as "smears" (gliding from one pitch to another), "scoops" (starting at a pitch lower than the intended pitch and swooping up to it), "falloffs" (performing a descending glissando from the final pitch of a phrase), and "shakes" (a very deliberate and exaggerated vibrato).

Improvisation At the heart of jazz lies improvisation. Jazz musicians create a special electricity as they simultaneously create and perform, making decisions at lightning speed. The creativity of great improvisers is staggering. Their recorded performances represent only a tiny fraction of the music they create almost nightly. Of course, not all jazz is improvised, and most contains both improvised and composed sections. Yet it is improvisation that contributes most to the freshness and spontaneity of jazz.

A jazz improvisation is usually in theme-and-variations form. The theme is often a popular song melody made up of thirty-two **bars,** or measures. The improviser varies this original melody by adding embellishments and changing its pitches and rhythms. Some jazz improvisations are based on a harmonic pattern, or series of chords. This harmonic pattern will be repeated over and over while the improviser creates melodies above it. In jazz, each statement of the basic harmonic pattern or melody is called a **chorus.**

A jazz performance usually includes improvised solos by various members of the ensemble. In addition, there may be sections of *collective* improvisation, during which several musicians make up different melodies simultaneously. Their music is held together by the underlying series of chords, which is repeated throughout the performance. Collective improvisation was typical of Dixieland jazz in New Orleans.

Rhythm, Melody, and Harmony Syncopation and rhythmic swing are two of the most distinctive features of jazz. We say that jazz performers *swing* when they combine a steady beat with a feeling of lilt, precision, and relaxed vitality. In most jazz styles, the beat is provided by the percussionist (on drums or cymbals) and by the bass player. There are usually four beats to the bar. Accents often come on the weak beats: 1–**2**–3–**4.** Many kinds of syncopated rhythms result when accented notes come *between* the beats. Jazz musicians also create a feeling of swing by playing a series of notes slightly unevenly. For example, the second note of a pair of eighth notes is typically shorter than the first. Performers differ in their ways of subdividing the beat for this pair of "swing eighths." Most often, the rhythm falls somewhere between two equal eighth notes ♫ and a triplet pattern in which a quarter note is followed by an eighth note ♩. ♪. The performed rhythms of jazz are so irregular that it is difficult to notate them accurately. A performer must deviate appropriately from the notated rhythms to get a true jazz feeling. As jazz has evolved, performers have developed the ability to play rhythms that are highly irregular and complex.

Jazz melodies can be as flexible in pitch as in rhythm. These melodies—whether improvised or composed—often use a major scale in which the third, fifth, and seventh notes are lowered, or flatted, as in vocal blues. Jazz uses chord progressions like those of the traditional tonal system. But over the years, the harmonic vocabulary of jazz has become increasingly complex, sophisticated, and chromatic. Along with traditional three- and four-note chords, jazz often uses five- or six-note chords that sound rich and lush.

Jazz Styles

New Orleans Style

From about 1900 to 1917, jazz developed in a number of American cities, but the major center was New Orleans. *Dixieland jazz,* one of the most popular musical styles to develop in New Orleans during this period, was typically played by a small group of five to eight performers: a *front line* of melodic instruments (cornet or trumpet; clarinet, and trombone) and a supporting rhythm section (drums; chordal instruments such as banjo, guitar, and piano); and a single-line low instrument such as a plucked bass or tuba. The front-line players improvised several contrasting melodic lines at once, producing a kind of polyphonic texture; and their syncopations and rhythmic independence created a marvelous sense of excitement. This collective improvisation, in which each instrument had a special role, was the most distinctive feature of New Orleans jazz, though as the style evolved during the 1920s (mainly in Chicago), solo playing was emphasized.

New Orleans jazz was usually based on a march or church melody, a ragtime piece, a popular song, or twelve-bar blues. Some well-known tunes associated with this style

New Orleans style (or Dixieland) was typically played by five to eight performers. King Oliver (standing, at left rear) is shown here with his Creole Jazz Band in 1923. The band included Louis Armstrong (seated, center) and Lil Hardin (at the piano).

are *When the Saints Go Marching In* and *Oh, Didn't He Ramble?* One or more choruses of collective improvisation generally occurred at the beginning and end of a piece. In between, individual players were featured in improvised solos, accompanied by the rhythm section or by the whole band. Sometimes there were brief unaccompanied solos, called **breaks.** The band's performance might begin with an introduction and end with a brief coda.

Notable figures of New Orleans jazz include Ferdinand "Jelly Roll" Morton and Joseph "King" Oliver. Oliver's *Blues* (1923) is a fine example of instrumental blues and New Orleans style. Especially important is the trumpeter and singer Louis "Satchmo" Armstrong (1901–1971), who was one of the greatest jazz improvisers. He revealed new dimensions of the trumpet, showing that it could be played in a higher register than had been thought possible.

Armstrong also popularized *scat singing,* vocalization of a melodic line with nonsense syllables. Starting in 1925, he made a series of recordings with bands known as Louis Armstrong's Hot Five and Louis Armstrong's Hot Seven. These recordings established his reputation as a leading jazz trumpeter.

Hotter Than That (1927), by Louis Armstrong and His Hot Five

Hotter Than That, an outstanding performance by Louis Armstrong and His Hot Five, is based on a tune written by Lillian Hardin Armstrong (1898–1971), who was Armstrong's wife and the pianist of the band. This performance shows how New Orleans style developed in Chicago during the 1920s. The emphasis is on improvisatory solos, based on the harmonic structure of the thirty-two-bar tune *Hotter Than That.* Collective improvisation—so important in earlier New Orleans style—is restricted to the introduction and the last of four choruses. Louis Armstrong performs as both trumpeter and vocalist. His vocal solo, an example of scat singing, is like his trumpet playing in sound and style. Other solos are by the clarinetist Johnny Dodds and the trombonist Kid Ory. At the middle and end of each chorus there is a brief unaccompanied solo, a break. Listen for the syncopations of Armstrong's vocal melody (chorus 3), the call and response between voice and guitar in the interlude following chorus 3, and the dissonant guitar chord that gives *Hotter Than That* an unusual, inconclusive ending.

Dippermouth Blues

Dippermouth Blues available in Connect Music

Listening Outline

LOUIS ARMSTRONG AND HIS HOT FIVE, *Hotter Than That*

Cornet, voice (Louis Armstrong), piano (Lillian Hardin Armstrong), clarinet (Johnny Dodds), trombone (Kid Ory), guitar (Lonnie Johnson)
Rapid tempo, quadruple meter ($\frac{4}{4}$)
Introduction—four choruses of thirty-two bars—coda
(Duration, 2:59)

Introduction (8 bars)
    0:00   **1.** All instruments, trumpet predominates, collective improvisation.
Chorus 1 (32 bars)
    0:09   **2.** Trumpet solo, accompanied by piano and guitar. Trumpet briefly alone, piano and guitar rejoin.
Chorus 2 (32 bars)
    0:43   **3.** Clarinet solo, piano and guitar accompany.

Chorus 3 (32 bars)	
1:19	**4.** Vocal solo, scat singing, guitar accompanies.
Interlude (20 bars)	
1:54	**5.** Voice imitated by guitar. Piano leads into
Chorus 4 (32 bars)	
2:17	**6. a.** Muted trombone solo, piano and guitar accompany.
2:33	**b.** Trumpet, other instruments join, collective improvisation.
Tag (4 bars)	**c.** Trumpet, guitar, dissonant chord at end.

Swing

A new jazz style called *swing* developed in the 1920s and flourished from 1935 to 1945 (the "swing era"). It was played mainly by *big bands*; the typical *swing band* had about fourteen or fifteen musicians grouped into three sections: saxophones (three to five players, some doubling on clarinet), brass instruments (three or four each of trumpet and trombone), and rhythm (piano, percussion, guitar, and bass). A band of this size needed music that was more composed than improvised and was also *arranged,* or notated in written-out parts for each musician to read. With swing, the arranger became an important figure in jazz.

Melodies were often performed by entire sections of a swing band, either in unison or in harmony. The main melody was frequently accompanied by saxophones and brasses playing short, repeated phrases called *riffs.* The saxophone became one of the most important solo instruments, and percussionists also had a more prominent and spectacular role.

The swing era produced hundreds of "name" bands—both black and white—for example, those of Count Basie, Glen Miller, Tommy Dorsey, and Benny Goodman (the "king of Swing"). Some of the swing bands included leading musicians like the saxophonists Coleman Hawkins and Lester Young and featured singers like Billie Holiday, Ella Fitzgerald, and Frank Sinatra. Duke Ellington (1899–1974) was perhaps the most important composer, arranger, and conductor of the swing era. Ellington's works are richer in harmony and more varied in form than those of his contemporaries. Their

Typically, a swing band included about fifteen musicians. The Benny Goodman Band was one of the leading swing ensembles.

Duke Ellington and his orchestra in 1943. Ellington was perhaps the most important swing composer, arranger, and conductor.

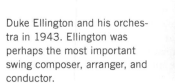

C-Jam Blues

Selection available on:
Connect Music
Mp3 download card
Mp3 disc

variety of mood may be sampled in such works as *KoKo, Harlem Air Shaft, In a Mellotone,* and *Blue Serge* (all included in *The Smithsonian Collection of Classic Jazz*).

C-Jam Blues (1942), in a rendition by Duke Ellington and his Famous Orchestra, was used as an example in Part I, Section 1 (see the listening outline on page 8). It illustrates how Ellington showcases the remarkable musicianship of his band members. Most of the performance is a series of improvised solos on the harmonic structure of twelve-bar blues, each solo introduced by a four-bar break (items 3, 4, 5, 6, 7). Therefore, every solo consists of sixteen bars: a four-bar break followed by a twelve-bar blues chorus. This pattern is unusual because breaks normally appear during the first four bars of a twelve-bar blues structure. The first four solos (violin, muted cornet, tenor saxophone, trombone with plunger mute) are lightly accompanied by the rhythm section. Only during the clarinet solo (item 7) do other instruments join with sustained chords. This buildup leads to a climactic ending chorus (twelve bars) played by the full ensemble.

Bebop

The early 1940s saw the development of **bebop** (or **bop**), a complex style of music usually for small jazz groups consisting of four to six players and meant for attentive listening, not dancing. It had sophisticated harmonies and unpredictable rhythms, and its performers were a special "in" group. A typical bebop ensemble might have a saxophone and a trumpet supported by a rhythm section of piano, bass, and percussion. The role of rhythm instruments was different from that in earlier jazz. The beat, often extremely fast, was marked not by the snare drum or bass drum, but mainly by the

Bebop was a complex style of music usually for small jazz groups. Charlie Parker (alto saxophone) is shown with Tommy Potter (bass), Miles Davis (trumpet), and Duke Jordan (piano).

pizzicato bass and ride cymbal (a large suspended cymbal). The drummer also supplied irregular accents, sometimes played with such power that they are called "bombs." Similarly, the pianist's left hand no longer helped emphasize the basic pulse but joined with the right hand to play complex chords at irregular intervals. Melodic phrases were often varied in length, and chords might have five to seven notes rather than the three or four characteristic of earlier jazz. A bop performance generally began and ended with a statement of the main theme (often derived from a popular song or twelve-bar blues) by a soloist, or by two soloists in unison. The remainder of the piece was made up of solo improvisations based on the melody or harmonic structure.

Notable bebop performers included the trumpeter Dizzy Gillespie (1917–1993) and the pianist Thelonius Monk (1917–1982). The alto saxophonist Charlie Parker (1920–1955) was a towering figure among bebop musicians and an important influence on instrumentalists.

KoKo (1945), by Charlie Parker

KoKo available in Connect Music

Bebop style and Parker's improvisatory genius are both illustrated in *KoKo,* which is performed in our recording by Parker (alto saxophone) and three other outstanding musicians: Dizzy Gillespie (trumpet and piano), Curly Russell (bass), and Max Roach (percussion). Parker based the melody of *KoKo* on the harmonies of the popular song *Cherokee* (1938), a big-band standard of the swing era. "I'd been getting bored with the stereotyped changes [chord progressions] that were being used all the time," said Parker about the composition of *KoKo*. "I kept thinking that there's bound to be something else. I could hear it sometimes but I couldn't play it. Well, that night, I was working over 'Cherokee,' and as I did, I found that by using the higher intervals of the chord as a melody line and backing them with appropriately related changes, I could play the things I'd been hearing. I came alive."

KoKo consists of an introduction, two choruses of alto saxophone solo, a drum solo, and a coda that is a varied and slightly abridged return of the introduction. The tempo is extremely fast, and the beat is usually marked by the pizzicato bass and by the "ride" cymbal played with brushes. Notice the "bombs," or irregular accents played by the bass drum. The introduction begins with a short melody played by the alto saxophone and trumpet in unison and continues with two brief solos played at breakneck speed by these instruments. Parker's extended solo is a torrential flow of rapid notes with asymmetrical phrases and unexpected accents and rests. Only during this solo is the full rhythm section heard. In the spectacular drum solo, complex rhythmic patterns make it difficult to perceive the beat.

Cool Jazz

Cool jazz (which emerged in the late 1940s and early 1950s) was related to bop but far calmer and more relaxed. Cool jazz pieces also tended to be longer than bebop works and relied more heavily on arrangements. They sometimes used instruments that were new to jazz, including the French horn, flute, and cello. The tenor saxophonists Lester Young (1909–1959) and Stan Getz (b. 1927), the pianist Lennie Trístano (1919–1978), and the trumpeter and bandleader Miles Davis (1926–1991) were important figures.

Free Jazz

Until about 1960, jazz improvisations tended to keep the length and chord structure of the original theme, if not its melody. But during the 1960s, some musicians created *free jazz,* a style that was not based on regular forms or established chord patterns.

Free Jazz, recorded in 1960 by Ornette Coleman (b. 1930) with several other musicians improvising individually and collectively, is an example; it can be compared to the chance music created by John Cage and his followers. Another musician who played an important role in the development of free jazz was John Coltrane (1926–1967), who was influential as an improviser, tenor and soprano saxophonist, and composer.

Jazz Rock (Fusion)

Rock became a potent influence on jazz starting in the late 1960s. This influence led to *jazz rock,* or **fusion,** a new style combining the jazz musician's improvisatory approach into a style employing rock musical forms, rhythms, and tone colors. Instruments used by a jazz rock group were either electronic or acoustic and often included synthesizers and electric piano, guitar, and bass. In jazz rock and fusion, the bass player assumes a more melodic role in addition to the more traditional functions of providing the beat and emphasizing the harmonic foundation. The percussion section was sometimes larger than that in earlier jazz groups and often included a percussionist—or sometimes multiple percussionists—performing on instruments from Africa, Latin America, or India.

Miles Davis, a leading musician in cool jazz, was also important in jazz rock. Herbie Hancock, Chick Corea, Joe Zawinul, and Wayne Shorter—who made recordings with both Zawinul and Davis—became pacesetters of jazz rock in the 1970s, 1980s, and 1990s. In addition to these jazz musicians who began to incorporate rock elements, a number of rock musicians began to incorporate jazz improvisation and other elements of the style into their recordings and performances. Two of the most successful of these jazz rock groups during the late 1960s and early 1970s were Chicago and Blood, Sweat & Tears.

Miles Runs the Voodoo Down (1969), by Miles Davis

Miles Runs the Voodoo Down available in Connect Music

Miles Runs the Voodoo Down is from the Miles Davis album *Bitches Brew,* one of the early milestones of jazz rock (fusion). It is performed by a large ensemble of twelve musicians including only three brass and woodwind instruments—trumpet (Miles Davis), soprano saxophone (Wayne Shorter), bass clarinet (Bennie Maupin)—but a very large rhythm section: drums (Lenny White, Jack De Johnette, Charles Alias), percussion (Jim Riley), electric pianos (Chick Corea, Larry Young), electric bass (Harvey Brooks), string bass (Dave Holland), and electric guitar (John McLaughlin). *Miles Runs the Voodoo Down* evokes the feeling of a ritual dance through its slow beat, unchanging harmony, and constant background of rock ostinatos in the electric bass and repeated rhythmic figures in African and South American percussion instruments. We focus on the opening four minutes of this extended piece (lasting fourteen minutes), which features a spectacular improvised solo by Miles Davis.

Miles Runs the Voodoo Down opens softly and ominously with repeated rhythmic and melodic figures in the percussion and electric bass. Other instruments gradually join, creating a hypnotic rhythmic background that becomes increasingly prominent during Miles Davis's solo, which begins half a minute into the piece. The solo conveys a blues feeling because Davis often slides from one pitch to another. It is a free and imaginative flow of musical ideas, not based on a regular form or an established chord pattern. The trumpet opens in a middle to low register. Later, Davis's improvisation moves through a very wide range and includes a variety of brief and extended phrases, screaming high held tones, rapid passages in bebop style, and many inflections that sound vocal. *Miles Runs the Voodoo Down* beautifully integrates jazz improvisation with the rhythms and electronic resources of rock.

Miles Davis.

Jazz rock is only one of the substyles that could be heard since the 1970s. Every kind of jazz we've studied—New Orleans, swing, bebop, cool jazz, and free jazz—has its fans and devoted performers. As they have done since the early days, jazz musicians continue to explore new resources to further the development of their art.

22 Music for Stage and Screen

Musical Theater

Along with jazz and rock, the *musical* was one of the most important American contributions to twentieth-century popular culture. Shows like *Oklahoma! South Pacific, West Side Story,* and *My Fair Lady* are performed and enjoyed all over the world.

Elements of the Musical

A **musical,** or **musical comedy,** is a type of theater that fuses script, acting, and spoken dialogue with music, singing, and dancing and with scenery, costumes, and spectacle. Most musicals are in fact comedies, though some are serious. Many have been produced in theaters around Broadway in New York (hence the term *Broadway musical*), but successful musicals reach nationwide and even worldwide audiences, and some are made into movies (such as *The Sound of Music, Hair, Evita, Chicago, Rent,* and *The Producers*).

Generally, a musical is in two acts, of which the second is shorter and brings back some of the melodies heard earlier. Traditionally, the songs consisted of an introductory section (called the *verse*) and a main section (called the *chorus*) in A A B A form (thirty-two bars). Hit tunes from musicals, like *Ol' Man River* (from *Show Boat*) or *Some Enchanted Evening* (from *South Pacific*), have often had lasting appeal, detached from their original theatrical context.

The American musical embraces a variety of styles, yet it is a distinct type of musical theater, separate from opera. In contrast to opera, it tends to use simpler harmonies, melodies, and forms; it contains more spoken dialogue and its songs have a narrower pitch range. Also, the musical is even more of a collaborative effort: one composer may create the songs, but other musicians are responsible for the orchestration, the overture, connective musical passages, and music accompanying dances. The spoken dialogue and lyrics are usually written by several people. Still, certain works, such as Stephen Sondheim's *Sweeney Todd* (1979), fall somewhere between musicals and operas; and some, like Sondheim's *A Little Night Music* (1973), are eventually performed by opera companies.

Development of the Musical

Sources of the American musical include a variety of musical and dramatic forms of the late nineteenth century and the early twentieth century, including operetta, vaudeville, and the revue. *Operetta,* or *comic opera,* combines song, spoken dialogue, and dance with sophisticated musical techniques. Examples are the operettas of the Englishmen W. S. Gilbert and Arthur Sullivan, such as *The Mikado* (1885); and those of the American Victor Herbert, such as *Babes in Toyland* (1903) and *Naughty Marietta* (1910). A more popular antecedent was *vaudeville,* a variety show with songs, comedy, juggling, acrobats, and animal acts, but no plot. The *revue,* a variety show without a plot but with a unifying idea, was often satirical and featured chorus girls and comedians.

The years from about 1920 to 1960 saw a golden era of the American musical, created by songwriters and composers like Irving Berlin (1888–1989), Jerome Kern (1885–1945), George Gershwin (1898–1937), Cole Porter (1893–1964), Richard Rodgers (1902–1979), Frank Loesser (1910–1969), and Leonard Bernstein (1918–1990). Plots became more believable and wider in range; song and dance were better integrated with the story, and musical techniques became more sophisticated.

During the 1920s and 1930s, despite unrealistic "boy meets girl" stories, lyrics were clever and witty, as in Cole Porter's song *You're the Top* (1934).

> You're the top! You're the Colosseum.
> You're the top! You're the Louvre Museum.
> You're a melody from a symphony by Strauss.
> You're a Bendel bonnet, a Shakespeare sonnet, you're Mickey Mouse. . . .

A pathbreaking musical with a serious plot was *Show Boat* (1927, music by Jerome Kern and lyrics by Oscar Hammerstein II), which treated interracial romance. Its songs—including *Ol' Man River* and *Why Do I Love You?*—revealed character and were smoothly woven into the action. In the 1930s, some musicals satirized social and political institutions. A prominent instance was George and Ira Gershwin's *Of Thee I Sing* (1931), which poked fun at American presidential elections. In the late 1930s, ballet became more significant and was used to carry the action forward. For example, the climax of the musical *On Your Toes* (1936) was a ballet by George Balanchine (1904–1989) called *Slaughter on Tenth Avenue. Oklahoma!*—by Richard Rodgers and the lyricist Oscar Hammerstein II—was a landmark in the integration of dance, songs, and plot; its ballets, created by Agnes de Mille and inspired by square dances, were important for the progress of the story. After World War II, however, an increasing number of shows were set in foreign lands, such as Siam (*The King and I;* 1951), France (*Fanny;* 1954), England (*My Fair Lady;* 1956), and Russia (*Fiddler on the Roof;* 1964). Postwar musicals also began to explore new kinds of serious subjects, such as teenage gang warfare in *West Side Story* (1957).

A scene from *Into the Woods,* a musical by Stephen Sondheim and James Lapine.

After 1960, some composers of Broadway shows continued to write traditional songs—a conservative trend also reflected in the many revivals of classic musicals. However, other composers departed from traditional A A B A form; and often their songs were so much a part of the context that they were unlikely to become hits on their own. Like jazz, the musical was affected by the "rock revolution" of the 1960s. One of the rock musicals was *Hair* (1967), which reflected the hippie movement and had a scene of total nudity. Rock elements were also incorporated into *Jesus Christ Superstar* (1971), by the British musician Andrew Lloyd Webber (b. 1948), who also created *Cats* (1982) and *Phantom of the Opera* (1987), the longest-running Broadway musical ever. The unusual prominence of European composers on the American musical scene was also reflected in *Les Misérables* (1986) and *Miss Saigon* (1989), written by the Frenchmen Claude-Michel Schönberg and Alain Boublil. Highly successful musicals of recent years include *Rent* (1996), *The Lion King* (1997), *Wicked* (2003), and *The Book of Mormon* (2011).

Perhaps the most original contributions to American musical theater since the 1960s have been made by the composer-lyricist Stephen Sondheim (b. 1930), who first became known as the lyricist for *West Side Story.* Many of his works are "concept musicals," based more on an idea than on a traditional plot. They include *Company* (1970); *Sunday in the Park with George* (1984); and his most ambitious work, *Sweeney Todd, the Demon Barber of Fleet Street* (1979), which blurs the boundary between the musical and opera. His musical style fuses elements of the traditional Broadway song with elements of Stravinsky, Copland, and Bernstein.

Leonard Bernstein

The extraordinarily versatile Leonard Bernstein (1918–1990) was a twentieth-century culture hero—conductor, pianist, author, lecturer, and composer of orchestral and vocal works, including *West Side Story.* Bernstein was born in Lawrence, Massachusetts; graduated from Harvard University; and studied piano and conducting at the Curtis

The versatile American musician Leonard Bernstein was a composer of musicals and symphonic works, as well as an outstanding conductor, concert pianist, and author-lecturer.

Institute in Philadelphia. His spectacular career was launched when a guest conductor became ill; Bernstein took the podium with no rehearsal and on a few hours' notice. The concert, which was broadcast on nationwide radio, was hailed as a "dramatic musical event" on the front page of the *New York Times*.

"I have a deep suspicion that every work I write, for whatever medium, is really theater music in some way." Bernstein's words apply not only to his musicals, operas, and ballets and his theater piece *Mass* (1971), but also to his choral work *Chichester Psalms* (1965) and his three programmatic symphonies—*Jeremiah* (1942), *The Age of Anxiety* (1949), and *Kaddish* (1963). His music is clearly tonal, enlivened by syncopations and irregular meters, and infused with jazz and dance rhythms. Like Stravinsky and Copland, who both influenced him, Bernstein wrote very successful ballets, including *Fancy Free* (1944) and *Facsimile* (1946). Dance numbers play an important and dramatic role in his musicals *On the Town* (1944), *Wonderful Town*, (1953) and *West Side Story* (1957). Bernstein accomplished the difficult feat of bridging the worlds of "serious" and popular music. He died in 1990, mourned by people all over the world.

West Side Story (1957)

On January 6, 1949, the choreographer Jerome Robbins first suggested to Leonard Bernstein that they collaborate on a modern version of Shakespeare's *Romeo and Juliet* set in the slums of New York. Bernstein was very enthusiastic about the "idea of making a musical that tells a tragic story in musical-comedy terms, using only musical-comedy techniques, never falling into the 'operatic' trap. Can it succeed? . . . I'm excited. If it can work—it's the first." *West Side Story*—with music by Bernstein, spoken dialogue by Arthur Laurents, and lyrics by Stephen Sondheim—was completed seven years later.

West Side Story deals with a conflict between gang rivalry and youthful love. The feud between the lovers' families in Shakespeare's *Romeo and Juliet* is transformed into warfare between two teenage street gangs: the Jets, native-born Americans led by Riff; and the Sharks, Puerto Ricans led by Bernardo. The plot revolves around a fight ("rumble") between the gangs and the doomed love of Tony (the Romeo character), a former member of the Jets; and Maria (the Juliet character), Bernardo's sister. Tony kills Bernardo after a vain attempt to break up a fight between the leader of the Sharks and Riff. Later he is shot by one of the Sharks and dies in Maria's arms.

Though it included rough street language and ended unhappily, *West Side Story* was a tremendous popular success and became an Oscar-winning musical film (1961). It was an unprecedented fusion of song and drama with electrifyingly violent choreography (by Jerome Robbins and Peter Gennaro). Compared with the average Broadway show, *West Side Story* had more music; more complex and unconventional music; and a wider range of styles, from vaudeville (*Gee, Officer Krupke*) and Latin rhythms (*America*) to bebop fugue (*Cool*) and quasi-operatic ensemble (*Tonight*). We focus on *America* and the *Tonight* Ensemble.

America

The energetic ensemble *America* brilliantly combines Latin-flavored song and dance. Two young women of the Sharks gang, Rosalia and Anita—Bernardo's girlfriend—express opposing feelings about their homeland, Puerto Rico, and their adopted country, America. The ensemble creates a lighter mood after the emotional intensity of previous scenes and helps develop the character of the witty and high-spirited Anita.

Tony and Maria meet on a fire escape in a scene from the film version of *West Side Story.*

America begins with an atmospheric introduction in a moderate tempo. The introduction is marked *Tempo di Seis,* and performed by the two soloists. (*Seis* is a type of Puerto Rican song and dance music.) The homesick Rosalia first sings the words *Puerto Rico, You lovely island, Island of tropical breezes,* eliciting Anita's mocking response—to the same melody—*Puerto Rico, You ugly island, Island of tropic diseases.*

The debate continues in the joyful main part of the song, in a faster tempo marked *Tempo de Huapango.* (*Huapango* refers to a type of Mexican dance.) In this part, the Shark women often join in Anita's praises of America. The three kinds of music heard in this part can be represented as sections A, B, and C in the outline. Section A is the refrain, or recurring main melody, first sung to the words, *I like to be in America* by Anita. Section B consists of brief solos by Rosalia, each followed by Anita's sarcastic responses. Instrumental interludes meant for dancing are referred to as section C. The last interlude is marked C′ because it is varied and shortened. These interludes illustrate the dramatic importance of dance throughout *West Side Story.*

The music of *America* has a Hispanic flavor with alternations between $\frac{6}{8}$ and $\frac{3}{4}$ meter, similar to those in *Final Dance: Malambo* by the Argentinean Alberto Ginastera (studied in Part VI, Section 18). As in *Final Dance: Malambo,* six fast pulses are divided into two groups of three pulses and three groups of two pulses.

Also contributing to the Latin atmosphere in *America* are the sounds of the claves, guiro—both percussion—and guitar, instruments typical of South America.

(In the film version of *West Side Story,* the music of *America* remains the same, but some words are changed and Bernardo and the Shark men sing and dance together with the young women.)

The following outline is meant to clarify the form of *America.* Most often, just the first line of text in a section is given.

Introduction, Moderato, Temo di Seis

Rosalia sings (*Puerto Rico you lovely island . . .*); then Anita sings "mockingly" to the same melody (*Puerto Rico, You ugly island . . .*). Introduction ends with Anita's solo (*I like the island Manhattan . . .*).

Tempo di Huapango, Fast tempo

A	*I like to be in America . . .*	Anita
B	*I like the City of San Juan . . .*	Rosalia and Anita
A	*Automobile in America . . .*	Anita and young women
B	*I'll drive a Buick through San Juan . . .*	Rosalia and Anita
A	*Immigrant goes to America . . .*	Anita and young women
C	Instrumental, dance around Rosalia	
B	*I'll bring a TV to San Juan . . .*	Rosalia and Anita
A	*I like the shores of America . . .*	Anita and young women
C	Instrumental, dance around Rosalia with whistling	
B	*When I will go back to San Juan . . .*	Rosalia and Anita
C′	Varied and shortened instrumental dance	

Tonight Ensemble

In the *Tonight* ensemble, Bernstein projects several different emotions at the same time: Riff, Bernardo, and their gangs excitedly planning for the upcoming fight; Anita looking forward to the "kicks" she's "gonna get"; and Tony and Maria anticipating the joy of being together. Riff, Bernardo, and Anita sing quick, staccato tones in a narrow range, whereas Tony and Maria sing the legato, soaringly lyrical *Tonight* melody, heard in an earlier "balcony scene" on Maria's fire escape. As Verdi did in the Quartet from *Rigoletto*, Bernstein lets us hear the voices separately before combining them in an ensemble. Such dramatic ensembles were uncommon in musicals, which tended to feature solo songs with "hit" potential.

Listening Outline

BERNSTEIN, *Tonight* Ensemble from *West Side Story*

Riff, Bernardo, Anita, Tony, Maria, gang members, orchestra
Fast and rhythmic.
(Duration, 3:38)

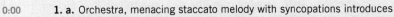

0:00	**1. a.**	Orchestra, menacing staccato melody with syncopations introduces
0:07	**b.**	Riff, Bernardo, and their gangs alternate and then sing together quick, staccato phrases with syncopations.

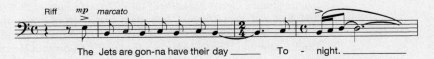

1:08	**c.**	Anita repeats previous phrases.
1:25	**d.**	Tony, lyrical *Tonight* melody.

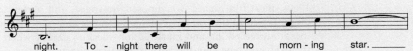

2:15	**2. a.**	Orchestra, *ff*.
2:23	**b.**	Riff, quick staccato phrases.
2:40	**c.**	Maria, lyrical *Tonight* melody, with Riff's staccato phrases, and brief interjections (*All right, Tonight*) by Tony and Anita. Tony joins Maria on *Tonight* melody.
3:29	**d.**	Voices join on sustained high tones (*Tonight*), *ff*.

Music in Film

Early Film Music

Music for film began in the 1890s and emerged as an important musical genre during the twentieth century. During the silent-film era (c. 1890–1926), live pianists, organists, and orchestras accompanied films, both to heighten the emotional effect and to drown out the noise of the movie projector. In the first "talking movie," *The Jazz Singer* (1927), starring Al Jolson, the sound was recorded on vinyl discs. By 1929, new technology enabled sound to be recorded directly on the celluloid filmstrip.

Functions and Styles of Film Music

Synchronized with images on a screen, *film music* provides momentum and continuity, and suggests mood, atmosphere, character, and dramatic action. As in opera and ballet, music in film can convey unspoken thoughts and the emotional implications of a setting. It can clarify the meaning of a scene and enhance the excitement of the action. Movies range widely in the amount and function of the music they contain. At one extreme are musicals and films about musicians, in which musical performer-actors appear on screen and music captures the viewers' attention. At the other extreme are films in which music discreetly accompanies the drama, without diverting viewers from the onscreen action and dialogue.

Most movie music is commissioned for specific films, but some sound tracks include segments of previously existing compositions. Film music is extraordinarily diverse in style, ranging from the rock and roll of *Pulp Fiction* (1994) to the minimalism, electronic sounds, and eerie string effects of *The Matrix* (1999). Many people have come to appreciate classical music by hearing it in such films as *Fantasia* of 1940 (Bach, Beethoven, Stravinsky); *2001: A Space Odyssey* of 1968 (Richard Strauss, Johann Strauss, Ligeti); *Amadeus* of 1984 (Mozart); *Shine* of 1996 (Rachmaninoff); and *The Pianist* of 2002 (Chopin). Important composers of American film music include Franz Waxman (*The Bride of Frankenstein,* 1935), Aaron Copland (*The Heiress,* 1948), Dimitri Tiomkin (*The Old Man and the Sea,* 1958), Bernard Herrmann (*Vertigo,* 1958, which we study), and John Williams (*Star Wars,* 1977; *Harry Potter and the Prisoner of Azkaban,* 2003). Recent composers who are well regarded include James Horner (*Titanic,* 1997) and Danny Elfman (*Spider-Man,* 2002 and 2004). Sometimes, a composer will collaborate with a particular director on many films, as John Williams did with Steven Spielberg (*Jaws,* 1975; *E.T. The Extra-Terrestrial,* 1982; *Schindler's List,* 1993).

Creating Film Music

Up to the 1950s, a major Hollywood film studio such as MGM or Paramount would have a resident orchestra and staff composers, conductors, and arrangers. Since the 1960s, most film music is composed, arranged, and performed by freelance musicians. Typically, the composer views the movie and—in collaboration with the director, producer, editor, and music editor—decides exactly where music will appear in the film, and how long the musical passage, known as a *cue,* will last. Composition, orchestration—usually by one or more orchestrators—and recording are often completed within a few months or less. John Williams has vividly described his preferred method of composing for film: "I'll get a sense of the film's kinetic ebb and flow. . . a sense of where the film may be slowing down, or where it's accelerating, and where I can pick up on the rhythms of the film." For Williams, the "most important issue in scoring films is tempo. Anyone who takes a home movie and puts records to it knows this: if you put one piece of music to it, the film will be one kind of musical experience, and another piece of music will change the experience totally." While composing, Williams will view the scene "many times and have a timing cue sheet that's been prepared for the scene and then I'll write three or four bars and go back and look at it and then write four bars more and look at it again. And it's a constant process of writing, looking, checking, running it in my mind's ear against the film, even conducting with a stopwatch against the action of the film."

Music and Image

In movie scores, musical themes—or leitmotifs—often become associated with specific characters, objects, emotions, or ideas in the film, a technique derived from the music dramas of Richard Wagner. The "shark theme" in *Jaws* (1975), the "007 theme" in the James Bond movies, and the "imperial march" (Darth Vader) theme in the *Star Wars* movies are well-known examples. As in Wagner's music dramas, these musical themes are varied and transformed to convey evolving dramatic situations and changes of character. They can remind the audience of the associated character, whether or not he or she appears onscreen.

The mood of movie music does not always match that of the synchronized visual image. In such instances, the music is meant to produce a distancing or ironic effect. Well-known instances are *Goodfellas* (1990) and *Kill Bill* (2003), in which scenes of horrific violence are accompanied by gentle or happy music, making the action seem almost unreal.

During the last few decades, the importance of music in film has become widely recognized. Interest in film music continues to grow, as many moviegoers have come to appreciate the significant contributions of this musical genre. Today, sound track albums and concert performances bring film music to millions of people outside the movie theater.

Vertigo (1958), Directed by Alfred Hitchcock, Music by Bernard Herrmann

One of the most important American composers of film was Bernard Herrmann (1911–1975), who wrote music for such movies as Orson Welles's *Citizen Kane* (1941); Martin Scorsese's *Taxi Driver* (1976); and Alfred Hitchcock's *Vertigo* (1958), *North by Northwest* (1959), *Psycho* (1960), and *Marnie* (1964). Herrmann's music plays a major role in creating the atmosphere of obsession that pervades *Vertigo*. This psychological thriller received mixed reviews when first released in 1958, but subsequently *Vertigo* and its musical score have been hailed as masterpieces.

Near the beginning of *Vertigo*, Scottie Ferguson (played by James Stewart), a detective in San Francisco, retires from the police force because of his fear of heights and vertigo—a medical condition that causes dizziness. Scottie is hired by an old college friend, Gavin Elster (played by Tom Helmore), to find out why his beautiful wife, Madeleine (played by Kim Novak), has behaved strangely in recent weeks.

While following Madeleine, Scottie saves her from drowning after she attempts suicide by jumping into San Francisco Bay. The two become increasingly attracted to each other. She tells him she has dreamed of a Spanish village with a church and tower, which Scottie realizes is the San Juan Bautista Mission south of San Francisco. He drives her there hoping to resolve her emotional problems. We focus on how Herrmann's music intensifies the dramatic effect of visual images in the climactic "Tower Scene" that occurs halfway through *Vertigo*, one of the best-known scenes in movie history.

Tower Scene (segment)

In the action-packed Tower Scene, Madeleine runs into the church and rushes up the bell tower stairway, followed by Scottie. But vertigo slows him down, preventing him from reaching her in time. Through a window, he sees Madeleine fall from the tower to her death.

This brief segment of *Vertigo* illustrates how Herrmann's music for orchestra raises the tension of the evolving dramatic situation through string tremolos, sustained dissonant chords, rapid whirring ostinatos, and loud repeated brass notes.

As the Tower Scene opens, a loud string tremolo suggests the ominous significance of Madeleine's run toward the church. Scottie's anxiety as he looks up to the tower is conveyed by three sustained dissonant chords: the first played by high muted brasses (as we see the tower), the second played louder by brasses in the middle register (as we see Scottie's face), and the third played softly by low woodwinds (after he cries out "Madeleine!"). Starting when Madeleine enters the church, a rapid whirring ostinato in the strings suggests terror and frenzied motion.

Scottie's frantic pursuit of Madeleine up the stairway takes place in three stages of increasing tension. The climb up to the first landing is accompanied by the whirring string ostinato, and single rising tones in loud, low brass instruments. A high, shrill brass chord, called the "vertigo chord," conveys Scottie's fear of heights as he momentarily stops climbing and looks down the tower stairwell. This dissonant chord is a polychord that combines E flat minor and D major triads.

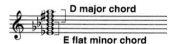

In the second stage of the climb, tension is increased by a loud, insistent figure of three rapid repeated notes in the brasses. Again the shrill "vertigo chord" evokes Scottie's terror as he looks down the stairwell from a greater height. In the last stage of the climb, high brasses play a quicker and more insistent repeated-note figure that suggests a racing heartbeat. Scottie hears the slam of the tower trapdoor followed by a woman's scream. He looks through the tower window and sees Madeleine's body fall to the roof of the church; her fall is evoked by a high, shrill sustained chord. As her body hits the roof, a timpani roll and an ascending two-note idea in the low brasses create a feeling of doom. This solemn two-note idea repeats as Scottie freezes in desperation at the end of the film segment.

To fully appreciate the enormous contribution of Herrmann's music to the scene's emotional intensity, turn down the volume completely as you watch this film clip. Probably, the Tower Scene will seem much less exciting to you without its music.

23 Rock

The mid-1950s saw the growth of a new kind of popular music that was first called *rock and roll* and then simply *rock*. Though it includes diverse styles, **rock** tends to be vocal music with a hard, driving beat, often featuring electric guitar accompaniment and heavily amplified sound.

Early rock grew mainly out of *rhythm and blues*, a dance music of African Americans that fused blues, jazz, and gospel styles. Rock also drew upon *country and western*, a folklike, guitar-based style associated with rural white Americans; and on pop music, a smooth, highly-polished style exemplified by such performers as Frank Sinatra and

Perry Como. In little more than a decade, rock evolved from a simple, dance-oriented style to music that was highly varied in its tone colors, lyrics, musical forms, and electronic technology.

Development of Rock

In the late 1940s, rhythm and blues became a dominant style among African Americans. Rhythm and blues (R & B) of the 1950s differed from earlier blues in its more powerful beat and its use of the saxophone and electric guitar. Among the leading performers were Little Richard, Chuck Berry, and vocal groups such as the Platters. During the 1950s many rhythm-and-blues hits were issued by white performers in versions ("covers") with less sexually explicit lyrics. Little Richard's *Tutti Fruiti* and *Long Tall Sally,* for example, were issued in "cover" versions by Pat Boone one month after the release of the originals.

One of the earliest important rock and roll groups was Bill Haley and His Comets, whose *Rock Around the Clock* is often identified as the first big hit of the new style, though this distinction could just as appropriately be awarded to any number of singles from the period. The song was recorded in 1954, but it did not become a number-one hit until a year later, when it was prominently featured in *The Blackboard Jungle,* a provocative movie about teenage delinquency in a contemporary setting: a New York City high school. To many people, the new music seemed rebellious in its loudness, pounding beat, and sexual directness; and the image of youthful rebellion was also projected by Elvis Presley, who reigned as "king" of rock and roll.

During the 1960s, much of the rock music by black performers was called *soul,* a term that emphasized its emotionality, its gospel roots, and its relationship to the black community. Soul musicians included James Brown, Ray Charles, and Aretha Franklin. *Motown*—derived from "Motor Town USA," a nickname for Detroit, the city from which the style emerged—was a type of music that blended rhythm and blues with elements of popular music; among its stars were Diana Ross and the Supremes and Stevie Wonder. With Motown, African American composers and performers entered the mainstream of popular music.

A new era of British influence began in 1964 with the American tour of the Beatles, an English rock group whose members probably have been the most influential

During the 1950s, Chuck Berry was a leading performer of rhythm and blues.

performers in the history of rock. The Beatles—the singer-guitarists Paul McCartney, John Lennon, and George Harrison; and the drummer Ringo Starr (all born in the early 1940s)—dominated the popular music scene in the United States, along with the Rolling Stones and other British groups. Under their influence, rock musicians of the middle and late 1960s explored a wider range of sources for sounds and musical ideas. They experimented with electronic effects, with "classical" and nonwestern instruments, and with unconventional scales, chord progressions, and rhythms. Apart from the influence of the British invasion, rock in the 1960s also absorbed elements of folk music and dealt with contemporary issues; *Blowin' in the Wind,* by the songwriter and singer Bob Dylan, is a well-known example. At rock festivals, like the three-day Woodstock Music and Art Fair in August 1969, more than 300,000 people listened in open fields to the music of Joan Baez, Janis Joplin, Jimi Hendrix, Jefferson Airplane, and Santana, among many others. The diversity of rock styles—which produced the first rock musical (*Hair,* 1967) and the first rock opera (*Tommy,* 1969)—is reflected in the many terms that describe the music of this period: *fusion, folk rock, jazz rock, psychedelic rock, acid rock, art rock.*

The 1970s saw the continuation of many 1960s styles, the revival of early rock and roll, and the rise of a dance music called *disco.* In addition to veteran performers, new stars emerged, such as Linda Ronstadt, Billy Joel, Bruce Springsteen, and Donna Summer.

A blend of country music and rock called *country rock* became popular; other musical styles included *reggae* (from the West Indies), *funk* (featuring electrification and syncopated rhythms), and *punk,* a raucous style of rock in which the musical material was typically ultrasimple and performers were not expected to be expert on their instruments. Some groups performed *art rock,* rock arrangements of earlier western art music or extended compositions using the language and sounds of rock music, and jazz rock reached a wider audience than ever before through groups like Chicago; Weather Report; and Blood, Sweat, & Tears.

In the early 1980s, new wave bands from Britain such as the Police and the Clash were popular with American rock audiences. This "second British invasion" was comparable to the one that had been led by the Beatles during the early 1960s. Though their styles varied, many British bands of this period, such as New Order and The Cure, made extensive use of electronic technology—synthesizers and computers—and often featured outlandish costumes. *Heavy metal* bands such as Quiet Riot, Iron Maiden, and Guns N' Roses played a type of basic rock with sexually explicit lyrics, bizarre costumes, and tremendous volume. The musical style of these heavy metal bands was greatly influenced by earlier recordings by Led Zeppelin and Black Sabbath.

During the later 1970s and 1980s, groups such as the Talking Heads, Peter Gabriel, and the Police—including Sting's solo recordings—also drew increasing inspiration from "exotic" sources, including African music and Jamaican reggae. Paul Simon's album *Graceland,* recorded in 1986 with South African musicians, also helped increase worldwide interest in African popular music. Four years later, Simon released *Rhythm of the Saints* (1990), an album incorporating west African, Brazilian, and zydeco elements. Another significant trend of the 1980s was increased awareness of "world music" in general and African popular music specifically. Youssou N'Dour of Senegal, whose music combined traditional African styles with contemporary European American pop accompaniments, became an international star. His rise to stardom was helped by his tours for Amnesty International with such rock icons as Bruce Springsteen and Sting.

Interest in world music was not limited to African popular music. There was also an interest in other styles that combined

Elvis Presley, who died in 1977 at the age of forty-two, was the "king" of rock and roll.

Performance Perspectives

Carlos Santana

The guitarist and songwriter Carlos Santana fuses rock with Latin and African rhythms as well as elements of jazz and the blues. A major figure in Spanish-language rock, and leader of the band Santana, he was inducted into the Rock and Roll Hall of Fame in 1998.

Santana, a fourth-generation musician, was born in 1947 in the town of Autlán de Novarra in Mexico. When he was five his father—a violinist and bandleader—began teaching him the violin, and at eight he switched to the guitar. In 1955, Santana moved with his family to Tijuana, Mexico, where he sang and played guitar on the streets for tourists. At age fourteen, he moved to San Francisco, and five years later he formed the Santana Blues Band. A turning point in Santana's career came in 1969, when his band created a sensation at the Woodstock rock festival and its first album, *Santana,* was hailed by *Rolling Stone* magazine as "an explosive fusion of Hispanic-edged rock, Afro-Cuban rhythms, and interstellar improvisation."

During the 1970s, Santana's band became one of the most famous in the world as a result of its best-selling recordings and concert tours in the United States, Europe, and Africa. Some of his band's albums of the early 1970s, including *Caravanserai* (1972), were close in style to jazz-rock fusion. Besides recording with his band, Santana has also made solo albums that have had a powerful impact on the rock scene. He often records with star performers in other fields like Bob Dylan (folk rock), Herbie Hancock (jazz), Wayne Shorter (jazz), and John McLaughlin (jazz-rock fusion). Remarkably for a rock performer, at age fifty-two Santana

created his biggest hit so far, the album *Supernatural* (1999), which was voted Best Rock Album of the Year and has sold more than 21 million copies worldwide.

Santana usually begins to create a song by recording his guitar improvisation for two or three hours. Then he selects the best segments, and works on them with a collaborator. Santana has vividly described the way he created the song *Love of My Life,* together with the singer and guitarist Dave Matthews. "I was picking up my son from school and I thought, OK, time to listen to some radio. I turned on a classical station and the first thing I heard was this melody. . . . They didn't say who the composer was." Santana went into a record store and sang the melody for a salesperson, who told him that it came from Brahms's Third Symphony (studied in Part V, Section 14). He bought the recording and later played Brahms's melody—with slightly changed rhythm—for Dave Matthews and recited the beginning of the lyrics. "Dave sat down and—bam—wrote the song lyrics right there on the spot, and we recorded it."

"Playing the guitar is both a physical and a meta-physical experience," Santana once wrote. "When you can play from your heart, you are being open and honest. . . . The instrument becomes the vehicle by which you can reach others with the music." Santana's guitar sound has a vocal quality. "When you listen to vocalists like Aretha Franklin and Dionne Warwick, you learn to phrase differently," Santana has said. "I love musicians who make you want to cry and laugh at the same time. . . . You want to bend notes, you want to be able to express joy . . . anger, and a cry."

traditional musical forms from around the world with the sounds of contemporary American and European popular music. Zouk, for example—a hybrid of Parisian and French Caribbean dance music—experienced widespread international appeal.

Among young urban blacks, *rap* developed. It began as a kind of rhythmic talking accompanied by a disk jockey who manipulated recordings on two turntables to create a collage of rhythmic effects. First popularized in black neighborhoods of east coast American cities, rap often depicts the anger and frustration of urban black youth. Rap is part of the *hip-hop* culture that also includes breakdancing and graffiti.

Heavy metal and rap continued to grow in popularity throughout the 1980s and into the 1990s. The audience for heavy metal has been, since its beginnings, mainly white working-class adolescents. Rap, on the other hand, had by 1990 adopted stylistic features that clearly distinguished it from other forms of popular music and had

Bob Dylan's songs of the 1960s often dealt with such contemporary issues as war and racial injustice.

Bruce Springsteen performs onstage at Madison Square Garden in New York City on November 7, 2009.

begun to attract a wider audience, crossing over ethnic and social lines. Some of the most successful rap artists of this period were Chuck D, Dr. Dre, Snoop Doggy Dogg, Ice Cube, Ice-T, and Scarface. An interesting hybrid of heavy metal and rap emerged in the early 1990s when Bodycount was formed by the rapper Ice-T. This group combined speed metal guitar riffs with rapped lyrics, initiating a period during which many groups, including Rage Against the Machine, Limp Bizkit, and Linkin Park, adopted a similar sound. By the end of the 1990s, rap and rap-flavored rhythm and blues moved into the mainstream and dominated the recording charts. Particularly influential were Dr. Dre, Tupac Shakur, Missy Elliot, and the Detroit rapper Marshall Mathers (Eminem). Recordings of the controversial *gangsta rap*—with its deliberately antisocial and sexually explicit lyrics—had enormous sales.

Many young people who had become disenchanted with the polished sounds of mainstream rock of the early 1990s embraced the brash grinding guitar sounds and angry lyrics of despair inherent in the music of alternative rock bands. One of the centers of alternative rock was the Seattle *grunge* scene from which Nirvana, Pearl Jam, Soundgarden, and Alice in Chains emerged. These groups encompassed a wide range of styles, although they were all influenced by 1970s punk, hard rock, and heavy metal. The continued success of alternative rock in the 1990s was confirmed by the popularity of such new bands as Smashing Pumpkins, Nine Inch Nails, and the female-led groups Belly and Hole. By the mid-1990s, this success engendered a punk resurgence with the success of Green Day, NOFX, and System of a Down.

At the end of the twentieth century, interesting trends included the emergence of Latino artists who incorporated pan-Latin influences in their music (Gloria Estefan and Ricky Martin); the appearance of crossover artists from the world of country music (Garth Brooks, and more recently, Tim McGraw), and a renewed interest in music from the 1970s. The 2000s have witnessed the popularity of garage rock, contemporary metal, electronic rock, and the crossover of indie rock into the mainstream.

Throughout the history of rock, superstars have struck it rich through record royalties, movie contracts, and astronomical concert fees. However, many leading rock performers also give concerts to benefit various social causes. An important event in 2012 was 12-12-12: The Concert for Sandy Relief, held in Madison Square Garden in New York City to benefit victims of Hurricane Sandy. The performers at this concert, which was broadcast worldwide, included Alicia Keys, Billy Joel, Bon Jovi, Bruce Springsteen, The Rolling Stones, Eric Clapton, Nirvana, and Paul McCartney.

Elements of Rock

Tone Color Having briefly examined the development of rock, we now consider its musical elements. Though some early rock performers used piano-based instrumentation, it was the electric guitar sound of rock that contrasted most with the brass-reed sound of the "big band" heard in the 1930s and 1940s. Rock music is powerfully amplified, and the guitar is often manipulated electronically to produce a wide range of tone colors. Along with singers (who often also play instruments), a rock group typically includes two electric guitars (lead and rhythm), electric bass, percussion, and keyboard instruments such as piano, electric piano, and synthesizer. Some groups also include one or more trumpets, trombones, or saxophones.

Starting in the 1960s, a wide range of instruments not normally associated with popular music—from the harpsichord to the Indian sitar—were occasionally added to the basic rock group, particularly for recording sessions. Rock recordings began to use such diverse sounds as electronic blips, crowd noises, and a symphony orchestra.

The Beatles have so far been the most influential performing group in the history of rock.

During the 1970s and 1980s, rock musicians such as Keith Emerson (Emerson, Lake, and Palmer) exploited the ever-expanding capabilities of synthesizers and computers. Sophisticated electronic technology made it possible for a few performers to sound like a large ensemble. By the 1990s and the early 2000s, the range of tone color in many rock groups was expanded by the inclusion of a disk jockey who manipulated vinyl recordings, and by the use of multiple computers in contemporary rock concerts.

The singing style of rock is drawn largely from black, folk, and country-and-western music. Although singing styles vary, they are all different from the crooning sound cultivated by earlier popular vocalists. Rock singers shout, cry, wail, growl, and use guttural sounds, as well as *falsetto,* a method of singing used by males to reach notes higher than their normal range. Nonsense syllables and repeated chants (such as *Yeah! Yeah! Yeah!*) are also featured.

Rhythm Most rock is based on a very powerful beat in quadruple ($\frac{4}{4}$) meter with strong accents on the second and fourth beats of the bar. The rhythmic excitement is heightened because each beat is usually subdivided into two equal notes. This produces eight faster pulses, which are superimposed on the four basic beats. To get the effect, count out the following: 1-and-2-and-3-and-4-and. Rock of the 1960s and 1970s often combined complicated rhythms with this basic pattern; for example, the bass player might emphasize the offbeats—the *ands*.

Form, Melody, and Harmony The earliest rock music was often in twelve-bar blues form (see pages 359–360), in thirty-two-bar A A B A form, or in a variant of these forms. Other common popular music structures include strophic and verse-chorus forms. Strophic form (see page 40), in which the musical accompaniment remains the same for each stanza of the lyrics, is commonly found in folk music. Because the accompaniment is repeated, the listener's attention is drawn to the words, which are particularly important both in folk music and in its rock-oriented derivation known as *folk rock*. Verse-chorus form, a variant of strophic form, is very commonly used in popular music. (The Beatles' song *Lucy in the Sky with Diamonds,* studied next, is in verse-chorus form.) In this musical structure, each verse, or stanza, is followed by a chorus, or refrain. In the verse sections, the different stanzas of text are set to a repeated melody and accompaniment, as in strophic form. In the chorus, however, both text and music are repeated. The chorus typically includes a "hook line," a repeated lyric and melody that become the most memorable part of the song.

Earlier popular songs usually consisted of four- or eight-bar phrases, but rock melodies sometimes contain phrases that are irregular in length. Rock songs tend to have short melodic patterns that are repeated or varied (or both) several times. They are occasionally built on modes, rather than on traditional major or minor scales.

The harmonic progressions of rock are usually quite simple, often consisting of just three or four basic chords. Sometimes, the harmony can be deliberately restricted to only two chords, as in *Eleanor Rigby,* by John Lennon and Paul McCartney. By the mid-1960s, the Beatles, the Beachboys, and other innovative artists began using chord progressions that were rarely found in earlier popular music.

Sgt. Pepper's Lonely Hearts Club Band (1967)

Sgt. Pepper's Lonely Hearts Club Band, a landmark of rock, was one of the first rock music recordings to be presented as a "concept album": its thirteen songs are linked by the ruling idea of a music hall show with a dazzling succession of acts. The sense of continuity is heightened by the varied reprise of the opening song (*Sgt. Pepper's Lonely Hearts Club Band*) as the next-to-last song on the recording. The impact of this record comes largely from its tremendous range of sounds and electronic effects—audience noises, barnyard sounds, weird orchestral tone clusters, and instruments such as the harpsichord, harp, and sitar. There is also a wide range of musical styles, including traditional rock and roll (the Sgt. Pepper theme), a parody of a 1920s music-hall tune (*When I'm Sixty-Four*), an old-fashioned melodramatic ballad (*She's Leaving Home*), and the exotic sounds of Indian music (*Within You, Without You*).

Lucy in the Sky with Diamonds, the third song of the cycle, evokes a world of daydream and fantasy. But the dreamlike mood is shattered by a brusque refrain. After the introduction, *Lucy in the Sky with Diamonds* is in verse-chorus form. The verse, which consists of subsections A-B (*Cellophane flowers*), is relatively soft, gently pulsating, and in triple meter. In contrast, the chorus, or refrain, section C (*Lucy in the Sky*), is loud, heavily accented, and in quadruple meter. The song can be outlined as follows:

Introduction

1. A-B (*Cellophane flowers*)	C (*Lucy in the Sky*)
2. A-B (*Newspaper taxis*)	C
3. A	CC (Fade-out at end)

The Twentieth Century and Beyond: Summary

Music in Society

- The early twentieth century was a time of revolt, with more fundamental changes in the language of music than any time since the baroque era.
- The variety of musical styles of the early twentieth century reflects the vast diversity of life during this time.
- The United States became a potent force in music.
- Recordings, radio, and television became new modes for hearing music, bringing music to larger audiences, and increasing the range of music available to everyone.
- Women and people of color began to play major roles in professional music making.
- American colleges and universities have indirectly become important patrons of music.

Characteristics of Twentieth-Century Music

- Tone color became a more important element of music than it ever was before.
- Noiselike and percussive sounds are used often.
- There is less emphasis on blended sound; individual tone colors are heard clearly.
- Melodies often are no longer tied to traditional chords, major or minor keys, or a tonal center.
- Traditional distinctions between consonance and dissonance were often abandoned.
- New chord structures and alternatives to the traditional tonal system were explored.
- Rhythm is one of the most striking elements of twentieth-century music, used to generate power, drive, and excitement.

Characteristics of Music since 1945

- The twelve-tone system was expanded to include elements other than pitch, such as rhythm, timbre, and dynamics.
- The element of chance was introduced to music composition and performance.
- Some composers have embraced tonal music and a return to tonality.
- The introduction of tape studios, synthesizers, computers, and mixed media are notable developments.
- The greatest expansion and experimentation have involved percussion instruments.
- Rhythm and form have undergone some of the most striking changes in music since 1945.

IMPORTANT TERMS

Glissando, p. 285
Polychord, p. 286
Fourth chord, p. 287
Tone cluster, p. 287
Polytonality, p. 288
Bitonality, p. 288
Atonality, p. 288
Polyrhythm, p. 289
Ostinato, p. 289
Pentatonic scale, p. 294
Whole-tone scale, p. 294
Sprechstimme, p. 304
Twelve-tone system, p. 305
Tone row (set, series), p. 305
Serialism, p. 340
Chance (aleatory) music, p. 340
Minimalist music, p. 341
Quotation music, p. 342
Electronic music, p. 344
Microtones, p. 346
Mixed media, p. 346
Prepared piano, p. 348
Call and response, p. 358
Twelve-bar blues, p. 359
Subdominant, p. 359
Rhythm section, p. 362
Bars, p. 363
Chorus, p. 363
Front line, p. 364
Break, p. 365
Scat singing, p. 365
Swing band, p. 366
Riff, p. 366

FEATURED STYLES

FEATURED COMPOSERS OR PERFORMERS

Claude Debussy (1862–1918)
Igor Stravinsky (1882–1971)
Arnold Schoenberg (1874–1951)
Alban Berg (1885–1935)
Anton Webern (1883–1945)
Béla Bartók (1881–1945)
Amy Beach (1867–1944)
Charles Ives (1874–1954)
George Gershwin (1898–1937)
William Grant Still (1895–1978)
Aaron Copland (1900–1990)
Alberto Ginastera (1916–1983)
John Cage (1912–1992)
Edgard Varèse (1883–1965)
Ellen Taaffe Zwilich (b. 1939)
John Adams (b. 1947)
Eric Whitacre (b. 1970)
Scott Joplin (1868–1917)
Bessie Smith (1894–1937)
King Oliver's Creole Jazz Band
Louis Armstrong (1901–1971)
  and His Hot Five
Duke Ellington (1899–1974)
  and his Famous Orchestra
Charlie Parker (1920–1955)
Miles Davis (1926–1991)
Leonard Bernstein (1918–1990)
Bernard Hermann (1911–1975)
The Beatles

Jazz

- Jazz developed in New Orleans around the turn of the century.
- Jazz features a small combo of three to eight players, or a big band of ten to fifteen.
- Improvisation lies at the heart of jazz, and adds freshness and spontaneity.
- Syncopation and rhythmic swing are distinctive features of jazz.

Music for Stage and Screen

- Along with jazz and rock, the musical was one of the most important American contributions to twentieth-century popular culture.
- The golden era in American musical theater was created from about 1920 to 1960. After 1960, some composers departed from traditional forms.

Rock

- Though it includes diverse styles, rock tends to be vocal music with a hard, driving beat, often featuring electric guitar accompaniment and heavily amplified sound.

Beyond the Classroom: Attending a Concert of Music Composed after 1900

Attending a concert of twentieth-century music can be one of the most unpredictable and exhilarating musical activities you can experience, regardless of whether the music you hear is classical, jazz, Broadway, film, or rock music. The range of styles and the number of new sounds you may hear are astonishing. Concerts today also can be visual extravaganzas, complete with digital effects, light shows, photography, film projections, dancing, and even pyrotechnics. Because the music is so wide-ranging in style, audience members, too, tend to be an extremely diverse group.

Professional ensembles devoted to the performance of music composed after 1900 are found in many cities and towns. Colleges and universities also are excellent sources of free lectures and concerts spanning a wide range of twentieth-century genres and styles.

When attending a concert of twentieth century music, go with an open mind. Plan to be challenged aurally, intellectually, and emotionally.

Ask yourself the following questions as you are listening:

- How are voices used? Do the singers make any special sound effects?
- Do the voices or instruments blend together, or are the individual tone colors unblended?

- What observations can you make regarding timbre? Are noiselike or percussive instruments used? If so, what do they look like, how are they played, and what is their effect on the music?
- Does the performance use taped music, special amplification, computers, synthesizers, or a combination of electronic and live music? What is their effect on your reaction to the music?
- Is the music consonant or dissonant? Does the music sound tonal or not? Do the program notes indicate if the music is twelve tone or aleatory?
- How would you describe the rhythm, tempo, and meter? Are they predictable and steady, or are they irregular? Do you notice any ostinatos?
- Do you notice instances of musical quotation?
- Does the performance include examples of mixed media?
- What performing forces do you hear? If instruments are used, are they traditional instruments of the western world, or are they from other locations? If you notice any unusual instruments, what do they look like and how are they played?
- Does the performance include any special effects, dancers, or other enhancements to the music?
- How did you react to the music in general?

■ All over the world, music is closely linked with religion, dance, and drama. Shown here is a gamelan, an Indonesian orchestra.

PART VII

Nonwestern Music

The highest aim of our music is to reveal the essence of the universe it reflects . . . through music one can reach God.

—Ravi Shankar

LEARNING OBJECTIVES

- Identify the characteristics of music in the nonwestern world

- Analyze the various functions of music in sub-Saharan Africa

- Describe the elements of music in sub-Saharan Africa

- Discuss the elements of Indian classical music

- Examine the life and career of Ravi Shankar

The Diversity of Nonwestern Music

Nonwestern music reflects and expresses the diversity of the world's languages, religions, geographical conditions, social and economic systems, values, beliefs, and ways of life. Each culture has its own characteristic instruments, performance practices, tonal systems, and melodic and rhythmic patterns. Nonwestern societies also differ in their range of musical styles: some have only folk music, some have both folk and popular music, and some have complex classical music as well. Thus nonwestern music can offer a wide range of listening experiences and cultural insights. Moreover, nonwestern traditions were an important source of inspiration for western music of the twentieth and twenty-first centuries. For example, they influenced the French composer Claude Debussy, the British rock star George Harrison, the African American jazz artist John Coltrane, and the American composer Elliott Carter.

African music is closely associated with dancing. While moving, a dancer often sings or plays an instrument.

The koto, a plucked string instrument, is important in traditional Japanese music.

1 Music in Nonwestern Cultures

Characteristics of Nonwestern Music

Music of the nonwestern world is too varied to allow easy generalizations. Yet some features are common to most traditions: All music is closely linked with religion, dance, and drama; it can be both entertainment and an accompaniment to everyday activities, magic rites, and ceremonies; and it is often used to send messages and to relate traditions.

Oral Tradition Nonwestern music is most often transmitted orally from parent to child or from teacher to student. Compositions and performance techniques are learned by rote and imitation. Music notation is far less important in nonwestern than in western culture. Many musical cultures do not have notation; and when notation exists, it traditionally serves only as a record, not for teaching or performance.

Improvisation Improvisation is important in many nonwestern musical cultures. Performers usually base their improvisations on traditional melodic phrases and rhythmic patterns. Often it is a highly disciplined art that requires years of training. Indian and Islamic musicians, for instance, create music within a framework of melody types, each associated with a specific mood, a specific set of tones, and characteristic phrases. Although in some cultures the traditional songs and instrumental pieces are performed similarly from generation to generation (as in Japan, where improvisation in classical music is practically nonexistent), in other traditions, pieces are treated with great flexibility. In Iran (Persia) and sub-Saharan Africa, for example, performers freely vary melodies and add sections.

Voices Singing is the most important way of making music in the vast majority of nonwestern cultures. Each tradition has its own preferred vocal timbres: for example, middle eastern and north African singers cultivate a nasal, intense, strained tone whereas singers in sub-Saharan Africa prefer a more relaxed, open-throated sound. Vocal techniques include shouting, crying, whispering, sighing, humming, yodeling, and singing through the teeth.

Instruments Nonwestern instruments produce a wealth of sounds and come in a wide variety of sizes, shapes, and materials. Scholars usually group these instruments into four categories, based on what generates the sound.

1. *Chordophones* are instruments—such as harps and lutes—whose sound generator is a stretched string.
2. *Aerophones* are instruments—such as flutes and trumpets—whose sound generator is a column of air.
3. *Membranophones* are instruments—basically, drums—whose sound generator is a stretched skin or another membrane.
4. *Idiophones* are instruments—such as bells, gongs, scrapers, rattles, and xylophones—whose own material is the sound generator (no tension is applied).

The musical style of a culture is an important factor in its choice of instruments. For example, chordophones (strings) are prominent in Islamic and Indian classical music, whose highly ornamented melodies require instruments with great flexibility of

Instruments are sometimes shaped like birds, animals, fish, or dragons. The *saron,* an idiophone, is part of the Indonesian gamelan.

pitch. Idiophones and membranophones (such as bells, rattles, and drums) are featured in sub-Saharan Africa, where rhythm is strongly emphasized and music is closely linked with dancing.

A second factor is geography, which determines the availability of raw materials. Bronze idiophones are prominent in southeast Asia; Indonesian orchestras (gamelans) include bronze gongs, chimes, and xylophones. Instruments made of animal skins and horns are common in parts of sub-Saharan Africa, where these materials are easily found. Among the Aniocha Ibo of Nigeria, for example, drums are made of animal skins, and some aerophones (winds) are made from elephant tusks. Where raw materials are scarce, as in the deserts of Australia, instruments may be few.

Along with musical style and geography, religious beliefs may influence the choice of materials. In Tibet, for example, trumpets and drums are made from the bones and skulls of criminals in order to appease demons. Instruments often have symbolic associations and are linked with specific gods and goddesses. They may be shaped like birds, animals, or fish.

Melody, Texture, and Rhythm
In Asia, the near east, and north Africa, most music emphasizes melody and rhythm, rather than harmony or polyphony. Texture is often monophonic, consisting of an unaccompanied melody or a melody supported by percussion. In India and the near east, the melodic line is frequently supported by a drone, one or more sustained tones. In many parts of the world—such as north Africa, the middle east, southeast Asia, and the far east—all parts may perform the same basic melody, with differing ornamentation or rhythm, a procedure called ***heterophonic texture.*** Homophonic and polyphonic textures tend to be more common in sub-Saharan Africa than in Asia.

Nonwestern music uses a wide variety of scales. Most often, scales have five, six, or seven tones. Nonwestern melodies commonly use intervals smaller or larger than those standard in the west. Microtones—intervals smaller than the western half step—are frequent in the music of India and the near east. And much nonwestern music has very complex rhythms; drummers in India and sub-Saharan Africa spend many years learning their sophisticated art.

Interaction between Nonwestern and Western Music

After 1900, nonwestern music felt the impact of American and European music. This influence resulted from increased urbanization, adoption of western technology, and access to radios, films, recordings, and western instruments. Western elements are often found in the popular music heard in the large cities of Africa, Asia, and the near east. One example of such popular music is the *high life* of west Africa, which combines European instruments with the steady rhythm characteristic of Africa. Some composers in the nonwestern world combine traditional elements with western forms and styles. And in many areas, western and traditional music exist side by side. Yet there are vast areas of the world where traditional music is dominant. Many governments subsidize traditional performing groups to preserve their rich national heritage.

In the sections that follow, the traditional music of sub-Saharan Africa and India is studied as a sample of the wealth of nonwestern music.

2 Music in Sub-Saharan Africa

The African continent can be subdivided into north Africa, which includes Morocco, Algeria, Tunisia, and Egypt; and sub-Saharan Africa, the area south of the Sahara Desert, which includes Ghana, Nigeria, Mozambique, and Angola, among many other countries. North Africa is predominantly Muslim and Arabic-speaking, and its music is closely related to that of the middle east. This section focuses on the music of sub-Saharan Africa, sometimes called "black Africa," and generally, throughout the section, the word *Africa* pertains to sub-Saharan Africa.

Sub-Saharan Africa, which is environmentally and culturally diverse, has several thousand peoples with different religions, social customs, and more than 700 different languages. Though urban growth and industrialization are transforming sub-Saharan Africa today, many Africans still hold to traditional ways of life. Most groups have polytheistic religions, live in villages, and devote themselves to traditional occupations such as agriculture and raising cattle.

The music of sub-Saharan Africa is as diverse as its people. Even so, most of it features complex rhythms and polyrhythms, percussive sounds, and a wide variety of instrumental ensembles. Vocal music is often performed by a soloist and a responding chorus. Of course, the different cultures of Africa have influenced each other. For example, in parts of sub-Saharan Africa, such as Ghana and northern Nigeria, musical styles have been influenced by Arabic culture.

Music in Society

Music permeates virtually every aspect of African life. It is used to entertain; to accompany dances, plays, religious ceremonies, and magic rites; and to mark such events as birth, puberty, marriage, and death. There are work songs; specific songs or dances to treat the ill; litigation songs; songs praising leaders, criticizing authority, and recounting history; and many songs for particular occasions (for example, among the Fon—a people in Dahomey in west Africa—children sing a special song when they lose their

Singing and playing instruments are interwoven into the fabric of African life.

first tooth). Singing and playing instruments are so interwoven into life that the abstract word *music*—as understood in the west—is not used by most African peoples, though there are words for *song, dance,* and *poetry.*

African music is closely associated with dancing; both arts are basic to many ceremonies, rituals, and celebrations. While moving, a dancer often sings or plays rattles or other idiophones that are held or tied to the body.

African music is also intimately linked with language. Many languages are *tone languages,* in which a word can have several different meanings, depending on its relative pitch. Tone languages permit the use of music for communication: drummers, trumpeters, and other musicians convey messages and tell stories by imitating the rhythms and pitch fluctuations of words. *Talking drums*—capable of two or more different pitches—are often used to send musical messages.

In Africa, music making is a social activity in which almost everyone participates. Music is usually performed outdoors, and there is spontaneous music making as well as performances by social and music groups at ceremonies and feasts. There is no musical notation; musical tradition, like folklore and history, is transmitted orally.

Elements of African Music

Rhythm and Percussion   Rhythm and percussive sounds are highly emphasized in African music, reflecting the close link between music and dance. African music tends to feature complex polyrhythms; usually, several different rhythmic patterns are played simultaneously and repeated over and over, and each instrument goes its own rhythmic way. Dancers may choose to follow any of several rhythmic patterns—one dancer may follow a pattern played with a bell while a second follows a rattle and a third a drum.

Percussion ensembles consist mainly of drums, xylophones, or rattles carefully chosen to provide contrasts of tone color and pitch. The human body itself is often used as a percussion instrument. Hand claps, foot stamps, and thigh or chest slaps are common sounds in African music.

Vocal Music   African singers use a wide variety of vocal sounds. Even within a single performance a singer may shift from an open, relaxed tone to one that is tighter and more constricted. Singers sometimes whisper, hum, grunt, shout, imitate animal noises, and yodel (move quickly from a chest voice to a falsetto).

Much African vocal music is characterized by a performance style known as **call and response,** in which the phrases of a soloist are repeatedly answered by those of a chorus. An exciting overlap often results when the leader resumes singing before the chorus has completed its response. Singers are often accompanied by percussion ostinatos (repeated rhythmic patterns). Typically, short musical phrases are repeated over and over to different words.

Texture   Unlike many other nonwestern cultures, African societies often have music that is homophonic or polyphonic in texture. Several voice parts may sing the same melody at different pitch levels, occasionally producing a series of parallel chords. Some African peoples also perform polyphonic music in which the different melodic lines are quite independent.

African Instruments

A great variety of instruments and instrumental ensembles are found in Africa. Ensembles have from two to twenty or more players and may consist of instruments of indefinite pitch (bells, rattles, log drums), definite pitch (flutes, trumpets, xylophones, plucked lutes), or a combination of both (flutes, drums, bells).

Idiophones The most common instruments in Africa are idiophones, such as bells, rattles, scrapers, xylophones, and log drums. Most are struck or shaken, but others are scraped, rubbed, plucked, or stamped against the ground. Many—such as rattles, bells, and stone clappers—are instruments of indefinite pitch. A few—such as the xylophone and *mbira,* or *thumb piano*—are tuned instruments.

Xylophones are particularly important in Africa; they are played solo, in small groups, and in larger orchestras and exist in different sizes ranging from soprano to double bass. In some parts of Africa, a single large xylophone is played by several performers simultaneously. Xylophones have ten to twenty or more slats, sometimes with gourd resonators. Spiderwebs are often placed over small holes in the resonators to create a buzzing sound.

The *mbira* (*sansa, kalimba,* or *thumb piano*) is a melodic idiophone capable of producing elaborate melodies. From eight to more than thirty tongues made of metal or bamboo are attached to a sounding board or box. The tongues are plucked with the thumbs and forefingers. Vocalists often use the mbira to accompany themselves.

Another important idiophone is the *slit drum,* a hollowed-out log with a long slit on top. Some slit drums are small enough to be held in the hand, whereas others are tree trunks more than twenty feet long. Variations in the width of the slit allow two and sometimes four different tones to be produced when the slit is struck. The slit drum is used both as a "talking drum" for signaling and as a musical instrument.

Membranophones Drums with stretched skins or other membranes are also important in African culture. They are essential to many religious and political ceremonies, and they are used for dancing and regulating the pace of work. Talking drums are used to send messages over long distances, and drums are often considered sacred or magical. The manufacture of drums is usually accompanied by special rites, and drums are sometimes housed in special shrines and given food and offered sacrifices. Drums are often regarded as the property of the group, rather than that of an individual, and they symbolize power and royalty.

Drums are usually played in groups of two to four, though some ensembles are made up of as many as fifteen drums, played by four to six performers. The drums are often tuned to different pitches and create melodic music similar to that of xylophone ensembles. The chief drummer is typically free to improvise within a traditional framework; the other drummers repeat certain rhythmic patterns. African drummers are among the most sophisticated in the world, producing complicated rhythms and a wide range of tone colors and pitches.

Drums come in many sizes, shapes, and forms. There are drums shaped like cones, cylinders, kettles, barrels, goblets, and hourglasses. They are made from logs, gourds, and clay. They may have one or two drumheads made from animal skins. Some drums produce a single sound; others—such as the hourglass-shaped *pressure drum* (which often imitates the spoken "tone language")—can produce a variety of pitches. Devices used for special effects include seeds or beads inside a closed drum or pieces of metal or small bells attached to a drum's rim.

Six musicians play
membranophones.

Aerophones and Chordophones The most common aerophones (winds)
are flutes, whistles, horns, and trumpets. Reed instruments are less widespread. Flutes
are usually made of bamboo, cane, or wood; horns and trumpets are made from animal horns, elephant tusks, wood, bamboo, and gourds.

Chordophones (strings) are plucked or struck, perhaps reflecting the African musician's preference for percussive sounds. One of the most widely used chordophones
is the musical bow, whose string is plucked or struck with a stick. Some musical bows
have a gourd resonator; with others, the player's mouth is used as the resonator.

Ompeh

Percussive sounds, complex polyrhythms, and a call-and-response pattern are featured
in *Ompeh,* a song from the central region of Ghana, recorded by the ethnomusicologist
Roger Vetter in the coastal town Winneba in 1992–1993. "Within this area," Vetter
observes, "are to be found several ethnic/linguistic identities and a colorful palette
of musical instruments, ensembles, and repertoires that fulfill the musical needs of
small and large communities alike." *Ompeh* is performed by a recreational amateur
ensemble of singers and percussionists who specialize in *ompeh,* a type of music of the
Akan-speaking peoples in Ghana.

In the performance, brief solo melodies for male voice are each followed by longer
responses from a chorus singing mostly in thirds. (From *do* to *mi* in the scale is an
interval of a third.) Each choral response is introduced by a single held tone sung by
a higher solo male voice. We also hear a percussion ensemble—consisting of a bamboo slit drum, pan rattles (made from aluminum pie plates), a two-headed cylindrical drum (*ogyamba*), a large barrel-shaped hand drum (*ompehkyen*), and a metal bell
(*afirikyiwa*)—producing a variety of rhythms, pitches, and tone colors. The metal bell
serves as the timekeeper of the group. Its repeated rhythm reflects the influence of *high
life,* a type of popular music from Ghana.

The text of *Ompeh* relates to the group's performances, for which chairs are set up
on the earth and the singers dance to the music. There are three references to death in
the song. The first, *I'm dying,* has to do with pairing contradictions in Akan poetry, as
in "I'm dying of laughter." The second and third references are more threatening. The
singers become combative when they realize that the *Tokoraba* people have arrived and

warn them that they will be sent to a distant place, *The land of the dead.* In this song, the performers combine two of the many languages spoken in Ghana: Ga and Fante.

Soloist

A woyaa woyaa	We go, we go,
E wo asi wo agwa e	They've set the chairs,
Asaase e	Earth,
Eba anadwo kakra	When night falls,
Wo asi wo agwa e	They've set the chairs,
Mere wuo o	I'm dying.

Chorus

E a woyaa woyaa	We go, we go,
Daa wo asi wo agwa e	They've set up chairs daily,
Asaase e	Earth,
Eba anadwo kakra	When night falls,
Wo asi wo agwa e	They've set the chairs,
Mere wuo o	I'm dying,
A woyaa woyaa	We go, we go,
Krohinko sane e	We swing back and forth,
Kowa e	Kowa e [perhaps a name]
Owuo e, sane e, Kowa e	Death, problem, Kowa e,
A woyaa Tokoraba wose wo ba	We are going, Tokoraba people say they are here,
Saman wa	The land of the dead is far.

Listening Outline

Ompeh

2 solo male voices, chorus, bamboo slit drum, metal bell, pan rattle, cylindrical drum, large barrel-shaped hand drum
(Duration, 2:08)

0:00	**1. a.**	Bamboo slit drum, followed by metal bell, pan rattles, cylindrical drum.
0:14	**b.**	Solo vocal melody joins.
0:23	**c.**	Higher solo voice introduces choral response in thirds.
0:34	**d.**	Barrel-shaped bass drum joins accompaniment to chorus, percussion continues throughout.
0:51	**2. a.**	Solo vocal melody.
1:00	**b.**	Higher solo voice introduces choral response in thirds.
1:25	**c.**	Percussion alone.
1:31	**3. a.**	Solo vocal melody.
1:40	**b.**	Higher solo voice introduces choral response in thirds.
2:04	**c.**	Percussion alone closes segment.

3 Classical Music of India

The musical traditions of India, which include folk and popular music, date back more than 3,000 years and are thus among the oldest in the world. Between the twelfth and sixteenth centuries, Indian classical music developed two distinct traditions: *Karnatak music,* of south India; and *Hindustani music,* of north India (an area that now includes Pakistan). The centers of north Indian music were the princely courts, whereas south Indian music was performed in temples. The music of north India absorbed many Persian elements because many of its rulers came from Persia and were Muslims. The music of south India developed more along its own lines.

When India came under British rule during the nineteenth century, north Indian classical music was still performed mainly for small, elite audiences at princely courts. But aristocratic patronage declined during the twentieth century as India made the transition from British rule to independence. Many musicians lost their jobs around 1947—the date of India's independence—when almost 600 princely states of India were abolished as political units and merged with neighboring territories. Indian performers turned to the general public for support, just as European musicians did during the eighteenth and nineteenth centuries.

Today, Indian musicians broadcast on radio and television, make recordings, and compose music for films. Some teach in colleges or give concerts for large audiences. Many Indian artists now travel and give concerts throughout the world.

Performers

Indian performers consider their music spiritual in character. "We view music as a kind of spiritual discipline that raises one's inner being to divine peacefulness and bliss," writes Ravi Shankar (1920–2012), one of the most important Indian musicians. "The highest aim of our music is to reveal the essence of the universe it reflects; . . . through music, one can reach God." This spiritual emphasis is reflected in the texts of south Indian songs, which have religious associations. Indian musicians venerate their *guru* (*master* or *teacher*) as representative of the divine. A special initiation ceremony usually occurs when a guru accepts a disciple. The student is then expected to surrender his or her personality to the guru.

Musical traditions are transmitted orally from master to disciple, who learns by imitation, not by studying textbooks or written music. For example, Indian music students imitate their teacher phrase by phrase at lessons and sing or play along at concerts. Although India has various systems of musical notation, they give only the basic melodic and rhythmic elements. The development of these elements—the essential ornaments and musical elaborations—cannot be notated and must be learned from a teacher.

Improvisation

Improvisation has an important role in Indian music. In few other cultures is improvisation as highly developed and sophisticated. The improviser is guided by complex melodic and rhythmic systems that govern the choice of tones, ornaments, and rhythms. Before being allowed to improvise, young musicians must study for years and practice many hours a day, mastering basic rules and techniques. Improvisations are generally performed by a soloist and a drummer. They last anywhere from a few minutes to several hours, depending on the occasion and the mood of the performers and audience. Both vocalists and instrumentalists improvise.

Elements of Indian Classical Music

Indian music is based on the human voice—so much so that the pitch range of all Indian music is restricted to less than four octaves. Instrumentalists often imitate a vocal style of performance. Composed pieces are songs performed by a singer or an instrumentalist, with the instrumentalist imitating vocal styles. And songs are used as a springboard for improvisation.

There have been many composers in south India, producing thousands of songs. The greatest composers were Tyagaraja (1767–1847), Muthuswamy Dikshitar (1775–1835), and Shyama Sastri (1762–1827). These three musicians were born in the same village and were contemporaries of Haydn, Mozart, and Beethoven; they are called the "musical trinity."

Highly embellished melody—both vocal and instrumental—is characteristic of Indian music. Melodies often move by microtones (intervals smaller than a half step). Melodic lines are subtly embellished by microtonal ornaments, tiny pitch fluctuations around notes. Slides of pitch provide graceful transitions from one note to another.

Indian melodies are almost always accompanied by a drone instrument that plays the tonic and dominant (or subdominant) notes throughout the performance. The basic texture of Indian music, therefore, consists of a single melody performed over an unchanging background. Rather than the harmonic progression and polyphonic texture of western music, Indian music has melodic and rhythmic tension and relaxation. The main drone instrument is the **tambura,** a long-necked lute with four metal strings that are plucked continually in succession. The constant sound of the drone contributes vitally to the atmosphere of the music. In addition to the soloist and the tambura players, a drummer maintains the rhythmic structure and may also perform rhythmic improvisations.

Melodic Structure: Raga In Indian classical music, melody is created within a melodic framework called *raga*. A **raga** is a pattern of notes. A particular raga is defined partly by the number of its tones and the pattern of its intervals. Each raga has an ascending and descending form with characteristic melodic phrases and tonal emphases. Particular ornaments and slides from one note to another give each raga its individuality.

The term *raga* comes from a word meaning *color* or *atmosphere,* and an ancient saying describes raga as "that which colors the mind." Ragas have many extramusical associations. Each raga is linked with a particular mood, such as tranquility, love, or heroism. Ragas are also associated with specific gods, seasons, festivals, and times of day or night. They involve so many dimensions that Indian musicians spend a long time learning each one. Some distinguished musicians restrict themselves to performing only about a dozen ragas. Within the framework of a raga, great artists can create and improvise a limitless variety of music.

Rhythmic Structure: Tala Rhythm is organized into cycles called *talas*. A **tala** consists of a repeated cycle of beats. Although beat cycles range from 3 to more than 100 beats in length, the most common cycles have 6 to 16 beats. A cycle is divided into groups of beats. For example, the 10-beat tala called *jhaptal* is divided 2-3-2-3, and the 10-beat tala called *shultal* is divided 4-2-4:

Jhaptal

| |1 | 2 | |3 | 4 | 5 | |6 | 7 | |8 | 9 | 10| |

Shultal

| |1 | 2 | 3 | 4 | |5 | 6 | |7 | 8 | 9 | 10| |

The sitarist Ravi Shankar is accompanied here by a tabla (a pair of single-headed drums) and a tambura (a drone instrument).

Each beat in a tala may be divided into smaller time values, just as a quarter note in western music may be divided into eighth or sixteenth notes. The most important beat of the tala cycle is the first. The soloist usually plays an important note of the raga on the first beat. Apart from the main beat, other beats receive secondary accents at the beginning of each group division. Singers and members of the audience often keep time with hand and finger movements on accented beats and hand waving on less important ones. Talas are performed in a variety of tempos ranging from slow to very fast.

The rhythm of Indian music is remarkably complex and sophisticated. Young drummers spend years with a master drummer memorizing hundreds of talas and their variations. Drummers and instrumental soloists sometimes have exciting dialogues in which rhythmically intricate phrases are rapidly tossed back and forth.

Instruments

Although the most important performing medium in India is the voice, there are a dazzling variety of instruments of all kinds. In north Indian classical music, instruments have become about as popular as the voice. Many instruments are associated with specific gods and goddesses. For example, the flute is associated with the Hindu god Krishna, and the *vina*—a plucked string instrument—is linked with Sarasvati, the Hindu goddess of wisdom. We describe only a few of the best-known instruments.

The **sitar** is the most popular chordophone of north India. It is a long-necked lute with nineteen to twenty-three movable frets. There are seven strings, which are plucked: five are used for melodies, and two supply drone and rhythmic effects. The sitar also has nine to thirteen sympathetically vibrating strings that give the instrument its characteristic sound. These strings lie under the frets, almost parallel to the plucked strings. The most famous sitarist is Ravi Shankar.

The *vina* is the most ancient plucked string instrument of south India. It has four strings for playing melodies, and three strings at the side of the fingerboard can be used for drone and rhythmic effects.

The *sarod* is a north Indian string instrument plucked with a plectrum of ivory or coconut shell. It has six main strings: four for melodies and two for drones and rhythm. Eleven to sixteen other strings vibrate sympathetically.

The *mridangam* is a two-headed barrel drum popular in south India. It is played with the open hands and fingers. The right drumhead is tuned to the tonic, and the left head functions as a bass.

The north Indian counterpart of the mridangam is the **tabla,** a pair of single-headed drums played by one performer. The right-hand drum is generally tuned to the tonic note, and the left-hand drum functions as a bass drum. These drums, which are played with the hands and fingers, can produce a wide variety of pitches and tone colors. The tabla is vital to north Indian concerts and is used for solos as well as accompaniments.

Maru-Bihag, by Ravi Shankar

The performance here is an improvisation by the sitarist Ravi Shankar on the evening raga *Maru-Bihag*. As usual, the sitar is accompanied by a pair of drums (tabla) with a *tambura* (a drone instrument) in the background. In his spoken introduction to the recorded performance, Shankar illustrates the raga pattern and the tala (beat cycle)

Performance Perspectives

Ravi Shankar, Sitarist, Performing *Maru-Bihag*

The sitarist and composer Ravi Shankar (1920–2012) exerted a greater influence on western culture than any other performer of Asian music in the twentieth century. Starting in the 1950s, he introduced audiences around the world to a new sonic universe in the art music of his homeland, India. At the same time, his collaborations with composers and performers from Philip Glass to the Beatles brought profound new ideas into our musical culture.

Shankar was born in the ancient holy city of Benares (Varanasi), where he was surrounded by traditional music. At age ten, he left his country for Paris to participate in a dance troupe led by his oldest brother Uday, a famous dancer and choreographer. When he was eighteen, Shankar returned to India, where he spent seven and a half years studying the sitar with a master musician who became his guru, or teacher. "Taking a guru was the most important decision of my life," Shankar later recalled. "It demanded absolute surrender, years of fanatical dedication and discipline." He learned from his guru "how sacred music is, and how it should be kept that way when you perform."

Around 1956, after becoming prominent in India as a performer and composer, Shankar began to give concert tours around the world. He collaborated with distinguished western musicians such as the violinist Yehudi Menuhin and the composer Philip Glass, and composed concertos for sitar and orchestra, as well as works combining the sitar with the western flute and the Japanese koto (a plucked stringed instrument). It was through these creative encounters that ideas and concepts from Indian musical traditions spread into western musical practice. He showed that in

Indian music, for example, improvisations "are not just letting yourself go, as in jazz—you have to adhere to the discipline of the ragas and the talas without any notation in front of you." This idea of "structured freedom" found its way into the music of Philip Glass and other composers. Shankar's performances also exemplified the idea that music has a spiritual role: "My goal has always been to take the audience along with me deep inside, as in meditation, to feel the sweet pain of trying to reach out for the supreme, to bring tears to the eyes, and to feel totally peaceful and cleansed."

It was this emphasis on the spiritual that made Shankar a superstar in the 1960s through his connection with the Beatles. In 1966, the Beatles went to India, where Shankar taught the sitar to their guitarist George Harrison. Subsequently, Harrison wrote songs permeated by the sounds of Indian music, including *Love You To,* from the album *Revolver.* George Harrison has aptly said that Shankar merits the title "godfather of world music" because "he has shown it is possible to introduce an apparently alien art form successfully into another culture." In the late 1960s, Shankar performed before hundreds of thousands at rock festivals including Monterey and Woodstock.

Shankar performed widely until his mid-eighties, and his musical legacy is continued by his two daughters: the sitar virtuoso Anoushka Shankar, who has made several solo albums and toured the world with her father's ensemble; and the pop singer Norah Jones, who has sold more than 50 million albums worldwide.

Ravi Shankar's performance of *Maru-Bihag* is included in the recordings.

used as a basis for this performance. The ascending and descending melodic forms of *Maru-Bihag* are as follows:

Raga *Maru-Bihag*

The tala, played by the tabla, consists of 10 beats divided to give 2-3-2-3. In the illustration as well as the performance, it is not easy to perceive the beats. Each one is often subdivided into shorter drum strokes, and accents often come off the beat.

The performance opens with an *alap,* a rhapsodic introductory section in which the sitar is accompanied only by the tambura playing the tonic and dominant notes of the raga pattern. The sitarist plays in free rhythm, without regular beat or meter. Shankar conveys the basic mood and character of the raga by gradually unfolding its melodic pattern, characteristic phrases, and important tones. There are many long notes, microtonal ornaments, and slides from tone to tone. After opening with a downward glissando (glide) across the sympathetic strings, Shankar first explores the lowest notes of the melody and then plays slightly higher ones. In this performance the introductory section (alap) is two minutes in length. (In other performances, however, the alap can last as long as an hour.)

The entrance of the tabla playing the tala (beat cycle) marks the second phase of the performance. Shankar presents the *gat,* a short composed phrase that recurs many times. Between these recurrences, there are longer sections of improvisation. As the improvisation progresses, Shankar generates excitement by using increasingly rapid notes and by moving through the low and high registers of the sitar. This performance is a spectacular display of virtuosity and musical imagination.

Nonwestern Music: Summary

Characteristics of Nonwestern Music

Oral Tradition
- Nonwestern music is often transmitted orally.
- Music notation is either nonexistent or far less important in nonwestern cultures than in western cultures.

Improvisation
- Improvisation is an important feature of many nonwestern musics, and in some cultures it is a highly sophisticated art requiring years of training.

Voices
- Singing is the most important way of making music in the vast majority of nonwestern cultures, but vocal timbres vary widely from one culture to another.
- Vocal techniques may include shouting, crying, whispering, sighing, humming, yodeling, and singing through the teeth.

Instruments
- Nonwestern instruments produce a wealth of sounds and come in a wide variety of shapes, sizes, and materials.
- A culture's use of instruments is influenced by its geography, raw materials available, and religious beliefs.

Melody, Texture, and Rhythm
- In many parts of the world, music often has a heterophonic texture.
- Nonwestern music uses a wide variety of scales.
- Nonwestern melodies commonly use intervals smaller or larger than those used in the western world, or they use microtones, particularly in India and the near east.
- Much nonwestern music has very complex rhythms.

Interaction between Nonwestern and Western Music

- After 1900, nonwestern music felt the impact of American and European music.
- In many areas, western and traditional music exist side by side.

Music in Sub-Saharan Africa
- The African continent is more than three times the size of the United States.
- Sub-Saharan Africa has several thousand peoples, more than 700 different languages, and music that is as diverse as its people.
- Music permeates virtually every aspect of African life.
- Music is essential to many African ceremonies, and a large number of songs are meant for particular occasions.
- Music is closely associated with dancing and closely linked with language.
- One word can have four different meanings, depending on its pitch.
- Music making is a social activity in which almost everyone participates.

IMPORTANT TERMS

Chordophone, p. 391
Aerophone, p. 391
Membranophone, p. 391
Idiophone, p. 391
Heterophonic texture, p. 392
Call and response, p. 394
Tambura, p. 399
Raga, p. 399
Tala, p. 399
Sitar, p. 400
Tabla, p. 401

FEATURED GEOGRAPHICAL REGIONS

Music in sub-Saharan Africa, p. 393
Classical music of India, p. 398

FEATURED PERFORMER

Ravi Shankar (1920–2012)

- African music emphasizes rhythm and percussive sounds. Singers use a wide variety of vocal sounds.
- Much African music uses call and response, which also is a major feature of early jazz.
- Unlike many other nonwestern cultures, African societies often have music that is homophonic or polyphonic in texture.
- The most common instruments in Africa are idiophones. Membranophones are also important in African culture.

Classical Music of India
- The musical traditions of India are among the oldest in the world. All Indian music is based on the human voice, yet there is a dazzling variety of instruments too.
- Two distinct traditions developed by the sixteenth century: Karnatak music of south India, and Hindustani music of north India.
- Indian performers consider their music spiritual in character, as reflected in the texts of south Indian songs, which have religious associations.
- Vocal and instrumental improvisation have an important role in Indian music, where it is highly developed and sophisticated, and takes years to master. Improvisations can last anywhere from a few minutes to several hours.
- Vocal and instrumental melodies are highly embellished, often move by microtones, and are almost always accompanied by a drone instrument.
- The rhythm of Indian classical music is remarkably complex and sophisticated.
- In Indian classical music, melody is created within a melodic framework called *raga*, a pattern of notes with extramusical associations. Rhythm is organized into cycles called *tala*, a repeated cycle of beats.

Beyond the Classroom: Attending a World Music Concert

One of the best ways to discover music of other countries is to attend a concert of world music. As the United States becomes more ethnically diverse, the music and traditions of nonwestern countries are performed and celebrated in many local communities. Numerous colleges and universities in the United States offer courses in world music and ethnomusicology, and these institutions often sponsor world music concerts and events.

When listening to world music, we should be aware that the culture, traditions, and music of various countries may be quite different from our own. Listen with an open mind. Evaluate the music you hear on the basis of its own qualities rather than comparing it with what you already know. For example, although we are accustomed to listening to music for pleasure alone, in other countries this concept may be completely alien. Understand that music is a cultural phenomenon that reveals much about the people and society that produce it. And the music of every country carries a rich history with its own unique story for you to explore.

When you go to a concert of world music, ask yourself the following questions:

- What geographical region is represented by the music you are hearing?
- Do the performers wear traditional clothing characteristic of the region? Does the performance include dancing representative of the area?
- If instruments are used, what do they look like, and from what materials are they constructed? How is the sound produced? It may be helpful to describe unfamiliar instruments as chordophones, aerophones, membranophones, or idiophones.
- Do you notice instances of heterophonic texture?
- Does the performance include the use of a drone?
- Pay careful attention to rhythm. Is the rhythm simple or complex? Do you notice any repeated patterns? Do you hear multiple rhythms simultaneously? Do you notice any changes to the rhythm or tempo? If

there are changes, how would you characterize them, and do they coincide with changes in other musical elements?

- Is there a distinctive melody? If so, how might you describe it? Who is singing or playing the melody? Are the intervals small or large? Does the melody span a small or wide range?

- How many scales are being used—one or more than one? Can you determine how many pitches are in the scale? Are the intervals small or large? Do you hear instances of microtones?

- Is the nonwestern music influenced by western music in terms of its instrumentation or harmony?

Glossary

A B form See *two-part form.*

A B A form See *three-part form.*

Absolute music Instrumental music having *no* intended association with a story, poem, idea, or scene; nonprogram music.

A cappella Choral music without instrumental accompaniment.

Accelerando Becoming faster.

Accent Emphasis of a note, which may result from its being louder, longer, or higher in pitch than the notes near it.

Accompanied recitative Speechlike melody that is sung by a solo voice accompanied by the orchestra.

Accordion Instrument consisting of a bellows between two keyboards (piano-like keys played by the right hand, and buttons played by the left hand) whose sound is produced by air pressure that causes free steel reeds to vibrate.

Adagio Slow.

Aerophone Any instrument—such as a flute or trumpet—whose sound is generated by a vibrating column of air.

Affections Emotional states like joy, grief, and agitation represented in baroque music through specific musical languages.

Aleatory music See *chance music.*

Allegretto Moderately fast.

Allegro Fast.

Alto (contralto) Female voice of low range.

Andante Moderately slow, a walking pace.

Answer Second presentation of the subject in a fugue, usually in the dominant scale.

Aria Song for solo voice with orchestral accompaniment, usually expressing an emotional state through its outpouring of melody; found in operas, oratorios, and cantatas.

Arpeggio See *broken chord.*

Ars nova (new art) A term used by musical theorists to describe the profound stylistic changes of Italian and French music in the fourteenth century.

Art song Setting of a poem for solo voice and piano, translating the poem's mood and imagery into music, common in the romantic period.

Atonality Absence of tonality, or key, characteristic of much music of the twentieth and early twenty-first centuries.

Augmentation Variation of a fugue subject in which the original time values of the subject are lengthened.

Bar Another term for *measure,* often used in jazz.

Baritone Male voice range lower than a tenor and higher than a bass.

Baritone horn Brass instrument similar in shape to the tuba, with a higher range, commonly used in bands.

Bass (1) Male voice of low range. (2) See *double bass.*

Bass clarinet Member of the clarinet family, having a low range. Its shape is curved at the end before flaring into a bell.

Bass clef Symbol on the staff indicating relatively low pitch ranges, such as those played by a pianist's left hand.

Bass drum Percussion instrument of indefinite pitch, the largest of the orchestral drums.

Basso continuo Baroque accompaniment made up of a bass part usually played by two instruments: a keyboard plus a low melodic instrument. (See also *figured bass.*)

Basso ostinato See *ground bass.*

Bassoon Double-reed woodwind instrument, made of wood, having a low range.

Baton Thin stick used by many conductors to beat time and indicate pulse and tempo.

Beam Horizontal line connecting the flags of several eighth notes or sixteenth notes in succession, to facilitate reading these notes.

Beat Regular, recurrent pulsation that divides music into equal units of time.

Bebop (bop) Complex jazz style, usually for small groups, developed in the 1940s and meant for attentive listening rather than dancing.

Binary form See *two-part form.*

Bitonality Approach to pitch organization using two keys at one time, often found in twentieth-century music.

Blues Term referring both to a style of performance and to a form; an early source of jazz, characterized by flatted, or "blue," notes in the scale; vocal blues consist of three-line stanzas in the form a a' b.

Bop See *bebop.*

Bow Slightly curved stick strung tightly with horsehair, used to play string instruments.

Brass instrument Instrument, made of brass or silver, whose sound is produced by the vibrations of the player's lips as he or she blows into a cup- or funnel-shaped mouthpiece. The vibrations are amplified and colored in a tube that is flared at the end.

Break Brief unaccompanied solo in jazz.

Bridge (transition) In the exposition of the sonata form, a section which leads from the first theme in the tonic, or home, key to the second theme, which is in a new key.

Broken chord (arpeggio) Sounding of the individual tones of a chord in sequence rather than simultaneously.

Cadence (1) Resting place at the end of a phrase in a melody. (2) Progression giving a sense of conclusion, often from the dominant chord to the tonic chord.

Cadenza Unaccompanied section of virtuoso display for the soloist in a concerto, usually appearing near the end of the first movement and sometimes in the last movement.

Call and response (1) In jazz, a pattern in which one voice or instrument is answered by another voice, instrument, or group of instruments. (2) Performance style in which the phrases of a soloist are repeatedly answered by those of a chorus, often found in African and other nonwestern music.

Camerata In Italian, *fellowship or society;* a group of nobles, poets, and composers who began to meet regularly in Florence around 1575 and whose musical discussions prepared the way for the beginning of opera.

Cantata Composition in several movements, usually written for chorus, one or more vocal soloists, and instrumental ensemble. The church cantata for the Lutheran service in Germany during the baroque period often includes chorales.

Castrato Male singer castrated before puberty to retain a high voice range; the most important category of vocal soloists in opera during the baroque period.

Celesta Percussion instrument of definite pitch, with metal bars that are struck by hammers controlled by a keyboard.

Cello (violoncello) String instrument with a range lower than that of the viola and higher than that of the double bass.

Chamber music Music using a small group of musicians, with one player to a part.

Chance (aleatory) music Music composed by the random selection of pitches, tone colors, and rhythms; developed in the 1950s by John Cage and others.

Chimes Percussion instrument of definite pitch, with suspended metal tubes that are struck with a hammer.

Chorale Hymn tune sung to a German religious text.

Chorale prelude Short composition for organ, based on a hymn tune and often used to remind the congregation of the melody before the hymn is sung.

Chord Combination of three or more tones sounded at once.

Chordophone Instrument—such as a harp or lute—whose sound is generated by a stretched string.

Chorus (1) A group of singers performing together, generally with more than one to a part. (2) In jazz, a statement of the basic harmonic pattern or melody.

Chromatic harmony Use of chords containing tones not found in the prevailing major or minor scale but included in the chromatic scale (which has twelve tones); often found in romantic music.

Chromatic scale Scale including all twelve tones of the octave; each tone is a half step away from the next one.

Church modes Scales containing seven tones with an eighth tone duplicating the first an octave higher, but with patterns of whole and half steps different from major and minor scales; used in medieval, Renaissance, and twentieth-century music and in folk music.

Clarinet Single-reed woodwind instrument with a beak-shaped mouthpiece, cylindrical in shape with a slightly flared bell.

Clavichord Baroque keyboard instrument in which sound is produced by means of brass blades striking strings, capable of making gradual dynamic changes, but within a narrow volume range.

Clef Symbol placed at the beginning of the staff to show the exact pitch of notes placed on each line and space.

Climax Highest tone or emotional focal point in a melody or a larger musical composition.

Coda In a sonata-form movement, a concluding section following the recapitulation and rounding off the movement by repeating themes or developing them further.

Complete cadence Definite resting place, giving a sense of finality, at the end of a phrase in a melody.

Computer Tool used to synthesize music, to help composers write scores, to store samples of audio signals, and to control synthesizing mechanisms.

Computer music Composition including sounds generated and manipulated by computer.

Concert overture Independent composition for orchestra in one movement, usually in sonata form, often found in the romantic period.

Concertmaster Principal first violinist in a symphony orchestra.

Concerto Extended composition for instrumental soloist and orchestra, usually in three movements: (1) fast, (2) slow, (3) fast.

Concerto grosso Composition for several instrumental soloists and small orchestra; common in late baroque music.

Conductor Leader of a performing group of musicians.

Consonance Tone combination that is stable and restful.

Contrabassoon Double-reed woodwind instrument with a register one octave lower than that of the bassoon.

Contralto See *alto.*

Contrast Striking differences of pitch, dynamics, rhythm, and tempo that provide variety and change of mood.

Cool jazz Jazz style related to bebop, but more relaxed in character and relying more heavily on arrangements; developed around 1950.

Cornet Brass instrument similar in shape to the trumpet, with a mellower tone.

Countermelody Melodic idea that accompanies a main theme.

Counterpoint Technique of combining two or more melodic lines into a meaningful whole.

Countersubject In a fugue, a melodic idea that accompanies the subject fairly constantly.

Countertenor Male who sings in a female pitch range using a special kind of voice production.

Crescendo Gradually louder. (Often abbreviated *cresc.*)

Cymbals Percussion instrument of indefinite pitch, consisting of a pair of metal plates, played by striking the plates against each other.

Da capo From the beginning; an indication usually meaning that the opening section of a piece is to be repeated after the middle section.

Da capo aria Aria in A B A form; after the B section, the term *da capo* is written; this means *from the beginning* and indicates a repetition of the opening A section.

Decrescendo (diminuendo) Gradually softer.

Development Second section of a sonata-form movement, in which themes from the exposition are developed and the music moves through several different keys.

Diminuendo See *decrescendo.*

Diminution Variation of a fugue subject in which the original time values of the subject are shortened.

Dissonance Tone combination that is unstable and tense.

Dixieland See *New Orleans jazz.*

Dominant chord Triad built on the fifth note of the scale, which sets up tension that is resolved by the tonic chord.

Dotted note Note with a dot to the right of it. This dot increases the note's undotted duration by half.

Dotted rhythm Long-short rhythmic pattern in which a dotted note is followed by a note that is much shorter.

Double bass (bass) Largest string instrument, having the lowest range of the string family.

Double-reed woodwinds Instruments whose sound is produced by two narrow pieces of cane held between the player's lips; these pieces vibrate when the player blows between them.

Double stop See *stop.*

Downbeat First, or stressed, beat of a measure.

Drone Long, sustained tone or tones accompanying a melody.

Duple meter Pattern of 2 beats to the measure.

Dynamics Degrees of loudness or softness in music.

Electronic instrument Instrument whose sound is produced, modified, or amplified by electronic means.

Electronic music Music in which sounds are produced by electronic devices such as computers and synthesizers.

English horn Double-reed woodwind instrument, slightly larger than the oboe and with a lower range, straight in shape with an egg-shaped bell.

Ensemble In opera, a piece performed by three or more solo singers.

Episode Transitional section in a fugue between presentations of the subject, which offers either new material or fragments of the subject or countersubject.

Estampie A medieval dance that is one of the earliest surviving forms of instrumental music.

Étude In French, *study*; a piece designed to help a performer master specific technical difficulties.

Euphonium Brass instrument similar in shape to the tuba and the baritone horn, with a higher range than the tuba's, commonly used in bands.

Exoticism Use of melodies, rhythms, or instruments that suggest foreign lands; common in romantic music.

Exposition First section of a sonata-form movement, which sets up a strong conflict between the tonic key and the new key; and between the first theme (or group of themes) and the second theme (or group of themes).

Expressionism Musical style stressing intense, subjective emotion and harsh dissonance, typical of German and Austrian music of the early twentieth century.

Figured bass Bass part of a baroque accompaniment with figures (numbers) above it indicating the chords to be played. (See also *basso continuo.*)

Film music Music accompanying a film.

Flag Wavy line attached to the stem on a note, indicating how long that note is to be held relative to the notes around it.

Flat sign (♭) Symbol which notates a pitch one half step lower than the pitch that would otherwise be indicated—for example, the next lower key on the piano.

Flute Woodwind instrument, usually made of metal, with a high range, whose tone is produced by blowing across the edge of a mouth hole.

Form Organization of musical ideas in time.

Forte (f) Loud.

Fortepiano Eighteenth-century or early nineteenth-century piano, which differs from the modern piano in sound and construction.

Fortissimo ($f\!f$) Very loud.

Fourth chord Chord in which the tones are a fourth apart, instead of a third; used in twentieth-century music.

Free jazz Jazz style which departs from traditional jazz in not being based on regular forms or on established chord patterns; developed during the 1960s.

French horn Brass instrument of medium range, whose tube is coiled into a roughly circular shape and fitted with valves; commonly used in symphony orchestras and in bands. (Sometimes called simply a *horn*.)

French overture Common opening piece in baroque suites, oratorios, and operas; usually in two parts: the first slow, with characteristic dotted rhythms, full of dignity and grandeur; the second quick and lighter in mood, often starting like a fugue.

Front line In New Orleans or Dixieland jazz, the group of melodic instruments that improvise on a melody, supported by the rhythm section.

Fugue Polyphonic composition based on one main theme, or subject.

Fusion See *jazz rock*.

Glissando Rapid slide up or down a scale.

Glockenspiel Percussion instrument of definite pitch, made up of flat metal bars set in a frame and played by striking with small metal hammers.

Gong (tam-tam) Percussion instrument of indefinite pitch, made up of a large flat metal plate that is suspended and struck with a mallet.

Grand staff Combination of the treble and bass staves, used in keyboard music to encompass the wide range of pitches produced by both hands.

Grave Very slow, solemn.

Gregorian chant Melodies set to sacred Latin texts, sung without accompaniment; Gregorian chant was the official music of the Roman Catholic church.

Ground bass (basso ostinato) Variation form in which a musical idea in the bass is repeated over and over while the melodies above it continually change; common in baroque music.

Guitar Plucked string instrument with six strings stretched along a fretted fingerboard.

Half step Smallest interval traditionally used in western music; for example, the interval between *ti* and *do*.

Harmonics Very high-pitched whistle-like tones, produced in bowed string instruments by lightly touching the string at certain points while bowing.

Harmony How chords are constructed and how they follow each other.

Harp Plucked string instrument, consisting of strings stretched within a triangular frame.

Harpsichord Keyboard instrument, widely used from about 1500 to 1775, whose sound is produced by plectra that pluck its wire strings. The harpsichord was revived during the twentieth century.

Heterophonic texture Simultaneous performance of the same basic melody by two or more voices or instruments, but in versions that differ in ornamentation or rhythm; common in nonwestern music.

Home key See *tonic key*.

Homophonic texture Term describing music in which one main melody is accompanied by chords.

Humanism The dominant intellectual movement of the Renaissance, focusing on human life and its accomplishments.

Idée fixe Single melody used in several movements of a long work to represent a recurring idea.

Idiophone Instrument—such as bells, a gong, a scraper, a rattle, or a xylophone—whose sound is generated by the instrument's own material (no tension is applied).

Imitation Presentation of a melodic idea by one voice or instrument that is immediately followed by its restatement by another voice or instrument, as in a round.

Impressionism Musical style which stresses tone color, atmosphere, and fluidity, typical of Debussy (flourished 1890–1920).

Improvisation Creation of music at the same time as it is performed.

Incidental music Music intended to be performed before and during a play, setting the mood for the drama.

Incomplete cadence Inconclusive resting point at the end of a phrase, which sets up expectations for the following phrase.

Interval "Distance" in pitch between any two tones.

Inversion Variation of a fugue subject in which each interval of the subject is reversed in direction.

Jazz Music rooted in improvisation and characterized by syncopated rhythm, a steady beat, and distinctive tone colors and performance techniques. Jazz was developed in the United States predominantly by African American musicians and gained popularity in the early twentieth century.

Jazz rock (fusion) Style which combines the jazz musician's improvisatory approach with rock rhythms and tone colors; developed in the 1960s.

Kettledrums See *timpani*.

Key (tonality) Central note, scale, and chord within a piece, in relationship to which all other tones in the composition are heard.

Key signature Sharp or flat signs immediately following the clef sign at the beginning of a piece of music, indicating the key in which the music is to be played.

Keyboard instrument Instrument—such as the piano, organ, or harpsichord—played by pressing a series of keys with the fingers.

Keynote (tonic) Central tone of a melody or larger piece of music. When a piece is in the key of C major, for example, C is the keynote.

Largo Very slow, broad.

Leap Interval larger than that between two adjacent tones in the scale.

Ledger lines Short, horizontal lines above or below the staff, used to indicate a pitch that falls above or below the range indicated by the staff.

Legato Smooth, connected manner of performing a melody.

Leitmotif Short musical idea associated with a person, object, or thought, characteristic of the operas of Wagner.

Librettist Dramatist who writes the libretto, or text, of an opera.

Libretto Text of an opera.

Lute Plucked string instrument shaped like half a pear; used in Renaissance and baroque music.

Madrigal Composition for several voices set to a short secular poem, usually about love, combining homophonic and polyphonic textures and often using word painting; common in Renaissance music.

Major key Music based on a major scale.

Major scale Series of seven different tones within an octave, with an eighth tone repeating the first tone an octave higher, consisting of a specific pattern of whole and half steps; the whole step between the second and third tones is characteristic.

Mass Sacred choral composition made up of five sections: Kyrie, Gloria, Credo, Sanctus, and Agnus Dei.

Mass ordinary Roman Catholic church texts that remain the same from day to day throughout most of the year: Kyrie, Gloria, Credo, Sanctus, and Agnus Dei.

Measure Rhythmic group set off by bar lines, containing a fixed number of beats.

Melody Series of single tones that add up to a recognizable whole.

Membranophone Instrument—basically, a drum—whose sound is generated by a stretched skin or another membrane.

Meter Organization of beats into regular groups.

Meter signature See *time signature*.

Metronome Apparatus that produces ticking sounds or flashes of light at any desired constant speed.

Mezzo forte (*mf*) Moderately loud.

Mezzo piano (*mp*) Moderately soft.

Mezzo-soprano Female voice of fairly low range, though not so low as alto.

Microtone Interval smaller than a half step.

Middle C Note C nearest to the center of the piano keyboard, notated as the pitch on the ledger line below the treble clef and above the bass clef.

Minimalist music Music characterized by steady pulse, clear tonality, and insistent repetition of short melodic patterns; its dynamic level, texture, and harmony tend to stay constant for fairly long stretches of time, creating a trancelike or hypnotic effect; developed in the 1960s.

Minor key Music based on a minor scale.

Minor scale Series of seven tones within an octave, with an eighth tone repeating the first tone an octave higher, composed of a specific pattern of whole and half steps; the half step between the second and third tones is characteristic.

Minuet and trio (minuet) Compositional form—derived from a dance—in three parts: minuet (A), trio (B), minuet (A). Often used as the third movement of classical symphonies, string quartets, and other works, it is in triple meter ($\frac{3}{4}$ time) and usually in a moderate tempo.

Mixed media Technique in which music is presented together with visual counterparts such as slide projections, films, or theatrical action.

Moderato Moderate tempo.

Modulation Shift from one key to another within the same piece.

Monophonic texture Single melodic line without accompaniment.

Motet Polyphonic choral work set to a sacred Latin text other than that of the mass; one of the two main forms of sacred Renaissance music.

Motive Fragment of a theme, or short musical idea that is developed within a composition.

Movement Piece that sounds fairly complete and independent but is part of a larger composition.

Musical (musical comedy) Type of American theater created to entertain through fusion of a dramatic script, acting, and spoken dialogue with music, singing, and dancing—and scenery, costumes, and spectacle.

Musical texture Number of layers of sound that are heard at once, what kinds of layers they are, and how they are related to each other.

Mute Device used to veil or muffle the tone of an instrument. For string instruments, the mute is a clamp that fits onto the bridge; for brass instruments, it is a funnel-shaped piece of wood, metal, or plastic that fits into the bell.

Nationalism Inclusion of folk songs, dances, legends, and other national material in a composition to associate it with the composer's homeland; characteristic of romantic music.

Natural sign (♮) Symbol used in notation of pitch to cancel a previous sharp or flat sign.

Neoclassicism Musical style marked by emotional restraint, balance, and clarity, inspired by the forms and stylistic features of eighteenth-century music, found in many works from 1920 to 1950.

New art See *ars nova*.

New Orleans (Dixieland) jazz Jazz style in which the front line, or melodic instruments, improvise several contrasting melodic lines at once, supported by a rhythm section that clearly marks the beat and provides a background of chords;

usually based on a march or church melody, a ragtime piece, a popular song, or twelve-bar blues.

Nocturne In French, *night piece;* a composition, usually slow, lyrical, and intimate in character, often for piano solo.

Notation System of writing down music so that specific pitches and rhythms can be communicated.

Note In notation, a black or white oval to which a stem and flags can be added.

Oboe Double-reed woodwind instrument with a relatively high range, conical in shape with a small flared bell.

Octave Interval between two tones in which the higher tone has twice the frequency of the lower tone.

Opera Drama that is sung to orchestral accompaniment, usually a large-scale composition employing vocal soloists, chorus, orchestra, costumes, and scenery.

Oratorio Large-scale composition for chorus, vocal soloists, and orchestra, usually set to a narrative text, but without acting, scenery, or costumes; often based on biblical stories.

Organ (pipe organ) Keyboard instrument with many sets of pipes controlled from two or more keyboards, including a pedal keyboard played by the organist's feet. The keys control valves from which air is blown across or through openings in the pipes. (The *electric organ* is an electronic instrument that is sometimes designed to imitate the sound of a pipe organ.)

Organ point See *pedal point.*

Organum Medieval polyphony that consists of Gregorian chant and one or more additional melodic lines.

Ostinato Motive or phrase that is repeated persistently at the same pitch, used in music of the twentieth and early twenty-first centuries to stabilize a group of pitches.

Overture (prelude) Short musical composition, purely orchestral, which opens an opera and sets the overall dramatic mood. Orchestral introductions to later acts of an opera are called *preludes.*

Passacaglia See *ground bass.*

Pedal point (organ point) Single tone, usually in the bass, which is held while the other voices produce a series of changing harmonies against it; often found in fugues.

Pentatonic scale Scale made up of five different tones, used in folk music and music of the far east.

Percussion instrument Instrument of definite or indefinite pitch whose sound is produced by striking by hand, or with a stick or hammer, or by shaking or rubbing.

Phrase Part of a melody.

Pianissimo (*pp***)** Very soft.

Piano Widely used keyboard instrument of great range and versatility, whose sound is produced by felt-covered hammers striking against steel strings.

Piano (*p***)** Soft.

Piccolo Smallest woodwind instrument, having the highest range; a smaller version of the flute.

Pipe organ See *organ.*

Pitch Relative highness or lowness of a sound.

Pitch range Distance between the highest and lowest tones that a given voice or instrument can produce.

Pizzicato Means of playing a string instrument by which the strings are plucked, usually with a finger of the right hand.

Plectrum Small wedge of plastic, leather, or quill used to pluck the strings of certain instruments, such as the guitar, koto, and harpsichord. (Plural, *plectra.*)

Polonaise Composition in triple meter with a stately character, often for piano solo; originally a Polish court dance.

Polychord Combination of two chords sounded at the same time, used in twentieth-century music.

Polyphonic texture Performance of two or more melodic lines of relatively equal interest at the same time.

Polyrhythm Use of two or more contrasting and independent rhythms at the same time, often found in music after 1900.

Polytonality Approach to pitch organization using two or more keys at one time, often found in twentieth-century music.

Postlude Concluding section; the section at the end of an art song that sums up its mood, played by the piano or orchestra, without the voice.

Prelude (1) Short piece usually serving to introduce a fugue or another composition; a short piece for piano. (2) See *overture.*

Prepared piano A piano whose sound is altered by placing objects such as bolts, screws, rubber bands, or pieces of felt between the strings of some of the keys.

Prestissimo As fast a tempo as possible.

Presto Very fast tempo.

Primitivism Evocation of primitive power through insistent rhythms and percussive sounds.

Program Explanatory comments specifying the story, scene, or idea associated with program music.

Program music Instrumental music associated with a story, poem, idea, or scene, often found in the romantic period.

Program symphony Symphony (a composition for orchestra in several movements) related to a story, idea, or scene, in which each movement usually has a descriptive title; often found in romantic music.

Progression Series of chords.

Prompter Person who gives cues and reminds singers of their words or pitches during an opera performance. The prompter is located in a box just over the edge of center stage, which conceals him or her from the audience.

Quadruple meter Pattern of four beats to the measure.

Quadruple stop See *stop.*

Quintuple meter Pattern of five beats to the measure.

Quotation music Works which make extensive use of quotations from earlier music; common since the mid-1960s.

Raga Pattern of notes serving as a melodic framework for the creation of an improvisation, characteristic of Indian classical music.

Ragtime Style of composed piano music, generally in duple meter with a moderate march tempo, in which the pianist's right hand plays a highly syncopated melody while the left hand maintains the beat with an "oom-pah" accompaniment. Ragtime was developed primarily by African American pianists and flourished from the 1890s to about 1915.

Range See *pitch range.*

Recapitulation Third section of a sonata-form movement, in which the first theme, bridge, second theme, and concluding section are presented more or less as they were in the exposition, with one crucial difference: all the principal material is now in the tonic key.

Recitative Vocal line in an opera, oratorio, or cantata that imitates the rhythms and pitch fluctuations of speech, often serving to lead into an aria.

Recorder Family of woodwind instruments whose sound is produced by blowing into a "whistle" mouthpiece, usually made of wood or plastic.

Reed Very thin piece of cane, used in woodwind instruments to produce sound as it is set into vibration by a stream of air.

Register Part of the total range of an instrument or voice. The tone color of the instrument or voice may vary with the register in which it is played or sung.

Renaissance Term used to describe the fifteenth and sixteenth centuries in Europe, a period of geographic exploration and adventure as well as intellectual curiosity and individualism.

Repetition Reiteration of a motive, phrase, or section, often used to create a sense of unity.

Resolution Progression from a dissonance to a consonance.

Rest In notation of rhythm, a symbol to indicate the duration of silence in the music.

Retrograde Variation of a fugue subject in which the subject is presented by beginning with its last note and proceeding backward to the first.

Rhythm Ordered flow of music through time; the pattern of durations of notes and silences in music.

Rhythm section Instruments in a jazz ensemble that maintain the beat, add rhythmic interest, and provide supporting harmonies. The rhythm section is usually made up of piano, plucked double bass, percussion, and sometimes banjo or guitar.

Riff In jazz, a short repeated phrase that may be an accompaniment or a melody.

Ritardando Becoming slower.

Ritornello In Italian, *refrain;* a repeated section of music usually played by the full orchestra, or tutti, in baroque compositions.

Ritornello form Compositional form usually employed in the baroque concerto grosso, in which the tutti plays a ritornello, or refrain, alternating with one or more soloists playing new material.

Rock First called *rock and roll,* a style of popular vocal music that developed in the 1950s, characterized by a hard, driving beat and featuring electric guitar accompaniment and heavily amplified sound.

Rondeau One of the main poetic and musical forms in fourteenth- and fifteenth-century France.

Rondo Compositional form featuring a main theme (A) that returns several times in alternation with other themes, such as A B A C A and A B A C A B A. Rondo is often the form of the last movement in classical symphonies, string quartets, and sonatas.

Rubato Slight holding back or pressing forward of tempo to intensify the expression of the music, often used in romantic music.

Saxophone Family of single-reed woodwind instruments.

Scale Series of pitches arranged in order from low to high or high to low.

Scat singing Vocalization of a melodic line with nonsense syllables, used in jazz.

Scherzo Compositional form in three parts (A B A), sometimes used as the third movement in classical and romantic symphonies, string quartets, and other works. A scherzo is usually in triple meter, with a faster tempo than a minuet.

Score Notation showing all the parts of a musical ensemble, with a separate staff for each part, and with simultaneously sounded notes aligned vertically; used by the conductor.

Secco recitative Speechlike melody that is sung by a solo voice accompanied only by a basso continuo.

Septuple meter Pattern of seven beats to the measure.

Sequence In a melody, the immediate repetition of a melodic pattern on a higher or lower pitch.

Serenade Instrumental composition, light in mood, usually meant for evening entertainment.

Serialism Method of composing that uses an ordered group of musical elements to organize rhythm, dynamics, and tone color, as well as pitch; developed in the mid-twentieth century.

Series See *tone row.*

Set See *tone row.*

Sextuple meter Pattern of six beats to the measure.

Sharp sign (♯) Symbol which notates a pitch one half step higher than the pitch that would otherwise be indicated—for example, the next higher black key on the piano.

Side drum See *snare drum.*

Single-reed woodwinds Instruments whose sound is produced by a single piece of cane, or reed, fastened over a hole in the mouthpiece. The reed vibrates when the player blows into the mouthpiece.

Sitar Most popular chordophone of north India. It is a long-necked lute with nineteen to twenty-three movable frets. Seven strings are plucked, and nine to thirteen strings vibrate sympathetically.

Snare drum (side drum) Percussion instrument of indefinite pitch, in the shape of a cylinder with a stretched skin at either end. A "snare" of gut or metal is stretched below the lower skin and produces a rattling sound when the drum is struck.

Solo concerto A piece for a single soloist and an orchestra.

Sonata In baroque music, an instrumental composition in several movements for one to eight players. In music after the baroque period, an instrumental composition usually in several movements for one or two players.

Sonata form Form of a single movement, consisting of three main sections: the exposition, where the themes are presented; the development, where themes are treated in new ways; and the recapitulation, where the themes return. A concluding section, the coda, often follows the recapitulation.

Sonata-rondo Compositional form that combines the repeating theme of rondo form with a development section similar to that in sonata form, outlined A B A—development—A B A.

Song cycle Group of art songs unified by a story line that runs through their poems, or by musical ideas linking the songs; often found in romantic music.

Soprano Female voice of high range.

Sound Vibrations that are transmitted, usually through air, to the eardrum, which sends impulses to the brain.

Sprechstimme In German, *speech-voice;* a style of vocal performance halfway between speaking and singing, typical of Schoenberg and his followers.

Staccato Short, detached manner of performing a melody.

Staff In notation, a set of five horizontal lines between or on which notes are positioned.

Stem Vertical line on a note indicating how long that note is to be held relative to the notes around it.

Step Interval between two adjacent tones in the scale.

Stop (double, triple, quadruple) Means of playing a string instrument by which the bow is drawn across two, three, or four strings at the same time or almost the same time.

Stretto Compositional procedure used in fugues, in which a subject is imitated before it is completed; one voice tries to catch the other.

String instrument Instrument whose sound is produced by the vibration of strings.

String quartet Composition for two violins, a viola, and a cello; usually consisting of four movements. (*Also,* the four instrumentalists.)

Strophic form Vocal form in which the same music is repeated for each stanza of a poem.

Style Characteristic way of using melody, rhythm, tone, color, dynamics, harmony, texture, and form in music.

Subdominant Fourth note (*fa*) of the scale, or the triad (chord) based on this note.

Subject Theme of a fugue.

Suite In baroque music, a set of dance-inspired movements all written in the same key but differing in tempo, meter, and character.

Swing Jazz style that was developed in the 1920s and flourished between 1935 and 1945, played mainly by "big bands." *Also,* verb for what jazz performers do when they combine a steady beat and precision with a lilt, a sense of relaxation, and vitality.

Swing band Typically, a large band made up of fourteen or fifteen musicians grouped in three sections: saxophones, brasses, and rhythm. They play swing, a jazz style (*see* above).

Symphonic poem (tone poem) Programmatic composition for orchestra in one movement, which may have a traditional form (such as sonata or rondo) or an original, irregular form.

Symphony Orchestral composition, usually in four movements, typically lasting between 20 and 45 minutes, exploiting the expanded range of tone color and dynamics of the orchestra.

Syncopation Accenting of a note at an unexpected time, as between two beats or on a weak beat. Syncopation is a major characteristic of jazz.

Synthesizer System of electronic components that can generate, modify, and control sound; used to compose music and to perform it.

Tabla Pair of single-headed drums in which the right-hand drum is generally tuned to the tonic note and the left-hand drum functions as a bass drum; the most important percussion instrument in north Indian music.

Tala Repeated cycle of beats organizing the rhythm in Indian classical music.

Tambourine Percussion instrument of indefinite pitch, consisting of a skin stretched across a shallow cylinder, with small circular plates set into the cylinder which jingle when the skin is struck or the cylinder is shaken.

Tambura Long-necked lute with four metal strings that are continually plucked in succession; the main drone instrument in Indian music.

Tam-tam See *gong.*

Tape studio Studio with tape recorders and other equipment used to create electronic music by modifying and combining recorded sounds.

Tempo Basic pace of the music.

Tempo indication Words, usually at the beginning of a piece of music and often in Italian, which specify the pace at which the music should be played.

Tenor Male voice of high range.

Terraced dynamics Abrupt alternation between loud and soft dynamic levels; characteristic of baroque music.

Thematic transformation Alteration of the character of a theme by means of changes in dynamics, orchestration, or rhythm, when it returns in a later movement or section; often found in romantic music.

Theme Melody that serves as the starting point for an extended piece of music.

Theme and variations Form in which a basic musical idea (the theme) is repeated over and over and is changed each time in melody, rhythm, harmony, dynamics, or tone color. Used either as an independent piece or as one movement of a larger work.

Three-part form (A B A) Form that can be represented as statement (A); contrast (B); return of statement (A).

Through-composed form Vocal form in which there is new music for each stanza of a poem.

Tie In notation of rhythm, an arc between two notes of the same pitch indicating that the second note should not be played but should be added to the duration of the first.

Timbre See *tone color.*

Time signature (meter signature) Two numbers, one above the other, appearing at the beginning of a staff or the start of a piece, indicating the meter of the piece.

Timpani (kettledrums) Percussion instruments of definite pitch, shaped like large kettles with calfskin or plastic stretched across the tops, played with soft padded mallets.

Tonality See *key.*

Tone Sound that has a definite pitch, or frequency.

Tone cluster Chord made up of tones only a half step or a whole step apart, used in music after 1900.

Tone color (timbre) Quality of sound that distinguishes one instrument or voice from another.

Tone-color melody (Klangfarbenmelodie) Succession of varying tone colors serving as a musical idea in a composition, used by Schoenberg and his followers.

Tone poem See *symphonic poem.*

Tone row (set, series) Particular ordering of the twelve chromatic tones, from which all pitches in a twelve-tone composition are derived.

Tonic See *keynote.*

Tonic chord Triad built on the first, or tonic, note of the scale, serving as the main chord of a piece and usually beginning and ending it.

Tonic key (home key) Central key of a piece of music, usually both beginning and ending the piece, regardless of how many other keys are included.

Transition See *bridge.*

Treble clef Notation on a staff to indicate relatively high pitch ranges, such as those played by a pianist's right hand.

Tremolo Rapid repetition of a tone, produced in string instruments by quick up-and-down strokes of the bow.

Triad Most basic of chords, consisting of three alternate tones of the scale, such as *do, mi, sol.*

Triangle Percussion instrument of indefinite pitch, consisting of a triangular length of metal suspended from a hook or cord, played by striking with a metal rod.

Trill Musical ornament consisting of the rapid alternation of two tones that are a whole or half step apart.

Trio sonata Baroque composition that has three melodic lines: two high ones, each played by one instrument; and a basso continuo, played by two instruments.

Triple meter Pattern of three beats to the measure.

Triple stop See *stop.*

Triplet In notation of rhythm, three notes of equal duration grouped within a curved line with the numeral 3, lasting only as long as two notes of the same length would normally last.

Trombone Brass instrument of moderately low range, whose tube is an elongated loop with a movable slide, commonly used in symphony orchestras, bands, and jazz ensembles.

Trumpet Brass instrument with the highest range, commonly used in symphony orchestras, bands, and jazz and rock groups.

Tuba Largest brass instrument, with the lowest range, commonly used in symphony orchestras and bands.

Tutti In Italian, *all;* the full orchestra, or a large group of musicians contrasted with a smaller group; often heard in baroque music.

Twelve-bar blues In vocal blues and jazz, a harmonic framework that is twelve bars in length, usually involving only three basic chords: tonic (I), subdominant (IV), and dominant (V).

Twelve-tone system Method of composing in which all pitches of a composition are derived from a special ordering of the twelve chromatic tones (tone row or set); developed by Schoenberg in the early 1920s.

Two-part form (A B) Form that can be represented as statement (A) and counterstatement (B).

Unison Performance of a single melodic line by more than one instrument or voice at the same pitch or in different octaves.

Upbeat Unaccented pulse preceding the downbeat.

Variation Changing some features of a musical idea while retaining others.

Vibrato Small fluctuations of pitch that make the tone warmer, produced in string instruments by rocking the left hand while it presses the string down.

Viola String instrument with a lower range than the violin and a higher range than the cello.

Violin String instrument with the highest range of the string family.

Violoncello See *cello*.

Vivace Lively tempo.

Voice categories of opera Voice ranges which include coloratura soprano, lyric soprano, dramatic soprano, lyric tenor, dramatic tenor, basso buffo, and basso profundo, among others.

Whole step Interval twice as large as the half step; for example, the interval between *do* and *re*.

Whole-tone scale Scale made up of six different tones, each a whole step away from the next, which conveys no definite sense of tonality; often found in the music of Debussy and his followers.

Woodwind instrument Instrument whose sound is produced by vibrations of air in a tube; holes along the length of tube are opened and closed by the fingers, or by pads, to control the pitch.

Word painting Musical representation of specific poetic images—for example, a falling melodic line to accompany the word *descending*—often found in Renaissance and baroque music.

Xylophone Percussion instrument of definite pitch, consisting of flat wooden bars set in a frame and played by striking with hard plastic or wooden hammers.

Acknowledgments

Musical Excerpts and Musical Texts

Arlen, Harold, and E. Y. Harburg. "Over the Rainbow" (from *The Wizard of Oz*). Music by HAROLD ARLEN. Lyrics by E. Y. HARBURG. © 1938 (Renewed) METRO-GOLDWYN-MAYER INC. © 1939 (Renewed) EMI FEIST CATALOG INC. All Rights Controlled and Administered by EMI FEIST CATALOG INC. (Publishing) and ALFRED PUBLISHING CO., INC. (Print). All Rights Reserved. Used by Permission of ALFRED PUBLISHING CO., INC.

Bach, Johann Sebastian. Cantata No. 140, *Wachet auf, ruft uns die Stimme.* English translation by Gerhard Herz. From *The Norton Scores* edited by Roger Kamien. Copyright © 1970 by W. W. Norton & Company, Inc. Used by permission of W. W. Norton & Company, Inc. This selection may not be reproduced, stored in a retrieval system, or transmitted in any form or by any means without the prior written permission of the publisher.

Berg, Alban. *Wozzeck.* English translation courtesy of RM Associates. Used by permission.

Hildegard of Bingen, *O successores.* English translation. Copyright Peter Dronke. Reprinted by permission.

Machaut, Guillaume de. *Puis qu'en oubli.* English translation by R. Barton Palmer. From Guillaume de Machaut, *La Messe de Nostre Dame; Songs from Le Voir Dit.* Oxford Camerata, Jeremy Summerly, Director. Naxos 553833. Reprinted by permission of R. Barton Palmer.

Ompeh. English translation by Kwasi Ampene, Ph.D., Department of Afroamerican and African Studies, University of Michigan. Reprinted by permission of the translator.

Penderecki, Krzysztof. *Threnody for the Victims of Hiroshima.* By KRZYSZTOF PENDERECKI. © 1961 (Renewed) EMI DESHON MUSIC, INC. Exclusive Worldwide Print Rights Administered by ALFRED MUSIC PUBLISHING CO., INC. All Rights Reserved. Used by Permission of ALFRED PUBLISHING CO., INC.

Schoenberg, Arnold. *A Survivor from Warsaw,* op. 46. Used by permission of Belmont Music Publishers.

Schubert, Franz. "Erlkönig." From *The Ring of Words: An Anthology of Song Texts,* translated by Philip L. Miller. Garden City, NY: Doubleday, 1963. Reprinted by permission of Robert M. Kuehn, executor of the estate of Philip L. Miller, New York.

Verdi, Giuseppe. English translation by William Weaver of "La donna è mobile" and Quartet from Act III, from *Rigoletto* from *Verdi Librettos* by William Weaver. Doubleday, 1963. Reprinted by permission of The Ned Leavitt Agency as agents for William Weaver.

Wagner, Richard. *Die Walküre.* English translation by William Mann. © William Mann. Commissioned and originally published by The Friends of Covent Garden. Reprinted by permission of Erika Mann.

Whitacre, Eric. *Lux Aurumque.* © 2001 by Walton Music Corporation. Used with permission. Latin translation © 2001 Charles Anthony Silvestri. Used with permission.

Literary Acknowledgments

Block, Adrienne Fried. *Amy Beach, Passionate Victorian: The Life and Work of an American Composer, 1867–1944.* New York: Oxford University Press, 1998.

Considine, J. D. "Viva Santana: The Man, the Myth, the Legend—gazing into the spiritual eye of the Latin guitar great, Carlos Santana," http://www.guitarworld.com/artistindex/9704.santana.html

Daverio, John. *Robert Schumann: Herald of a "New Poetic Age."* New York: Oxford University Press, 1997.

Ellis, Andy. "Carlos Santana on Spirit Guides, Rainbow Music & Passionate Guitar," *Guitar Player,* August 1999.

Holsinger, Bruce W. *Music, Body, and Desire in Medieval Culture: Hildegard of Bingen to Chaucer.* Stanford, CA: Stanford University Press, 2001, p. 113.

Hume, Paul. "The Fireworks of Alberto Ginastera," *The Washington Post,* January 29, 1978.

Levine, Lawrence. *Highbrow/Lowbrow: The Emergence of Cultural Hierarchy in America.* Cambridge, MA: Harvard University Press, 1990.

Page, Christopher. *Voices and Instruments of the Middle Ages: Instrumental Practice and Songs in France, 1100–1300.* Berkeley: University of California Press, 1986, pp. 59–60.

Pavarotti, Luciano, and William Wright. *Pavarotti: My World.* New York: Crown, 1995.

Pavarotti, Luciano, and William Wright. *Pavarotti: My Own Story.* Garden City, NY: Doubleday, 1981.

Reich, Steve. Comments in interview with D. Sterritt, "Artists and Their Inspiration: Tradition Reseen," *Christian Science Monitor,* October 23, 1980.

Santana, Carlos. Liner notes to the album *Dance of the Rainbow Serpent.*

Shankar, Ravi. *Raga Mala: The Autobiography of Ravi Shankar,* edited and introduced by George Harrison. New York: Welcome Rain Publishers, 1999.

Stravinsky, Igor. *Chronicle of My Life.* London: Gollancz, 1936.

Stravinsky, Igor, and Robert Craft. *Expositions and Developments.* Garden City, NY: Doubleday, 1962.

Whitacre, Eric. L. O., "The Q&A: Eric Whitacre, Composer," *The Economist,* online, June 14, 2011.

Zwilich, Ellen Taaffe. Comments on *Concerto Grosso.*

Photo Credits

Front Matter

iii © Roger Kamien; **iv** © Laura Doss/Media Bakery; **v** © Rick Diamond/Getty Images; **vii** © The Pierpont Morgan Library/Art Resource; **viii** © Universal Images Group/Getty Images; **ix** © AKG London; **xi** © Johann Zoffany/The Bridgeman Art Library/Getty Images; **xii, xiii** © AKG London; **xiv** © Gianni Dagli Orti/The Art Archive at Art Resource; **xv** © SEF/Art Resource; **xvii** © The Museum of Modern Art/Licensed by SCALA/Art Resource; **xviii** © The Granger Collection; **xix** © Clive Barda/ArenaPal/The Image Works; **xx, xxi** © Michael Ochs Archives/Getty Images; **xxiii** © C. Osborne/Lebrecht Photo Library.

Part I

1 © Laura Doss/Media Bakery; **2 (top)** © Dougal Waters/Getty Images; **2 (bottom)** © Ron Sherman/Stock Boston; **3 (top)** © Michael Ochs Archives/Getty Images; **3 (bottom left)** © Odie Noel/Lebrecht Photo Library; **3 (bottom right)** © Mango Productions/Media Bakery; **10** © Jim Wright/Star Ledger/Corbis; **11** © Jacques Sarrat/Sygma/Corbis; **13 (top left)** © akg-images/Marion Kalter/Newscom; **13 (top right)** © Clive Barda/Topham/The Image Works; **13 (bottom left)** © Alex Wong/Getty Images; **13 (bottom right)** © David R. Frazier/Danita Delimont Photography/Newscom; **14 (left)** © Darrin Klimek/The Image Bank/Getty Images; **14 (right)** © Nicky J. Sims/Redferns/Getty Images; **16 (top left)** © Lebrecht Photo Library/Alamy; **16 (top right)** © Richard E. Aaron/Redferns/Getty Images; **16 (bottom left)** © Chris Stock/Lebrecht/The Image Works; **16 (bottom right)** © Joshua Kamien; **17 (top left)** © Chris Stock/Lebrecht Photo Library; **17 (top right)** © Steve Morley/Redferns/Getty Images; **17 (bottom left)** © Joshua Kamien; **17 (bottom right)** © Lebrecht Photo Library/Alamy; **18 (left)** © David Redferns/Redferns; **18 (right)** © Tim Mosenfelder/Corbis; **19 (top left)** © Lawrence Migdale/Science Source; **19 (top right)** © G. Salter/Lebrecht Photo Library; **19 (bottom left)** © David Redfern/Redferns/Getty Images; **19 (bottom right)** © Chris Stock MR/Lebrecht Photo Library; **21 (top left)** © Dan Porges/ArenaPAL/The Image Works; **21 (top right)** © Harold Smith/Alamy; **21 (bottom left)** © Chris Stock/Lebrecht/The Image Works; **21 (bottom right)** © Wladimir Polak/Lebrecht Photo Library; **22 (top left)** © ArenaPal/Topham/The Image Works; **22 (top right)** © Rolf Haid/dpa/Corbis; **22 (bottom left)** © Richard Haughton/Lebrecht Photo Library; **22 (bottom right)** © G. Salter/Lebrecht Photo Library; **23 (top left)** © Wladimir Polak/Lebrecht Photo Library; **23 (top right)** © Leon Morris/Redferns; **23 (bottom)** © Bill Gallery/Stock Boston; **24 (top)** © KEYSTONE/Urs Flueeler/AP Images; **24 (bottom)** © Richard Lewis/AP Images; **25 (top)** © Lawrence Migdale/Science Source; **25 (bottom)** © Beth A. Keiser/AP Images; **26** © Steve Prezant/Blend Images/Corbis; **29** © Jack Vartoogian; **41** © Rick Diamond/Getty Images; **43** © Roger Kamien

Part II

59 © Visual Arts Publishing Ltd./Art Resource; **60** © Interfoto/Lebrecht Photo Library; **61 (top)** © Royalty-Free/Corbis; **61 (bottom)** © Art Resource; **62 (left)** © Scala/Art Resource; **62 (right)** © Bridgeman-Giraudon/Art Resource; **63 (left)** ©

DeAgostini/Getty Images; **63 (right)** © National Gallery of Art, Washington (1949.7.1[1048]); **64 (left)** © Art Resource; **64 (right)** © Royalty-Free/Corbis; **65, 66** © Erich Lessing/Art Resource; **69** © The Pierpont Morgan Library/Art Resource; **73** © Interfoto/Lebrecht Photo Library; **74** © By permission of The British Library, shelfmark: Royal 20 A. XVII, f.9; **75** © R. Strange/PhotoLink/Getty Images; **79** © Hiroyuki Ito/Getty Images; **84** © DeA Picture Library/Art Resource; **90** © The Metropolitan Museum of Art/Art Resource; **91** © The Pierpont Morgan Library/Art Resource

Part III

97 © Universal Images Group/Getty Images; **98 (top)** © AKG London; **98 (middle)** © Scala/Art Resource; **98 (bottom)** © AKG London; **99 (left)** © Museo e Gallerie Nazionali di Capodimonte, Naples, Italy/The Bridgeman Art Library; **99 (right)** © Scala/Art Resource; **100 (top)** © Museum of Fine Arts, Boston/Augustus Hemenway Fund and Arthur William Wheelright Fund/Bridgeman Art Library; **100 (bottom)** © Scala/Art Resource; **101 (top)** © National Gallery of Art; **101 (bottom)** © Robert Harding World Imagery/Getty Images; **106** © Réunion des Musées Nationaux/Art Resource; **116** © Gail Mooney/Corbis; **119** © Scala/Art Resource; **120** © AKG London; **121** © Erich Lessing/Art Resource; **122** © Bildarchiv Preussischer Kulturbesitz/Art Resource; **126** © AKG London; **130** © Dean Macdonell/Courtesy Tafelmusik Baroque Orchestra and Chamber Choir, Toronto; **131** © AKG London; **134** © The Art Archive/Corbis; **141** © AKG London

Part IV

151 © Johann Zoffany/The Bridgeman Art Library/Getty Images; **152 (top left)** © AKG London; **152 (top right)** © Erich Lessing/Art Resource; **152 (middle left)** © AKG London; **152 (middle right)** © Geoffrey Clements/Corbis; **152 (bottom left)** © AKG London; **152 (bottom right)** © Scala/Art Resource; **153** © Norton Simon Museum; **154 (top)** © The Metropolitan Museum of Art/Art Resource; **154 (bottom)** © PhotoLink/Photodisc; **155 (top)** © Erich Lessing/Art Resource; **155 (bottom)** © Scala/Art Resource; **160, 174** © AKG London; **175** © Museen der Stadt Wein; **176** © AKG London; **182** © Jack Vartoogian; **189** © Hiroyuki Ito/Hulton Archive/Getty Images; **190** © AKG London

Part V

205 © Gianni Dagli Orti/The Art Archive at Art Resource; **206 (top right)** © Burstein Collection/Corbis; **206 (left)** © Gemaeldegalerie, Staatliche Museen, Berlin, Germany/Art Resource; **206 (bottom right)** © AKG London; **207** © Scala/Art Resource; **208 (left)** © AKG London; **208 (right)** © *The Gleaners*, 1857 (oil on canvas), Millet, Jean-Francois (1814–75)/Musee d'Orsay, Paris, France/Giraudon/The Bridgeman Art Library International; **209 (top)** © Gemaeldegalerie, Staatliche Museen, Berlin, Germany/Art Resource; **209 (bottom)** © Museum of Fine Arts, Boston/Warren Collection, William Wilkins Warren Fund/The Bridgeman Art Library; **210** © Burstein Collection/Corbis; **215** © The Art Archive/Corbis; **216** © Art Resource;

Index

Digital Music Collection for Music: *An Appreciation Brief,* 8th edition

These audio selections are available in three ways, making accessing the music on a computer or portable device easier than ever:

- Connect Music, where selections stream via computer, tablet, or smartphone in two ways: in a simple audio player or in interactive Listening Outlines.

- Mp3 download card, which instructors can opt to package with the text. Simply use the unique code printed on the card to access and download all of the music to your music device of choice.

- Mp3 disc, which replaces the multi-disc audio CD set. This disc contains high-quality mp3s that can be uploaded to a personal computer or other devices. Instructors can choose to package the mp3 disc with the text.

PAGE #	COMPOSER	TITLE
8	Stravinsky	*The Firebird,* Scene 2
8	Ellington	*C-Jam Blues*
28	Britten	*The Young Person's Guide to the Orchestra*
38	Arlen	*Over the Rainbow*
42	Chopin	Prelude in E Minor for Piano, Op. 28, No. 4
49	Bizet	*Farandole* from *L'Arlésienne,* Suite No. 2
51	Tchaikovsky	*Dance of the Reed Pipes* from *Nutcracker* Suite
53	Bach	Bourrée from Suite in E Minor for Lute
70	Anon.	*Alleluia: Vidimus stellam*
72	Hildegard of Bingen	*O successores*
74	Anon.	*Estampie*
77	Machaut	*Puis qu'en oubli*
78	Machaut	*Notre Dame* Mass, Agnus Dei
82	Josquin	*Ave Maria . . . virgo serena*
85	Palestrina	*Pope Marcellus* Mass, Kyrie
87	Weelkes	*As Vesta Was Descending*
89	Dowland	*Flow My Tears*
110	Bach	*Brandenburg* Concerto No. 5 in D Major, I
113	Bach	Fugue in G Minor (*Little Fugue*)
122	Monteverdi	*Orfeo,* "Tu se' morta"
124	Purcell	*Dido and Aeneas,* Act III, *Dido's Lament*
128	Vivaldi	*La Primavera (Spring)* Concerto for Violin and String Orchestra, Op. 8, No. 1 from *The Four Seasons,* I
129	Vivaldi	*La Primavera (Spring)* Concerto for Violin and String Orchestra, Op. 8, No. 1 from *The Four Seasons,* II
129	Vivaldi	*La Primavera (Spring)* Concerto for Violin and String Orchestra, Op. 8, No. 1 from *The Four Seasons,* III
133	Bach	Suite No. 3 in D Major, S. 1068, Bourrée
139	Bach	Cantata No. 140: *Wachet auf, ruft uns die Stimme,* IV
140	Bach	Cantata No. 140: *Wachet auf, ruft uns die Stimme,* VII
143	Handel	*Messiah, Ev'ry Valley Shall Be Exalted*
145	Handel	*Messiah, Hallelujah Chorus*
164	Mozart	Symphony No. 40 in G Minor, K. 550, I
166	Haydn	Symphony No. 94 in G Major (*Surprise*), II

Online Supplements

Connect Music with LearnSmart One-Term Online Access for Music: An Appreciation, Eighth Brief Edition

McGraw-Hill Connect is a digital teaching and learning environment that improves performance over a variety of critical outcomes. With Connect, instructors can deliver assignments, quizzes and tests easily online. Students can practice important skills at their own pace and on their own schedule.

HOW TO REGISTER

Using a <u>Print Book</u>?
To register and activate your Connect account, simply follow these easy steps:
1. **Go to the Connect course web address provided by your instructor or visit the Connect link set up on your instructor's course within your campus learning management system.**
2. **Click on the link to register.**
3. **When prompted, enter the Connect code found on the inside back cover of your book and click Submit. Complete the brief registration form that follows to begin using Connect.**

Using an <u>eBook</u>?
To register and activate your Connect account, simply follow these easy steps:
1. **Upon purchase of your eBook, you will be granted automatic access to Connect.**
2. **Go to the Connect course web address provided by your instructor or visit the Connect link set up on your instructor's course within your campus learning management system.**
3. **Sign in using the same email address and password you used to register on the eBookstore. Complete your registration and begin using Connect.**

Note: Access Code is for one use only. If you did not purchase this book new, the access code included in this book is no longer valid.

Need help? Visit mhhe.com/support

Topics from the Restless

BOOK TWO

Selections That Intrigue Developing Readers

Third Edition

JAMESTOWN PUBLISHERS

a division of NTC/CONTEMPORARY PUBLISHING GROUP
Lincolnwood, Illinois USA

Cover Illustration: "Separation of the Praying Masses" by Mario Castillo

ISBN: 0-89061-117-3

Published by Jamestown Publishers,
a division of NTC/Contemporary Publishing Group, Inc.,
4255 West Touhy Avenue,
Lincolnwood (Chicago), Illinois 60712-1975 U.S.A.
© 1999 by NTC/Contemporary Publishing Group, Inc.

00 01 02 03 04 VH 10 9 8 7 6 5 4 3 2

ACKNOWLEDGMENTS

Acknowledgment is gratefully made to the following publishers, authors, and agents for permission to reprint these works. Every effort has been made to determine copyright owners. In the case of any omissions, the Publisher will be pleased to make suitable acknowledgments in future editions.

"The Science of Being Santa" by Roger Rapoport. © 1973 by Saturday Review Co. First appeared in *Saturday Review/Science* December 23, 1972.

Excerpts from Jessie Lopez De La Cruz's "La Causa" reprinted by permission of The Feminist Press from Ellen Cantarow with Susan Gushee O'Malley and Sharon Hartman Strom, *Moving the Mountain: Women Working for Social Change* (New York: The Feminist Press at The City University of New York, 1980). Copyright © 1980 by Ellen Cantarow, Susan Gushee O'Malley and Sharon Hartman Strom.

Excerpts from *Organ Hunter* by Andrew C. Revkin. Copyright © 1988 Andrew C. Revkin. Reprinted with permission of *Discover Magazine*.

Excerpt from *Killer: Autobiography of a Mafia Hit Man* by Joey with Dave Fisher. Copyright © 1973 by Playboy Press.

Excerpt from *The Peter Principle* by Laurence J. Peter and Raymond Hull. Copyright © 1969 by William Morrow & Company, Inc. By permission of William Morrow & Company, Inc.

Excerpt from "Field Trip" by Naomi Shihab Nye. Reprinted by permission of the author.

Excerpt from *The Autobiography of Malcolm X* by Malcolm X with the assistance of Alex Haley. Copyright © 1964 by Alex Haley and Malcolm X. Copyright © 1965 by Alex Haley and Betty Shabazz. Reprinted by permission of Random House, Inc.

"A Beloved Professor's Last Lessons" by Mitch Albom. From *The New York Times,* November 2, 1997. Copyright © 1997 by The New York Times Co. Reprinted by permission.

"A Whole Society of Loners and Dreamers" by William Allen. Reprinted by permission of the author. (William Allen is a nationally recognized personal essayist and Professor Emeritus of The Ohio State University.) "A Whole Society of Loners and Dreamers" was originally published in *The Saturday Review,* November 11, 1972.

"The Excellence of Welby Stitch Jr" by Russell Baker. Reprinted by permission of Don Congdon Associates, Inc. Copyright © 1969 by Time Inc., renewed 1997 by Russell Baker.

"Henry Ford's Fabulous Flivver" by Irwin Ross. From *Our Sun* magazine of the Sun Oil Co.

"First Flight Across America" by Ray Helminiak. From *Northliner,* the inflight magazine of North Central Airlines.

"British Eccentricity on Four Wheels" by Kirk Kraeutler. From *The New York Times,* August 10, 1997. Copyright © 1997 by The New York Times Co. Reprinted by permission.

"Why Not Bicycle to Work?" by Robert Petersen. From *Bicycling* magazine, December 1968. Copyright © 1968 by *Bicycling.*

"The Pedestrian." From *The Golden Apples of the Sun* by Ray Bradbury. Reprinted by permission of Don Congdon Associates, Inc. Copyright © 1951 by the Fortnightly Publishing Co., renewed 1979 by Ray Bradbury.

"Ebola: An Early Outbreak." From *The Hot Zone* by Richard Preston. Copyright © 1994 by Richard M. Preston. Reprinted by permission of Random House, Inc.

"Winning the Battle of the Bug" by William Shelton. From *Exxon USA,* quarterly magazine of the Exxon Company USA.

"A Day's Wait" by Ernest Hemingway. Reprinted with permission of Scribner, a Division of Simon & Schuster, from *Winner Take Nothing* by Ernest Hemingway. Copyright 1933 by Charles Scribner's Sons. Copyright renewed © 1961 by Mary Hemingway.

"Conquering Polio." From *Jonas Salk* by Victoria Sherrow. Copyright © 1993 by Victoria Sherrow. Reprinted by permission of Facts on File, Inc.

Excerpt from "Needles & Nerves" by Catherine Dold, *Discover Magazine,* September 1998. Catherine Dold/© 1998. Reprinted with permission of *Discover Magazine.*

Photographs

Page 7: Tony Stone Images/Steward Cohen.

Page 10: The Image Bank/Patti McConville.

Page 16: UPI/Corbis-Bettmann.

Page 22: Ken Shung, © 1988. Reprinted with permission of *Discover Magazine.*

Page 28: The Image Bank/Bertran Henry.

Page 33: The Image Bank/Larry Dale Gordon.

Page 39: Tony Stone Images/Lonnie Duka.

Page 42: NTC/Contemporary photo by Jeff Ellis, courtesy of Dream Color, Inc.ß

Page 47: UPI/Corbis-Bettmann.

Page 53: Copyright © 1997 Heather Pillar.

Page 59: The Image Bank/Gary Russ.

Page 65: The Stock Market/Jon Feingersh.

Page 71: Tony Stone Images/ Greg Probst.

Page 74: © FPG International 1993

Page 80: Corbis-Bettmann.

Page 86: FPG International/© Navaswan 1991.

Page 91: The Image Bank/Alan Becker.

Page 97: © Tony Stone Images/Yves Marcoux.

Page 103: Tony Stone Images/David Joel.

Page 106: Agence France Presse/Corbis-Bettmann.

Page 112: The Image Bank/Will Crocker.

Page 118: The Image Bank/Bob Elsdale.

Page 124: UPI/Corbis-Bettmann.

Page 130: Tony Stone Images/Nick Vedros, Vedros & Associates.

CONTENTS

Introductory Selection

READING PURPOSE —
The following passage will tell you about the selections in this book and how they are structured. As you read, decide which selection part will help you improve your reading most. (After you have completed the vocabulary activity and before you begin reading, turn to page 4 and record the hours and minutes in the box labeled *Starting Time*.)

VOCABULARY—PART ONE

All of these words are in the selection you are about to read. Study each word and its meaning. Then answer the questions below. As you read the selection, notice how each vocabulary word is used.

intent: purpose

aspects: parts; features; elements

oppression: persecution; great hardship

compelling: very interesting or attention-getting

slant: angle; viewpoint

efficient: performing a task easily and skillfully

consecutively: coming one after another in order

corresponding: matching

diagnostic: helping to analyze or find problems in

discriminating: able to see differences and distinctions

---

1. Which word could describe a person who works without wasting any effort?

2. Which word would describe a person who could easily tell the difference between real and fake emeralds?

3. Which word could describe a movie that held your interest so strongly you could hardly stand for it to end?

4. If you counted from 1 to 100 in order, how would you be presenting the numbers?

5. Which word would you use if you were describing a test that told you about your reading strengths and weaknesses?

(Enter your starting time on page 4 now.)

1   You are using this text for two purposes: (1) to improve your reading and study skills and (2) to read stories and articles about topics that will both interest you and make you think.

2   The topics and selections in these books span the range of human experience. The editors' intent in choosing them was to show aspects of the real world, but another, equally important, purpose was to present materials simply because they are interesting. Serious or amusing, the topics in these books will help you get involved with the reality of today's world.

3   The other purpose for using this series, that of reading and study improvement, recognizes another kind of reality. The series will help you to develop skills and techniques necessary for success.

4   In the books in *Topics from the Restless* you will read not only about serious matters like preserving the environment, knowing the dangers of alcohol and other drugs, and recognizing injustice and oppression. You will also find less serious stories and articles about interesting ways that people make a living, fascinating cities and regions around the world, and thrilling encounters with disaster. Though you may not find each selection equally compelling, there are enough choices to get you interested in reading and to show you how exciting stories in books, newspapers, and magazines can be.

5   Each book in this series is divided into units of five reading selections. These selections will cover different aspects of the unit topic, or perhaps present different opinions on that topic. Sometimes one selection in the unit will be a bit more difficult than the others, and sometimes you will see how a writer of fiction can give a new and different slant to a topic. By the time you have finished reading the selections in a unit, you should be something of an expert on the topic. At the very least, you will be familiar with various ways to look at it.

6   Included with each selection is a study skills exercise. In these exercises, you will learn methods of understanding, critical thinking skills, techniques of comprehension, and many other key ways to improve your reading ability. The study skills exercises are designed to help you develop efficient reading techniques. As you read the selections in this book, you will find that often one study skills exercise leads to the next. It is important to read

and work the study skills exercises consecutively to understand each subject fully. You will come to see that each kind of reading matter demands a corresponding reading technique.

Using the Topics

7   The 20 selections following this introductory one are designed to be read in numerical order, starting with Selection 1 and ending with Selection 20. Because the selections generally increase in difficulty as you progress through the book, the earlier ones may prepare you to handle the upcoming ones successfully.

8   Here are the procedures to follow for reading each selection:

9   **1. Answer the Vocabulary Questions.** At the beginning of each lesson, immediately preceding the selection, is a vocabulary-previewing activity. The activity includes 10 vocabulary words from the selection, their meanings as they are used in the selection, and 5 questions related to those words. To answer each question, you will choose from and write one of the 10 vocabulary words. Previewing the vocabulary in this way will give you a head start on understanding the words when you encounter them in the selection. In the selection itself the words are underlined for easy reference.

10   **2. Preview Before Reading.** Previewing acquaints you with the overall content and structure of the selection before you actually read. It is like consulting a road map before taking a trip: planning the route gives you more confidence as you proceed and, perhaps, helps you avoid any unnecessary delays. Previewing should take about a minute or two and is done in this way:

11   a) Read the title. Learn the writer's subject and, possibly, his or her point of view on it.

12   b) Read the opening and closing paragraphs. These contain the introductory and concluding remarks. Important information is frequently presented in these key paragraphs.

13   c) Skim through. Try to discover the author's approach to the subject. Does he or she use many examples? Is the writer's purpose to convince you about certain ideas? What else can you learn now to help you when you read?

14   **3. Establish a Reading Purpose.** After you have previewed the selection, establish a purpose for reading it. The suggestion that precedes the selection will help you complete the activities.

15 **4. Read the Selection.** Do not try to race through. Read carefully so that you can answer the comprehension questions that follow.

16 Keep track of your reading time by noting when you start and finish. A table on page 136 converts your reading time to a words-per-minute rate. Select the time from the table that is closest to your reading time. Record those figures in the boxes at the end of the selection. There is no one ideal reading speed for everything. The efficient reader varies reading speed as the selection requires.

17 **5. Answer the Comprehension Questions.** After you have read the selection, find the comprehension questions that follow. These have been included to test your understanding of what you have read. The questions are diagnostic, too. Because the comprehension skill being measured is identified, you can detect your areas of weakness.

18 Read each question carefully and select one of the four choices that answers the question most accurately or most completely. Frequently all four choices, or options, given for a question are *correct*, but one is the *best* answer. For this reason some comprehension questions are highly challenging and require you to be highly discriminating. You may, from time to time, disagree with an answer. When this happens, you can sharpen your powers of discrimination. Study the question again and seek to discover why the listed answer may be best. When you disagree with the text, you are thinking. When you objectively analyze and recognize your errors, you are learning.

19 A profitable habit for you to acquire is analyzing the questions you have answered incorrectly. If time permits, return to the selection to find and underline the passages containing the correct answers. This helps you see what you missed the first time. Some interpretive and generalizing questions are not answered specifically in the text. In these cases, bracket the part of the selection that refers to the correct answer.

20 **6. Answer Additional Vocabulary Questions.** Following the comprehension section are two sets of sentences using the 10 vocabulary words introduced earlier. Each fill-in-the-blank sentence requires you to choose the correct word by looking at the context (surrounding words). This format helps you improve your ability to use context to understand words. The efficient use of context is a valuable vocabulary tool.

21 The boxes following the vocabulary activity contain space for your comprehension score and your vocabulary score. Each correct vocabulary item is worth 10 points, and each correct comprehension answer is worth 10 points.

22 A profitable habit for you to acquire is analyzing the questions you have answered incorrectly. If time permits, return to the selection to find and underline the passages containing the correct answers. This helps you see what you missed the first time. Some interpretive and generalizing questions are not answered specifically in the text. In these cases, bracket the part of the selection that refers to the correct answer.

23 Pages 137 and 138 contain graphs to be used for plotting your scores and tallying your incorrect responses. On page 137 record your comprehension score at the appropriate intersection of lines, using an X. Use a circle on the same graph to record your vocabulary results. Some students prefer to use different color inks, or pencil and ink, to distinguish between comprehension and vocabulary plottings.

24 On page 138 darken the squares to indicate the comprehension questions you have missed. By referring to the Skills Profile as you progress through the text, you and your instructor will be able to tell which questions give you the most trouble. As soon as you detect a specific weakness in comprehension, consult your instructor to see what supplementary materials he or she can provide or suggest.

25 **7. Write About the Selection.** A brief writing activity allows you to offer your own opinions about some aspect of the selection. Here you are always asked to respond briefly, which means you do not have to go on for pages. A clearly written paragraph or two, using as many specific facts or examples as possible, is enough to complete each writing assignment.

26 **8. Complete the Study Skills Exercises.** Concluding each lesson is a passage on study skills followed by five completion questions to be answered after you have finished the passage. One or two of these questions will always ask you to apply the study skill to the selection you have just read.

Using the Topic Review

27 At the end of each unit of selections is a Topic Review consisting of six questions. These questions deal with the unit as a whole and so may

ask you to think about the selections in new ways, such as by comparing and contrasting them or by making generalizations about their content. One question will always require you to apply a study skill from the unit to one or more of the selections.

28   The questions in the Topic Review are designed to be answered in writing. Your instructor, however, may choose to have you discuss some or all of them in class. He or she may also suggest that you answer only certain questions or may have you pick a certain number of them to answer.

29   Each lesson and each Topic Review is set up in the manner just described. When you have finished doing the activities in this introductory material, go on to the first selection for Topic 1.

Starting Time

Finishing Time

Reading Time

Reading Rate

COMPREHENSION

Read the following questions and statements. For each one, put an X in the box before the option that contains the most complete or accurate answer.

1. How much time should be spent on previewing?
   ☐ a. Your time will vary with each selection.
   ☐ b. Previewing should take one or two minutes.
   ☐ c. No specific time is suggested.
   ☐ d. None—the instructor times the selection.

2. The way the vocabulary exercises are described suggests that
   ☐ a. the meaning of a word often depends on how the word is used in the selection.
   ☐ b. the final authority for word meaning is the dictionary.
   ☐ c. words have precise and permanent meanings.
   ☐ d. certain words are always difficult to understand.

3. The writer of this passage presents the facts in order of
   ☐ a. importance.   ☐ c. time.
   ☐ b. purpose.   ☐ d. operation.

4. *Topics from the Restless* is based on which of the following premises?
   ☐ a. Students should know about today's world.
   ☐ b. Students learn best from reading newspapers and magazines.
   ☐ c. The only worthwhile articles are long and serious.
   ☐ d. Traditional reading improvement texts rarely accomplish their purpose.

5. How does the writer feel about reading speed?
   ☐ a. It is a minimal aspect of the total reading situation.
   ☐ b. It is second (following comprehension) in the ranking of skills.
   ☐ c. It is connected to comprehension.
   ☐ d. It should be developed at an early age.

6. The introductory selection
   ☐ a. eliminates the need for oral instruction.
   ☐ b. explains the proper use of the text in detail.
   ☐ c. permits the student to learn by doing.
   ☐ d. allows for variety and interest.

7. The introductory selection suggests that
   ☐ a. most readers are not flexible.
   ☐ b. students should learn to use different reading skills for different types of reading matter.
   ☐ c. students today read better than students of the past did.
   ☐ d. 20 selections is an ideal number for a reading improvement text.

8. The overall tone of this passage is
   ☐ a. serious.   ☐ c. humorous.
   ☐ b. suspenseful.   ☐ d. sarcastic.

9. The author of this selection is probably
   ☐ a. a doctor.   ☐ c. an educator.
   ☐ b. an accountant. ☐ d. a businessman.

10. The writer of this passage makes his or her point clear by
    ☐ a. telling a story.
    ☐ b. listing historical facts.
    ☐ c. using metaphors.
    ☐ d. giving directions.

Comprehension Skills Key

1. recalling specific facts
2. retaining concepts
3. organizing facts
4. understanding the main idea
5. drawing a conclusion
6. making a judgment
7. making an inference
8. recognizing tone
9. understanding characters
10. appreciating literary forms

VOCABULARY—PART TWO

Write the word that makes the most sense in each sentence.

aspects
intent
oppression

efficient
consecutively

1. The purpose of this series was not to make reading dull and boring; instead, its _____ was to show how interesting reading can be.

2. The selections deal with amusing topics as well as serious ones, such as injustice and other forms of _____ .

3. Many _____ of each topic are presented, so the reader can have contact with a wide range of viewpoints about that topic.

4. Because the study skills are presented in order, it is important to study each lesson _____ .

5. Learning to apply the study skills as you go through this book will make you a more _____ reader.

diagnostic
corresponding
slant

discriminating
compelling

6. Though a few selections may bore you, you should find most of them _____ .

7. Most selections were chosen because the writers have a distinct point of view and an interesting _____ on their topics.

8. When answering the comprehension questions following a selection, you should mark the blank _____ to the right response.

9. Some of the questions are difficult and require you to be _____ between the possible answers.

10. You can use your wrong answers in a _____ way to figure out your reading weaknesses.

Comprehension [ ]

Vocabulary [ ]

UNDERSTANDING THROUGH WRITING

Think about the weaknesses you might have as a reader. In what ways do you think the selections in this book will be most helpful in overcoming them? Write a paragraph explaining what you think. Be as specific as you can.

_____

_____

_____

_____

_____

_____

_____

BUILDING STUDY SKILLS

Read the following passage and answer the questions that follow it.

Why Learn Study Skills?

You may wonder why you still need to learn how to study at this point in your life. You may feel you know all there is to know about studying.

But do you really? Have you ever found yourself in the same situation as these people?

- A student quickly reads the directions to his friend's house and thinks he knows where he's going. But he gets lost on the way.
- A woman needs to find one small fact in an 800-page biography. After 45 minutes, she has looked through the first 250 pages and still has not found what she wanted.
- A businessman enjoys reading fiction and can get through a mystery novel in two nights. But when he reads documents at work, he has trouble understanding them.

Maybe you recognized the problem each of these people had. The student could have jotted down notes or drawn a rough map to help himself remember the directions. The woman could have found the information she needed by using the book's index. The businessman should have slowed down when he read more difficult materials, such as business documents.

It is clear that study skills are skills that can help you far beyond the classroom. Whenever you have to read, locate, or understand information, your job will be easier if you call on the appropriate study skill.

Today's reader must be flexible enough to choose the skills that suit each reading task. As you complete the selections and exercises in this book, you will find yourself improving your reading technique. The more techniques you master, the easier you will make your life in school, as well as in the outside world.

1. You may feel you know a lot about

_____ already.

2. You may remember that to find information in a book, you can use the book's

_____ .

3. Study skills can help you whenever you have to read, locate, or _____ information.

4. Today's reader must be _____ enough to choose a suitable skill for each reading task.

5. The selections and exercises in this book will help you grow in _____ .

I was born to live, not to work!

—Unknown Portuguese fisherman

A LIVING WAGE

The Science of Being Santa

Roger Rapoport

R E A D I N G   P U R P O S E —
This selection tells about the preparation workers go through to become in-house Santas. Read to find out some of the things the Santas have to learn

VOCABULARY—PART ONE

All of these words are in the selection you are about to read. Study each word and its meaning. Then answer the questions below. As you read the selection, notice how each vocabulary word is used.

hirsute: hairy

gross: earn before taxes are taken out

comprehensive: broad in scope

yielded: produced

matronly: like a dignified, stately woman

hygiene: cleanliness and health

patter: special vocabulary for a group or situation

minimal: very low

steadfast: not moving or changing

compliance: yielding to a command or law

1. Which word could describe an examination that covered all areas of study from a course?

2. Which word could include such things as frequent bathing and hair washing?

3. Which word might describe a friend who stands by you no matter what wrong things you have done?

4. Which word could describe a person with a mustache and full beard?

5. Which word could describe the efforts of a working person who barely did anything to keep his job?

1 Mrs. Gail Plowe slapped her hand on a red velveteen suit trimmed with white fur as she addressed her students: "Now, class, under no circumstances does Western Girl tolerate 'Ho, Ho, Ho'-ing from our Santas. You'll frighten the smaller children right out of the store. Try to remember you're in there as a customer draw. A Santa can make or break a store at Christmas time."

2 Mrs. Plowe's twenty-two Santa trainees shifted uneasily in their chairs at the Oakland office of Western Girl, the international temporary-employment agency. They ranged from eighteen to seventy, from the unemployed to the retired. But primarily they were hirsute, young college students eager to make a few hundred extra dollars by playing St. Nicholas. Theirs was one of seventy-five pre-Christmas Santa schools conducted across the country by Western Girl's Santa Division. With a full-time Santa selling for $1,200 to $1,500, the company expects to gross roughly $500,000 on the rental of 500 full- and part-time Santas this season.

3 Western Girl has become the nation's largest supplier of Santas, thanks in large part to a comprehensive training program pioneered by Richard Westerman of the North Pole Santa Claus Rental Agency in Los Angeles. Three years ago Western Girl bought out the North Pole Agency and took Westerman's total-service-Santa concept national. Today a store anywhere in the country can rent a fully trained and costumed Western Girl Santa, "bonded to $100,000 and covered with $1 million worth of insurance for bodily injury and property damage." In case of illness a backup Santa is available. This approach has yielded an average annual sales gain of 30 per cent, as such department-store chains as Sears, Ward's, and Penney's rent more and more Western Girl Santas each year in order to free themselves from the headaches of the Santa business.

4 The temporary employment agency screens carefully; only one out of every twenty-three Santa applicants is selected. A week before Thanksgiving matronly Mrs. Plowe stressed this point to her Oakland students: "Age and weight have very little to do with your being here tonight. When you get dressed up in the suit, all about anyone can see is your eyes. All of you have been chosen primarily because of that essential twinkle in your eyes." Her students blushed and winked at each other.

5 Mrs. Plowe glanced down at her thick, red Santa manual and continued lecturing: "There are several ground rules you must observe to stay in the Santa corps. I don't want to catch any of you with a bright red nose brought on from nipping at a bottle of Old Granddad. You're not allowed to flirt with the young women who work as Santa's helpers. Please remove your beard before you light a cigarette, or it might catch fire. Don't let the kids catch you smoking.

6 "If you're not working, don't let the kids see you in a Santa suit. Don't be like the off-duty Santa who brushed a friendly child aside, grumbling, 'Go away, little girl; I'm not on until the afternoon shift.' When you change shifts with another Santa, make sure that you are back in the dressing room before your replacement shows up in front of the children—it confuses the kids when they see two Santas at the same time. And please, please, pay attention to personal hygiene. We had to send one Santa home last year because of b. o. So remember, it's: 'On Right Guard, on Dial, on Certs, on Pepsodent, on Listerine, and on Brylcreem.'

7 "Now the most important thing you have to learn before you go to work is the names of the reindeer…Dasher, Dancer, Prancer, Vixen, Comet, Cupid, Donner, and Blitzen."

8 One bearded student wearing a work shirt and jeans raised his hand and asked: "What about Rudolph?"

9 Mrs. Plowe nodded: "Yes, of course, Rudolph. And let's all remember that Rudolph has a new girlfriend this year, named Violet."

10 Consulting her manual once again, the instructor began teaching Santa patter guaranteed to engage even the toughest kid: "The three basic parts of our Santa talk are the invitation, recognition of the child, and questions-closing. To save time that would normally be devoted to finding out the child's name, simply invite each 'young man' or 'young woman' to sit down with you. Next, recognize how they've grown since last year: 'Young man, you've sprouted up like a weed,' or, 'You're even prettier than last year, young woman.' Then ask what they want for Christmas and close by telling them to behave, eat their vegetables, drink their milk, and brush their teeth twice daily. Adjust your speed to the number of youngsters standing in line. Under pressure, speed up your pitch so that you can get more youngsters through faster.

11 "Never promise anything. Always say you'll see what you can do. If they ask for a baby brother, tell them: 'That's out of my department. If you want a

baby brother, you should pray for one. If God wants you to have one, then you will get one.' Never mention the word 'parents.' Use the term 'folks,' because a large percentage of kids today are not living with their original mothers and fathers. Many are in foster homes, or with grandparents or other relatives. If you say 'parents,' they might break out sobbing, 'I haven't any daddy or mommy,' and become semihysterical."

12   When Mrs. Plowe had finished teaching the Santa patter, her class broke for coffee and doughnuts. Much of their conversation was about the $500 to $700 that each expected to make during the Yuletide season. Although wages would be <u>minimal</u>, everyone was confident about regular overtime opportunities. The students seemed delighted that Western Girl was paying them to attend Santa school.

13   Gradually the pupils clustered around four classmates with previous Santa experience. Skip Ball, a nineteen-year-old student at nearby Diablo Valley College, encouraged the new Santas to limit themselves to four-hour shifts when possible: "Going eight hours is a real strain, with all these kids tugging at your beard and asking for weird things like pet rats. Last year I worked in a Walnut Creek department store where one of the Santas freaked out. He started running through the toy department, giving things away. The guy thought he really was Santa Claus. They had to fire him."

14   Another Santa returnee, who works as a handyman during the off-season, warned everyone to beware of adults: "Last year I worked at Penney's, and a lot of grownups sat down on my lap and told me what they wanted for Christmas. One woman must have weighed 250 pounds."

15   Marvin Meyers, a husky, twenty-year-old black singer with an Oakland band, alerted the students to special problems brought on by Western Girl's <u>steadfast</u> <u>compliance</u> with federal equal-employment-opportunity regulations. "I worked at

"Recognize how they've grown since last year: 'Young man, you've sprouted up like a weed.'"

Ward's here in Oakland last Christmas and split the day with a white Santa. One little kid showed up twice in a single day and became really confused. He gave me a long look and asked: 'Santa, what's happened to your face?' I told him I'd just been out here in the California sun too long." Another student mentioned that he had heard about similar problems caused by Western Girl's occasional use of women Santas. Curious children have asked Santa why he suddenly had sprouted breasts.

16   James McMahan, another twenty-year-old black from Oakland, mentioned that once he had played Santa to a child who happened to glance out the store window and noticed another Santa riding on top of a parade bus: "I told the kid that was Santa and I was St. Nick. He believed me. Generally, though, I think you'll find the younger generation heavier than our own. They really know what they want."…

17   When class had resumed, Mrs. Plowe held up a pair of Santa pants and showed how a drawstring makes one size fit all. Next, she pointed out a special secret pocket: "This was invented several years ago after eleven Santas had their wallets stolen out of dressing rooms. We encourage you to use it for your valuables."

18   Then, with the help of Bruce Leiper, a tall, twenty-two-year-old Berkeley student, she showed everyone how to put on the pants, jacket, belt, spats, eyeshadow, wig, and beard. At this point the class was officially over, but Mrs. Plowe simply couldn't resist the temptation offered by two students: "You guys look so adorable as Santas. Would one of you consider dressing up?"

19   Marvin Meyers and James McMahan flipped a nickel, and McMahan lost. He suited up quickly, to the cheers of his classmates. A moment later Western Girl's Oakland office cleaning lady showed up with her young daughter. McMahan promptly

bounced the child onto his knee and asked, "What do you want for Christmas, young lady?"

20   The little girl stared out at the classroom full of future Santas but refused to utter a word.

Starting Time	
Finishing Time	
Reading Time	
Reading Rate	

COMPREHENSION

Read the following questions and statements. For each one, put an X in the box before the option that contains the most complete or accurate answer.

1. Western Girl Santa is an outgrowth of
   - ☐ a. North Pole Santa Claus Rental Agency.
   - ☐ b. pre-Christmas Santa schools.
   - ☐ c. temporary employment agencies.
   - ☐ d. the national unemployment situation.

2. An important qualification for being hired to play Santa is
   - ☐ a. proven maturity.
   - ☐ b. expressive eyes.
   - ☐ c. body size.
   - ☐ d. short stature.

3. People enroll in Santa school
   - ☐ a. in order to apply for a job as Western Girl Santas.
   - ☐ b. after being hired as Western Girl Santas.
   - ☐ c. in order to become freelance Santas.
   - ☐ d. if they have difficulty adjusting to their role as Santa.

4. The purpose of this article is to
   - ☐ a. recruit more Santas.
   - ☐ b. describe an unusual service.
   - ☐ c. revive the spirit of Christmas.
   - ☐ d. promote good relations.

5. Stores who hire Santas from Western Girl
   - ☐ a. cannot train their own Santas.
   - ☐ b. must take out insurance in order to protect themselves.
   - ☐ c. select and train their own candidates.
   - ☐ d. want to attract parents of small children.

6. Department store Santas must expect to
   - ☐ a. see unpredictable behavior.
   - ☐ b. be recognized.
   - ☐ c. write during the off-season.
   - ☐ d. be fired.

7. Being a department store Santa can be
   - ☐ a. frightening.
   - ☐ b. stressful.
   - ☐ c. embarrassing.
   - ☐ d. tiring.

8. The tone of Mrs. Plowe's lecture was
   - ☐ a. matter-of-fact.
   - ☐ b. discouraging.
   - ☐ c. impatient.
   - ☐ d. humorous.

9. The Santa trainees in this selection were
   - ☐ a. desperate for money.
   - ☐ b. easily embarrassed.
   - ☐ c. willing pupils.
   - ☐ d. unwilling pupils.

10. This selection is
   - ☐ a. a biography.
   - ☐ b. an autobiography.
   - ☐ c. a piece of informative nonfiction.
   - ☐ d. a short story.

Comprehension Skills Key	
1. recalling specific facts	6. making a judgment
2. retaining concepts	7. making an inference
3. organizing facts	8. recognizing tone
4. understanding the main idea	9. understanding characters
5. drawing a conclusion	10. appreciating literary forms

VOCABULARY—PART TWO

Write the word that makes the most sense in each sentence.

hirsute   hygiene
patter   minimal
matronly

1. You may think that visiting Santa has a

   _____ influence on a child's life,

   but in fact it is an important thing for most kids.

2. Pulling on the beard of the fat,

   _____ gentleman is a memory

   many kids treasure.

3. Sometimes a serious, _____

   woman sits nearby dressed as Mrs. Santa Claus.

4. Mr. and Mrs. will engage in lively

   _____ to get the child to talk as

   well.

5. A clean, carefully dressed child may be compli-

   mented on his or her _____ .

gross   comprehensive
yielded   steadfast
compliance

6. Having Santas around has _____

   high profits for many stores at Christmas.

7. For this reason, stores should pay these workers

   plenty—not just be in _____ with

   minimum-wage laws.

8. A store's _____ sales, of course,

   are larger than after taxes are taken out.

9. Nevertheless, they should make a

   _____ commitment—and stick to

   it—to pay their Santas well.

10. For a store making a(n) _____

    plan to increase yearly sales, having a Santa

    around is definitely one step they should take.

Comprehension [   ]

Vocabulary [   ]

UNDERSTANDING THROUGH WRITING

What sort of person do you think would want to be a Santa? Write a short explanation of your ideas. Use information from the story to help you.

_____

_____

_____

_____

_____

_____

_____

_____

BUILDING STUDY SKILLS

Read the following passage and answer the questions that follow it.

Paragraphs of Introduction

Textbook writers work through paragraphs. The effectiveness with which they communicate with readers depends on how well and how carefully they have structured those paragraphs.

In each chapter or article, the writer begins with an introductory paragraph. Like a speaker, the writer offers prefacing remarks to open his or her discussion of a particular topic or subject.

We have all heard speakers who tell a story or two to "warm up" listeners before they get into the body of their talks. Writers have a much more difficult task—they are not face to face with their listeners, and must do more than tell an amusing story to get the readers ready for the presentation. Recognizing this limitation of the printed page, writers strive to create an effective opening with which to introduce their subject.

The opening paragraph is called the paragraph of introduction—used as a kind of announcement of what is to follow. Frequently writers will state the purpose they hope to accomplish in the following paragraphs; they may offer a brief outline of their major concepts; they may merely mention one or two of the ideas the reader can expect later in the chapter.

Obviously a paragraph of introduction is important. Because it offers such a preview of what is to come, it is one of the only two paragraphs read when previewing. In magazine articles and similar leisure reading publications, the paragraph of introduction has a spe-

cial function to perform—it's used frequently as bait to lure the reader into the account. Feature writers know that they must capture the reader's interest and attention with just a few words. The reader can expect any kind of interest-compelling devices to be employed for this purpose—this is where skilled writers show off their best work.

1. The textbook writer depends on carefully structured _____ for effective communication.

2. Recognizing their limits within the _____ , writers must try to create an effective way to introduce the subject to the reader.

3. The paragraph of introduction is used as a sort of _____ of things to come.

4. In magazine articles such as "The Science of Being Santa," the paragraph of introduction is often used to _____ the reader into the account.

5. In this article the writer uses a direct _____ from the Santa trainer to get readers interested.

2

La Causa

Jessie Lopez De La Cruz

READING PURPOSE—
In the following selection a woman tells of her experiences organizing migrant farm-workers into a union. Read to find out some of the things that happened to her.

VOCABULARY—PART ONE

All of these words are in the story you are about to read. Study each word and its meaning. Then answer the questions below. As you read the story, notice how each vocabulary word is used.

excluded: kept out of

benefits: services such as health insurance and pension funds provided by employers

exploiting: taking advantage of

migrant: worker who moves from place to place

radical: person with extreme views or beliefs

aggressive: taking the first step in an argument or other situation; bold

scabs: workers who replace striking union workers

pesticides: chemicals used to kill pests, especially insects

aliens: people who are not citizens

disputes: arguments; fights

---

1. Which word tells what some gardeners spray on their flowers to keep the bugs away?

   _____

2. Which word could describe a comedian who in three nights has performed in Kansas City, St. Louis, and Memphis?

   _____

3. Which word could describe what you did to a troublemaker when you refused to let her attend a community meeting?

   _____

4. Which word could be an antonym for *timid*?

   _____

5. Which word could be a synonym for *disagreements*?

   _____

1   I think I was made an organizer because in the first place I could relate to the farmworkers, being a lifelong farmworker. I was well-known in the small towns around Fresno. Wherever I went to speak to them, they listened. I told them about how we were <u>excluded</u> from the NLRB [National Labor Relations Board] in 1935, how we had no <u>benefits</u>, no minimum wage, nothing out in the fields—no restrooms, nothing. I would talk about how we were paid what the grower wanted to pay us, and how we couldn't set a price on our work. I explained that we could do something about these things by joining a union, by working together. I'd ask people how they felt about these many years they had been working out in the fields, how they had been treated. And then we'd all talk about it. They would say, "I was working for so-and-so, and when I complained about something that happened there, I was fired." I said, "Well! Do you think we should be putting up with this in this modern age? You know, we're not back in the twenties. We can stand up! We can talk back! It's not like when I was a little kid and my grandmother used to say, 'You have to especially respect the Anglos,' 'Yessir,' 'Yes, Ma'am!' That's over. This country is very rich, and we want a share of the money these growers make of our sweat and our work by <u>exploiting</u> us and our children!" I'd have my sign-up book and I'd say, "If anyone wants to become a member of the union, I can make you a member right now." And they'd agree!

2   So I found out that I could organize them and make members of them. Then I offered to help them, like taking them to the doctor's and translating for them, filling out papers that they needed to fill out, writing their letters for those that couldn't write. A lot of people confided in me. Through the letter-writing, I knew a lot of the problems they were having back home, and they knew they could trust me, that I wouldn't tell anyone else about what I had written or read. So that's why they came to me.

3   There was a <u>migrant</u> camp in Parlier. And these people, the migrants, were being used as strike-breakers. I had something to do with building that camp. By that time, I had been put on the board of the Fresno County Economic Opportunity Commission, and I was supporting migrant housing for farmworkers. But I had no idea it was going to be turned almost into a concentration camp or prison. The houses were just like matchboxes—square, a room for living, a room for cooking, a bathroom that didn't have a door, just a curtain. The houses are so close together that if one catches fire, the next one does, too, and children have burned in them. It happened in Parlier.

4   So I went to the camp office and said I wanted to go in and visit. By this time, I was well-known as a <u>radical</u>, an educator, and a troublemaker! The man in the office asked what I wanted to talk about. I just wanted to visit, I said.

5   "Well, you have to sign your name here." I said, "I also would like to know when I can use the hall for a meeting."

6   "What kind of meeting?"

7   "An organizing meeting." You see, when it was built, they told us there was supposed to be a hall built for parties and whatever. I felt we could use it for a meeting to talk to the people. But he said, "We can't authorize you to come in here and talk to the people about a union, but you can write Governor Reagan and ask for permission." I left.

8   I met a nurse who had to go to this camp. She said, "Why don't you come with me as my translator?" Even though she spoke perfect Spanish! So both of us went in, and she said she was from the Health Department and I was her translator. I got in there and talked to the people and told them about our union meetings, and at our next meeting they were there. I had to do things like that in order to organize.

9   It was very hard being a woman organizer. Many of our people my age and older were raised with the old customs in Mexico: where the husband rules, he is king of his house. The wife obeys, and the children, too. So when we first started it was very, very hard. Men gave us the most trouble—neighbors there in Parlier! They were for the union, but they were not taking orders from women, they said....

10 We'd have a union meeting every week. Men, women, and children would come. Women would ask questions and the men would just stand back. I guess they'd say to themselves, "I'll wait for someone to say something before I do." The women were more <u>aggressive</u> than the men. And I'd get up and say, "Let's go on, let's do it!"...

11 The women took the lead for picketing, and we would talk to the people. It got to the point that we would have to find them, because the men just wouldn't go and they wouldn't take their wives. So we would say, "We're having our picket line at the

Safeway in Fresno, and those that don't show up are going to have to pay a five-dollar fine." We couldn't have four or five come to a picket line and have the rest stay home and watch tv. In the end, we had everybody out there.

12   One time we were picketing—I think it was the early part of 1972—White River Farms in Delano, for a new contract. To go picket, we had to get up early. See, a lot of these growers were chartering buses, and at four or five o'clock in the morning they'd pick up the <u>scabs</u>. So we would follow these labor bosses who chartered the buses.

13   At White River Farms one morning very early, we were out there by the hundreds by the road, and these people got down and started working out there in the grapes. We were asking them not to work, telling them that there was a strike going on. The grower had two guards at the entrance, and there was a helicopter above us. At other White River Farm ranches they had the sheriff, the county police, *everybody*. But there were pickets at three different ranches, and where we were picketing there wasn't anybody except these two guards. So I said, "Hey! What about the women getting together and let's rush 'em!" And they said, "Do you think we could do that?" And I said, "Of course we can! Let's go in there. Let's get 'em out of there any way we can." So about fifty of us rushed. We went under the vines. We had our banners, and you could see them bobbing up and down, up and down, and we'd go under those rows on our knees and roll over. When the scabs saw us coming they took off. All of them went and they got on the bus. The guards had guns that they would shoot, and something black like smoke or tear gas would come out. That scared us, but we still kept on. After we saw all those workers get back on the buses, we went back. Instead of running this time, we rolled over and over all the way out. The vines are about four feet tall, and they have wire where you string up the vines. So you

"We were asking [the strikebreakers] not to work, telling them that there was a strike going on."

can't walk or run across one of these fences. You have to keep going under these wires. So I tripped, and rolled down about three or four rows before I got up. I rolled so they wouldn't get at me when they were shooting. When I got out there on the road they were getting these big, hard dirty clods and throwing them at us. And then the pickets started doing the same thing. When the first police car came, somebody broke the windshield. We don't know if it was the scabs or someone on the picket lines, but the picketers were blamed.

14   When we women ran into the fields, we knew we'd be arrested if they caught us. But we went in and we told the scabs, "If you're not coming out we're gonna pull you out!" Later I told Arnold, "See? See what women can do? We got all those men out there to come out!"

15   At another place, in Kern County, we were sprayed with <u>pesticides</u>. They would come out there with their sprayers and spray us on the picket lines. They have these big tanks that are pulled by a tractor with hoses attached, and they spray the trees with this. They are strong like a water hose, but wider. They get it started and spray the vines and the trees. When we were picketing, they came out there to spray the pickets. What could we do? We tried to get as far away as we could, and then we would come back.

16   They had goons with these big police dogs on leashes. I think they were trying to scare us by letting them loose on us…. When the growers realized how strong we were getting and how we had so many members, when our contracts were up for renewal they called the Teamsters in. And even before we bargained for our new contract, the growers signed up with the Teamsters. Then they claimed they already had a union and couldn't recognize ours. That was another way they had of not signing with UFW [United Farm Workers]. They were signing hundreds of what we called "sweetheart contracts."

17   Another thing the growers did to break our strikes was to bring in "illegal <u>aliens</u>." I would get a list of names of the scabs and give them to the border patrol. At that time, you see, we were pitted against each other, us and the people from Mexico, so it was either us or them. When I went to the border patrol office, I'd go in and say, "Can I come in?" They'd say, "You can't come in. This is a very small office." They kept telling us they were short of men. But every time I went there, there were all of them with their feet up on the desks in their air-conditioned office. They told me they were under orders not to interfere with labor <u>disputes</u>. So I called Bernie Sisk's office and talked to them about it. Then I came home and called a lot of students who'd been helping us, and other people, and the next morning, there we were at the border patrol. I said, "We're paying our tax money, but not for you to sit here while the illegal aliens are being used to break our strike."

Starting Time	
Finishing Time	
Reading Time	
Reading Rate	

COMPREHENSION

Read the following questions and statements. For each one, put an X in the box before the option that contains the most complete or accurate answer.

1. The people that De La Cruz organized were
   - ☐ a. farmworkers.
   - ☐ b. truck drivers.
   - ☐ c. cowboys.
   - ☐ d. factory workers.

2. In the town of Parlier, De La Cruz
   - ☐ a. organized a demonstration.
   - ☐ b. held a union meeting.
   - ☐ c. took over a whole neighborhood.
   - ☐ d. had migrant housing built.

3. De La Cruz develops her story mainly through
   - ☐ a. a time-order retelling of events.
   - ☐ b. a series of incidents showing the difficulty of her work.
   - ☐ c. spatial-order descriptions of the workplace settings.
   - ☐ d. a letter of complaint to President Reagan.

4. Which of the following best summarizes how De La Cruz might explain her work?
   - ☐ a. I had to use a lot of techniques to get the results I wanted.
   - ☐ b. The men I dealt with, both workers and bosses, made me very irritated.
   - ☐ c. I enjoyed being well known in the Fresno area.
   - ☐ d. I was timid when I started, but I got over that very quickly.

5. De La Cruz worked more with women than with men because
   - ☐ a. she had more in common with them.
   - ☐ b. the men were usually on the bosses' side.
   - ☐ c. the men were less willing to get involved.
   - ☐ d. she had trouble with men telling her what to do.

6. The men at the border patrol office
   - ☐ a. secretly sympathized with De La Cruz.
   - ☐ b. didn't try to keep illegal strike breakers out of the country.
   - ☐ c. didn't have enough help to do their job adequately.
   - ☐ d. were basically lazy.

7. In paragraph 8 De La Cruz pretends to be a translator in order to
   - ☐ a. help out the public health nurse, who didn't speak Spanish.
   - ☐ b. lead the people in Spanish cheers.
   - ☐ c. show the bosses how willing she was to help.
   - ☐ d. give out union information without the bosses understanding her.

8. The atmosphere that De La Cruz establishes in paragraph 13 is
   - ☐ a. mysterious.   ☐ c. angry.
   - ☐ b. frightening.   ☐ d. humorous.

9. De La Cruz can best be characterized as
   ☐ a. outspoken and courageous.
   ☐ b. reckless and foolhardy.
   ☐ c. a man hater.
   ☐ d. an immigrant hater.

10. In paragraph 3 when De La Cruz says that "migrant housing… turned almost into a concentration camp or prison," she is using
    ☐ a. literal description.
    ☐ b. a simile.
    ☐ c. a metaphor.
    ☐ d. exaggeration.

Comprehension Skills Key

1. recalling specific facts
2. retaining concepts
3. organizing facts
4. understanding the main idea
5. drawing a conclusion
6. making a judgment
7. making an inference
8. recognizing tone
9. understanding characters
10. appreciating literary forms

VOCABULARY—PART TWO

Write the word that makes the most sense in each sentence.

exploiting   scabs
pesticides   aliens
disputes

1. _____ were crossing the border from Mexico to work in the fields.

2. These people did not belong to the union; they were _____ .

3. The bosses were _____ their poverty by offering them a chance to work.

4. They knew nothing of the bitter _____ between the bosses and the local workers.

5. They didn't know that protesters had been sprayed with _____ and other chemicals.

excluded   aggressive
migrant   radical
benefits

6. The _____ workers usually had no permanent homes.

7. They had no medical _____ to protect them when they were ill.

8. The bosses made sure they were _____ from organizations that could help them.

9. Instead of being _____ , they were generally meek and frightened.

10. It often took a _____ to stand up for their rights.

Comprehension [ ]

Vocabulary [ ]

UNDERSTANDING THROUGH WRITING

Pretend you are one of the migrant workers that De La Cruz has helped organize. Write a short letter to a friend telling what you think of this woman. Use information from the story to back up what you say.

_____

_____

_____

_____

_____

_____

_____

_____

_____

BUILDING STUDY SKILLS

Read the following passage and answer the questions that follow it.

Paragraphs of Illustration

As the name suggests, paragraphs of illustration present examples, illustrations, stories, anecdotes, and so on. They are used by the author to illustrate, clarify, demonstrate, or amplify some idea or concept for the reader. Authors use many paragraphs of illustration to help the reader understand the subject.

These paragraphs are also easy to recognize and identify because of the use of key words and phrases like "For example," "An illustration of this," "By way of illustration," and so on. These and similar phrases tell the reader that an example or illustrative story is coming up.

Surprisingly, half a chapter, lesson, or article may consist of paragraphs of illustration. Unlike lecturers who are face-to-face with their students, authors are confined by the limitations of print. Because they have no way of knowing whether they are getting their ideas across to their readers, they must use more illustrations than they would when speaking. They cannot take chances; they must be sure that everyone will get the point.

Furthermore, the writer cannot be questioned over a misunderstood concept; there is no way to pause and clarify. It must be certain the first time that the student gets it—there are no second chances. For all of these reasons, we can see why much of what we read is illustrative, even in textbooks.

Selective readers are flexible in their approach to textbook reading. This means that while they may pause over paragraphs of definition, they often speed past paragraphs of illustration. After all, if you understand the point being illustrated, it is not necessary to linger over additional paragraphs illustrating this same point. You can move on to the place where something new is being presented.

1. Paragraphs of illustration are used by the author to help the reader understand a(n)

   _____ .

2. For example, in paragraph 13 of her selection, Jessie Lopez De La Cruz illustrates what conditions can be like on a _____ line.

3. Because authors cannot see their

   _____ , they are unable to tell how effectively their ideas are coming across.

4. Writers must be certain that their concepts are not questioned or _____ .

5. If you understand the point being made in a paragraph of illustration, you can move on to the place where something _____ is being presented.

Organ Hunter

Andrew C. Revkin

READING PURPOSE—
The following selection describes the job of a man who must deal with families at a very difficult time. Read to find out how he tries to make the circumstances work for everyone.

VOCABULARY—PART ONE

All of these words are in the selection you are about to read. Study each word and its meaning. Then answer the questions below. As you read the selection, notice how each vocabulary word is used.

potential: having the capacity to; able

limbo: nothingness; emptiness

sustained: supported; maintained

trauma: wound or other external injury

prospective: future; coming

collaborated: worked together

litany: series of words said over and over again

sullen: crabby; gloomy

dissipated: lessened; disappeared

recipient: one who receives

1. Which word could describe what you did if you planned a project with a classmate or other associate?

2. Which word could describe a severe cut you received falling off a motorcycle?

3. Which word could be an antonym for *sender*?

4. Which word could describe your mood if you have a bad headache and don't want to talk to anyone?

5. Which word could tell what happened to smoke that finally cleared away?

1   Bill Cantirino is home in Brooklyn on a Tuesday night, relaxing after dinner, when a shrill beeping sound tells him there is work to be done. He turns off the electronic page on his belt and is soon on the phone with a doctor at nearby Maimonides Medical Center. The doctor says they have a man in intensive care who looks ideal. He was carried into the emergency room the night before with a bullet in his neck.

2   Two policemen said the man had tried to gun them down after they pulled over the stolen Cadillac he was driving. They had both opened fire. The bullet cut a carotid artery, one of the main sources of blood to the brain. A surgeon worked for five hours trying to piece together the torn artery while others tried to keep the man alive. They finally stabilized him, but they were too late. His body was being kept alive on a variety of machines, but his brain had died.

3   Cantirino gets the name of the man's family and says he'll be in the next day. He thanks the doctor and hangs up the phone.

4   For Cantirino, tragedy means business. In an average week he has two or three such conversations. As one of two organ hunters for the Gift of Life Organ Procurement Organization, he is on 24-hour call, waiting to get word of <u>potential</u> organ donors....

5   The nonprofit Brooklyn-based group, part of a growing nationwide organ-sharing network, seeks hearts, livers, corneas,[1] even skin. But its stock-in-trade is kidneys: 8,976 kidney transplants were performed in this country in 1986. There were another 10,000 people with kidney failure on waiting lists for transplants....

6   "It costs more than thirty thousand dollars a year to keep someone on an artificial kidney," Cantirino says. "A transplant for the first year costs forty-five or fifty thousand. But the second year's cost drops to five thousand, and it goes down from there as dosages of antirejection drugs drop and office visits become less frequent. In terms of money alone, who could question the need for more transplants?"

7   The problem is that the demand for organs now far exceeds the supply. Patients waiting for transplants of vital body parts must wait for an anonymous death and for people like Cantirino to go to work. His job calls for him first to locate a special

kind of death—a death in which the brain is completely destroyed but the body hangs in a sort of <u>limbo,</u> <u>sustained</u> with machines and drugs but never able to be resurrected as a living person. Such deaths are usually caused by physical <u>trauma</u> to the head or lack of oxygen.

8   Deaths that make for good organ donors are therefore usually of the unexpected kind—the result of car accidents, shootings, or suicides. Once he has located such a case, Cantirino must try to convince parents or children or spouses in the depths of grief to donate organs from the deceased. Cantirino has to be a diplomat and psychologist, social worker and undertaker, rolled into one. He is often asked why he does such a thing. And his reply is always the same: "Because I was once given a second chance." Twelve years ago a kidney transplant saved his life.

9   On Wednesday morning Cantirino calls the family of the shooting victim and arranges to meet them at the hospital that afternoon. He says he usually tries to talk with the whole family, even though he needs the consent of only the next of kin. "They all have to live with this later on," he says.

10   He drives to Maimonides hospital early, to get a look at the <u>prospective</u> donor and to talk things over with the hospital staff. As he weaves his Oldsmobile around the potholes and broken bottles that pock Fort Hamilton Parkway, he says he can afford to give this family a few days to make up their mind. "As much as I would want the kidneys tonight, I would never press the family," Cantirino says. "I would never make it a point of saying, 'Look, if we don't get them now it's too late.' I would rather lose them and walk away."...

11   In the small intensive care unit on the fourth floor of Maimonides hospital, Cantirino meets with the young doctor who called him the night before. They had <u>collaborated</u> several weeks earlier on another donation. A 19-year-old boy had been shot while trying to hold up a store. The doctor called Cantirino, and after three days of talks with the family, they got the consent. Cantirino says he has developed personal contacts in emergency rooms and intensive care units throughout New York City; it helps speed the search. He brings the doctor up-to-date on the previous case: the recipients of both kidneys are doing fine.

12   Their attention now turns to the prospective donor. The doctor produces a blue folder labeled

[1]corneas: transparent parts of the outer eyeball

"Patient Record Number Eight." Cantirino thumbs through page after page of scribbled entries—blood pressure, heart rate, doses of dopamine and other drugs, electrocardiograms,[2] and electroencephalograms. "Looks good," he grunts. "Good donor."…

13   A nurse tells Cantirino that the family is out in the hall—a few cousins and uncles, the victim's parents, and his sisters. "Most of our cases are either gunshot wounds or auto accidents," Cantirino says. "This is typical of how you have to deal with a family, because there's a guy who all of a sudden goes out. It's not a case of where he had been sick or something."

14   Cantirino greets them and leads the immediate family into an empty conference room. Three sisters sit stiffly along one wall. The mother, a small, birdlike woman, sits opposite Cantirino, at the far end of a long walnut table. She sits sideways in her chair. No one looks directly at anyone else. The father sits to one side, overdressed in a heavy camel hair coat and a hat pulled down low. He periodically adjusts his brown-tinted glasses and stares at an empty blackboard.

15   Cantirino begins his pitch slowly, speaking gently. He says the doctors did all they could do. There is no hope. Repeating words already delivered to the family by a doctor, Cantirino says, "Your son is dead. The brain is gone completely. He lost so much blood that there was no oxygen to the brain. And the brain, when it's deprived of oxygen, it dies."

16   Cantirino carefully punctuates his delivery with pauses, giving the family time to absorb the blows. He tells them an electroencephalogram, or EEG, a test of the brain's electrical activity, was done that day. He says it was "flat-line" for at least a half-hour—not even a spark of life.…

17   There is a long silence. The father looks at the floor, glances at his fingernails. Then one of the sisters sobs. The two others immediately follow suit. The room fills with the sounds of their grief.

"Cantirino has to be a diplomat and psychologist, social worker and undertaker, all rolled into one."

The sisters shuffle out, hugging one another, leaving only the mother and father. The mother twists her wedding ring slowly. The room is silent.

18   "The only good that can come out of this is that two people can have a new life," Cantirino says, now shifting to a positive tack. "It could be anybody from the age of three to the age of fifty. It could be a woman with children; it could be a girl getting married."

19   The only sound is the humming of an electric clock. "I don't know if you know anybody on dialysis,[3] but it's not very pleasant," he says. "This is the only chance these people have to have some sort of life." The victim's mother hardly moves. She stares at the metal legs on one of the plastic chairs. "It's a very hard thing to ask you people, when you are losing a life, to give someone else a life," Cantirino says. "But it's the only time it can be done."

20   There is a long silence, finally broken by the father. "I know what it is all about, these things," he says. He speaks with a Spanish accent, slowly hefting each word like a heavy object. Cantirino, seeing he has gotten them over the first big hump, starts to lay out the situation in more detail. He says there will be an autopsy, as in any gunshot case. Giving up the kidneys will not affect any legal situation.…

21   The father rises slowly, almost painfully. "I understand you perfectly," he says. His wife moves to his side. Cantirino hands the father a business card and tells them to go home, to think it over. The door closes behind the couple, leaving Cantirino alone in the silent room.

22   He returns to the intensive care unit to tell the doctor that it will be at least two or three days before they get a decision. "They've just been told their son is dead," Cantirino says. "Regardless of what he did, he's dead. Now they have to accept this, to come to terms with it. Then they have to say okay—which I think they might, because we

---

[2]electrocardiograms: tests used to find diseases of the heart

[3]dialysis: procedure, done by machine, to remove liquid wastes from the body

didn't get a flat no. The father seems to be the strong one, yet the mother's the one who holds the key. You can see just by looking at her that no matter what he wants, she's the one who'll say, and whatever she says will go."...

23   The family is due at noon, but they don't show up until midafternoon, and then it's just the three sisters. Cantirino repeats his <u>litany</u>, sitting with them in the same conference room. The three women are a still life. Each stares in a different direction—numb. Each has an elbow propped on the table and cups her chin in her palm. They seem <u>sullen</u>, even resentful. The shock seems to have <u>dissipated</u> somewhat, but it has been replaced by suspicion. They start to ask questions. Where will the kidneys go? Are they sold or given to anyone who needs them? When will the body be turned over to the family?

24   Cantirino carefully, patiently answers each question. The body will go to the Office of the Chief Medical Examiner of New York City. Because matching an organ donor with a <u>recipient</u> is first attempted locally, the kidneys will probably go to someone from Brooklyn. "It's people like us," he says....

25   A match is made from a list of potential recipients at New York's various transplant centers. The selection is based on the length of time a patient has waited, the direness of the need, and the degree of tissue compatibility. "No one can buy a kidney, rich or poor," Cantirino says. "It's strictly through luck."...

26   Thursday night the sisters return with their mother, who is now dressed in black. She sits in a chair in the hallway, beneath a cheap print of yellow flowers that hangs on the cinder block wall. The doctor stands to one side, talking quietly with a friend of the family's. Cantirino hands the consent form to the mother. She and her daughters read it slowly. At 7:50 P.M. the mother signs the paper, indicating that she speaks for her husband as well. The doctor signs the form and makes a final entry on the patient's chart: he pronounces him dead.

27   The family goes for a last look at the victim-turned-donor. There are a few sobs, but mostly silence. After several minutes they leave for the last time. The young man lies still. An endless line of heartbeats parades across a monitor over his head. The bellows hisses; his chest rises and falls. A radio somewhere squawks tinny rock and roll.

28   Cantirino does some paperwork and telephones the organ recovery team at the Health Science

Center. Within a day the kidneys will be sutured[4] into place in the abdomens of two people. Cantirino heads for the door, his job done. A nurse waves to him, smiling. "Happy hunting," she says.

---

[4]sutured: sewed together the edges of a cut or wound

Starting Time	
Finishing Time	
Reading Time	
Reading Rate	

COMPREHENSION

Read the following questions and statements. For each one, put an X in the box before the option that contains the most complete or accurate answer.

1. The best organ donors are frequently victims of
    ☐ a. drug overdoses.
    ☐ b. drownings and stabbings.
    ☐ c. gunshot wounds and car accidents.
    ☐ d. terminal illness.

2. Cantirino needs to get the permission of
    ☐ a. all living relatives of the victim.
    ☐ b. the victim's next of kin.
    ☐ c. the victim's immediate family.
    ☐ d. the victim's family and their lawyer.

3. Cantirino approaches a victim's family only after he is sure the victim is
    ☐ a. under the age of fifty.
    ☐ b. brain dead.
    ☐ c. covered by medical insurance.
    ☐ d. a legal resident of the state of New York.

4. Cantirino performs a task that is
    ☐ a. boring but necessary.
    ☐ b. difficult but valuable.
    ☐ c. financially draining.
    ☐ d. ethically questionable.

5. Parents who donate the organs of their child take comfort in the knowledge that
  - ☐ a. their child is better off dead.
  - ☐ b. they will receive an autopsy report.
  - ☐ c. their actions will save the country money.
  - ☐ d. their actions will save the lives of other people.

6. Donating the organs of a brain-dead relative is a
  - ☐ a. gruesome act.
  - ☐ b. noble act.
  - ☐ c. selfish act.
  - ☐ d. mindless act.

7. Recipients of organ donations feel
  - ☐ a. grateful for the chance at a new life.
  - ☐ b. confused by the process.
  - ☐ c. guilty about benefiting from another's misfortune.
  - ☐ d. criticized by society.

8. The mood that dominated the conference room was one of
  - ☐ a. hopelessness.
  - ☐ b. regret.
  - ☐ c. sorrow.
  - ☐ d. fury.

9. Cantirino has great sympathy for
  - n a. the doctors who treat accident victims.
  - n b. people in need or organ donations.
  - n c. victims of shootings.
  - n d. people who refuse to donate organs.

10. Cantirino's statement that "the mother's the one who holds the key" is an example of
  - ☐ a. a simile.
  - ☐ b. a metaphor.
  - ☐ c. hyperbole.
  - ☐ d. personification.

Comprehension Skills Key

1. recalling specific facts	6. making a judgment
2. retaining concepts	7. making an inference
3. organizing facts	8. recognizing tone
4. understanding the main idea	9. understanding characters
5. drawing a conclusion	10. appreciating literary forms

VOCABULARY—PART TWO

Write the word that makes the most sense in each sentence.

limbo	**sustained**
trauma	**prospective**
dissipated	

1. Hanging between life and death, the gunshot victim was in a kind of _____ .

2. Cantirino saw him as a _____ organ donor because only his brain was dead.

3. The patient had received a severe _____ to the head.

4. Because he was no longer conscious, his pain had completely _____ .

5. His life was being _____ by machines and drugs.

recipient	**collaborated**
litany	**sullen**
potential	

6. A good team player, Cantirino had _____ with doctors from this hospital before.

7. Together, they identified many brain-dead patients as _____ organ donors.

8. Cantirino understood why many families were _____ and gloomy.

9. To each of them he repeated his _____ about the need for kidneys.

10. The dying person would be giving the _____ the gift of life.

Comprehension ☐

Vocabulary ☐

UNDERSTANDING THROUGH WRITING

What personal qualities does it take to be successful at a job like Cantirino's? Write down your ideas. Try to use information from the story to support what you say.

_____

_____

_____

_____

_____

_____

_____

_____

_____

_____

BUILDING STUDY SKILLS

Read the following passage and answer the questions that follow it.

Paragraphs of Information

The next paragraphs to examine are the ones used by the author to pass along information on the subject. These paragraphs of information contain names, dates, details, facts, explanations, and other factual information.

In a particular chapter or lesson, the reader can expect to find the meat of the matter in paragraphs like these. This is where the author gets down to business and presents the facts. The essential terms have been defined and illustrated, and now the reader is ready for the substance of the lesson.

Paragraphs of information contain important instructional material—the data that later may appear on tests.

In presenting information, the author will probably use one of the following methods of development.

1. State an opinion and give reasons. Look for a clue word used to introduce a series of reasons.

2. Pose a problem and offer a solution. Authors use this method frequently because it incorporates questioning as an aid to learning.

3. Draw a conclusion and then present proof. Actually the proof may come first, preceding the conclusion. Check to be sure that the conclusion logically follows from the proof.

4. Present steps in an argument. Expect here a list of points. Look for the introductory signal and circle the points.

5. Make a comparison or draw a contrast. Frequently used in paragraphs of illustration, this method may be used to present information too.

Paragraphs of information are the heart of the lesson. It's a good idea to study them well.

1. In paragraphs of information, the author gets down to business and presents the _____.

2. In a paragraph of information, the author may state an opinion and give _____.

3. An author may pose a _____ and offer a solution, as the author of "Organ Hunter" does in paragraph 7.

4. If an author presents steps in an _____, you should expect to see a list of points.

5. Making a comparison or drawing a contrast is a technique used in paragraphs of _____ as well as paragraphs of information.

4

Killer: Autobiography of a Mafia Hit Man

Joey with Dave Fisher

READING PURPOSE—
In this selection you will learn about a line of work you have probably only heard about in the movies. Read to find out about a real hit man.

VOCABULARY—PART ONE

All of these words are in the selection you are about to read. Study each word and its meaning. Then answer the questions below. As you read the selection, notice how each vocabulary word is used.

purveys: supplies; furnishes

efficiency: ability to perform a task easily and skillfully

punctual: on time; prompt

albeit: even though

graft: thievery; corruption

verify: prove the accuracy of

mellow: good-natured; agreeable

invariably: constantly; unchangingly

cynic: sarcastic, untrusting individual

conjecture: guess

---

1. Which word could describe a person who always arrived at exactly the time she said she would?

_____

2. Which word would tell what you are doing if you check the facts in an article you found on the Internet?

_____

3. Which word might describe a person who is always willing to go along with what the group wants?

_____

4. Which word might name an answer you made up on a test because you weren't sure what was right?

_____

5. Which word might be used in a discussion of the activities of dishonest politicians?

_____

(Foreword by Chris Borgen, TV crime reporter)

1   Joey is a businessman. Over the years, he has held various positions from salesman to collecting agent and company troubleshooter. Generally his organization has been satisfied with his work.

2   Joey's business is crime. Two of the services he purveys are death and destruction—services that are in high demand in his industry. He is never begging for employment.

3   I met Joey a number of years ago. At that time he was on his way down the ladder. He turned into the one thing his employers did not like. He is a bettor—a strung-out gambler willing and eager to get down on any and everything: horses, basketball, football, cards, dice, even cockroaches. If it is a gamble—Joey is ready, hand in pocket. He will bet his lungs.

4   Today he is no longer quite the sought-after "executive" he once was—not because he cannot perform. That he can do with outstanding efficiency. But he is no longer punctual. The job he is contracted to do may have to wait while he checks his bets for the day. Money advanced for travel may "get down" on the 3rd at Aqueduct. The trip is then delayed while Joey tries to get it back betting the 4th, 5th, and 6th. If he succeeds, then it's on with business, albeit a little late. But in the business of organized crime, late is absent. Joey, over the last few years, has gotten a reputation for being a little absent a little too often. The "jobs" still come, at least they are still offered. But Joey, more and more, would rather go to the betting window than to the office.

5   Though I knew of Joey by reputation while I was still a detective, I didn't actually meet Joey until after I had left the police department. The meeting was more of Joey's doing than my searching. He had seen a number of reports I had made about organized crime. He thought they were good—but he knew more. Perhaps it was because he knew how much I knew—that he wanted to impress me with how much I didn't know.

6   He took it upon himself to fill me in. Police graft in New York City? Look, he would say, you're right, but here is the way a pad works. Then he would give me a lesson in corruption that was like a graduate course in government finance.

7   Never mind who shot Columbo, he would say—better, why was he shot? Again, right on. In time Joey became one of my experts and I could cross-check his information against others. He was always in the know, but true to that peculiar code that ensures continuity of life, he would never name the names. If I did, he would verify. But he never volunteered names. Joey is not a squealer. He is a stand-up guy. But he has a funny twist. He wants your information to be right. To him, too much of the story about organized crime is told wrong. And to Joey, that is more of a crime than crime itself. He only murdered men, while too many so-called organized-crime experts murder the truth about organized crime....

8   Joey is now in semiretirement. He'll still "do a job," but only if he needs the money, which is to say if he has lost more than he has won or if a "friend" asks a favor; an important friend—an important favor. Joey was a "hit man." A killer for pay. A murderer. Joey is still one son-of-a-bitch. I don't know how many men he has killed. He says 38. Joey is many things, but I have not known him to be a liar—at least not to me. Perhaps this is because I have never found it necessary to ask him embarrassing questions like "who, where, or when."

9   In a mellow moment Joey talks of old times. He will mention names, but not so you can make a case. "____'s job was to hit the bastard and leave him so that the others would get the message." The message is invariably the same—pay back a loan-shark or stop trying to muscle in on some other crime boss's territory or don't try to move up the ladder too fast. Joey was more a privateer in syndicated crime than he was a member of any particular organized-crime family. It is perhaps because he was a privateer that he was so sought-after. Not being identified with any one group, he was free to work for all. His operations were coast to coast. His tools—a baseball bat, a sawed-off cue stick, a gun. He, like all craftsmen, had a preference. For him—the gun, a .38-caliber revolver.

10   What makes a man a killer for hire? I don't know. Put the same question to Joey and he will give you 2000 rambling words in explanation. He doesn't know either. But that is what he admits to having been—a killer. A man who kills coldly for profit and claims to have no regrets. A highly paid, eagerly sought-after functioning member of our sick society.

11   Joey is a cynic. He believes in very little, except friendship. That he holds dear. But he is a demanding friend. He demands understanding, affection,

acceptance; and he is serious and unforgiving. If you are *his friend*, don't, for God's sake, tell him that someone has done you a disservice. Joey's eyes grow cold, he leans close. What happened, he asks. Once he has the story, Joey will suddenly leave. It may be a day or a week later, but Joey will have done his thing. The someone who did you a disservice has had a visitor who left him with a cracked skull or a broken nose, arm or leg. Joey is very serious about friendship.

12　It is easy to say that if time and circumstances had been different Joey could have been a great doctor, lawyer or business chief. I don't think so. I don't say Joey doesn't have the brains. But Joey is Joey because he wanted to succeed. Perhaps, more important, Joey is Joey because society gave a value to success in terms of money. And Joey found the quick way available to him to make a buck.

13　…Men like Joey don't look for forgiveness, that is an alien feeling in their emotional makeup. Recognition, praise, respect—these are the social-emotional rewards they look forward to. If you ask the right people inside organized crime about Joey, they will know him. Few by sight, the majority by reputation. The bosses know him. They are the ones who hired him. The button men know of him. He was the one sent in to clean up their mistakes. The hood on the street—they have only heard about him. He was something else.

14　I know him—but not his real name. He has used a lot of names. I don't know where he lives. I don't know his phone number. Joey gets in touch with me. I don't get in touch with Joey.

15　Now you are going to know about him. He chose to tell. Why? The answer is a guessing game. He chose to tell for his own reasons… too numerous even to <u>conjecture</u> about. But there are two certainties. High on the list will be money and

"He, like all craftsmen, had a preference. For him—the gun, a .38-caliber revolver."

ego. Money because he is still a strung-out bettor and a bettor always needs money. Ego? Because Joey, like all men past their prime, wants to know that he was very good in his day—better than that—he wants you to know.

16　So—yes, Virginia, there is a Joey. And the fact that he exists is the shame of the world in which we live.

Starting Time	
Finishing Time	
Reading Time	
Reading Rate	

COMPREHENSION

Read the following questions and statements. For each one, put an X in the box before the option that contains the most complete or accurate answer.

1. Joey's favorite weapon is a
   ☐ a. sawed-off cue stick.
   ☐ b. baseball bat.
   ☐ c. knife.
   ☐ d. revolver.

2. Among other professionals in the business, Joey used to be known as
   ☐ a. a family man.
   ☐ b. a man who could get the job done.
   ☐ c. lazy.
   ☐ d. a liar.

3. Joey's status among Mafia leaders fell when he
   - ☐ a. botched an important job.
   - ☐ b. started talking to the author.
   - ☐ c. refused to accept certain contracts.
   - ☐ d. became a gambler.

4. Which of the following best expresses the main idea of the selection?
   - ☐ a. Society is punished by the monsters it has helped to create.
   - ☐ b. There is honor among thieves.
   - ☐ c. Virtue is its own reward.
   - ☐ d. The true test of friendship is to make no demands upon friends.

5. Joey has been unable to
   - ☐ a. concentrate entirely on business.
   - ☐ b. keep up with the demand.
   - ☐ c. accept important contracts.
   - ☐ d. find needed employment.

6. Employment in Joey's work does not depend on
   - ☐ a. his ability to meet deadlines.
   - ☐ b. his skill with his equipment.
   - ☐ c. the economic climate of the country.
   - ☐ d. the decisions of his competitors.

7. It is important to Joey that the public
   - ☐ a. receives accurate information.
   - ☐ b. be kept in the dark.
   - ☐ c. understands his motives.
   - ☐ d. forgives his crimes.

8. The selection ends on a note of
   - ☐ a. hope.
   - ☐ b. humor.
   - ☐ c. sorrow.
   - ☐ d. bitterness.

9. A serious flaw in Joey's character is his
   - ☐ a. compulsion to succeed.
   - ☐ b. tendency to drink.
   - ☐ c. passion for gambling.
   - ☐ d. passion for cars.

10. Saying that Joey will "do a job" means that he will still
   - ☐ a. honor a friendship.
   - ☐ b. commit a murder.
   - ☐ c. give police information about the Mafia.
   - ☐ d. obey the code of silence.

Comprehension Skills Key

1. recalling specific facts
2. retaining concepts
3. organizing facts
4. understanding the main idea
5. drawing a conclusion
6. making a judgment
7. making an inference
8. recognizing tone
9. understanding characters
10. appreciating literary forms

VOCABULARY—PART TWO

Write the word that makes the most sense in each sentence.

purveys	punctual
verify	cynic
conjecture	

1. A killer like Joey _____ a special service that only a few people can provide.

2. Without ever meeting such a killer, we can only _____ what he is like.

3. He has to be _____ ; he has to do a job exactly when he says he will.

4. He is probably a _____ , a person without much faith in human nature.

5. His "employer" will check up on him to _____ that he has done the job.

albeit   **mellow**
invariably   **efficiency**
graft

6. To ensure that a job isn't botched, a killer like Joey has to demonstrate his

_____ .

7. He also has to show that his routine

_____ remains the same.

8. His personality does not matter: he can be either unpleasant or _____ .

9. He can get revenge for _____ in political life or settle private arguments.

10. His basic goal is to get his employers to admit, _____ unwillingly, that they are satisfied with a job.

Comprehension [   ]

Vocabulary [   ]

UNDERSTANDING THROUGH WRITING

Why would someone with a clearly illegal "job" like Joey's want to talk about what he does? Write an explanation of your ideas about this.

_____
_____
_____
_____
_____
_____
_____
_____
_____

BUILDING STUDY SKILLS

Read the following passage and answer the questions that follow it.

Paragraphs of Definition

The next paragraph we are going to examine is the one used to define or explain an idea or concept.

Fortunately, these paragraphs of definition are easily recognizable. Frequently, the word, phrase, or concept being defined is shown in italics (or sometimes quotation marks)—this tells the reader that the word or words are being studied and analyzed. Certain key words appear regularly in these paragraphs. Look for phrases like "We can define this as…" or "This simply means…" or the word *define*.

It is essential to recognize paragraphs of definition because what is defined is important to understand. Much of what follows in a chapter may hinge on a clear understanding of the new word or concept.

Study carefully each word in a definition because every word is loaded with essential information. Question the author: "What exactly does this word add to the meaning? How would the definition change with this word left out?" No other single paragraph may be so essential to comprehension of a chapter as a paragraph of definition.

1. Paragraphs of definition are easily

_____ .

2. Words being studied or analyzed may be shown in _____ or quotation marks.

3. A one-word definition for *hit man* provided in paragraph 8 of the selection you just read is

_____ .

4. Authors use certain _____ words when they are defining things.

5. Every word in a definition is a source of essential

_____ .

The Peter Principle

Laurence J. Peter and Raymond Hull

READING PURPOSE—

The following description of a pattern of events in work situations has become famous because of its accuracy. Read to discover exactly what the Peter Principle is.

VOCABULARY—PART ONE

All of these words are in the selection you are about to read. Study each word and its meaning. Then answer the questions below. As you read the selection, notice how each vocabulary word is used.

incompetent: lacking ability; unqualified

complied: agreed; gave in to

hierarchy: organization in which some people are ranked above others

inherent: built-in or essential quality of something

affability: pleasantness; courtesy

demoralized: weakened the spirit or discipline of

subordinates: people who work for or under another

obscure: not well known or important

renowned: famous; notable

ostensible: apparent; presumable

---

1. What characteristic does a person show when he gets along well with everyone in a group?

   _____

2. Which word could describe how a woman feels when she has lost only three pounds after four weeks of exercise?

   _____

3. Which word could describe a person like Michael Jordan or President Clinton?

   _____

4. Which word identifies an organization that has a president, senior vice presidents, junior vice presidents, senior members, and associate members?

   _____

5. Which word would describe a person who seems unable to do any job he is given?

   _____

1   When I was a boy I was taught that the men upstairs knew what they were doing. I was told, "Peter, the more you know, the further you go." So I stayed in school until I graduated from college and then went forth into the world clutching firmly these ideas and my new teaching certificate. During the first year of teaching I was upset to find that a number of teachers, school principals, supervisors and superintendents appeared to be unaware of their professional responsibilities and incompetent in executing their duties. For example my principal's main concerns were that all window shades be at the same level, that classrooms should be quiet and that no one step on or near the rose beds. The superintendent's main concerns were that no minority group, no matter how fanatical, should ever be offended and that all official forms be submitted on time. The children's education appeared farthest from the administrator's mind.

2   At first I thought this was a special weakness of the school system in which I taught so I applied for certification in another province. I filled out the special forms, enclosed the required documents and complied willingly with all the red tape. Several weeks later, back came my application and all the documents!

3   No, there was nothing wrong with my credentials; the forms were correctly filled out; an official departmental stamp showed that they had been received in good order. But an accompanying letter said, "The new regulations require that such forms cannot be accepted by the Department of Education unless they have been registered at the Post Office to ensure safe delivery. Will you please remail the forms to the Department, making sure to register them this time?"

4   I began to suspect that the local school system did not have a monopoly on incompetence.

5   As I looked further afield, I saw that every organization contained a number of persons who could not do their jobs.

A Universal Phenomenon

6   Occupational incompetence is everywhere. Have you noticed it? Probably we all have noticed it....

7   Seeing incompetence at all levels of every hierarchy—political, legal, educational and industrial—I hypothesized that the cause was some inherent feature of the rules governing the placement of employees. Thus began my serious study of the ways in which employees move upward through a hierarchy, and of what happens to them after promotion.

8   For my scientific data hundreds of case histories were collected. Here are three typical examples.

9   MUNICIPAL GOVERNMENT FILE, CASE NO. 17
J. S. Minion[1] was a maintenance foreman in the public works department of Excelsior City. He was a favorite of the senior officials at City Hall. They all praised his unfailing affability.

10   "I like Minion," said the superintendent of works. "He has good judgment and is always pleasant and agreeable."

11   This behavior was appropriate for Minion's position: he was not supposed to make policy, so he had no need to disagree with his superiors.

12   The superintendent of works retired and Minion succeeded him. Minion continued to agree with everyone. He passed to his foreman every suggestion that came from above. The resulting conflicts in policy, and the continual changing of plans, soon demoralized the department. Complaints poured in from the Mayor and other officials, from taxpayers and from the maintenance-workers' union.

13   Minion still says "Yes" to everyone, and carries messages briskly back and forth between his superiors and his subordinates. Nominally a superintendent, he actually does the work of a messenger. The maintenance department regularly exceeds its budget, yet fails to fulfill its program of work. In short, Minion, a competent foreman, became an incompetent superintendent.

14   SERVICE INDUSTRIES FILE, CASE NO. 3
E. Tinker was exceptionally zealous and intelligent as an apprentice at G. Reece Auto Repair Inc., and soon rose to journeyman mechanic. In this job he showed outstanding ability in diagnosing obscure faults, and endless patience in correcting them. He was promoted to foreman of the repair shop.

15   But here his love of things mechanical and his perfectionism become liabilities. He will undertake any job that he thinks looks interesting, no matter how busy the shop may be. "We'll work it in somehow," he says.

16   He will not let a job go until he is fully satisfied with it.

---

[1]Some names have been changed in order to protect the guilty.

17   He meddles constantly. He is seldom to be found at his desk. He is usually up to his elbows in a dismantled motor and while the man who should be doing the work stands watching, other workmen sit around waiting to be assigned new tasks. As a result the shop is always overcrowded with work, always in a muddle, and delivery times are often missed.

"Occupational incompetence is everywhere. Have you noticed it? Probably we all have noticed it."

18   Tinker cannot understand that the average customer cares little about perfection—he wants his car back on time! He cannot understand that most of his men are less interested in motors than in their pay checks. So Tinker cannot get on with his customers or with his subordinates. He was a competent mechanic, but is now an incompetent foreman.

19   MILITARY FILE, CASE NO. 8   Consider the case of the late <u>renowned</u> General A. Goodwin. His hearty, informal manner, his racy style of speech, his scorn for petty regulations and his undoubted personal bravery made him the idol of his men. He led them to many well-deserved victories.

20   When Goodwin was promoted to field marshal he had to deal, not with ordinary soldiers, but with politicians and allied generalissimos.

21   He would not conform to the necessary protocol. He could not turn his tongue to the conventional courtesies and flatteries. He quarreled with all the dignitaries and took to lying for days at a time, drunk and sulking, in his trailer. The conduct of the war slipped out of his hands into those of his subordinates. He had been promoted to a position that he was incompetent to fill.

An Important Clue!

22   In time I saw that all such cases had a common feature. The employee had been promoted from a position of competence to a position of incompetence. I saw that, sooner or later, this could happen to every employee in every hierarchy.

23   HYPOTHETICAL CASE FILE, CASE NO. 1   Suppose you own a pill-rolling factory, Perfect Pill Incorporated. Your foreman-pill roller dies of a perforated ulcer. You need a replacement. You naturally look among your rank-and-file pill rollers.

24   Miss Oval, Mrs. Cylinder, Mr. Ellipse and Mr. Cube all show various degrees of incompetence. They will naturally be ineligible for promotion. You will choose—other things being equal—your most competent pill roller, Mr. Sphere, and promote him to foreman.

25   Now suppose Mr. Sphere proves competent as foreman. Later, when your general foreman, Legree, moves up to Works Manager, Sphere will be eligible to take his place.

26   If, on the other hand, Sphere is an incompetent foreman, he will get no more promotion. He has reached what I call his "level of incompetence." He will stay there till the end of his career.

27   Some employees, like Ellipse and Cube, reach a level of incompetence in the lowest grade and are never promoted. Some, like Sphere (assuming he is not a satisfactory foreman), reach it after one promotion.

28   E. Tinker, the automobile repair-shop foreman, reached his level of incompetence on the third stage of the hierarchy. General Goodwin reached his level of incompetence at the very top of the hierarchy.

29   So my analysis of hundreds of cases of occupational incompetence led me on to formulate *The Peter Principle:*

30   *In a Hierarchy Every Employee Tends to Rise to His Level of Incompetence...*

This Means You!

31   My Principle is the key to an understanding of all hierarchical systems, and therefore to an understanding of the whole structure of civilization. A few eccentrics try to avoid getting involved with hierarchies, but everyone in business, industry,

trade-unionism, politics, government, the armed forces, religion and education is so involved. All of them are controlled by the Peter Principle.

32 Many of them, to be sure, may win a promotion or two, moving from one level of competence to a higher level of competence. But competence in that new position qualifies them for still another promotion. For each individual, for you, for me, the final promotion is from a level of competence to a level of incompetence.

33 So, given enough time—and assuming the existence of enough ranks in the hierarchy—each employee rises to, and remains at, his level of incompetence. Peter's Corollary[2] states:

34 *In time, every post tends to be occupied by an employee who is incompetent to carry out its duties.*

Who Turns the Wheels?

35 You will rarely find, of course, a system in which *every* employee has reached his level of incompetence. In most instances, something is being done to further the ostensible purposes for which the hierarchy exists.

36 *Work is accomplished by those employees who have not yet reached their level of incompetence.*

---

[2]corollary: something proved from something else that has already been proved

Starting Time	
Finishing Time	
Reading Time	
Reading Rate	

COMPREHENSION

Read the following questions and statements. For each one, put an X in the box before the option that contains the most complete or accurate answer.

1. As a first-year teacher, the author observed that administrators at his school cared little about
   □ a. public opinion.
   □ b. outward appearances.
   □ c. the quality of students' education.
   □ d. rules and regulations.

2. The author was conditioned to believe that
   □ a. education was for the rich.
   □ b. teachers lacked professionalism.
   □ c. manual labor should be avoided.
   □ d. authority should not be questioned.

3. The author discovered the way hierarchy works
   □ a. while struggling through his first year as a teacher.
   □ b. after working as an automobile repair-shop foreman.
   □ c. during a chance encounter with J. S. Minion.
   □ d. after noting widespread incompetence in several organizations.

4. The case histories of Minion, Tinker, and Goodwin suggest that
   □ a. competence at one level doesn't mean competence at the next level.
   □ b. people should not be promoted.
   □ c. promotion should not be determined by seniority.
   □ d. journeymen mechanics do not make good foremen.

5. School administrators seemed unable to distinguish between
   □ a. the important and the unimportant.
   □ b. the minorities and the majority.
   □ c. work and play.
   □ d. professionals and nonprofessionals.

6. A person's level of incompetence should be
   □ a. concealed carefully.
   □ b. faced squarely.
   □ c. charitably overlooked.
   □ d. generally tolerated.

7. The author's first year of teaching left him
   □ a. discouraged with the system.
   □ b. bitter.
   □ c. indifferent to his superiors.
   □ d. bored.

8. The author's presentation is
   □ a. filled with examples.
   □ b. prejudiced.
   □ c. amusing but inaccurate.
   □ d. contradictory and embarrassing.

9. A. Goodwin was most happy when
    - ☐ a. drunk.
    - ☐ b. acting as field marshal.
    - ☐ c. holding the rank of general.
    - ☐ d. dealing with politicians.

10. The selection is written in the form of
    - ☐ a. an analysis.
    - ☐ b. a list.
    - ☐ c. an application.
    - ☐ d. a short story.

Comprehension Skills Key

1. recalling specific facts
2. retaining concepts
3. organizing facts
4. understanding the main idea
5. drawing a conclusion
6. making a judgment
7. making an inference
8. recognizing tone
9. understanding characters
10. appreciating literary forms

VOCABULARY—PART TWO

Write the word that makes the most sense in each sentence.

incompetent affability renowned inherent subordinates

1. The Peter Principle is based on qualities that are _____ in the human character.

2. Peter believes that although everyone is good at something, all people also reach a point where they are _____ .

3. Some people, for example, are great thinkers and thus are _____ for their powers of concentration.

4. But these people are usually solitary types not known for their _____ .

5. Put them at the head of an outgoing group of _____ and things probably won't go well.

complied obscure demoralized hierarchy ostensible

6. After working for several not-very-good supervisors, Peter became _____ .

7. They were not happy with him even when he _____ with their requests.

8. They never seemed to see the big picture, but instead worried over _____ issues.

9. Their most important goal was rising within the _____ of their company.

10. The _____ reasons for the company's existence—for example, turning out a good product—had no importance for them at all.

Comprehension ☐

Vocabulary ☐

UNDERSTANDING THROUGH WRITING

Do you believe in the truth of the Peter Principle? To answer this question, think of various work situations you have been in. Then write an explanation of why you do or do not believe in the principle. Use specific examples from your own experience as much as you can.

_____

_____

_____

_____

_____

_____

_____

BUILDING STUDY SKILLS

Read the following passage and answer the questions that follow it.

Paragraphs of Transition

The recognizable feature of paragraphs of transition is their brevity—they are normally short.

As the name implies, these paragraphs are used by the author to pass logically from one aspect of the subject to another. Through paragraphs of transition, authors show a change of thought or introduce a new side to the matter under discussion.

When they see paragraphs of transition, readers should know the author is about to switch tracks and change to a new topic. This knowledge helps the student to organize the reading because it is obvious that the current discussion is ending and that something new is coming.

Transitional paragraphs are valuable in other ways too. Because they introduce something new, they may function as a paragraph of introduction, offering a brief preview of the new concepts the author now plans to discuss. They may state the purpose the author hopes to accomplish by presenting the following information or try to arouse the reader's interest in what is to follow.

In another way, paragraphs of transition may function as concluding paragraphs, summing up for the reader the important points of the aspect being concluded. Or a restatement of the central thought may be presented to help the reader understand the subject before moving on.

It is this combination of functions and its contribution to the reader's understanding of a text's organization that makes this brief paragraph so valuable.

1. Paragraphs of transition are normally

   _____ .

2. The reader knows that the current discussion is coming to an _____ when he sees a paragraph of transition.

3. Paragraphs of transition sometimes function as paragraphs of _____ when they state new concepts the author plans to discuss.

4. These paragraphs may be used as _____ paragraphs when they restate a central thought before moving on.

5. In "The Peter Principle" paragraph 8 is a transition paragraph that also serves as a paragraph of

   _____ .

T O P I C   R E V I E W
React to Topic 1

Respond to one or more of these questions as your instructor directs.

1. There are certain similarities between Jessie Lopez De La Cruz in "La Causa" and Bill Cantirino in "Organ Hunter." Go through each selection and list three or more ways the two characters are alike.

_____

_____

_____

_____

_____

_____

2. Using the list you made in item 1, write a paragraph showing the similarities between Jessie Lopez De La Cruz and Bill Cantirino.

_____

_____

_____

_____

_____

_____

3. In Building Study Skills 1 you learned that authors can use a number of techniques in writing paragraphs of introduction. Look at the introductory paragraphs in selections 2–5. Write a short explanation of what you think each writer was trying to accomplish in his or her introduction.

_____

_____

_____

_____

_____

_____

4. Assume that you are doing some of the public relations work for a job fair. Pick one of the occupations discussed in selections 1–4 and prepare a brochure pointing up the advantages of that line of work. The brochure should be a mixture of words and illustrations; if you cannot find appropriate art or photos, draw a rough sketch of what they should be.

_____

_____

_____

_____

_____

_____

5. What makes people choose the occupations they do? Are most jobs the result of a well-thought-out plan, or do people just fall into them? Are there ways to ensure getting a job that will make a person happy? Write your thoughts about planning for, getting, and keeping the right job.

_____

_____

_____

_____

_____

_____

6. Either alone or with a partner, think of two or three job situations that would prove the truth of the Peter Principle. Then write a plan for a TV script that would dramatize those situations. For each job, you will need to make clear what the person was like before and after getting the job that he or she was incompetent at.

_____

_____

_____

_____

_____

_____

Draw from others the lesson that may profit yourself.

—Terence (190–159 B.C.)

YOU LEARN SOMETHING EVERY DAY

6

Field Trip

Naomi Shihab Nye

READING PURPOSE —
In the following selection the writer tells of taking her students on a disastrous field trip. Read to find out what happened.

VOCABULARY—PART ONE

All of these words are in the selection you are about to read. Study each word and its meaning. Then answer the questions below. As you read the selection, notice how each vocabulary word is used.

collation: arrangement of the pages of something in proper order

severance: act of cutting off

suspended: as if hanging in space

tediously: in a boring or tiresome manner

stricken: wounded

archival: having to do with the storing of historical records

monitor: keep track of

excruciating: very painful

incredible: unbelievable

bonded: connected; joined

---

1. Which word could describe the feeling of a very severe wound?

   _____

2. Which word would describe how a lecturer spoke if she had no expression in her voice and constantly repeated herself?

   _____

3. Which word could describe what you do if you keep a record of how long you exercise every day?

   _____

4. In what kind of file would you expect to find 50-year-old documents?

   _____

5. Which word could describe a story in which the main character lived to be 160 years old?

   _____

1   Only once did I ever take a large group of children on a field trip. I took a creative writing workshop to a printing office to see how pages were bound together to make books, and our cheerfully patient guide chopped her finger off with a giant paper cutter.

2   I had not prepared the children for experiences beyond typeface, camera-ready copy, <u>collation</u>. Standing toward the back like a shepherd, I felt their happy little backs stiffen at the moment of <u>severance</u>. A collective gasp rose from their throats as a blot of blood grew outward in a rapid pool, staining all the pages. Cupping her wounded hand against her chest, the woman pressed through the crowd, not screaming, but mouthing silently, "Hospital. Now. Let's go."

3   The children stood motionless, <u>suspended</u>. The motion of the workers was like the flurry of feathers and wings when anyone steps too quickly into a chicken coop. People dialed, then asked one another why they were dialing. Couldn't they drive her to the hospital themselves? Someone at the emergency room said to place the severed finger on ice, and a man who, moments before, had been <u>tediously</u> pasting up layouts ran for ice.

4   One boy tugged my shirt and croaked, "The last thing she said was—you have to be very careful with this machine."

5   Someone dropped a ring of keys, and I immediately crawled around on the floor, reaching under a desk for them. It felt good to fall to my knees. For a second the <u>stricken</u> woman loomed above me, and I stuttered, apologizing for having distracted her from business, but she was distracted by something else.

6   "Honey, look at that thing!" she said, staring into the cup of ice where the index finger now rested like a rare <u>archival</u> specimen. "It's turning white! If that finger stays white, I don't want it on my body!"

7   We laughed long and hard and straight, and the children stared, amazed. Had we lost our senses? That she could joke at such a moment, as the big fans whirred and the collating machines paused over vast mountains of stacked paper... I wanted to sing her blackness, the sweet twist of her joy, to call out to those boys and girls, "This, my friends, is what words can do for you—make you laugh when your finger rests in a plastic cup!"

8   But she went quickly off into the day, and I shuffled an extremely silent group of budding writers back onto our bus. I wanted to say something promising recovery, or praising our guide's remarkable presence of mind, but my voice seemed lost among the seats. No one would look at me.

9   Later I heard how they went home and went straight to their rooms. Some had nightmares. A mother called my assistant to say, "What in the world happened on that field trip? Sarah came over today, and she and Molly climbed up on the bed and just sobbed."

10   At our next meeting we forgot poetry and made get-well cards. Or come-together-again cards. May the seam hold. May the two become one. They thought up all kinds of things. I had been calling the printing office to <u>monitor</u> her progress, and the reports sounded good. The students had been gathering stories: someone's farmer-uncle whose leg was severed in a cornfield but who lived to see it joined; someone's brother's toe.

11   I went to her home with a bundle of hopeful wishes tied in loops of pink ribbon. She was wearing a terry-cloth bathrobe and sitting in a comfortable chair, her hand hugely bandaged.

12   She shook her head. "I guess none of those cute kids will ever become printers now, will they? Gee, I hope they don't stop reading and writing! And to think of it happening in front of such an interested audience! Oh, I feel just terrible about it."

13   Reading their messages made her chuckle. I asked what the doctors had said about the finger turning black again. She said they thought it would, but it might be slightly paler than the rest of her hand. And it would be stiff, for a long time, maybe forever.

14   She missed being at work; vacations weren't much fun when they came this unexpectedly. The pain had been <u>excruciating</u> at first but was easing now, and wasn't modern medicine <u>incredible</u>, and would I please thank those kids for their flowers and hearts!

15   Once I'd dreamed of visiting every factory in town, the mattress factory, the hot sauce factory, the assembly line for cowboy boots, but I changed my mind. Now I took my workshops out onto the schoolyard, but no farther. I made them look for

buttons and feathers, I made them describe the ways men and women stood as they waited for a bus.

16   By the time our workshops ended that summer, we felt more deeply <u>bonded</u> than other groups I'd known. Maybe our sense of mortality linked us, our shared vision of the fragility of body parts. One girl went on to become one of the best young writers in the city. I'd like to think her hands were blessed by our unexpected obsession with hands.

"'The last thing she said was—you have to be very careful with this machine.'"

Starting Time   [   ]

Finishing Time   [   ]

Reading Time   [   ]

Reading Rate   [   ]

COMPREHENSION

Read the following questions and statements. For each one, put an X in the box before the option that contains the most complete or accurate answer.

1. The field trip was taken in connection with a
   □ a. printing class.
   □ b. drawing class.
   □ c. creative writing class.
   □ d. drama class.

2. The story paints a good picture of
   □ a. the ways people respond to a bad accident.
   □ b. how government bureaucracy keeps things from getting done.
   □ c. the kind of work done at a printing shop.
   □ d. the difference between ages.

3. The main event in the story
   □ a. does not occur until the end.
   □ b. starts when the woman goes to the hospital.
   □ c. is described in a series of flashbacks.
   □ d. happens in the very first paragraph.

4. As a teacher, how might the author sum up this story?
   □ a. Students will bounce back from any experience.
   □ b. We don't always learn the lessons we expect.
   □ c. Easy come, easy go.
   □ d. Students need to be consoled when they are frightened.

5. The accident seemed to have the greatest effect on
   □ a. the injured woman.
   □ b. the woman's co-workers.
   □ c. the students on the field trip.
   □ d. the narrator.

6. Students and teacher developed close ties because
   □ a. they had shared a frightening experience.
   □ b. they wanted to befriend the injured woman.
   □ c. the students could not discuss what had happened with their parents.
   □ d. the teacher frequently invited the students to her house.

7. The students taken on the field trip were probably
   □ a. in preschool.
   □ b. in third or fourth grade.
   □ c. in junior high school.
   □ d. in high school.

8. The tone the author uses to tell this story is
   □ a. light-hearted.   □ c. critical.
   □ b. sad.   □ d. angry.

9. The woman involved in the accident
   ☐ a. was a timid, fearful sort.
   ☐ b. had a good sense of humor.
   ☐ c. had little patience with children.
   ☐ d. would probably never work again.

10. The kind of narrator used in this selection is
   ☐ a. third person limited.
   ☐ b. third person omniscient.
   ☐ c. second person.
   ☐ d. first person.

Comprehension Skills Key

1. recalling specific facts
2. retaining concepts
3. organizing facts
4. understanding the main idea
5. drawing a conclusion
6. making a judgment
7. making an inference
8. recognizing tone
9. understanding characters
10. appreciating literary forms

VOCABULARY—PART TWO

Write the word that makes the most sense in each sentence.

**collation   suspended
stricken   monitor
excruciating**

1. The teacher wanted to _____ her students so none would leave the group.

2. In the print shop, they saw copies of book pages go through the process of _____ .

3. No one was sure how to help the _____ tour guide.

4. The students walked around in a daze, as if _____ in midair.

5. Though the pain must have been _____ , the woman was calm.

**tediously   severance
bonded   archival
incredible**

6. At one time, the _____ of a finger meant that it was lost forever.

7. Old-time doctors would find it _____ that a finger can now be reattached.

8. Restitching lost fingers is now so routine that it is no longer done _____ .

9. In several weeks the severed part is usually _____ back onto the body.

10. In a hundred years _____ records will show how common body-part reattachment has become.

Comprehension ☐

Vocabulary ☐

UNDERSTANDING THROUGH WRITING

Pretend you are the teacher from this class and are writing in your journal. Write a summary of how you felt on the day of the accident.

_____
_____
_____
_____
_____
_____
_____
_____

BUILDING STUDY SKILLS

Read the following passage and answer the questions that follow it.

Closing Paragraphs

The function of the closing paragraph is to give the reader the author's concluding remarks or final words on the subject. The author may do this in one of several ways.

First, although this is quite rare, the author may draw a conclusion based on the information contained in the lesson or chapter. Authors are reluctant to do this because conclusions based on an entire chapter are much too important to be mentioned just once, at the end. We can expect to find the conclusion given early in the chapter and the facts supporting it to follow. It is likely, though, that such an important conclusion would be repeated or restated in the final paragraph.

Second, the author may use the final paragraph to summarize. In effect the author is saying, "Above all, remember this. This is what it's all been about." These summarizing remarks are valuable to the learner and a definite aid in reviewing.

Last, the author may choose to leave the readers with one final thought—the central, all-inclusive idea around which the chapter was developed. Occasionally this will be done with an anecdote, story, or moral used as a cap to the discussion.

The concluding paragraph is the author's last chance to reach the audience. If he or she wants to leave the readers with a last thought, here is where it will be.

1. The paragraphs used by the author to finish his or her remarks on a subject are called _____ paragraphs.

2. The reader can usually expect the conclusion to be given early in the chapter and the _____ supporting it to follow.

3. Summarizing remarks is a definite aid in _____ .

4. Often the author will close with one final thought, as did Naomi Shihab Nye when she mentioned some of the _____ the accident had on her and her students.

5. Sometimes the final thought is presented in the form of an anecdote, story, or _____ .

7

The Autobiography of Malcolm X

READING PURPOSE—
In this selection Malcolm talks about the problems he had with reading and how he overcame them. Read to learn about the method he followed.

VOCABULARY—PART ONE

All of these words are in the selection you are about to read. Study each word and its meaning. Then answer the questions below. As you read the selection, notice how each vocabulary word is used.

emulate: imitate

painstaking: very careful

succeeding: following

inevitable: unavoidable

inmate: person confined in a prison

circulation: the lending of library books and other materials

rehabilitation: restoring to a level of usefulness through therapy or other help

devour: take in with the eyes in a hungry way

engrossing: absorbing; interesting

feigned: pretended

---

1. Which word could describe a book that was so fascinating you couldn't put it down?

2. Which word would tell what you do when you model yourself after another person?

3. Which word could describe an accident when two speeding cars are coming into an intersection at the same time?

4. Which word could tell what a guest at a party does if she eagerly checks out the clothing of everyone in the room?

5. Which word names something the head of a library should be concerned with?

1   Many who today hear me somewhere in person, or on television, or those who read something I've said, will think I went to school far beyond the eighth grade. This impression is due entirely to my prison studies.

2   It had really begun back in the Charlestown Prison, when Bimbi first made me feel envy of his stock of knowledge. Bimbi had always taken charge of any conversation he was in, and I had tried to <u>emulate</u> him. But every book I picked up had few sentences which didn't contain anywhere from one to nearly all of the words that might as well have been in Chinese. When I just skipped those words, of course, I really ended up with little idea of what the book said. So I had come to the Norfolk Prison Colony still going through only book-reading motions. Pretty soon, I would have quit even these motions, unless I had received the motivation that I did.

3   I saw that the best thing I could do was get hold of a dictionary—to study, to learn some words. I was lucky enough to reason also that I should try to improve my penmanship. It was sad. I couldn't even write in a straight line. It was both ideas together that moved me to request a dictionary along with some tablets and pencils from the Norfolk Prison Colony school.

4   I spent two days just riffling uncertainly through the dictionary's pages. I'd never realized so many words existed! I didn't know *which* words I needed to learn. Finally, just to start some kind of action, I began copying.

5   In my slow, <u>painstaking</u>, ragged handwriting, I copied into my tablet everything printed on that first page, down to the punctuation marks.

6   I believe it took me a day. Then, aloud, I read back, to myself, everything I'd written on the tablet. Over and over, aloud, to myself, I read my own handwriting.

7   I woke up the next morning, thinking about those words—immensely proud to realize that not only had I written so much at one time, but I'd written words that I never knew were in the world. Moreover, with a little effort, I also could remember what many of these words meant. I reviewed the words whose meanings I didn't remember. Funny thing, from the dictionary first page right now, that "aardvark" springs to my mind. The dictionary had a picture of it, a long-tailed, long-eared, burrowing African mammal, which lives off termites caught by sticking out its tongue as an anteater does for ants.

8   I was so fascinated that I went on—I copied the dictionary's next page. And the same experience came when I studied that. With every <u>succeeding</u> page, I also learned of people and places and events from history. Actually the dictionary is like a miniature encyclopedia. Finally the dictionary's A section had filled a whole tablet—and I went on into the B's. That was the way I started copying what eventually became the entire dictionary. It went a lot faster after so much practice helped me to pick up handwriting speed. Between what I wrote in my tablet, and writing letters, during the rest of my time in prison I would guess I wrote a million words.

9   I suppose it was <u>inevitable</u> that as my word-base broadened, I could for the first time pick up a book and read and now begin to understand what the book was saying. Anyone who has read a great deal can imagine the new world that opened. Let me tell you something: from then until I left that prison, in every free moment I had, if I was not reading in the library, I was reading on my bunk. You couldn't have gotten me out of books with a wedge. Between Mr. Muhammad's teachings, my correspondence, my visitors—usually Ella and Reginald—and my reading of books, months passed without my even thinking about being imprisoned. In fact, up to then, I never had been so truly free in my life.

10   The Norfolk Prison Colony's library was in the school building. A variety of classes was taught there by instructors who came from such places as Harvard and Boston universities. The weekly debates between <u>inmate</u> teams were also held in the school building. You would be astonished to know how worked up convict debaters and audiences would get over subjects like "Should Babies Be Fed Milk?".

11   Available on the prison library's shelves were books on just about every general subject. Much of the big private collection that Parkhurst had willed to the prison was still in crates and boxes in the back of the library—thousands of old books. Some of them looked ancient: covers faded, old-time parchment-looking binding. Parkhurst, I've mentioned, seemed to have been principally interested in history and religion. He had the money and the special interest to have a lot of books that you

wouldn't have in general <u>circulation</u>. Any college library would have been lucky to get that collection.

12 As you can imagine, especially in a prison where there was heavy emphasis on <u>rehabilitation</u>, an inmate was smiled upon if he demonstrated an unusually intense interest in books. There was a sizable number of well-read inmates, especially the popular debaters. Some were said by many to be practically walking encyclopedias. They were almost celebrities. No university would ask any student to <u>devour</u> literature as I did when this new world opened to me, of being able to read and *understand*.

13 I read more in my room than in the library itself. An inmate who was known to read a lot could check out more than the permitted maximum number of books. I preferred reading in the total isolation of my own room.

14 When I had progressed to really serious reading, every night at about ten P.M., I would be outraged with the "lights out." It always seemed to catch me right in the middle of something <u>engrossing</u>.

15 Fortunately, right outside my door was a corridor light that cast a glow into my room. The glow was enough to read by, once my eyes adjusted to it. So when "lights out" came, I would sit on the floor where I could continue reading in that glow.

16 At one-hour intervals the night guards paced past every room. Each time I heard the approach-

"This new world opened to me, of being able to read and *understand*."

ing footsteps, I jumped into bed and <u>feigned</u> sleep. And as soon as the guard passed, I got back out of bed onto the floor area of that light-glow, where I would read for another fifty-eight minutes—until the guard approached again. That went on until three or four every morning. Three or four hours of sleep a night was enough for me. Often in the years in the streets I had slept less than that.

Starting Time	
Finishing Time	
Reading Time	
Reading Rate	

COMPREHENSION

Read the following questions and statements. For each one, put an X in the box before the option that contains the most complete or accurate answer.

1. The action in this story takes place mostly in
   - ☐ a. Charlestown Prison.
   - ☐ b. Norfolk Prison Colony.
   - ☐ c. Parkhurst Prison.
   - ☐ d. Attica.

2. Malcolm X changes in this selection from
   - ☐ a. a bitter to a happy man.
   - ☐ b. a nonreader to a reader.
   - ☐ c. a follower to a leader.
   - ☐ d. a performer to a librarian.

3. The first thing Malcolm did to accomplish his goal was
   ☐ a. begin reading harder books.
   ☐ b. stop feeling sorry for himself,
   ☐ c. improve his vocabulary.
   ☐ d. stop watching television in the prison lounge.

4. Malcolm's main purpose in this selection is to
   ☐ a. describe a process of learning.
   ☐ b. describe a jail setting.
   ☐ c. talk about how jail can break a person's spirit.
   ☐ d. complain how he was unfairly imprisoned.

5. Malcolm's handwriting improved because he
   ☐ a. took a penmanship course.
   ☐ b. got a lot of practice copying the dictionary.
   ☐ c. began writing on paper with lines.
   ☐ d. became the recorder of notes at all inmate meetings.

6. The attitude in Malcolm's prison was to
   ☐ a. let inmates improve themselves if they want to.
   ☐ b. keep inmates in their cells most of the time.
   ☐ c. force inmates to learn to read.
   ☐ d. make reading a reward for good behavior.

7. Parkhurst was
   ☐ a. one of the prison guards.
   ☐ b. one of the inmates.
   ☐ c. a wealthy man who wanted to help prisoners get an education.
   ☐ d. a relative of Malcolm's who regularly sent him books.

8. The general tone of this selection is
   ☐ a. angry.
   ☐ b. serious.
   ☐ c. bitter.
   ☐ d. humorous.

9. A good word to describe Malcolm in this selection is
   ☐ a. dedicated.
   ☐ b. competitive.
   ☐ c. lazy.
   ☐ d. talkative.

10. When Malcolm says in paragraph 9, "Up to then, I never had been so truly free in my life," he means that
    ☐ a. he had been freed from jail.
    ☐ b. he had been given a jail cell by himself.
    ☐ c. he was now allowed to go out to the prison yard.
    ☐ d. reading freed his mind and spirit.

Comprehension Skills Key

1. recalling specific facts
2. retaining concepts
3. organizing facts
4. understanding the main idea
5. drawing a conclusion
6. making a judgment
7. making an inference
8. recognizing tone
9. understanding characters
10. appreciating literary forms

VOCABULARY—PART TWO

Write the word that makes the most sense in each sentence.

succeeding	inevitable
circulation	devour
feigned	

1. Before Malcolm could read, he was so embarrassed that he sometimes _____ that he could.

2. As he learned more words, though, it was _____ that his reading skill would increase.

3. Once he became a reader, he loved books so much that he just wanted to _____ them.

4. He started slowly, but in each _____ month his reading skills grew.

5. Soon, most of the books in _____ in the library found their way into his cell.

inmate   **engrossing**
emulate   **painstaking**
rehabilitation

6. Reading made Malcolm feel that he was no longer a(n) _____ in a prison.

7. A book could be so _____ that it would give him a mental escape.

8. The _____ way he had taught himself gave him confidence about learning other things.

9. He began to look up to and _____ some of the more intellectual prisoners.

10. Once he became a serious reader, his _____ was practically complete.

Comprehension [ ]

Vocabulary [ ]

UNDERSTANDING THROUGH WRITING

Malcolm learned to read because he was determined to succeed despite all hardships. Think of a situation where you have overcome hardships to succeed at something. Write a short explanation of what happened.

_____

_____

_____

_____

_____

_____

_____

_____

_____

_____

BUILDING STUDY SKILLS

Read the following passage and answer the questions that follow it.

Inflexible Readers

If the reading habits of most of today's adults were to be described, the single adjective *inflexible* would be the most appropriate description.

To illustrate what is meant by inflexible reading, take the situation that many doctors find themselves in. To succeed, they must understand the content of textbooks and journals thoroughly; 100 percent comprehension is required. Accordingly, medical students develop an appropriate reading skill—a thorough, slow, and careful technique leading to mastery of many critically important details. The problem comes later, after medical school, when the doctor wants to settle down for an evening's enjoyment with a good novel. Most novels don't require the painstaking attention to detail that a medical text demands. But because of habits formed during years of study, the doctor has become an inflexible reader and plods intensively through whatever kind of reading material that comes to hand. The same thing happens in other professions as well.

As students, we also are guilty of inflexible reading. One factor leading to this is in the way we are first taught to read. Most of us were required to read aloud from our beginning texts. By listening to us, teachers could evaluate our progress and see how well we were learning to recognize, identify, and understand words. Our parents, too, could tell how we were doing by listening to us read.

But as beginning readers, we often learn other things at the same time: we are taught to read quite slowly and to pronounce words carefully, we are taught not to skip words, and we are conditioned to read in this one acceptable fashion. So, as we learn to read, the habits that will later make us inflexible readers are being established.

1. A word that can be used to describe the reading habits of many adults is _____ .

2. No dedicated doctor is satisfied with less than _____ comprehension.

3. One factor leading to inflexibility can be found in the way students are _____ to read.

4. As beginners, we are _____ to read in one acceptable fashion.

5. Following this fashion, when some students read even something as easy as the Malcolm X selection, they read it quite _____ .

8

A Beloved Professor's Last Lessons

Mitch Albom

READING PURPOSE—
In this selection the writer has a chance to revisit an old professor. Read to find out what he learned from those visits.

VOCABULARY—PART ONE

All of these words are in the selection you are about to read. Study each word and its meaning. Then answer the questions below. As you read the selection, notice how each vocabulary word is used.

engaged: charmed; captivated

interaction: communication; contact

impersonal: lacking direct human contact

forged: shaped; formed

aback: confused by something unexpected

intact: in one piece

thesis: essay based on research

compassion: concern and sympathy for others

angst: suffering; anxiety

prime: the best time or stage

---

1. What quality does a woman show if she brings flowers to her sick neighbor?

2. Which word could tell how you created something by putting pieces together?

3. Which word describes the condition of a vase that fell to the floor but didn't break?

4. Which word could describe a relationship where you leave notes for another person but never speak directly?

5. Which word names something you might write in school?

1   The old man who lay dying before me was a friend and a respected professional. But mostly he was a teacher. I still thought of him that way. A teacher. *My* teacher. And I was his student.

2   Never mind that in 16 years since my college graduation, I had lost track of him, building a work-stuffed life as a journalist. And although Morrie Schwartz, my former sociology professor, had thinning gray hair now and sunken eyes, he still offered me the same delightful smile that <u>engaged</u> me as a freshman at Brandeis University. The moment we were reunited, I was back in class again, my ego much smaller, my sense of wonder renewed.

3   Good teachers do that.

4   If I could wish anything for students today, it would be that they might find their own Morrie, and see how much learning goes on when you put down the books. With the trend today toward larger classes on some campuses, and less personal <u>interaction</u> with professors, many students are missing something special.

5   For me, such an <u>impersonal</u> situation would have meant missing one of my life's most important relationships, <u>forged</u> with a man who taught me how to live when he was healthy and now, even more, was teaching me how to live through his dying.

6   "Which do you prefer, Mitch or Mitchell?" Morrie asked me that first day at Brandeis.

7   I was taken <u>aback</u>. No teacher had ever asked this before.

8   "My friends call me Mitch," I replied.

9   "Well then, Mitch it is. And Mitch?"

10   "Yes?"

11   "I hope one day you will think of me as your friend."

12   Two decades earlier, that was our first conversation.

13   We had now reunited to share our last.

14   Morrie was dying of Lou Gehrig's disease, amyotrophic lateral sclerosis, a terrible illness that melts your nerves like a candle's flame and leaves your body a pile of wax. Morrie had but a few months left.

15   I had learned about his fate while watching "Nightline." I had lost track of Morrie in pursuit of my career in newspapers, television and radio. I was successful, financially if not spiritually. I lived in suburban Detroit with my wife, in a large house on a hill. It was there, one night, that I was startled to see my old professor talking earnestly with Ted Koppel. I felt ashamed at losing touch, yet was immediately drawn to his soothing conversation and engaging intelligence. Once teachers touch you, I believe they always will.

16   Watching the program that night, I learned that the silver lining to Morrie's illness—the only one—was that his mind would remain <u>intact</u>. As long as he had that, he could do what he loved most: teach.

17   And that is what he did with me. He taught me one last class, on the meaning of life.

18   Shortly after I saw Morrie on "Nightline," we reunited, rediscovered our affection for each other and began to meet at his home every Tuesday, the same day we used to meet for most of his classes in college.

19   In those years, it was an office at Brandeis; now it was the study in his house in West Newton, Mass., where he lived with his wife and a small visiting army of health care workers who tended to him around the clock. Back in college, I would scurry up the campus hill to Morrie's classes, always late, always out of breath. Now I flew in from Detroit each week to sit by my old teacher's side.

20   But there was still the same magic, the teacher-student chemistry, a relationship I have never really duplicated since.

21   Each Tuesday, Morrie would rest in a reclining chair, where he could watch his beloved hibiscus plant on the windowsill. He was unable to move his legs or torso. He needed me to wipe his brow and place his glasses on the bridge of his nose. He was weak and frail, 78 years old.

22   We talked about life, a different topic every week. I asked about things that perplexed many Americans. Marriage. Career. Aging. Death. Morrie saw these things through the eyes of a man who knew his fate. His wisdom was a precious fountain, offering answers to that eternal question: how would I change my life if I knew I had only a few months left?

23   So I asked about wealth. "I can tell you right now, as I'm sitting here dying," Morrie said, "when you need it most, neither money nor power will give you the feeling you're looking for."

24   I asked about aging. Morrie answered: "Aging is not just decay. It's growth. If you've found meaning in your life, you won't want to go back."

25   Often, I asked about his new specialty, death. "It ends a life," he said, "but not a relationship."

26   Throughout the process, we laughed. We held hands. I took notes and taped our conversations for the book we would do together, "Tuesdays With Morrie," something Morrie called our last thesis. As the weeks went on, my old professor spoke more and more about compassion, being fully human. He whispered warnings for the young and healthy. "Love each other or perish," he said, echoing Auden[1].

27   I wrote it all down, just as I had years ago.

28   Finally, one Tuesday, I arrived at the house in West Newton, but Morrie was no longer in his study. He was tucked in bed, his body shriveled to the size of a boy's. He was crying. I began to cry, too.

29   Our last class was brief, only a few words, and a funeral followed instead of graduation.

30   At the memorial service, hundreds of former students paid their respects. I found a common theme: few of us remembered textbooks and papers; all of us remembered Morrie. The way he spoke with us in his office. The way he listened to our student angst. The walks we took. The coffees we drank. The jokes we made.

31   Maybe they don't do this on college campuses anymore. Maybe you get something from large lecture halls and graduate assistants. Maybe it is a

"I…was immediately drawn to his soothing conversation and engaging intelligence."   Copyright © Heather Pillar

more efficient use of time, of resources. I don't know.

32   All I know is that I was never quite as good as I was when I was by my favorite professor's side, once in the prime of his life, once in his final days.

Starting Time	
Finishing Time	
Reading Time	
Reading Rate	

---

[1]W. H. Auden was a well-known British poet of the 1930s.

COMPREHENSION

Read the following questions and statements. For each one, put an X in the box before the option that contains the most complete or accurate answer.

1. The author had known Morrie as a
   - ☐ a. high school student.
   - ☐ b. college student.
   - ☐ c. sportswriter.
   - ☐ d. elementary school student.

2. The author wanted to talk to Morrie because
   - ☐ a. he felt he had lost touch with the real values of life.
   - ☐ b. his agent wanted him to write a book about his old teacher.
   - ☐ c. he was looking for financial success.
   - ☐ d. he wanted to introduce Morrie to his wife.

3. The way the author develops this selection is mainly through
   - ☐ a. memories from the past and examples from the present.
   - ☐ b. comparing Morrie's teaching style with that of his other teachers.
   - ☐ c. a physical description of Morrie.
   - ☐ d. having Morrie tell his story in his own words.

4. The main point of this article is that
   - ☐ a. you can't relive the past.
   - ☐ b. having a good teacher is a wonderful gift.
   - ☐ c. students don't appreciate their instructors until it is too late.
   - ☐ d. schools now are not like they used to be.

5. If the author had his way, students today would
   - ☐ a. have to study harder.
   - ☐ b. start college later.
   - ☐ c. visit their instructors at their homes.
   - ☐ d. have smaller, more personal classes.

6. The author feels that teachers like Morrie
   - ☐ a. can be found in most schools.
   - ☐ b. need their former students to stay in contact with them.
   - ☐ c. teach only at East Coast schools.
   - ☐ d. can make one's education special.

7. The author talked with Morrie about the meaning of life because
   - ☐ a. they had little else in common at this point.
   - ☐ b. he needed the information for his book.
   - ☐ c. it was something a dying man would have a good perspective on.
   - ☐ d. it was something they had never talked about in class.

8. The tone the author uses in talking about Morrie is
   - ☐ a. amusing.
   - ☐ b. regretful.
   - ☐ c. impersonal.
   - ☐ d. respectful.

9. Morrie and the author were alike in that both were
   - ☐ a. ill.
   - ☐ b. teachers of a sort.
   - ☐ c. eager to talk about life.
   - ☐ d. looking forward to changes.

10. When the author says of Morrie, "His wisdom was a precious fountain," he is using
    - ☐ a. a simile.
    - ☐ b. a metaphor.
    - ☐ c. a literal comparison.
    - ☐ d. personification.

Comprehension Skills Key

1. recalling specific facts
2. retaining concepts
3. organizing facts
4. understanding the main idea
5. drawing a conclusion
6. making a judgment
7. making an inference
8. recognizing tone
9. understanding characters
10. appreciating literary forms

VOCABULARY—PART TWO

Write the word that makes the most sense in each sentence.

interaction   aback
intact   compassion
prime

1. When the author first revisited Morrie, he was taken _____ by the professor's poor health.

2. The author had known Morrie in the _____ of his life; now he was an old man.

3. He felt _____ for Morrie and tried to ease his suffering.

4. He wanted to have a meaningful _____ with the old man before he died.

5. Morrie's body was broken down, but his mind was _____ .

impersonal	**forged**
thesis	**angst**
engaged	

6. The friendship between the two men had been

   _____ through their earlier

   relationship.

7. Morrie had _____ the author

   with his warmth and personality.

8. Far from being a(n) _____

   instructor, he wanted to really get to know his

   students.

9. Now that Morrie was old and disease-ridden, the

   author would be a witness to his

   _____ .

10. Together they would write a(n)

    _____ based on what Morrie had

    learned from life.

Comprehension ☐

Vocabulary ☐

UNDERSTANDING THROUGH WRITING

Think of an instructor you've had somewhere in your schooling who made a big impression on you. Write a short description of this person. Explain why he or she affected you so much.

_____

_____

_____

_____

_____

_____

_____

_____

_____

_____

_____

_____

BUILDING STUDY SKILLS

Read the following passage and answer the questions that follow it.

Flexible Readers

Good readers are flexible, varying their reading technique to suit the occasion. Some materials demand a slow, analytical approach; insurance policies and contracts are good examples. Light fiction calls for a breezy, casual kind of reading at a fairly rapid rate. Another kind of material permits the reader to quickly glance down the column of print, snatching ideas on the run. This is called skimming.

Comprehension is another aspect of flexible reading. There are degrees, or levels, of comprehension that are appropriate for certain materials. For example, a very practical and thorough kind is needed to follow directions accurately. Obviously we don't need this for reading the comics. Textbooks require the student to remember concepts and to understand relationships. The student, moreover, is expected to use comprehension as a tool for thinking. But simple articles of passing interest require only a temporary kind of comprehension.

We often run across articles, accounts, and stories that are of just casual or passing interest to us. These may be unrelated to school or the job; they may contain very little factual content; and they may be very simply written. To read these materials analytically like contracts, documents, and textbooks would be a waste of time. These materials need only to be skimmed to be understood.

1. Good readers _____ their reading technique to suit the occasion.

2. Light fiction calls for an informal kind of reading at a fairly _____ rate.

3. Textbooks should be read slowly because they require the student to remember _____ and understand relationships.

4. Simple articles of only passing interest need only to be _____ to be understood.

5. Because the selection about Morrie is written very _____ , it does not have to be read as carefully or analytically as a textbook.

9

A Whole Society of Loners and Dreamers

William Allen

READING PURPOSE—
In this selection a young boy decides to answer a magazine ad promising to teach him to write. Read to see what he learns from his experience.

VOCABULARY—PART ONE

All of these words are in the selection you are about to read. Study each word and its meaning. Then answer the questions below. As you read the selection, notice how each vocabulary word is used.

geared: aimed; designed

pore: look at intently or steadily

critiques: critical reviews

arduous: difficult; strenuous

raw: undeveloped

fortitude: strength of mind; determination

spurred: urged on; encouraged

option: choice

panorama: wide-angle view of a landscape or scene

curt: to the point; blunt

---

1. Which word describes the view you would get from the top of a mountain?

_____

2. Which quality would a woman show if she refused to let her poverty get the better of her?

_____

3. Which word could describe a man who makes brief, almost rude comments?

_____

4. Which word could describe a cross-country hike in which you had to sleep on the ground and try to swim across raging rivers?

_____

5. Which word would describe what you do if you spend half an hour closely studying every element of a map?

_____

1   On Sunday afternoons here, if you're tired of taking walks in the country and fighting off the green-bellied hogflies, your next best choice is thumbing magazines at the downtown drugstore. One Sunday not long ago, when I ran out of anything else to thumb, I started looking through one of those magazines geared toward helping new writers achieve success. I used to pore over them a lot when I was a teen-ager, and the first thing I noticed now was that the ads haven't changed much over the past fifteen years:

2   "IMAGINE MAKING $5,000 A YEAR WRITING IN YOUR SPARE TIME! Fantastic? Not at all…. Hundreds of People Make That Much or More Every Year—and Have Fun Doing It!"

3   "TO PEOPLE WHO WANT TO WRITE FOR PROFIT BUT CAN'T GET STARTED. Have You Natural Writing Ability? Now a Chance to Test Yourself—FREE!"

4   "I FIRE WRITERS… with enthusiasm for developing God-given talent. You'll 'get fired' too with my 48-lesson home study course. Over-the-shoulder coaching… personalized critiques! Amazing sales opportunity the first week. Write for my FREE STARTER KIT."

5   The ad that struck me the most showed a picture of a handsome and darkly serious young man sitting on a hill, picking his teeth with a weed, and gazing out over the countryside. The caption read: DO YOU HAVE THE "FAULTS" THAT COULD MEAN YOU WERE MEANT TO BE A WRITER? The ad went on to list the outstanding characteristics of writers. They are dreamers, loners, bookworms. They are too impractical, too intense, too idealistic.

6   When I was fourteen and had just started trying to write, I saw an ad much like this and was overwhelmed by it. That fellow on the hill was just like me, I thought. It was a tremendous feeling to discover that I might not be alone—that there was a whole society of loners and dreamers, that they were called writers, and that by sending off for a free writing IQ test I could find out by return mail if I qualified to climb the hill and chew straw with them.

7   I took that test and blew the top off it. The writing school said I demonstrated a rare creative potential unlike anything they had seen in years. They did wonder, though, if I had what it took to stick with them through long months of arduous training to develop my raw talent. If I really did have that kind of fortitude, the next step would be to send in some actual samples of my writing.

8   Spurred, I sent off everything I had ever written—two stories of about 200 words each. One was about some unidentified creatures who lived in dread of an unidentified monster who came around every week or so to slaughter as many of them as he could. Some of the persecuted creatures had the option of running, hopping, scurrying, or crawling to safety, but the others, for some unexplained reason, couldn't move and had just to stand there and take it. There was a description of the monster's roaring approach. Then the last line hit the reader like a left hook: "The lawn mower ran swiftly over…"

9   The other story I have preserved these many years:

THE RACE

10   Two gleaming hot rods stand side by side, poised and tensed—eager to scream down the hot asphalt track, each secretly confident that he will be the supreme victor. The time is drawing close now; in just a few minutes the race will be on.

11   There is a last minute check of both cars… everything is ready. A yell rings out for everyone to clear the track. The flagman raises the starting flag above his head, pauses for a second, and with a downward thrust of the flag, he sends the cars leaping forward with frightening speed.

12   They fly down the track, side by side, neither able to take the lead. They are gaining speed with every second. Faster and faster they go, approaching the half-way mark with incredible momentum….

13   Wait! Something is wrong—one of the cars is going out of control and skidding toward the other car! The rending sound of ripping metal and sliding tires cuts through the air as the two autos collide and spin crazily off the track.

14   For a moment the tragic panorama is hidden by a self-made curtain of dust, but it isn't a second before the curtain is pulled away by the wind, revealing the horrible sight. There are the two hot rods, one turned over, both broken and smashed. All is quiet….

15   Two small children, a boy and a girl, get up from the curb where they have been sitting. They eye each other accusingly as they walk slowly across the street where the two broken toy cars lay silent…. "Woman driver," grumbles the little boy.

The End

16 The correspondence school's copy desk quickly replied that the writing samples confirmed my aptitude test results and that they looked forward to working with me to the point of publication and beyond. I couldn't imag-

"The writing school said I demonstrated a rare creative potential."

ine what could be beyond publication but finally figured out they meant to handle my work later as agent-representative. They praised my choice of subject matter, sense of drama, and powerful surprise endings—all of which they said indicated I could sell to the sci-fi market. This made sense, because science fiction was all I had ever read voluntarily except for *Comic Classics* and, as a child, *Uncle Wiggily*. The school was particularly impressed by my style, which they said was practically poetry, in places. They made reference to my use of alliteration ("rending sound of ripping metal") and of metaphor ("self-made curtain of dust...pulled away by the wind").

17 They were quick to make clear, however, that what I had here were only germs of stories. They needed to be expanded to publishable lengths and had to have better character development—particularly the one about the bugs and grass being slaughtered by the lawn mower. They said a good writer could give even an insect an interesting personality.

18 The next step was to send them $10 for each of the two stories—the standard fee for detailed, over-the-shoulder copy-desk criticism. Then after these stories had been redone and rushed off for publication, I should enroll in their thirty-six-lesson course, in which I would be taught the ins and outs of plotting, characterization, point of view, theme, tone, and setting. The fee was $10 a lesson, and after my successful completion of the course they would then handle my literary properties, protect my legal rights, etc., for the regular 10 per cent.

19 At this point I began to wonder if I might be going in over my head. I was getting only a dollar a week from my folks and didn't understand half of what the writing school was talking about. In English class I had heard of such terms as "alliteration," "tone," and "point of view" but had no clear idea what they meant. Also I felt like an imposter. I had given my age as twenty-one. Of course, I was strutting because at fourteen I was doing better than anybody they had worked with in years, but I wondered if I could keep it up. "Rending sound of ripping metal" was genius, but could I crank out lines like that on a daily basis? I decided to try.

20 First I wrote them that I was a little short of cash this month and asked if, just to get started, it would be all right to work on one story for $10 instead of two for $20. They replied that that would be fine—just send in the ten bucks so they could get rolling.

21 Meanwhile I hadn't been able to get even that much money together. I approached my family and was turned down flat because my father thought there was something unhealthy about people who wanted to write. He was bothered by the school's remark that my writing was like poetry. "If you were a girl, it might be different," he said, and showed me a copy of *Men's Adventure*. "Look here, why don't you get one of these two ninety-eight worm ranches? Or one of these small-game boomerangs?"

22 After a few days of trying to drum up work around the neighborhood, I realized I wasn't going to be able to pull it off and decided just not to write back. But in a week I got a <u>curt</u> note saying they wanted to help me, were trying to be patient, but I was going to have to be more responsible. They said that writing was 1 per cent inspiration and 99 per cent perspiration and wondered if in my case the figures might be reversed.

23 This both goaded and scared me. I wrote back that on account of unexplained medical expenses I

could afford to give them only $5 at first. Could they possibly let me have a cut rate? They replied that it was strictly against their policy, but in view of my undeniably vast potential the copy-desk team had voted to go along with me just this once—send the $5.

24   By mowing lawns and selling bottles, I had by this time scraped together $3, but there my earning potential dropped sharply. Another week went by, and I made only 48 cents more. Then a letter arrived stamped in red, front and back: URGENT! IMPORTANT! DO NOT DISCARD! It said I had violated an agreement based on mutual trust and had exactly twenty-four hours to send in the $5. Without exactly spelling it out, they gave the impression that legal action might be taken. The letter ended: "Frankly, Mr. Allen, we're about at our wits' end with you."

25   I was hurt as well as shaken. I felt that I just didn't have what it takes. If there ever had been a chance of my climbing that hill and sitting with that elite group of loners and dreamers, it was gone now. I had my mother write them that I had suddenly been struck down with polio and was unable even to write my name, much less take their course. I hung onto the little money I had in case I had to give it to them to avoid a lawsuit, but I didn't hear from them after that. In a few weeks I relaxed and mailed off for the $2.98 worm ranch.

Starting Time	
Finishing Time	
Reading Time	
Reading Rate	

COMPREHENSION

Read the following questions and statements. For each one, put an X in the box before the option that contains the most complete or accurate answer.

1. When he became desperate, the author asked his mother to
   - ☐ a. loan him $5.
   - ☐ b. write a letter to the school.
   - ☐ c. help him complete a story.
   - ☐ d. buy him a worm ranch.

2. The author feared the school would
   - ☐ a. take legal action against him.
   - ☐ b. close before he completed his course.
   - ☐ c. not accept him into their 36-lesson course.
   - ☐ d. decide he had no talent as a writer.

3. The school refused to provide detailed criticism of the author's story until he
   - ☐ a. sent them some money.
   - ☐ b. offered proof that he was 21.
   - ☐ c. agreed to enroll in a 36-lesson course.
   - ☐ d. demonstrated a real desire to improve his writing skills.

4. The selection is critical of
   - ☐ a. raw talent.
   - ☐ b. young writers.
   - ☐ c. correspondence schools.
   - ☐ d. business schools.

5. The magazine ads were designed to appeal to the
   - ☐ a. inexperienced.   ☐ c. wealthy.
   - ☐ b. talented.   ☐ d. educated.

6. The strategy of the correspondence school illustrates which of the following?
   - ☐ a. A satisfied customer always returns.
   - ☐ b. To succeed, one should seem a fool but be wise.
   - ☐ c. Talent is only a starting point.
   - ☐ d. A sucker is born every minute.

7. The writing school was quick to recognize
   - ☐ a. a person with rare talent.
   - ☐ b. an overtrustful person.
   - ☐ c. an applicant with little potential.
   - ☐ d. a candidate unwilling to work.

8. As the time passed, the tone of the letters sent by the writing school changed from
   - ☐ a. doubtful to excited.
   - ☐ b. surprised to uninterested.
   - ☐ c. promising to threatening.
   - ☐ d. cheerful to discouraging.

9. At age fourteen, the author felt that he was
   - ☐ a. an idler and a drifter.
   - ☐ b. a loner and a dreamer.
   - ☐ c. misunderstood.
   - ☐ d. superior.

10. In view of the author's age, the stories he submitted were
    - ☐ a. good.
    - ☐ b. fantastic.
    - ☐ c. unusual
    - ☐ d. typical.

Comprehension Skills Key

1. recalling specific facts
2. retaining concepts
3. organizing facts
4. understanding the main idea
5. drawing a conclusion
6. making a judgment
7. making an inference
8. recognizing tone
9. understanding characters
10. appreciating literary forms

VOCABULARY—PART TWO

Write the word that makes the most sense in each sentence.

geared	critiques
arduous	raw
option	

1. The boy sent a writing sample to a company and received _____ of his work from their experts.

2. They said that while he was not a polished writer, he displayed a lot of _____ talent.

3. They pointed out that he had the _____ of either developing this talent or letting it go to waste.

4. Their course, they pointed out, was _____ to help young writers just like him.

5. Learning to write could be _____ , but they knew he was up to the challenge.

fortitude   spurred
pore   panorama
curt

6. The boy was _____ by the encouraging words of the experts.

7. He climbed a hill near his home to view the _____ he had described.

8. He vowed to develop the _____ to succeed at his challenging goal.

9. He vowed to _____ over every comment the critics made.

10. He would have only _____ answers for anyone who tried to distract him.

Comprehension   [   ]

Vocabulary   [   ]

UNDERSTANDING THROUGH WRITING

What kind of people are ads like the one in this story meant to appeal to? Have you ever answered a similar ad yourself? Write your opinion of these ads.

_____

_____

_____

_____

_____

_____

_____

_____

_____

BUILDING STUDY SKILLS

Read the following passage and answer the questions that follow it.

Skimming for Facts

Skimming is a skill—it is not careless reading. Skimming is often done with study-type matter in which the student wishes to locate certain facts. Actually this is a reference skill—skimming through a chapter or lesson to see if a particular topic is discussed or covered. When the student finds what he or she is looking for, other reading and study techniques can then be used. Skimming is a more thorough kind of previewing.

When skimming for facts, here is how to proceed.

1. Read the Title. This may tell you if the subject might include the information you need.

2. Read the Subhead. Be alert for a word pertaining to your topic. See if the author announces a category or classification that might include it.

3. Study the Illustration. Look for graphic information relating to what you are seeking.

4. Read First Sentences. Look for paragraphs that contain information and definitions. These are the ones most likely to contain factual data. Skim through these looking for your topic. Paragraphs of introduction may tell you that what you are seeking is coming next. Paragraphs of illustration will probably not contain factual data—these may be glossed over or skipped entirely. The closing paragraph is not likely to help, either.

1. Skimming is a skill—it is not _____ reading.

2. One kind of material that permits the reader to skim is _____ matter in which the student locates certain facts.

3. Reading the _____ may tell you if the subject contains information that you need.

4. Look for paragraphs that contain information and _____ .

5. If you were skimming "A Whole Society of Loners and Dreamers," you might stop to look at the sentences that stand out—the ones printed in _____ .

10

The Excellence of Welby Stitch Jr.

Russell Baker

READING PURPOSE—
In the following selection a young man is recommended as a candidate for Harvard based on certain strong points in his character. Read to find out what those fine points are.

VOCABULARY—PART ONE

All of these words are in the selection you are about to read. Study each word and its meaning. Then answer the questions below. As you read the selection, notice how each vocabulary word is used.

perjury: lying, especially when under oath

impeccable: flawless; excellent

eminence: prominence; glory

maimed: injured; destroyed

pliable: easily bendable

neurosis: less severe type of mental disorder

arrogant: excessively proud and self-important

pedagogy: teaching

tenure: permanent teaching position at a school or university

inflict: cause to suffer

---

1. Which word describes a crime that people are sometimes sent to jail for?

2. Which word would describe a soft metal pipe that with little effort you bent in half?

3. Which word could describe the condition of a horse whose leg has been broken?

4. Which word could describe a person who thinks she knows everything?

5. Which word could describe an ice-skating performance that didn't contain even one mistake?

Dear Harvard,

1   Welby Stitch Jr., age seventeen, of 174 Hemlock Terrace, has asked me to write you a letter of recommendation supporting his application for admission to your college next fall. No one else, it seems, is willing to recommend Welby, which just goes to show how few people recognize excellence when they see it.

2   I am not going to resort to the usual <u>perjury</u>, which you probably expect in letters of recommendation, and tell you that Welby's mastery of Greek irregular verbs, <u>impeccable</u> table manners and singular dedication to extracurricular activities mark him for a future of dazzling <u>eminence</u>. Welby's peculiar excellences are so rare among today's college applicants that it would be criminal not to tell you quite candidly about them.

3   Frankly, about Greek verbs Welby knows from nothing. Even his English verbs tend to buckle under the pressure of formal composition. A glance at his academic record—monotonous battalions of Cs, broken here and there by a forlorn D—will give you a clear idea of how Welby feels about verbs, as well as quadratic equations, the laws of thermodynamics and "The Scarlet Letter."

4   It is clear enough from the record that Welby has protected himself with great cunning against tyrants who tried to litter his mind with the sort of knowledge most adults spend years struggling to forget. Thanks to his successful resistance, he brings you the finest gift it is possible to present to a university—a pure mind, unused, untouched and unscarred by the educational production line. A mind ripe for wakening.

5   This is not all. You should note particularly Welby's extraordinarily healthy lack of interest in extracurricular activities. Through twelve long years of schooling, he has never joined the stamp club, never <u>maimed</u> fact or taste for the school newspaper, never tormented his elders by taking part in "The Desert Song" on the school stage, never ranted through megaphones to packed grandstands.

6   After school one day I ran into him as he was about to enter a burlesque house. "Welby," I asked him, "why don't you spend your afternoons at the high-school government club learning Robert's Rules of Order? You know how Harvard likes its applicants to show an early interest in public life."

7   "To do that," Welby explained, "I'd have to take time out from my education," and he went into the burlesque house to observe, if memory serves me, Ima Peach perform an ancient dance.

8   Despite many obstacles placed in his way by schools, Welby has achieved a well-rounded education. Aside from familiarity with ancient dance, he has become expert in the care of tropical fish and has assisted competently at the birth of three litters of cats. He drives with confidence, spends with ease and does a devastating imitation of his father throwing a scene at the dinner table.

9   Welby has learned something more valuable than the distinction between the indicative and subjunctive moods (of which he is totally unaware). He has learned that it is ridiculous to decide at seventeen what he will do when he becomes an adult.

10   "When I'm forty years old," he asked me recently, "why should I have to spend my days sitting around courtrooms because some kid decided at the age of seventeen that I'd have to be a lawyer?"

11   I mention this, Harvard, only because if you ask him what he plans to do with his life he is likely to tell you he wants to be a Beatle. Do not assume that he is being juvenile. This is merely Welby's polite way—he is exceedingly polite to old people—of reminding you that people who ask juvenile questions usually get juvenile answers.

12   Of all Welby's excellences, the most commendable is his indifference to proving his excellence. "If you want to get into Harvard, Welby," his father told him at the age of six, "you'll have to get straight A's for the rest of your life."

13   Young and <u>pliable</u>, Welby pursued A's for a few weeks. Then he observed that many of his fellow first-graders were pursuing A's with such intensity that they were coming down with gastric ulcers. And he saw others being led away for psychiatric treatment. After that, Welby never pursued an A again.

14   "The way I look at it," he told me recently, "if I make a big deal out of proving my excellence in order to get into Harvard, I'll either be a physical wreck or a very unpleasant person by the time I get there, and I won't enjoy it."

15   Today, at seventeen, Welby is a fine physical specimen, notably free of <u>neurosis</u>. He is full of good humor, gentle intentions, affection for life,

and indulgence for his less fortunate schoolmates who have shattered duodenum[1] and psyche in the pursuit of A's. He is capable of feeling humble about not understanding the subjunctive mood. If he did understand it, however, he would be incapable of feeling <u>arrogant</u> about the accomplishment.

"Welby's peculiar excellences are so rare among today's college applicants that it would be criminal not to tell you quite candidly about them."

16   Can Harvard fulfill its obligation to the nation if it denies Welby the privilege of higher education and consigns him, instead, to feed cannon? I think not. Consider, Harvard, the contributions that Welby will almost certainly make to humanity.

17   Indifferent to <u>pedagogy</u>, he will never take up scholarship and start producing those incredibly dreary scholastic books written to win professional <u>tenure</u>. With Welby Stitch Jr., Harvard will lighten humanity's burdens by at least six unnecessary books.

18   Indifferent to the flaunting of excellence, Welby will surely never enter politics. And so, with Welby, Harvard will assure itself of at least one graduate who can be relied upon not to visit yet more taxes and wars upon mankind.

19   Welby's admirable lack of brilliance makes it certain that he will make immense contributions to human happiness by never becoming a Wall Street lawyer, an advertising executive, a Secretary of State or a world-renowned psychiatrist.

20   Welby's absolute incompetence at science argues its own case. Thanks to Welby, Harvard will produce at least one graduate who can be counted upon to make life better by never building a bigger computer or synthesizing a deadlier nerve gas.

21   Not accept Welby Stitch Jr.? Harvard cannot refuse him. In years to come when his class

reunites at Cambridge, Harvard will feel mighty bad as the old grads get up one by one and boast that it was Harvard that made it possible for them to <u>inflict</u> unreadable books, taxes, wars, lawsuits, bigger computers and deadlier nerve gas upon humanity.

22   On that grim day, Harvard will feel proud of itself when, at last, Welby's turn comes to speak, and he rises, and says, "I guess I'm the only fellow here who hasn't made the world just a little more unbearable. I might have, with proper encouragement, but thanks to Harvard I learned early that there's a place in life for everybody, even for a few who refuse to do their worst."

Sincerely yours,
WELBY STITCH SR.

Starting Time	
Finishing Time	
Reading Time	
Reading Rate	

---

[1] *duodenum*: organ just below the stomach

COMPREHENSION

Read the following questions and statements. For each one, put an X in the box before the option that contains the most complete or accurate answer.

1. The writer of the letter wants Welby Stitch Jr. to go to
   - ☐ a. Harvard.
   - ☐ b. Princeton.
   - ☐ c. Yale.
   - ☐ d. the University of Illinois.

2. The letter seems to be critical of
   - ☐ a. lazy students.
   - ☐ b. people who try too hard to get into good schools.
   - ☐ c. alumni of Princeton and Yale.
   - ☐ d. newspaper columnists.

3. The purpose of the letter writer is to
   - ☐ a. describe.
   - ☐ b. tell a story.
   - ☐ c. persuade.
   - ☐ d. explain.

4. The writer of the letter seems to agree with the following statement:
   - ☐ a. A little knowledge is a dangerous thing.
   - ☐ b. Young people shouldn't clutter their minds with unnecessary learning.
   - ☐ c. Going to college is not necessary in this day and age.
   - ☐ d. Why put off until tomorrow what you can do today?

5. Becoming a lawyer or a college professor is
   - ☐ a. not what Welby Stitch Sr. wants for his son.
   - ☐ b. better, according to Welby Stitch Sr., than becoming a psychiatrist.
   - ☐ c. what Welby Stitch Jr. is thinking of doing.
   - ☐ d. what Welby Stitch Sr. thought of doing when he was in college.

6. A father might seriously consider writing a letter like this if he
   - ☐ a. knew the president of the university.
   - ☐ b. knew that his son was doing the best he could in high school.
   - ☐ c. had the money to send his son to any college.
   - ☐ d. was trying desperately to make his son look good.

7. Russell Baker probably
   - ☐ a. agrees with some of the points that the letter writer makes.
   - ☐ b. totally disagrees with the letter writer's ideas.
   - ☐ c. wrote this letter to help a friend's son get into college.
   - ☐ d. thinks too much value is placed on the need for a college education.

8. The tone of this letter is
   - ☐ a. serious.
   - ☐ b. angry.
   - ☐ c. humorous.
   - ☐ d. sad.

9. As portrayed in this letter, Welby Stitch Jr. is
   - ☐ a. a serious student who just doesn't learn well.
   - ☐ b. a show-off eager to take advantage of his father's money.
   - ☐ c. very popular with his female classmates.
   - ☐ d. a pleasant, easygoing fellow.

10. The line in paragraph 5 about "rant[ing] through megaphones to packed grandstands" is a reference to
    - ☐ a. football players.
    - ☐ b. cheerleaders.
    - ☐ c. baton twirlers.
    - ☐ d. alumni at homecoming games.

Comprehension Skills Key

1. recalling specific facts
2. retaining concepts
3. organizing facts
4. understanding the main idea
5. drawing a conclusion
6. making a judgment
7. making an inference
8. recognizing tone
9. understanding characters
10. appreciating literary forms

VOCABULARY—PART TWO

Write the word that makes the most sense in each sentence.

impeccable   **eminence**
pliable   **neurosis**
perjury

1. My son is a humble fellow who will never go out of his way to seek _____ .

2. His personality is _____ rather than rigid.

3. His manners are _____ : he always does the correct thing in social situations.

4. He would never commit _____ , for he is always truthful and honest.

5. He suffers from no _____ that makes him strange or unacceptable to other people.

maimed   **tenure**
inflict   **arrogant**
pedagogy

6. By contrast, a professor with _____ does not have to seek work in the real world.

7. He is concerned more with _____ than with his students' feelings.

8. He can _____ severe mental anguish on a boy like my son.

9. My son does *not* need a(n) _____ instructor who thinks he knows everything.

10. My boy can be _____ for life dealing with such insensitive people.

Comprehension ☐

Vocabulary ☐

UNDERSTANDING THROUGH WRITING

Pretend that you are the admissions officer who received this letter from Welby Stitch Sr. Write a letter back, explaining why you have or have not accepted Welby Stitch Jr. as a student. Use information from the letter to support what you say.

_____

_____

_____

_____

_____

_____

_____

_____

_____

_____

_____

_____

_____

BUILDING STUDY SKILLS

Read the following passage and answer the questions that follow it.

Dynamic Skimming

One type of high speed skimming can be labeled dynamic skimming. The label *dynamic* is appropriate because of the impressive results this kind of skimming yields at such high speeds. The steps to dynamic skimming are these.

1. Preview. As you no doubt have begun to realize, previewing is necessary in any kind of reading. In dynamic skimming, previewing is more essential than ever. Before skimming, the reader must perform a thorough and comprehensive preview of the entire article. The steps to previewing do not change. It's just that more time is spent on previewing to form a clear mental outline of the article for skimming.

2. Skim. This time let your eyes flow down the column of print, snatching ideas on the run. Do not stop to read—do not pause to reflect. Strive to let the words trigger your thinking as you skim by.

This kind of skimming is difficult at first because most people are in the habit of reading line by line. To overcome this natural tendency, use your finger as a pacer to force your eyes down the page. You may wish to move your finger in a zigzag fashion, letting the eyes fixate (stop and read) twice on each line. Gradually speed up until you are able to cover the page in 10 or 12 seconds.

3. Reread. This is the third step to dynamic skimming. Rereading is done like previewing, attempting to fill any gaps in your understanding of the article.

To be successful, you must have easy material and perform each of the three steps: preview, skim, and reread.

1. High-speed skimming is called

   _____ skimming.

2. _____ , the first step, is necessary

   for reading of any kind.

3. While skimming, the second step, your eyes flow

   down the column of print, snatching

   _____ on the run.

4. Following these steps with Baker's selection

   would have revealed that it includes several direct

   _____ from both father and son.

5. Through _____ , the third step,

   you would have learned something of the father's

   opinion of his son.

TOPIC REVIEW

React to Topic 2

Respond to one or more of these questions as your instructor directs.

1. The characters of Malcolm X and Welby Stitch Jr. are different in many ways. Review the selections in which they appear, and then make a list of at least three differences between them.

_____

_____

_____

_____

_____

2. Mitch Albom in "A Beloved Professor's Last Lessons" and William Allen in "A Whole Society of Loners and Dreamers" had very different relationships with their instructors. Go through each selection and make a list of three differences. Then write a short paper contrasting the two situations.

_____

_____

_____

_____

_____

3. In Building Study Skills 10 you learned a technique called dynamic skimming. After reviewing the technique, practice it on either selection 11, 12, or 13. Apply only the first two steps of the technique at this time. Then write a brief statement of what you think the selection will be about. Later, when you actually study the selection, compare its contents with what you wrote about it in this activity.

_____

_____

_____

_____

_____

4. Diagram a setting from either "Field Trip" or "The Autobiography of Malcolm X." For "Field Trip" you will probably want to diagram the room where the accident occurred. For the Malcolm X selection, you might choose the cell block or perhaps the prison library. Use information from the selection but add to that information, using your own ideas. Label all important elements in your diagram.

_____

_____

_____

_____

_____

5. As "A Beloved Professor's Last Lessons" makes clear, many of the best lessons people learn in the course of their schooling have nothing to do with studying or academic subjects. Think of such a lesson that you learned while a student. It may have had to do with dealing with other people or finding out what the world is really like. Write a short explanation of what you learned and how you learned it.

_____

_____

_____

_____

_____

6. Assume that a movie is being made about the characters in either "Field Trip" or "The Excellence of Welby Stitch Jr." Choose one of the selections, and decide whom you would cast in the leading parts. For "Field Trip" you will want to cast the teacher, the woman who cut off her finger, and perhaps one of the children. For the Welby Stitch selection you should cast both Welby Sr. and Welby Jr. Write whom you chose to play each role and a brief explanation of why you chose that person.

_____

_____

_____

_____

_____

To travel hopefully is a better thing than to arrive.

—Robert Louis Stevenson (1850–1894)

YOU CAN'T GET THERE FROM HERE

11

Henry Ford's Fabulous Flivver

Irwin Ross

READING PURPOSE—
This selection describes the most popular car in the early days of automobiles. Read to find out what the car was like and why people liked it so much.

VOCABULARY—PART ONE

All of these words are in the selection you are about to read. Study each word and its meaning. Then answer the questions below. As you read the selection, notice how each vocabulary word is used.

obsolescent: outdated

wrought: brought about; made

prodigious: huge; immense

attributes: features; qualities

conceded: gave in to; accepted

placate: pacify; appease

depressed: pushed down on

disdained: refused with contempt; scorned

proliferated: spread widely

castigated: criticized; chastised

---

1. Which word could describe the action of a baby-sitter who feeds candy to a child to get her to stop crying?

   _____

2. Which word might describe a 30-foot wave on an ocean or sea?

   _____

3. Which word could describe a washing machine with a hand-fed wringing attachment on it?

   _____

4. Which word could describe what you did if you admitted your opponent at cards had beaten you?

   _____

5. Which word describes what a parent did when he spoke harshly to his children for misbehaving?

   _____

1   In this era of gaudy, expensive, annually <u>obso-lescent</u> automobiles, it is difficult to realize that an American once grew rich by manufacturing the same car in the same model for 19 years. And the same color for 11 of those years.

2   The man was Henry Ford and the car was his remarkable Model T.

3   It was an odd-looking contraption, seven feet tall from top to pavement, as ungraceful as a village pump, as eccentric as the village hermit. It went its way making a noise like the end of the world. But it <u>wrought</u> <u>prodigious</u> changes in our nation's living; it was a revolution on wheels.

4   The Model T Ford—more familiarly referred to as the "flivver," "Tin Lizzie," or the "Leaping Lena"—made its debut in 1908. By 1927, when he finally discontinued it, Henry Ford had produced more than 15 million Model Ts. This was as many cars as had been turned out by all other automobile companies put together.

5   Where Mr. Ford's competitors issued new models every year, the Model T remained largely unchanged. There were occasional improvements, but it kept its same strange, three-pedal floor-board (clutch pedal on the left; reverse pedal in the center; brake on the right). And it was an unvarying black. Thus the famous quote by Mr. Ford:

6   "A customer can have a car painted any color he wants, so long as it is black."

7   But black had a reason. In the beginning, the touring model was painted red or a silver gray called "French Gray" and trimmed in highly polished brass. Then in 1914, Henry Ford began making cars on a fast production line basis that kept the cost low. The only color that would dry fast enough to keep the line moving was black Japan enamel. It wasn't until 1926 and 1927, the last two years of production, that colors were again made available.

8   The Model T had other quaint characteristics. On the touring car there was no left-hand door—only the outline of one stamped into the metal. There was no water pump. When the engine overheated, you lifted the sides of the hood and folded them under. This, as one person described it, gave the car the "appearance of a hen with her wings akimbo." There was no gas gauge. To find out how much fuel you had, you got out of the car, removed the front seat, unscrewed the gas cap beneath it and thrust in a stick or a ruler.

9   The lights of the Model T operated, not on a battery, but on a magneto[1] (introduced after 1914), and glowed or faded according to the speed of the engine. If you became lost at night and stopped to get your bearings, you had to race your engine for enough light to read a sign or peer up the road ahead.

10   Starting a flivver was a massive test of patience, timing, and strength. You turned the ignition switch, jerked the spark down, shoved the accelerator up (in early models both were levers under the steering wheel), set the emergency brake, and walked resolutely to the front of the car. Pulling the choke wire which extended through the radiator, you grabbed the crank and gave it a hearty spin. If the engine caught, you raced back and jerked the accelerator down again before your snorting, quivering mount shook itself to pieces.

11   Yet with all its eccentricities, the Model T had three hugely endearing <u>attributes</u>. It was cheap (as low as $265 at one time). It was easy to drive. And it was durable. "She may not be pretty," flivver owners <u>conceded</u>, "but she gets you there and she brings you back."

12   A farmer wrote to the Ford factory that he had bought a secondhand Model T roadster two years old. He used it for 13 years as a farm truck, never had to overhaul it, put it in a repair shop only twice, and spent just $40 on mechanical upkeep.

13   Henry Ford was in the automobile business five years before he started producing the Model T. He had begun, logically, with the Model A, a two-cylinder car generating eight horsepower. He went from that to the four-cylinder Model B and on through the alphabet, although some of the models got no further than the drawing board.

14   Model K, when it came along, almost broke the infant Ford Motor Company. To <u>placate</u> stockholders who thought cars were only for the rich, Mr. Ford priced the Model K at $2,750—and had to sell every one at a loss.

15   This experience stiffened his determination to produce a cheap car. In due course, there emerged from his factory in the Highland Park suburb of Detroit, a Ford known as the Model T. As one student of the era has since observed, "That car had integrity. Perhaps nothing in it was beautiful—but nothing in it was false."

---

[1]*magneto:* small electric generator that uses a magnetic field to produce an electric current.

16 Standardized parts, mass-produced, were a prime reason for the cheapness of the Model T. You could buy a muffler for $2, a front fender for $6, a carburetor for $6. Model T parts were available almost every-where—including five-and-ten-cent stores.

17 But the marvel of the Model T was its planetary transmission. There was no gearshift to be jiggled until, with grinding and snarling, you slipped into gear. All you did was push the clutch pedal nearly to the floor, which put you in low gear, and gave her the gas. When you were hurtling along at 20 miles an hour, you released the clutch to go into high. For reverse, you <u>depressed</u> the center pedal. A young-ster could do it.

18 Attracted by their simplicity as well as their economy, people bought flivvers in droves. For a long time Mr. Ford couldn't make enough of them to supply the demand. From 1918 to 1923, although local Ford dealers advertised, Mr. Ford <u>disdained</u> to do so. He didn't have to.

19 And so the flivver <u>proliferated</u>. One wisecrack of the period was: "Two flies can manufacture 48,876,552,154 new flies in six months, but they haven't anything on two Ford factories." Model Ts rattled through the towns and cities and along the country roads. Farmers installed tractor wheels and did their plowing with Model Ts. They jacked up the rear end, removed a tire, attached a belt, and ran buzz saws, pumped water, churned butter, ground feed, and generated electricity. Railroads put flanged wheels on Model Ts and used them as inspection cars. Movie companies made Model Ts collapsible and used them in the Keystone Cop comedies.

20 In the wake of its popularity there sprang up a whole school of Model T humor:

21 "Why is a Ford like a bathtub?"

22 "You hate to be seen in one."

23 "Didja know that Ford's going to paint his cars yellow so they can be hung outside of grocery stores and sold in bunches like bananas?"

"Attracted by their simplicity as well as their economy, people bought flivvers in droves."

24 "Heard the one about the farmer? He stripped the tin roof off his barn, sent it to Ford, and got back a letter saying, "While your car was an exceptionally bad wreck, we will be able to complete repairs and return it by the end of the week!"

25 These Model T jokes grew so plentiful that ultimately they were anthologized into books.

26 Henry Ford told the stories himself and plainly recognized that Model T jokes—complimentary or otherwise—were fine free publicity. One of his own favorite stories concerned the time he was traveling in a Ford car, inspecting some Michigan lumber properties with several aides. They came onto a farmer who was having trouble with his automobile—a beaten-up Ford. Mr. Ford and his men stopped, went to work on the car and, after replacing some spark plugs, got it running again.

27 "How much do I owe you fellers?" asked the farmer.

28 "Nothing," said Henry Ford rolling down his sleeves.

29 The farmer looked at him dubiously. "Can't make you out," he puzzled. "You talk as if money didn't mean anything to you, but if you've got so much money, why are you running around in a Ford?"

30 Henry Ford did indeed make a lot of money out of the Model T. He became, in fact, one of the two or three wealthiest men in the world. Moreover, the Model T brought fantastic returns to his original stockholders before he bought them all out. In all, $28,000 was invested in the Ford Motor Company by 12 people, and in ten years they made back a quarter-billion.

31 Henry Ford <u>castigated</u> competitors who brought out new models every year. "It does not please us to have a buyer's car wear out or become obso-lete," he said. "We want the man who buys one of our products never to have to buy another."

32 But in the mid-1920s, the flivver began to encounter sales resistance. Other makes, with their gearshifts, accessories, lively colors, and annual

model changes, were catching the fancy of the public. Mr. Ford blamed the Model T's loss of popularity on almost everything except the Model T. He said that the dealers' "mental attitude" was bad. He said that the American people had "fallen under the spell of salesmanship." But at last, reluctantly, he agreed that the Model T had to give way to mechanical progress.

33 The whole nation waited in tingling suspense for news of the new Ford. When the new car appeared with stylish lines and in different colors, it made the front page of practically every newspaper in the United States. And with it came one final Ford joke: "Henry's made a lady out of Lizzie."

34 Not everyone greeted the changeover with great joy. When an elderly woman in New Jersey heard that the Model Ts were being discontinued, she bought seven of them and stored them away so she would have Model Ts for the rest of her life and never have to change.

35 On May 26, 1927, the 15 millionth Model T rolled off the assembly line. Shortly afterward production of the phenomenal flivvers stopped entirely. An era had ended.

Starting Time	
Finishing Time	
Reading Time	
Reading Rate	

COMPREHENSION

Read the following questions and statements. For each one, put an X in the box before the option that contains the most complete or accurate answer.

1. The first car Henry Ford built had
   - ☐ a. two cylinders.
   - ☐ b. four cylinders.
   - ☐ c. six cylinders.
   - ☐ d. eight cylinders.

2. The automobile
   - ☐ a. changed America's lifestyle.
   - ☐ b. was a hazard to livestock.
   - ☐ c. threatened the American economy.
   - ☐ d. was a familiar sight in the early days.

3. From 1918 to 1923, Henry Ford
   - ☐ a. experimented with different types of Model Ts.
   - ☐ b. lost millions with his Model K.
   - ☐ c. produced red and gray touring cars.
   - ☐ d. didn't bother to advertise his product.

4. The public in Mr. Ford's day appreciated
   - ☐ a. luxury and versatility.
   - ☐ b. speed and safety.
   - ☐ c. economy and durability.
   - ☐ d. style and color.

5. Owners and drivers of the Model T had to be
   - ☐ a. wealthy and educated.
   - ☐ b. influential.
   - ☐ c. patient and resourceful.
   - ☐ d. uncaring.

6. Henry Ford's early domination of the automotive industry resulted from
   - ☐ a. daring financial investments.
   - ☐ b. a proud family tradition.
   - ☐ c. questionable business techniques.
   - ☐ d. a successful formula.

7. In the early days of the automobile, Henry Ford was
   - ☐ a. the only producer of automobiles.
   - ☐ b. the controlling force in the stock market.
   - ☐ c. the main supporter of labor unions.
   - ☐ d. the major manufacturer of automobiles.

8. Henry Ford's statement that he didn't want his cars to become obsolete was
   - ☐ a. sarcastic.
   - ☐ b. ironic.
   - ☐ c. sincere.
   - ☐ d. sorrowful.

9. Henry Ford believed in giving consumers
   ☐ a. a host of options.
   ☐ b. an honest value.
   ☐ c. occasional gifts.
   ☐ d. detailed instructions.

10. The selection is written in the form of a
    ☐ a. conversation.
    ☐ b. short story.
    ☐ c. historical essay.
    ☐ d. narrative.

Comprehension Skills Key

1. recalling specific facts
2. retaining concepts
3. organizing facts
4. understanding the main idea
5. drawing a conclusion
6. making a judgment
7. making an inference
8. recognizing tone
9. understanding characters
10. appreciating literary forms

VOCABULARY—PART TWO

Write the word that makes the most sense in each sentence.

obsolescent   attributes
conceded   depressed
proliferated

1. Dad's grandfather hated to admit it, but he finally _____ that the Model T was his all-time favorite car.

2. According to him, its best _____ were its shape (square) and its color (black).

3. Some parts had to be pulled up to make the car work; others had to be _____ .

4. A flivver never became _____ : it barely changed from year to year.

5. So many people bought the car that it quickly _____ all over the country.

placate   castigated
prodigious   wrought
disdained

6. Great-grandfather finally had to replace his old Model T to _____ his hard-to-please wife.

7. Wanting a fancy car, she _____ the rattling, bumpy-riding flivver and called it a tin can.

8. In fact, she had _____ him when he first bought it, saying he had no taste at all.

9. Great-grandpa used to tell her, "You do a _____ amount of complaining for a sweet-looking little lady."

10. Her new car _____ a tremendous change in her riding comfort, but it never did improve her personality.

Comprehension   [   ]

Vocabulary   [   ]

UNDERSTANDING THROUGH WRITING

Put yourself in the position of someone buying a car—a Model T—for the first time. What are your feelings? Are you nervous, excited, or both? Write a short explanation of your feelings and why you feel as you do.

_____

_____

_____

_____

_____

_____

_____

_____

_____

_____

BUILDING STUDY SKILLS

Read the following passage and answer the questions that follow it.

Building Vocabulary

An academic curriculum incorporates many subjects, each of which is characterized by its own vocabulary of specialized terms. These terms must be understood if the subject is to be mastered.

All teachers, when evaluating and grading students, reward those who can express their understanding of key concepts and fundamental facts clearly and concisely. Students display this kind of understanding through their use of appropriate terminology. Thus, familiarity with the vocabulary of a subject opens the avenues of communication between student and instructor.

This is not to say that random flaunting of specialized terms will deceive instructors, but it stands to reason that as you acquire the vocabulary of a subject, you will also be accumulating fundamental knowledge in that field. This becomes the base on which new knowledge is acquired and assimilated during your regular study.

It is a fact that familiar material is more easily read and understood than new material. This explains why we all tend to read articles in our field of interest with ease; we already have the necessary background of information. And this also explains why we sometimes find new subjects dull and uninteresting. Learning the basic vocabulary of a subject gives us a foundation to build on and assures that our study of that field will be profitable.

1. The specialized vocabulary of a subject must be understood if the subject is to be

   _____ .

2. Knowledge of vocabulary enables a student to express his or her _____ of the key concepts of a subject.

3. Acquiring a specific vocabulary also adds to fundamental _____ in a particular field.

4. For example, if when reading paragraph 7 of Ross's article, you did not know what a _____ line is, you would not understand why using it kept the cost of making cars low.

5. And if you did not know that the word _____ in paragraph 19 meant "spread widely," you might not understand the wisecrack about the flies in that paragraph.

12

First Flight Across America

Ray Helminiak

READING PURPOSE—
In this selection the writer describes the effort it took to make the first transcontinental flight. Read to find out some of the things that made the flight difficult.

VOCABULARY—PART ONE

All of these words are in the selection you are about to read. Study each word and its meaning. Then answer the questions below. As you read the selection, notice how each vocabulary word is used.

garb: costume

infinitesimal: exceedingly small

rudimentary: basic; not fully developed

precluded: prevented

scion: heir; descendant

Pullman: sleeping car on a train

originated: began

flail: beat; thrash

capers: tricks

frenzied: wild; crazy

---

1. Which word might describe things that happen on Halloween night?

2. Which word could be an antonym for *ended*?

3. Which word names something you might find on Amtrak?

4. Which word could be used in describing the size of an atom?

5. Which word might describe a person so upset that he runs screaming through the streets?

1   Back in 1911, air travel wasn't too long on refinements.

2   In September of that year, an adventurous soul named Cal Rodgers made the first flight across America, in an aircraft called the *Vin Fiz*.

3   It wasn't easy, not at all like an airplane trip today.

4   First off, Rodgers sat outside in a maze of wires and braces, with two whirling propellers at his back. This necessitated his wearing a cap backwards, in the early flying tradition. Goggles, a leather coat, and cotton for his ears were also part of the aviator's <u>garb</u>.

5   The horsepower rating of the aircraft engine was an <u>infinitesimal</u> 35. There were no such things as windshields, arm rests, or instrument panels. Rodgers's only flying instrument was a string dangling before him. If it hung straight down, the plane was either on the ground or in a dead stall. In other positions, the string indicated with varying accuracy the degree of climb or descent, or a yawing[1] action to the right or left.

6   In spite of its <u>rudimentary</u> appearance—an open boxlike affair wired to 32-foot fabric-covered wings—the plane was the Wright brothers' latest design.

7   Smoking restrictions aboard the *Vin Fiz* were nonexistent, so Rodgers's stogie was his constant companion. Describing his journey later, Rodgers remarked, "I could light a cigar with ease at any stage of the flight."

8   The man had nerves of steel and lungs of leather.

9   He was certainly equal to the task of being the first man to span America by air. A 6'4", 190-pounder, he was from a long line of American heroes. His great-grandfather, Commodore Matthew Perry, opened Japan's doors to the world. A grand uncle, Oliver Hazard Perry, won the Battle of Lake Erie during the War of 1812. Rodgers's father, an Army officer, was killed before the boy was born.

10   A childhood attack of scarlet fever left Rodgers partially deaf and <u>precluded</u> the military career he had hoped for. But aviation offered the challenge and excitement that suited his temperament. He attended the Wright brothers' flying school and after 90 minutes of instruction was a qualified solo pilot.

11   Rodgers bought a Wright biplane for $5,000 and, at 32, began his flying career.

12   Rodgers entered aviation competition whenever possible and established an American flight endurance record of 3 hours, 42 minutes. At a flying meet in Chicago's Grant Park, Rodgers met J. Ogden Armour, the meat packing <u>scion</u>, who was then marketing a soft drink named Vin Fiz.

13   Armour was so impressed that he offered to back Rodgers in a cross-country flight. Such a feat would not only publicize Armour's grape-flavored drink but would also capture the $50,000 prize offered by publisher William Randolph Hearst for the first plane trip across America.

14   Hearst's only rule was the flight had to take no more than 30 days.

15   Rodgers accepted the challenge.

16   Armour guaranteed Rodgers $5 for every mile flown, and provided a special train to accompany him. The train consisted of a <u>Pullman</u>, a diner, several cars with spare parts, a complete machine shop, and a first aid center.

17   Passengers aboard the train included Rodgers's wife, his mother, and the Wright brothers' best mechanic. Since there were no navigational aids and few airports, Rodgers needed all the help he could get.

18   September 11—the magic day—arrived, and so did a huge crowd of well-wishers at Sheepshead Bay, New York, where the flight <u>originated</u>.

19   "Stand back or someone will be killed," Rodgers shouted as the chain-driven props began to <u>flail</u> the air. His concern was real. The plane had no throttle and the engine had only two speeds: off and wide open.

20   When Rodgers became airborne, he cut a few <u>capers</u> over Brooklyn at 800 feet. After dropping some leaflets advertising Vin Fiz, he headed west, sputtering along at 55 miles per hour, his top speed.

21   The days that followed saw a series of <u>frenzied</u> takeoffs and desperate landings, including a nose dive into a chicken coop.

22   There were endless delays for repairs, replacements, injuries, and a few visits to local cigar stores.

23   Getting lost was also a problem. Once, Rodgers followed the wrong railroad tracks and ended the day with a net advance of 15 miles.

24   A big hazard of the flight was the crowds gathering at Rodgers's advertised landings. At Middle-

---

[1]*yawing:* turning from a straight course by a motion around a plane's vertical axis

town, New York—his first controlled stop—9,000 people were waiting. About 500 autos were parked in a circle to mark a landing spot, but the crowd flooded into the area.

25 "I had to herd them up before they would clear a space," Rodgers said, "but I came down so easily I didn't even knock the ashes off my cigar."

"I am bound for Los Angeles and the Pacific Ocean.... I mean to get there."

alight and step from his machine, there came a sensation as if they had seen a messenger from Mars."

32 In Dallas, 7,500 people gathered at his landing. On November 1, he was in Tucson and a day later over California.

33 On November 5, he reached Los Angeles.

34 Though he had officially completed his journey, Rodgers insisted on flying all the way to the Pacific Ocean. He succeeded, but not without another serious crackup and a broken ankle. (Next day he remarked, "I hit the ground a mighty hard whack, but I'm going to finish the flight and finish it with that machine.")

26 Other crowds were less cooperative. When Rodgers made a forced landing near Scranton, Pennsylvania, he had a rough time saving his machine. "The crowd went crazy. There wasn't a name on my wings when I started, but in 10 minutes there wasn't an inch free from pencil marks…I nearly lost my temper when a man with a chisel tried to punch out his monogram."

27 Rodgers hoped to reach Chicago four days after his initial takeoff. But things didn't go right and it was 21 days and three mishaps before he saw the Windy City, where he displayed his plane at Grant Park.

28 At this late date, he knew he couldn't complete his flight within the 30-day period. The prize money was lost. There was no reason to continue—except the pure feat of conquering the United States by air, and Cal Rodgers rose to the occasion:

29 "I am bound for Los Angeles and the Pacific Ocean. Prize or no prize, that's where I'm going, and if canvas, steel, and wire together with a little brawn, tendons, and brain stick with me, I mean to get there."

30 He flew on to Kansas City where, according to the *Star*, he gave the populace "an aerial thrill the likes of which it had never experienced before. Rodgers was the first to fly over the city, and he did it with daring, along the Missouri River at 700 feet and buzzing the business district."

31 Next was Muskogee, Oklahoma, where the newspaper reported, "To those who saw Rodgers

35 When he finally taxied his *Vin Fiz* into the Pacific waters at Long Beach, Rodgers had logged 82 flying hours, and 69 landings.

36 The aircraft was in terrible shape. In fact, only the vertical rudder and a few struts[2] remained of the original *Vin Fiz*. The rest was scattered across the American landscape: a wheel here, a wing there, wire everywhere. It had been rebuilt three times.

37 But, Cal Rodgers philosophized, "That's all part of the game."

38 Rodgers's crazy game—to publicize a soft drink—helped pave the way for modern transcontinental air travel.

39 And today, you'd be hard put to find anyone who's ever sipped a Vin Fiz…or even heard of it.

---

[2]struts: supporting braces

Starting Time	
Finishing Time	
Reading Time	
Reading Rate	

COMPREHENSION

Read the following questions and statements. For each one, put an X in the box before the option that contains the most complete or accurate answer.

1. Rodgers came from a family of
   - ☐ a. great wealth.
   - ☐ b. politicians.
   - ☐ c. pilots.
   - ☐ d. adventurers.

2. After Rodgers knew he had lost the prize money, his
   - ☐ a. ambition fizzled.
   - ☐ b. plane was destroyed.
   - ☐ c. determination intensified.
   - ☐ d. sponsor withdrew.

3. The flight to the Pacific took approximately
   - ☐ a. 30 days.
   - ☐ b. 40 days.
   - ☐ c. 50 days.
   - ☐ d. 70 days.

4. Rodgers's accomplishment
   - ☐ a. had no lasting value.
   - ☐ b. helped shape the future of aviation.
   - ☐ c. made him a legend in aviation history.
   - ☐ d. proved that planes had little commercial value.

5. It could be said of Rodgers that he
   - ☐ a. flew by the seat of his pants.
   - ☐ b. risked the lives of spectators.
   - ☐ c. observed the rules of safety.
   - ☐ d. relied on electronic equipment

6. The $50,000 prize offered by William Randolph Hearst most probably
   - ☐ a. damaged Hearst's publishing empire.
   - ☐ b. advanced the cause of flying.
   - ☐ c. alarmed the military establishment.
   - ☐ d. attracted no other entry.

7. The *Vin Fiz* caused a sensation everywhere because
   - ☐ a. Rodgers was well liked.
   - ☐ b. flying was a popular sport.
   - ☐ c. airplanes were expensive.
   - ☐ d. flying was a novelty.

8. Rodgers's statements reveal
   - ☐ a. an insensitive nature.
   - ☐ b. a high level of tension.
   - ☐ c. a scornful view of the world.
   - ☐ d. a devil-may-care attitude.

9. The word best describing Rodgers's personality is
   - ☐ a. unstable.
   - ☐ b. predictable.
   - ☐ c. greedy.
   - ☐ d. determined.

10. The opening sentence is an example of
    - ☐ a. an understatement.
    - ☐ b. an overstatement.
    - ☐ c. a metaphor.
    - ☐ d. a simile.

Comprehension Skills Key

1. recalling specific facts
2. retaining concepts
3. organizing facts
4. understanding the main idea
5. drawing a conclusion
6. making a judgment
7. making an inference
8. recognizing tone
9. understanding characters
10. appreciating literary forms

VOCABULARY—PART TWO

Write the word that makes the most sense in each sentence.

precluded   **Pullman**
originated   **scion**
rudimentary

1. The plane Rodgers flew in was very
   _____ ; it had few of the parts present on airplanes today.

2. The cockpit was so small that it
   _____ any additional persons from entering.

3. The flight was the brainchild of a wealthy
   _____ of the meat-packing industry.

4. The plan _____ as a way to sell a soft drink, but then it quickly developed into something more exciting.

5. Rodgers was followed on the ground by a train that even had a _____ car.

flail   **capers**
infinitesimal **garb**
frenzied

6. Excited, sometimes _____ crowds met Rodgers at almost every stop he made.

7. Sometimes he would perform midair _____ to delight and thrill them.

8. He might _____ around to make it appear he was going to crash.

9. Or he would skim along close to the ground, leaving a(n) _____ space between the plane and the hard earth.

10. Dressed in his fancy flying _____ , he must have greatly impressed the crowds.

Comprehension [   ]

Vocabulary [   ]

UNDERSTANDING THROUGH WRITING

Pretend you are Cal Rodgers. You have to convince J. Ogden Armour that you are the person he should choose to make the first transcontinental flight. Write a letter convincing him to select you. Use information from the story in making your case.

_____

_____

_____

_____

_____

_____

_____

_____

_____

_____

_____

BUILDING STUDY SKILLS

Read the following passage and answer the questions that follow it.

Specialized Word Lists, I

The two prime sources of words for your specialized lists are your instructors and your textbooks.

Listen during lectures for words the speaker repeats and emphasizes. These are likely candidates. Identifying key words will present no problem because experienced lecturers understand the limitations of their listeners. They know that major points need the emphasis of repeated exposure. What would be in bold print in a textbook must be conveyed to students verbally. Be alert to certain words that are stressed and repeated. These are considered important by the lecturer. Especially important terms are often written on the blackboard.

Listen to questions that the lecturer asks. Oral quizzing is often used to draw greater attention to important points under discussion.

Another clue to identifying important words and ideas may be found in the length of time devoted to discussion of a single topic. Important points deserve more time.

When you discover that a major term is being presented, try to record the exact definition or explanation given. Being a specialist, your instructor will use precise terminology when defining a concept. Be sure to capture new words exactly as they are used. Indicate with an asterisk or star in your notes that here is a word for your specialized list.

1. Two prime sources for specialized vocabulary lists are your _____ and your textbooks.

2. Experienced instructors make it easy to _____ key words.

3. Important words are stressed, _____ , and often written on the board.

4. Because he or she is a specialist, the instructor will use _____ terminology when defining a concept.

5. To help you understand the unsteady airplane movement described in paragraph 5 of "First Flight Across America," an instructor might make sure you knew the meaning of the technical term _____ .

13

British Eccentricity on Four Wheels

Kirk Kraeutler

READING PURPOSE—
The author of this article is given a unique driving experience. Read to find out what it is.

VOCABULARY—PART ONE

All of these words are in the selection you are about to read. Study each word and its meaning. Then answer the questions below. As you read the selection, notice how each vocabulary word is used.

venerable: worthy of respect because of age

inconceivable: unimaginable; unbelievable

ungainly: awkward; clumsy

bevy: group; collection

languorous: lazy-looking

joie de vivre: enjoyment of life

superfluous: unnecessary; excessive

fixated: intensely focused

smitten: hard hit by love

quintessential: being the most perfect example of something

---

1. Which word describes a coat that you no longer need because you got a new one?

   _____

2. Which word would describe a 14-year-old girl who spends all of her time talking to, or about, her new boyfriend?

   _____

3. Which word could describe the elderly company owner whom everyone thinks highly of because of his commitment to his employees?

   _____

4. Which word describes a person who trips every time he gets up?

   _____

5. Which word could describe an event that you never expected to happen?

   _____

1 I cannot say I wasn't warned. I was warned, and the warning went something like this: "The worst part of this weekend will be when you have to return the car. When you're driving a Morgan, you're somebody. The moment you hand over those keys, you're nobody again."

2 My friend and I were standing in central London in an alleyway in front of a small garage, one of the few places in England and perhaps the world where one can rent a Morgan, that venerable English sports car. As we surveyed the field, the whole idea seemed inconceivable. Not so much the renting of the thing, but the driving itself. Looking at them now, they seemed too beautiful, too delicate, too lilting and lovely to be taken out on the cruel roads of a modern nation, to be driven alongside boorish trucks and vans and ordinary passenger cars that, by comparison, suddenly seemed as ungainly as ox carts.

3 Morgans, I was informed, were still handmade. The original was a three-wheeler built early in the century. After that, the very classic design evolved and has not been substantially changed since the 1930s. Even now, the frame of the body is ash wood. Each is made to order, and only about 500 are turned out each year. To buy one, there is a five-year waiting list. But there they were, a small bevy of Morgans: red, silver, indigo, British racing green, canary yellow. With the long, languorous curves of the front fender sloping down into a kind of running board, they looked more like perfectly oversized Matchbox race cars than driveable automobiles. But you could drive them, and they were ours for the picking, for three days, at about $177 a day per car.

4 That weekend in February was my friend Colin's 30th birthday. As part of the celebration he had decided to rent a country house in Wales with a group of friends and supply them with four Morgans, a gesture as telling of his joie de vivre as his generosity. This was the start of the trip, and my first encounter with the car and English roads.

5 Something should be said right up front: I know nothing about cars. An automobile (actually, roadster is probably the proper term) this special could hardly be more wasted, except that I do love to drive. As the train of us pulled away from the garage and out through the city streets, I have to admit that I was not thinking of the engine's bore and stroke of 80.6-by-88 mm., or even its compression ratio of 10.0:1. All I was thinking was what I

repeated to myself softly (over the gentle purr of the exhaust system's cast manifold to stainless steel down pipe): "Keep to the left, keep to the left."

6 The nice man at the garage had given each of us a dutiful lecture on how to get the canvas top off and on, where to find the windshield wiper switch (where the turn signal usually was) and where to find the turn signal (you guessed it). At the time, I thought the tutorial was endearing in its British formality, but entirely superfluous. I was pretty much fixated on how to work a left-handed shift. (This was England, remember—everything was on the wrong side of the car, not just the road.)

7 I followed Colin and the others back to his flat, a 10-minute drive that went off without a hitch and, more important, without a bump, dent or scratch. They went on to Wales that afternoon, about four hours straight west on the M-4 highway. I waited back in London for my traveling companion, navigator and co-pilot—that is, for my girlfriend, Radhika, who was to arrive directly from New York early the next day.

8 Once there, she immediately poured herself into the Morgan's single passenger seat. Having a navigator made things much easier. Suddenly, my intimidation melted away. Instead of heading directly to Wales, we stopped in Oxford along the way, got lost, and stopped in Oxford again. I quickly discovered one of the great hidden advantages of a Morgan: Even if you did drive like a lost tourist, your fellow drivers seemed that much more inclined toward forgiveness.

9 We took the scenic route west toward mid-Wales, along the M-40, and then a series of two-lane highways. Jet-lagged from an overnight flight, Radhika found the charm of the Morgan more in its looks than in its creature comforts. Once she was sure we were pointed in the right direction, she tried to get some sleep. After about a half-hour, she opened her eyes and made a simple, horrifying statement.

10 "I hate this car," she said. (I had been afraid of this.) "How much did this cost to rent?"

11 "Probably twice as much as a regular car," I said.

12 "You mean a regular car that you could sleep in, that had heat and where we wouldn't have to shout to hear each other?" It would grow on her, I assured myself, but she would need just a little more time.

13 As for me, by the time we arrived in Wales, I was already feeling comfortable enough to

acknowledge, unashamedly, my unfamiliarity with some of England's more peculiar road signs, and I asked Colin to spare some guidance. "What are those numbers inside the little red circle?" I asked.

14 "That's the speed limit," he said.

15 I explained that I thought they were road markers or something, because

"They seemed too beautiful, too delicate, too lilting and lovely to be taken out on the cruel roads of a modern nation."

the numbers always seemed far too small. I think he understood. This was, after all, the same man who later in the weekend would remark how much driving a Morgan was like playing a video game, only he had to keep reminding himself that he did not have three lives.

16 Driving up through the hills of Wales was beyond being beautiful and romantic, far more work than I had imagined. I began to understand what put the sport in sports car. The steering was so direct, you were forced to keep your eyes on the road constantly. It was also so heavy that, after working the car over the winding hills on a country road, my arms were exhausted from pulling the car around the turns while also climbing up and down through the gears.

17 It was not until we were driving back to London on Monday morning that things got serious. By now—although still too timid to get behind the wheel—Radhika was smitten, and suggested a little spin through the Cotswolds, the quintessential English countryside. Soon it became clear that we were not returning the car that day. I made a phone call late that afternoon that began: "Hi, my name is Kraeutler and I have one of your Morgans." I would make the same call twice more over the next three days, and it began to sound like a hostage-taking. There were also calls to the airline, postponing the flight home and gladly explaining the reason, even though no one had asked. "We've rented this car and can't take it back," Radhika told one friendly ticket agent. "It's really changed our lives."

18 We stayed two nights in Stratford-on-Avon, where a Shakespeare play seemed to be required viewing. I remember discussing whether it would be worth going if we couldn't drive to the theater, which was two blocks away. We toured the region's old sheep-trading towns, sped along narrow country lanes and drove past the wondrous quilt of farmland neatly sewn together by tree lines and hedgerows. We bundled up in hats and gloves and took the top down in 40-degree weather and lacy drizzle. I grew a beard. We were beginning to understand. The real mystique of the Morgan lay in its total impracticality, which by now seemed to inform every part of our lives.

19 Finally, the day came that we could put off no longer. As I (gulp) handed back the keys, Radhika and I tried to make the moment more bearable by discussing plans to ship a Morgan home. The nice man at the garage seemed perplexed, as though he couldn't quite figure out if we were serious or joking. But, then, neither could we.

20 Back on the streets, we tested our legs again, with a wobbliness more appropriate to passengers disembarking a boat. We walked through the city center in search of food, drink and solace, all our belongings in a knapsack that seemed to weigh more heavily on my shoulder than it had before. Then I reminded myself that I was someone, after all. I had Radhika, and we had the memory of having driven a Morgan.

Starting Time	
Finishing Time	
Reading Time	
Reading Rate	

COMPREHENSION

Read the following questions and statements. For each one, put an X in the box before the option that contains the most complete or accurate answer.

1. The author was to drive the car from London to
   ☐ a. Brighton. ☐ c. Wales.
   ☐ b. Scotland. ☐ d. Manchester.

2. The rental had been arranged
   ☐ a. as part of a birthday celebration.
   ☐ b. so the author and his girlfriend could have a special vacation.
   ☐ c. so the Morgan could be displayed in an antique car show.
   ☐ d. with one of the six London garages that handled such cars.

3. The author meets up with his girlfriend
   ☐ a. as soon as he arrives in London.
   ☐ b. just before he goes to get the car.
   ☐ c. the day after he picks up the car.
   ☐ d. when he arrives at his final destination.

4. The chief point the author makes in this article is
   ☐ a. how confusing it is to drive in England.
   ☐ b. that driving a Morgan grows on you.
   ☐ c. that a Morgan is a very uncomfortable car for long-distance traveling.
   ☐ d. that it's much easier traveling in a strange place if you have a navigator.

5. The author
   ☐ a. has never driven in England before.
   ☐ b. has driven before on English back roads, but never on main highways.
   ☐ c. feels comfortable in an English car because he is left-handed.
   ☐ d. would rather drive a regular car.

6. The author's friend Colin is
   ☐ a. an Australian. ☐ c. a race-car driver.
   ☐ b. a college student. ☐ d. rather wealthy.

7. Driving a Morgan requires
   ☐ a. joie de vivre.
   ☐ b. understanding of its compression ratio.
   ☐ c. skill and attentiveness.
   ☐ d. a special permit.

8. By the end of the story, the author's tone is
   ☐ a. bored. ☐ c. unconcerned.
   ☐ b. regretful. ☐ d. joyful.

9. The author may be described as a person who
   ☐ a. has always been a sports-car enthusiast.
   ☐ b. relies on his girlfriend's opinion when making a decision.
   ☐ c. would like to move permanently to England.
   ☐ d. likes to make the most of new opportunities.

10. When the author says "the wondrous quilt of farm-land neatly sewen together by tree lines," he is using
    ☐ a. personification. ☐ c. a metaphor.
    ☐ b. a simile. ☐ d. a literal comparison.

Comprehension Skills Key

1. recalling specific facts
2. retaining concepts
3. organizing facts
4. understanding the main idea
5. drawing a conclusion
6. making a judgment
7. making an inference
8. recognizing tone
9. understanding characters
10. appreciating literary forms

VOCABULARY—PART TWO

Write the word that makes the most sense in each sentence.

languorous **venerable**
fixated **inconceivable**
quintessential

1. The author had never imagined driving a Morgan; it was _____ .

2. The Morgan was not a new car, but age had made it particularly _____ .

3. The car may have looked _____ , but actually it had a lot of pep and power.

4. The author could not take his eyes off the car; he was _____ by its beauty.

5. It was the _____ sports car, the standard that all others could only strive for.

joie de vivre   **smitten**
superfluous   **ungainly**
bevy

6. At a local auto show a _____ of sports cars were on display.

7. Some were loaded with _____ gadgets that did nothing to improve performance.

8. Others looked too front-heavy and seemed as if they'd be _____ to drive.

9. If a person falls in love with a car, he may remain _____ for life.

10. Owning a sports car gives people a sense of _____ .

Comprehension [   ]

Vocabulary [   ]

UNDERSTANDING THROUGH WRITING

What kind of car would you like to drive if given the chance? Write a short description of your dream car.

_____

_____

_____

_____

_____

_____

_____

_____

BUILDING STUDY SKILLS

Read the following passage and answer the questions that follow it.

Specialized Word Lists, II

Another source of specialized terms is your textbook. Frequently a textbook chapter hinges on only five or six major concepts. Often there are key words associated with these concepts; these are the words to collect and learn.

Such words are often highlighted in bold print or included in headings. Refer to questions or summaries that frequently appear at the end of the chapter. These summaries will emphasize points the writer wants you to understand and remember.

When you have located the important terms for the unit you are studying, write them down with accompanying definitions and explanations. As you read through the chapter, try to understand these new words and the concepts they represent as fully as you can.

Frequently, the words you list will be the same ones that are emphasized in class. When this is the case, the instructor will often explain the new terms in words different from those in the text. Be alert to catch these variances because they enrich the meaning of an idea, often making it easier to understand.

1. Key words associated with _____ concepts are the words to learn.

2. Questions and _____ at the end of the chapter emphasize important points.

3. Write down important terms with accompanying _____ and explanations.

4. Instructors often add to the meaning of a word defined in the text, thereby _____ its significance.

5. For example, with the story about the Morgan, in addition to the meaning of "group; collection," the word _____ also refers to a flock of birds such as larks.

14

Why Not Bicycle to Work?

Robert Petersen

READING PURPOSE—
The author of this article explains why commuting by bicycle can be done in most kinds of weather. Read to learn the steps he takes to make cycling to work successful.

VOCABULARY—PART ONE

All of these words are in the selection you are about to read. Study each word and its meaning. Then answer the questions below. As you read the selection, notice how each vocabulary word is used.

proclaimed: declared publicly

hefty: substantial; considerable

notoriously: well known because of something bad

unruffled: calm

stability: ability to stand firmly

efficient: working without waste of time or energy

shoulder: edge of a road, usually unpaved

conspicuous: obvious; attracting attention

optimal: most favorable; best

panoply: impressive exhibit or array

---

1. Which word describes the personality of someone who never gets upset no matter how often she is interrupted?

_____

2. Which word could describe a house painter who works without wasting any effort?

_____

3. Which word describes what you are checking when you make sure a huge billboard won't blow over in the wind?

_____

4. Which word might describe a 40-pound box that you struggle to carry?

_____

5. Which word could tell what a company manager did when he made a general announcement about a big sale?

_____

1   Cycle to work? "An appealing idea, but impractical" may be your first reaction. But is it? I and many of my coworkers at the National Institute of Health (N.I.H.) in Washington, D.C., do just that. What's more, many of us do it four out of five days of the week. Recently the *Washington Post* newspaper even <u>proclaimed</u> the bicycle the new status symbol at N.I.H.! The benefits? Better health, real savings in commuting costs, and the added bonus of cycling regularly year round.

2   Let's examine how we do it and just how practical an idea it is. To begin with there's the question of distance. Just how far from work can you live and still use a bicycle as a means of commuting? I live five miles away and can make the trip comfortably in fifteen or twenty minutes. That includes several <u>hefty</u> hills and a few stoplights on the way. Up to ten miles away would still be well within the limits of reasonable commuting. And when you get there, there's no need to waste time trying to find a place to put the car or paying expensive parking fees. You can usually park in or near the building in which you work at no cost whatever.

3   What about the weather? In the Washington area summers are <u>notoriously</u> hot and humid. Winters, while they do not rival those of Maine or Minnesota, are still well below freezing part of the year. The solution? During the warmest part of the year, you are riding to work early in the day— before it's had a chance to warm up. I usually leave by about eight. By making maximum use of the wide range of gears of the modern lightweight bicycle it's possible to choose ratios that are minimally likely to overheat your personal radiator. I usually leave off my tie and suit jacket in warm weather, unbutton an extra button on my shirt, and can count on being sufficiently "air-conditioned" to arrive at work without needing a shower. Since I can shower after returning home, I often make the return trip a more active one. I place my tie in my suitjacket pocket and carefully fold the jacket inside out—as you might for packing it in a suitcase. I then place the jacket on the luggage carrier secured by an elastic band or so-called shock cord (this can easily be obtained from your local cycle dealer). As a result my jacket and tie arrive as <u>unruffled</u> as I do.

4   During the winter I generally wear a coat over my business suit. A car coat is of convenient length for cycling and yet formal enough for attending a business lunch. My particular coat comes equipped with a hood attached to the collar which provides extra warmth and yet folds out of sight when not needed. On the very coldest days I add a wool sweater or suit vest for additional warmth. Part of the secret of being comfortable when cycling in winter is in wearing a hat and gloves. As the army discovered in World War II, the use of a hat and gloves greatly reduces heat losses and adds greatly to your comfort in cold weather. The other part of the secret lies in using your bicycle's gear ratios wisely. While in summer I choose among my gears for minimal effort so as to avoid becoming overheated, in winter I make my choice so as to insure enough effort to keep me warm. Hard as it may be to believe until you've actually tried it, the effort of cycling even in cold weather will keep you comfortably warm. And unlike the closed-in, overheated feeling you get in an automobile in winter, you're breathing really fresh air.

5   The only time I skip cycling to work is when it's actually raining or snowing when I start out in the morning. I suppose by a careful choice of rain gear I might even be able to ride in the rain. I generally avoid snow and icy road conditions because of the reduced <u>stability</u> of two-wheeled vehicles under these conditions. Despite eliminating riding when it's raining, snowing, or icy, I've been able to use my bicycle to commute more than 80 percent of the time. Even in more severe climates it's possible to cycle for much of the year.

6   People frequently ask me about traffic problems in commuting by bicycle. But remember, by cycling to work you're combining business with pleasure. What is the most <u>efficient</u> route by car is not necessarily the most efficient or most pleasant by bicycle. You're frequently better off choosing those secondary streets or roads disdained by the motorist as too narrow or slow for him. But by contrast, you're likely to find them fine for riding and delightfully free of carbon-monoxide fumes. You may even discover you're able to observe the world around you in a way you never could traveling by car. Even when it's necessary to use a major thoroughfare for part of the distance, I've found that there is frequently a <u>shoulder</u> out of the mainstream of traffic which is perfect for cycling. Motorists generally seem to give cyclists a wide berth. Perhaps it's because they associate bikes with children, but even on streets without shoul-

ders, I've found that the typical motorist is usually considerate. He generally passes me with far more than enough room.

7   What type of bicycle is best for commuting? I myself now use a fifteen-speed touring model equipped with dropped handlebars and a generator set. Before that I used a ten-speed bike with higher gear ratios, but I found it too highly geared for cycling with minimal effort in summer. My present bicycle is the same one I use for recreational riding. I chose the dropped handlebars because they offer a wider choice of riding positions than do other handlebar shapes. Most prospective cyclists have visions of themselves contorted into a pretzel-like shape if they use dropped bars. But as more experienced riders know, the advantage of that type of handlebar is that it provides a wider choice of riding positions for greater comfort and efficiency. You can ride with your hands on the upper or middle portion of the bars—in a more or less upright position—or with hands on the lower part of the bar for extra power.

8   While fifteen-gear ratios are convenient for touring under heavy load, ten-gear ratios with a sufficiently wide range of choices are more than adequate for commuting.

9   I personally use toe clips on the pedals, since this makes for more efficient pedaling. By keeping the straps loose enough, there is plenty of room for even heavy dress shoes to enable you to remove your feet quickly from the pedals as needed.

10   The generator set is especially convenient in winter when it is usually dark by late afternoon. I used to have a battery-operated headlamp, but the generator eliminates worries over dead batteries. I also have a rear light and a large red reflector on the back of the bicycle. To be absolutely certain of being seen, you can even add an orange visibility vest over your outer clothing. If that seems a bit too <u>conspicuous</u>, the reflector, reflecting tape on the bicycle, and the headlamp make it pretty

"The biggest bonus of all, is the sheer pleasure of cycling regularly and feeling better for doing so."

difficult for any motorist to miss seeing you.

11   Because I often carry a briefcase to work, my bicycle has both front and rear luggage carriers, although one or the other would really be enough. Instead of a luggage carrier, a basket might be substituted with equal ease.

12   Another point sometimes brought up is any problems that might arise from riding in good clothing. Actually by wiping off excess oil from the chain drive and using fenders, this has never been a problem for me. Extra oil serves no useful purpose anyway, and lightweight fenders add very little to the weight of the bicycle.

13   Now that you're more than half convinced that cycling to work just might be practical after all, what are the health benefits? Dr. Kenneth Cooper, author of a best-selling book on physical fitness, *Aerobics,* highly recommends cycling as one of the best means of maintaining general fitness. By cycling as little as three miles to work and back at a pace just over fifteen miles per hour, it's possible to earn the thirty points a week Dr. Cooper suggests for <u>optimal</u> fitness. That level of fitness is, by the way, a higher level of physical well-being than Dr. Cooper found in nearly two-thirds of Air Force recruits—all men in their late teens or early twenties.

14   As for commuting costs, even if you figure as little as six cents per mile for operating the cheapest car, my ten miles of daily cycling save me at least 60 cents a day, $3 a week, or $150 a year. That's without taking into account extra auto-insurance costs, parking fees I don't pay, and other commuting expenses. In addition, using my bicycle for commuting has eliminated the need for a second car despite suburban living—a very substantial savings.

15   Last, but probably the biggest bonus of all, is the sheer pleasure of cycling regularly and feeling better for doing so. Perhaps I could discipline myself enough to exercise regularly, but bicycle commuting makes it a certainty. Cycling brings me

closer to the world around me in a way that driving never would. I watch the changing seasons and the small events en route to my office in a way I never could while driving. Whether it's the arrival of the first birds from the south in spring or the changing colors as summer turns into fall, I am a more relaxed observer, better able to enjoy the <u>panoply</u> of seasons. And after the accumulated tensions of the workday, what better way to unwind than by pedaling home dissipating your tensions as you go?

Starting Time	
Finishing Time	
Reading Time	
Reading Rate	

COMPREHENSION

Read the following questions and statements. For each one, put an X in the box before the option that contains the most complete or accurate answer.

1. The limit of a reasonable commuting distance is about
   - ☐ a. five miles.
   - ☐ b. eight miles.
   - ☐ c. ten miles.
   - ☐ d. twelve miles.

2. Cycling to work offers
   - ☐ a. a means of reducing highway accidents.
   - ☐ b. physical and financial benefits.
   - ☐ c. social and political advantages.
   - ☐ d. a practical solution to the crime rate.

3. Before setting out for a morning commute by bicycle, a person should
   - ☐ a. consider the weather.
   - ☐ b. notify his or her employer.
   - ☐ c. consult his or her doctor.
   - ☐ d. calculate how much money will be needed to make the trip.

4. The purpose of the selection is to
   - ☐ a. promote the manufacture and sale of bicycles.
   - ☐ b. convince the public to exercise on a regular basis.
   - ☐ c. encourage more people to cycle to work.
   - ☐ d. advertise the need for bicycle trails.

5. Most people who bicycle to work
   - ☐ a. do so for monetary reasons.
   - ☐ b. enjoy this particular form of commuting.
   - ☐ c. are careless about basic safety rules.
   - ☐ d. endure teasing by their coworkers.

6. The author's claim that in the summer he arrives at work without needing a shower seems
   - ☐ a. reasonable.
   - ☐ b. impossible.
   - ☐ c. questionable.
   - ☐ d. miraculous.

7. A one-speed bicycle would
   - ☐ a. be sufficient to meet the needs of most commuters.
   - ☐ b. cost too much money to justify its use as a commuting vehicle.
   - ☐ c. not offer enough options for a comfortable commute.
   - ☐ d. reduce the risk of cycling accidents.

8. The author's personal knowledge and experience gives the selection a tone of
   - ☐ a. bravado.
   - ☐ b. boredom.
   - ☐ c. repetition.
   - ☐ d. authority.

9. The author is a
   - ☐ a. modest person.
   - ☐ b. persuasive person.
   - ☐ c. reclusive person.
   - ☐ d. forgiving person.

10. The author tries to appeal to the reader's
    - ☐ a. poetic impulses.
    - ☐ b. common sense.
    - ☐ c. desire for dignity.
    - ☐ d. compassion.

Comprehension Skills Key

1. recalling specific facts
2. retaining concepts
3. organizing facts
4. understanding the main idea
5. drawing a conclusion
6. making a judgment
7. making an inference
8. recognizing tone
9. understanding characters
10. appreciating literary forms

VOCABULARY—PART TWO

Write the word that makes the most sense in each sentence.

unruffled   conspicuous
optimal   panoply
notoriously

1. The author claims that people can commute by bicycle even in places with _____ bad climates.

2. When it's hot out, the _____ time to ride is early in the morning.

3. You may get very warm going home, but your sweaty body won't be so _____ at that time of day.

4. Besides, you can ride through parks and gardens and witness nature's _____ of blooming things.

5. The scenery should be so calming that you arrive home totally _____ .

stability   efficient
shoulder   proclaimed
hefty

6. The most _____ route to work is the one that gets you there the fastest.

7. Some cyclists pass cars by riding on the _____ , but this isn't always safe.

8. It can be especially dangerous carrying a loaded briefcase or other _____ package.

9. It is always smarter to ride on paved surfaces where the _____ of the bicycle won't be compromised.

10. If cities publicly _____ the importance of bike safety, there would probably be fewer accidents.

Comprehension [ ]

Vocabulary [ ]

UNDERSTANDING THROUGH WRITING

Do you think it would be possible for you to commute to school or work by bicycle? If you think you could, write the exact route that you would follow and tell about how long the trip would take. If you could not do it, write an explanation of why you couldn't.

_____

_____

_____

_____

_____

_____

_____

_____

_____

BUILDING STUDY SKILLS

Read the following passage and answer the questions that follow it.

Using Specialized Lists

You will naturally want your lists of specialized terms to be readily accessible and easy to use when you need them. There are different ways to accomplish this.

Some students list each word on its own 3-by-5 card along with the definition and an explanation. The cards can be filed alphabetically or by unit. Words recorded in this fashion are easily sorted, located, and reviewed.

Others prefer to use their notebooks. This arrangement allows new terms to be recorded close to the notes accompanying the lecture or chapter where the new terms were first used. Words catalogued this way make reviewing easier since you are able to use your knowledge of the terms as an aid to recall important concepts from the lecture or text.

Each night new terms should be studied during the review and memorization segment of your study period. The words will then be fresh in your mind for class the following day.

Periodically (before midterm examinations, for example), all specialized terms should be reviewed and studied. It is prudent at this time to attempt to write the definition of each term from memory. It is important to recall the exact wording since precise definitions are more useful to you both in understanding the subject matter and in demonstrating your understanding to your instructor.

1. Index cards enable you to file new words _____ or by unit.

2. Words listed in a _____ can be recorded close to the notes from the lecture where the words were first used.

3. New terms should be _____ each night during the review part of your study period.

4. Periodically, you should attempt to write the definition of each term from _____ .

5. Memorization could help you recall that the meaning of _____ in the story you just read is "obvious; attracting attention."

15

The Pedestrian

Ray Bradbury

READING PURPOSE—

The following story describes a man who gets into trouble simply for being on the street at night. Read to find out more about what the society he lives in is like.

VOCABULARY—PART ONE

All of these words are in the selection you are about to read. Study each word and its meaning. Then answer the questions below. As you read the selection, notice how each vocabulary word is used.

phantoms: ghosts
manifest: appear; be displayed
ceaseless: without stopping

jockeying: maneuvering
illumination: source of light
ebbing: declining
metallic: similar to the sound when metal is struck
peered: looked searchingly
riveted: fastened by a metal bolt with a head at each end
regressive: backward; reactionary

1. Which word could describe the music coming from your neighbor's apartment for 24 hours straight?

2. Which word would describe entities that haunt a house?

3. Which word could describe what the light is doing as the sun sets?

4. Which word could describe how the inside structure of a skyscraper is held together?

5. Which word could describe a group that never wants to change its regulations, no matter how out-of-date they get?

1   To enter out into that silence that was the city at eight o'clock of a misty evening in November, to put your feet upon that buckling concrete walk, to step over grassy seams and make your way, hands in pockets, through the silences, that was what Mr. Leonard Mead most dearly loved to do. He would stand upon the corner of an intersection and peer down long moonlit avenues of sidewalk in four directions, deciding which way to go, but it really made no difference; he was alone in this world of 2053 A.D., or as good as alone, and with a final decision made, a path selected, he would stride off, sending patterns of frosty air before him like the smoke of a cigar.

2   Sometimes he would walk for hours and miles and return only at midnight to his house. And on his way he would see the cottages and homes with their dark windows, and it was not unequal to walking through a graveyard where only the faintest glimmers of firefly light appeared in flickers behind the windows. Sudden gray <u>phantoms</u> seemed to <u>manifest</u> upon inner room walls where a curtain was still undrawn against the night, or there were whisperings and murmurs where a window in a tomblike building was still open.

3   Mr. Leonard Mead would pause, cock his head, listen, look, and march on, his feet making no noise on the lumpy walk. For long ago he had wisely changed to sneakers when strolling at night, because the dogs in intermittent squads would parallel his journey with barkings if he wore hard heels, and lights might click on and faces appear and an entire street be startled by the passing of a lone figure, himself, in the early November evening.

4   On this particular evening he began his journey in a westerly direction, toward the hidden sea. There was a good crystal frost in the air; it cut the nose and made the lungs blaze like a Christmas tree inside; you could feel the cold light going on and off, all the branches filled with invisible snow. He listened to the faint push of his soft shoes through autumn leaves with satisfaction, and whistled a cold quiet whistle between his teeth, occasionally picking up a leaf as he passed, examining its skeletal pattern in the infrequent lamplights as he went on, smelling its rusty smell.

5   "Hello, in there," he whispered to every house on every side as he moved. "What's up tonight on Channel 4, Channel 7, Channel 9? Where are the cowboys rushing, and do I see the United States Cavalry over the next hill to the rescue?"

6   The street was silent and long and empty, with only his shadow moving like the shadow of a hawk in mid-country. If he closed his eyes and stood very still, froze, he could imagine himself upon the center of a plain, a wintry, windless Arizona desert with no house in a thousand miles, and only dry river beds, the streets, for company.

7   "What is it now?" he asked the houses, noticing his wristwatch. "Eight-thirty P.M.? Time for a dozen assorted murders? A quiz? A revue? A comedian falling off the stage?"

8   Was that a murmur of laughter from within a moon-white house? He hesitated, but went on when nothing more happened. He stumbled over a particularly uneven section of sidewalk. The cement was vanishing under flowers and grass. In ten years of walking by night or day, for thousands of miles, he had never met another person walking, not one in all that time.

9   He came to a cloverleaf intersection which stood silent where two main highways crossed the town. During the day it was a thunderous surge of cars, the gas stations open, a great insect rustling and a <u>ceaseless</u> <u>jockeying</u> for position as the scarab-beetles, a faint incense puttering from their exhausts, skimmed homeward to the far directions. But now these highways, too, were like streams in a dry season, all stone and bed and moon radiance.

10   He turned back on a side street, circling around toward his home. He was within a block of his destination when the lone car turned a corner quite suddenly and flashed a fierce white cone of light upon him. He stood entranced, not unlike a night moth, stunned by the <u>illumination</u>, and then drawn toward it.

11   A <u>metallic</u> voice called to him:

12   "Stand still. Stay where you are! Don't move!"

13   He halted.

14   "Put up your hands!"

15   "But—" he said.

16   "Your hands up! Or we'll shoot!"

17   The police, of course, but what a rare, incredible thing; in a city of three million, there was only *one* police car left, wasn't that correct? Ever since a year ago, 2052, the election year, the force had been cut down from three cars to one. Crime was <u>ebbing</u>; there was no need now for the police, save for this one lone car wandering and wandering the empty streets.

18   "Your name?" said the police car in a metallic whisper. He couldn't see the men in it for the bright light in his eyes.

19 "Leonard Mead," he said.

20 "Speak up!"

21 "Leonard Mead!"

22 "Business or profession?"

23 "I guess you'd call me a writer."

24 "No profession," said the police car, as if talking to itself. The light held him fixed, like a museum specimen, needle thrust through chest.

25 "You might say that," said Mr. Mead. He hadn't written in years. Magazines and books didn't sell anymore. Everything went on in the tomb-like houses at night now, he thought, continuing his fancy. The tombs, ill-lit by television light, where the people sat like the dead, the gray or multi-colored lights touching their faces, but never really touching them.

26 "No profession," said the phonograph voice, hissing. "What are you doing out?"

27 "Walking," said Leonard Mead.

28 "Walking!"

29 "Just walking," he said simply, but his face felt cold.

30 "Walking, just walking, walking?"

31 "Yes, sir."

32 "Walking where? For what?"

33 "Walking for air. Walking to *see*."

34 "Your address!"

35 "Eleven South Saint James Street."

36 "And there is air *in* your house, you have an *air conditioner*, Mr. Mead?"

37 "Yes."

38 "And you have a viewing screen in your house to see with?"

39 "No."

40 "No?" There was a crackling quiet that in itself was an accusation.

41 "Are you married, Mr. Mead?"

42 "No."

43 "Not married," said the police voice behind the fiery beam. The moon was high and clear among the stars and the houses were gray and silent.

44 "Nobody wanted me," said Leonard Mead with a smile.

"In ten years of walking…, for thousands of miles, he had never met another person walking."

45 "Don't speak unless you're spoken to!"

46 Leonard Mead waited in the cold night.

47 "Just *walking*, Mr. Mead?"

48 "Yes."

49 "But you haven't explained for what purpose."

50 "I explained; for air, and to see, and just to walk."

51 "Have you done this often?"

52 "Every night for years."

53 The police car sat in the center of the street with its radio throat faintly humming.

54 "Well, Mr. Mead," it said.

55 "Is that all?" he asked politely.

56 "Yes," said the voice. "Here." There was a sigh, a pop. The back door of the police car sprang wide. "Get in."

57 "Wait a minute. I haven't done anything!"

58 "Get in."

59 "I protest!"

60 "Mr. Mead."

61 He walked like a man suddenly drunk. As he passed the front window of the car he looked in. As he had expected, there was no one in the front seat, no one in the car at all.

62 "Get in."

63 He put his hand to the door and peered into the back seat, which was a little cell, a little black jail with bars. It smelled of riveted steel. It smelled of harsh antiseptic; it smelled too clean and hard and metallic. There was nothing soft there.

64 "Now if you had a wife to give you an alibi," said the iron voice. "But—"

65 "Where are you taking me?"

66 The car hesitated, or rather gave a faint whirring click, as if information, somewhere, was dropping card by punch-slotted card under electric eyes. "To the Psychiatric Center for Research on Regressive Tendencies."

67 He got in. The door shut with a soft thud. The police car rolled through the night avenues, flashing its dim lights ahead.

68 They passed one house on one street a moment later, one house in an entire city of houses that were dark, but this one particular house had all of

its electric lights brightly lit, every window a loud yellow illumination, square and warm in the cool darkness.

69   "That's *my* house," said Leonard Mead.

70   No one answered him.

71   The car moved down the empty river-bed streets and off away, leaving the empty streets with the empty sidewalks, and no sound and no motion all the rest of the chill November night.

Starting Time   ☐

Finishing Time   ☐

Reading Time   ☐

Reading Rate   ☐

COMPREHENSION

Read the following questions and statements. For each one, put an X in the box before the option that contains the most complete or accurate answer.

1. Leonard Mead had no
   ☐ a. parents.
   ☐ b. air conditioner.
   ☐ c. viewing screen.
   ☐ d. money.

2. During the evening the city streets were
   ☐ a. dangerous.   ☐ c. well patrolled.
   ☐ b. off limits.   ☐ d. crowded.

3. The number of police cars had been reduced because
   ☐ a. the city was trying to save money.
   ☐ b. people objected to the invasion of privacy.
   ☐ c. criminals now controlled the city.
   ☐ d. the crime rate had dropped to a new low.

4. The purpose of the story is to
   ☐ a. demonstrate the efficiency of a scientifically run police force.
   ☐ b. show how city streets can be made safe for pedestrians.
   ☐ c. explain how electrical energy can be preserved in a crisis situation.
   ☐ d. describe what happens when people lose control over their government.

5. The police car was operated by
   ☐ a. two policemen.
   ☐ b. remote control.
   ☐ c. a phantom policeman.
   ☐ d. a skeletal force.

6. Which of the following best indicates how different Mr. Mead was from everyone else?
   ☐ a. He was a former writer.
   ☐ b. He was not married.
   ☐ c. He did not own a viewing screen.
   ☐ d. He was an old man.

7. The city described by the author seems to be maintained and controlled by
   ☐ a. an impersonal authority.
   ☐ b. an efficient police force.
   ☐ c. a power from outer space.
   ☐ d. an indifferent citizens' council.

8. The tone of the story is
   ☐ a. annoying.
   ☐ b. frightening.
   ☐ c. encouraging.
   ☐ d. amusing.

9. Mr. Leonard Mead is
   ☐ a. representative of the general public.
   ☐ b. a threat to law and order.
   ☐ c. an exception to the general rule.
   ☐ d. suffering from severe mental disorder.

10. The story is an example of
   ☐ a. high adventure.
   ☐ b. science fiction.
   ☐ c. nonfiction.
   ☐ d. biographical writing.

Comprehension Skills Key

1. recalling specific facts	6. making a judgment
2. retaining concepts	7. making an inference
3. organizing facts	8. recognizing tone
4. understanding the main idea	9. understanding characters
5. drawing a conclusion	10. appreciating literary forms

VOCABULARY—PART TWO

Write the word that makes the most sense in each sentence.

phantoms   **peered**
illumination   **metallic**
regressive

1. Leonard Mead's street was dark except for the _____ coming from his windows.

2. Now and then he saw weird shadows on other people's windows that appeared to be _____ .

3. Sometimes he thought he heard _____ clangings from pipes hitting against each other.

4. When he _____ through people's half-opened drapes, he saw them watching childlike cartoons.

5. The whole society seemed _____ rather than forward looking.

jockeying   **riveted**
ceaseless   **ebbing**
manifest

6. During the day, the roads were completely filled with _____ traffic.

7. One could watch the cars _____ from lane to lane in order to move faster.

8. Once the sun went down, though, the traffic began _____ .

9. By dark, not one car would _____ itself on the road.

10. It was as if their garages were _____ shut and they could not escape.

Comprehension [ ]

Vocabulary [ ]

UNDERSTANDING THROUGH WRITING

Where do you think Leonard Mead is taken by the police? What happens to him? Write a short explanation of Mead's fate. Base what you say on ideas you get from the story.

_____

_____

_____

_____

_____

_____

_____

_____

_____

_____

_____

_____

BUILDING STUDY SKILLS

Read the following passage and answer the questions that follow it.

Other Word Study, I

1. Contextual Aids. By seeing a word in context, we come to know it better and better with every exposure. At first, the word becomes part of our reading vocabulary. This means that we have seen it often enough to recognize it and remember its meaning. Many words remain just in our reading vocabulary. Other new words are repeated in print often enough for us to come to know them well; these words are then assimilated into our writing vocabulary. When a word finally becomes totally familiar, it may join our speaking vocabulary.

When read in context, words often have different shades of meaning that are not noticeable when they are read from a list. A simple word like *root,* for example, has at least 22 different meanings. The word *perception* has very different meanings in law and in psychology. You can't even know how to pronounce *precedent,* let alone know its meaning, without seeing how it is being used. And the only way to avoid confusion between words like *precept* and *percept* is to learn them in context.

Further, relating a word to the way it is used increases our understanding not only of the word, but also of the idea the word represents. Consequently, words learned though context are more permanent than those learned from lists.

2. Affixes and Roots. Still another kind of word study centers around prefixes, suffixes, and roots. Because both prefixes and suffixes are added to words, they are collectively called affixes.

1. Every time we see a word in context we get to know it _____ .

2. When we know a word completely it, becomes part of our _____ vocabulary.

3. Some _____ of meaning are not noticeable when words are not read in context.

4. For example, the word _____ in "The Pedestrian" means "maneuvering," but it can also refer to riding a horse in a race.

5. Prefixes and suffixes are both _____ to words.

TOPIC REVIEW
React to Topic 3

Respond to one or more of these questions as your instructor directs.

1. The Model T and the Morgan were made for very different purposes, but certain parts of their designs were similar. Write about at least two similarities and two differences between the two kinds of cars.

_____

_____

_____

_____

_____

2. Using the notes you made for question 1, write a short paper comparing and contrasting the Model T and the Morgan.

_____

_____

_____

_____

_____

3. Building Study Skills 12 and 13 gave you information about specialized word lists and how they can help you better understand a subject. Begin now to apply what you learned by previewing selections 16 and 17 in the next unit. Write six to eight words that seem related to the general topic of the unit and memorize their definitions. See if you find the selections easier to read as a result of this activity.

_____

_____

_____

_____

_____

4. Suppose your task is to sell either the antique airplane from "First Flight Across America" or a new bicycle designed especially for commuting. Create an ad that will make the vehicle attractive to an audience. In addition to writing copy describing the vehicle's special qualities, you might also want to sketch a picture of it or write an advertising jingle that could be used to sell it.

_____

_____

_____

_____

_____

5. What do you think will happen to the ways people get around in the next 20 years? Will cars get bigger or smaller? Will more people have private planes or helicopters? Will walking become more or less common? Either write your opinion on these questions or give your own ideas about how transportation will change.

_____

_____

_____

_____

_____

6. Think of a movie or TV show in which a method of transportation played an important part. For example, one TV show was set on a cruise ship; many movies are set on airplanes. Identify one movie or program, and write about why a vehicle or other means of transportation in it was important.

_____

_____

_____

_____

_____

_____

A wise man should consider that health is the greatest of human blessings.

—Hippocrates (460–400 B.C.)

FEELING BETTER ALREADY

16

Ebola: An Early Outbreak

Richard Preston

READING PURPOSE—
This passage describes an early case of the Ebola virus, one of the most contagious and deadly infections ever seen in humans. Read to find out the virus's symptoms and what happened as a result of the infection.

VOCABULARY—PART ONE

All of these words are in the selection you are about to read. Study each word and its meaning. Then answer the questions below. As you read the selection, notice how each vocabulary word is used.

orifices: openings

hemorrhages: heavy discharges of blood

amplify: expand; make more extensive

devastated: destroyed

lethal: deadly

detonation: sudden violent explosion

subsided: died down

emergence: a coming into existence or development

ravaged: laid waste; destroyed

mutate: change

1. Which word tells what happened when a severe storm suddenly lessened in intensity?

_____

2. Which word might be used for secret entranceways into caves?

_____

3. Which word could be used in talking about the blowing up of a gunpowder factory?

_____

4. Which word names the likely result of severe wounds to the body?

_____

5. Which word tells what happens to music when it is heard through many loudspeakers?

_____

1   On July 6, 1976, five hundred miles northwest of Mount Elgon, in southern Sudan, near the fingered edge of the central-African rain forest, a man who is known to Ebola hunters as Yu. G. went into shock and died with blood running from the <u>orifices</u> of his body. He is referred to only by his initials. Mr. Yu. G. was the first identified case, the index case, in an outbreak of an unknown virus.

2   Mr. Yu. G. was a storekeeper in a cotton factory in the town of Nzara. The population of Nzara had grown in recent years—the town had experienced, in its own way, the human population explosion that is occurring throughout the equatorial regions of the earth. The people of that area in southern Sudan are the Zande, a large tribe. The country of the Zande is savanna mixed with riverine forest, beautiful country, where acacia trees cluster along the banks of seasonal rivers. African doves perch in the trees and call their drawn-out calls. The land between the rivers is a sea of elephant grass, which can grow ten feet high. As you head south, toward Zaire, the land rises and forms hills, and the forest begins to spread away from the rivers and thickens into a closed canopy, and you enter the rain forest. The land around the town of Nzara held rich plantations of teak and fruit trees and cotton. People were poor, but they worked hard and raised large families and kept to their tribal traditions.

3   Mr. Yu. G. was a salaried man. He worked at a desk in a room piled with cotton cloth at the back of the factory. Bats roosted in the ceiling of the room near his desk. If the bats were infected with Ebola, no one has been able to prove it. The virus may have entered the cotton factory by some unknown route—perhaps in insects trapped in the cotton fibers, for example, or in rats that lived in the factory. Or, possibly, the virus had nothing to do with the cotton factory, and Mr. Yu. G. was infected somewhere else. He did not go to a hospital, and died on a cot in his family compound. His family gave him a traditional Zande funeral and left his body under a mound of stones in a clearing of elephant grass. His grave has been visited more than once by doctors from Europe and America, who want to see it and reflect on its meaning, and pay their respects to the index case of what later became known as Ebola Sudan.

4   He is remembered today as a "quiet, unremarkable man." No photograph was taken of him during his lifetime, and no one seems to remember what he looked like. He wasn't well known, even in his hometown. They say that his brother was tall and slender, so perhaps he was, too. He passed through the gates of life unnoticed by anyone except his family and a few of his co-workers. He might have made no difference except for the fact that he was a host.[1]

5   His illness began to copy itself. A few days after he died, two other salaried men who worked at desks near him in the same room broke with bleeding, went into shock, and died with massive <u>hemorrhages</u> from the natural openings of the body. One of the dead men was a popular fellow known as P. G. Unlike the quiet Mr. Yu. G., he had a wide circle of friends, including several mistresses. He spread the agent far and wide in the town. The agent jumped easily from person to person, apparently through touching and sexual contact. It was a fast spreader, and it could live easily in people. It passed through as many as sixteen generations of infection as it jumped from person to person in Sudan. It also killed many of its hosts. While this is not necessarily in the best interest of the virus, if the virus is highly contagious, and can jump fast enough from host to host, then it does not matter, really, what happens to the previous host, because the virus can <u>amplify</u> itself for quite a while, at least until it kills off much of the population of hosts. Most of the fatal cases of Ebola Sudan can be traced back through chains of infection to the quiet Mr. Yu. G. A hot strain radiated out of him and nearly <u>devastated</u> the human population of southern Sudan. The strain burned through the town of Nzara and reached eastward to the town of Maridi, where there was a hospital.

6   It hit the hospital like a bomb. It savaged patients and snaked like chain lightning out from the hospital through patients' families. Apparently the medical staff had been giving patients injections with dirty needles. The virus jumped quickly through the hospital via the needles, and then it hit the medical staff. A characteristic of a <u>lethal</u>, contagious, and incurable virus is that it quickly gets into the medical people. In some cases, the medical system may intensify the outbreak, like a lens that focuses sunlight on a heap of tinder.

7   The virus transformed the hospital at Maridi into a morgue. As it jumped from bed to bed, killing patients left and right, doctors began to notice signs of mental derangement, psychosis,

---

[1] host: person in which a disease lives

depersonalization,[2] zombie-like behavior. Some of the dying stripped off their clothes and ran out of the hospital, naked and bleeding, and wandered through the streets of the town, seeking their homes, not seeming to know what had happened or how they had gotten into this condition. There is no doubt that Ebola

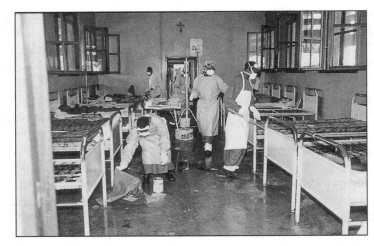

"The virus jumped quickly through the hospital via the [dirty] needles."

damages the brain and causes psychotic dementia.[3] It is not easy, however, to separate brain damage from the effects of fear. If you were trapped in a hospital where people were dissolving in their beds, you might try to escape, and if you were a bleeder and frightened, you might take off your clothes, and people might think you had gone mad.

8   The Sudan strain was more than twice as lethal as Marburg virus—its case-fatality rate was 50 percent. That is, fully half of the people who came down with it ended up dying, and quickly. This was the same kind of fatality rate as was seen with the black plague during the Middle Ages. If the Ebola Sudan virus had managed to spread out of central Africa, it might have entered Khartoum in a few weeks, penetrated Cairo a few weeks after that, and from there it would have hopped to Athens, New York, Paris, London, Singapore—it would have gone everywhere on the planet. Yet that never happened, and the crisis in Sudan passed away unnoticed by the world at large. What happened in Sudan could be compared to the secret detonation of an atomic bomb. If the human race came close to a major biological accident, we never knew it.

9   For reasons that are not clear, the outbreak subsided, and the virus vanished. The hospital at Maridi had been the epicenter[4] of the emergence. As the virus ravaged the hospital, the surviving medical staff panicked and ran off into the bush. It

was probably the wisest thing to do and the best thing that could have happened, because it stopped the use of dirty needles and emptied the hospital, which helped to break the chain of infection.

10   There was another possible reason why the Ebola Sudan virus vanished. It was exceedingly hot. It killed people so fast that they didn't have much time to infect other people before they died. Furthermore, the virus was not airborne. It was not quite contagious enough to start a full-scale disaster. It traveled in blood, and the bleeding victim did not touch very many other people before dying, and so the virus did not have many chances to jump to a new host. Had people been coughing the virus into the air…it would have been a different story. In any case, the Ebola Sudan virus destroyed a few hundred people in central Africa the way a fire consumes a pile of straw—until the blaze burns out at the center and ends in a heap of ash—rather than smoldering around the planet, as AIDS has done, like a fire in a coal mine, impossible to put out. The Ebola virus, in its Sudan incarnation, retreated to the heart of the bush, where undoubtedly it lives to this day, cycling and cycling in some unknown host, able to shift its shape, able to mutate and become a new thing, with the potential to enter the human species in a new form.

Starting Time	
Finishing Time	
Reading Time	
Reading Rate	

---

[2]*depersonalization:* condition of having lost one's personality or individuality
[3]*dementia:* insanity
[4]*epicenter:* place of origin

COMPREHENSION

Read the following questions and statements. For each one, put an X in the box before the option that contains the most complete or accurate answer.

1. The Ebola outbreak described in this selection took place in the African country of
   - ☐ a. Egypt.
   - ☐ b. Sudan.
   - ☐ c. Zaire.
   - ☐ d. Liberia.

2. This particular outbreak
   - ☐ a. could be blamed on the hospital at Maridi.
   - ☐ b. was caused by rats in the cotton factory.
   - ☐ c. spread across the continent of Africa.
   - ☐ d. was an isolated event.

3. The events described in this selection take place
   - ☐ a. in one day.
   - ☐ b. in three days.
   - ☐ c. over two or three weeks.
   - ☐ d. over seven or eight months.

4. The author's point in this selection is that
   - ☐ a. this particular outbreak came and went mysteriously.
   - ☐ b. Ebola is very similar to AIDS.
   - ☐ c. hospitals are to blame for many of our serious illnesses.
   - ☐ d. if this outbreak hadn't occurred where it did, it probably would have soon happened somewhere else.

5. Killing its host is usually not in the best interest of a virus because
   - ☐ a. if the host is dead, he or she can't infect anyone else.
   - ☐ b. the death weakens the strength of the virus.
   - ☐ c. this helps doctors figure out a way to cure the virus.
   - ☐ d. a funeral is not a good place for a virus to spread.

6. The doctors who go to visit the grave of Mr. Yu. G.
   - ☐ a. knew his family personally.
   - ☐ b. are grateful that he died without spreading the disease too much.
   - ☐ c. had worked at the hospital at Maridi.
   - ☐ d. respect and fear the power of the virus.

7. The author believes that this particular type of Ebola
   - ☐ a. eventually turned into AIDS.
   - ☐ b. is now gone forever.
   - ☐ c. was spread through coughing.
   - ☐ d. may some day recur in a new form.

8. The writer's intent in paragraph 8 is to
   - ☐ a. alarm his audience.
   - ☐ b. anger his audience.
   - ☐ c. amuse his audience.
   - ☐ d. inform his audience.

9. Mr. Yu. G.
   - ☐ a. got the virus from a man known as P. G.
   - ☐ b. was a quiet, unassuming man.
   - ☐ c. had sexual contact with a lot of women.
   - ☐ d. was the last person to die in this outbreak.

10. When the writer says that the medical system can be "like a lens that focuses sunlight on a heap of tinder," he is using
   - ☐ a. a literal comparison.
   - ☐ b. a simile.
   - ☐ c. a metaphor.
   - ☐ d. alliteration.

Comprehension Skills Key

1. recalling specific facts
2. retaining concepts
3. organizing facts
4. understanding the main idea
5. drawing a conclusion
6. making a judgment
7. making an inference
8. recognizing tone
9. understanding characters
10. appreciating literary forms

VOCABULARY—PART TWO

Write the word that makes the most sense in each sentence.

hemorrhages	amplify
detonation	emergence
ravaged	

1. The Ebola virus swept through the community and _____ it, leaving death and destruction in its wake.

2. The _____ of the virus began with a storekeeper named Mr. Yu. G.

3. Soon the epidemic began to _____ and to kill others in the area.

4. Many died in pools of blood caused by _____ .

5. The virus exploded in the area like the _____ of a bomb.

orifices	mutate
subsided	devastated
lethal	

6. The virus was so _____ that it could kill in a matter of hours.

7. Blood poured out of victims' mouths and other bodily _____ .

8. When the virus had _____ and the worst was over, hundreds of people had died.

9. The _____ families grieved as they buried their dead.

10. There is fear that the virus will _____ and return one day in a new form.

Comprehension	
Vocabulary	

UNDERSTANDING THROUGH WRITING

Pretend you live in the town where the virus has struck. Write a letter to a friend describing what is going on. Include information about your own feelings in the midst of this epidemic.

_____

_____

_____

_____

_____

_____

_____

_____

_____

_____

_____

_____

108

BUILDING STUDY SKILLS

Read the following passage and answer the questions that follow it.

Other Word Study, II

When a prefix is added to the beginning of a word, it causes a change in the meaning of that word. For example, the prefix *un-*, when added to a word like *happy,* gives the word a completely opposite meaning.

Suffixes are added to the ends of words. Although they do not affect the basic meaning of a word, suffixes frequently alter its part of speech. For example, a verb, *hate,* can become an adjective, *hateful,* when a suffix is added.

Word roots are often Latin and Greek stems on which many of our English words are based. *Bio,* which means "life," is a Greek root word. From it we get such English words as *biology* and *antibiotic*.

Through the study of affixes and roots, you can get a better feel for the meaning of many new words. Understanding how a word has acquired its particular meaning makes it much more likely that the word will become a part of your vocabulary. Check each new word you encounter in a good dictionary. The origin of the root of the word is usually explained.

As you become more familiar with words—their origins (etymology) and their formative parts—you will find that encountering new and difficult words will be much less daunting.

1. A prefix is an affix added to the
   _____ of a word.

2. A suffix is an affix added to the
   _____ of a word.

3. In the selection about the Ebola virus, the affix *-tion* changes the word *infection* from a verb, *infect,* to a _____ .

4. Word roots are often _____ on words of Greek or Latin origin.

5. To discover the origin of a word, one should consult a good _____ .

Winning the Battle of the Bug

William Shelton

READING PURPOSE—
   The mosquito has been a carrier of lethal disease from ancient times. Read to find out its history and the problems in overcoming it.

VOCABULARY—PART ONE

   All of these words are in the selection you are about to read. Study each word and its meaning. Then answer the questions below. As you read the selection, notice how each vocabulary word is used.

confrontation: conflict; battle

coagulating: thickening

rancid: rotten; putrid

contained: held back; restrained

pestilence: epidemic

undiluted: not thinned or weakened by adding water

ingest: consume; eat

immunity: resistance to poison or disease

formidable: arousing fear or dread

ominous: threatening; menacing

---

1. Which word tells what you should get from a flu shot?

---

2. Which word might describe a bowl of potato salad left outside in the hot sun for
   six days?

---

3. Which word could describe the condition of whiskey if someone drank it straight?

---

4. Which word could tell what a dam did to floodwaters?

---

5. Which word describes what you do when you sit down to a meal?

---

1   The confrontation begins when a small, fragile insect lights gently on your hand. It thrusts a hollow probe through the tender cells of your skin and into a vessel where your blood courses. You feel a slight sting. Because you are hurt, you react instinctively. A mosquito! Swat it!

2   If you are quick and your attacker is slow, you demolish this most ancient of enemies. But who really won? The million-year-old man? Or the 50-million-year-old mosquito? Perhaps you've won the battle, but the mosquito may win the war. For among the 150 diseases which the mosquito is known to carry are yellow fever and malaria which together have accounted for one-half of all human deaths in history.

3   In order to dine, the mosquito first injects a saliva-like liquid into your flesh which keeps your blood from coagulating as she sucks it out. (Only the females bite.) In that saliva medical science has identified the causes of such worldwide plagues as dengue fever, filariasis (which results in elephantiasis[1]), and epidemic hemorrhagic fever, which in one five-month period in South Vietnam caused 116 deaths. In the United States alone, scientists have found five types of human encephalitis viruses, including the dreaded Western and St. Louis encephalitis which causes swelling of human brain tissues. The Venezuelan variety (VEE) usually causes only influenza-like symptoms in man, but in the summer of 1971, VEE killed over half the horses it infected in the Southwest.

4   Like the tiny Lilliputians that subdued Gulliver, the "skeeter" acquires strength through sheer numbers. There are several hundred varieties of *Culicidae* in the United States, and over 2,000 worldwide. They surpass in population and total weight all the other animals of the earth combined. And mosquitoes breed equally as well in polar region ice pools, tree holes in tropical rain forests, or in the numerous receptacles of technological man—from tin cans to cemetery urns.

5   "The mosquito, except for man himself," says scientist Gilbert Chambers who researched the mosquito problem at the request of Exxon Oil & Refining Company, "is the cleverest, most destructive, and most adaptable animal on the face of the earth today. Man has always fought the mosquito, but has only experienced a measure of success in the last 60 years or so."

1*elephantiasis:* disease which causes parts of the body to greatly enlarge

6   If he had nothing with which to defend himself but his swat, man would have little chance against the mosquito. Early man smeared rancid grease on his body as a mosquito repellent, or hid within a cloud of woodsmoke from his campfire. The ingenious Egyptians improved on the campfire by developing the smudge pot and learning to weave mosquito netting. Hordes of mosquitoes from the Pontine Marshes surrounding ancient Rome so plagued the Caesars that they began what may have been man's first organized effort to fight back on a large scale. They drained the marshes, a mosquito control project which took fourteen centuries to complete.

7   The mosquito is partly responsible for the fact that the official language of the United States is neither Spanish nor French. Yellow fever and malaria contained early Spanish expansion in the New World, and turned back Napoleon's expeditionary forces in the Caribbean in 1802. Late in the nineteenth century, the same pestilence halted French attempts to dig a canal across the Isthmus of Panama.

8   Mosquito-borne diseases prevented mankind from expanding into the lush tropic zones of the earth, with the result that (with the exception of the polar regions) the vast equatorial lands are still the least populated of the world. Colonists settling the eastern shores of North America suffered from malaria, and some authorities believe it was the *Anopheles* mosquito which forced the English to move their capital from Jamestown to Williamsburg in 1699.

9   Until recently, few methods existed for controlling mosquito infestations. As early as 1793, Philadelphians poured expensive whale oil onto the surface of water in rain barrels to prevent mosquitoes from breeding there. With the birth of the oil industry, kerosene came into experimental use as a mosquito control during the 1890s. A major breakthrough came around the turn of the century when Dr. Walter Reed identified the female *Aedes aegypti* mosquito as the carrier of yellow fever. With this information, the United States took over the job of digging the Panama Canal. A massive program of swamp drainage and spraying with kerosene brought mosquitoes under control sufficiently to permit completion of the Canal in 1914.

10   In the early part of this century, mosquitoes got so bad in New Jersey that farmers were unable to farm and industry around Newark had to shut down temporarily on several occasions. To combat the

"New Jersey Terror," the state established the first U.S. mosquito control program. They sprayed millions of gallons of undiluted diesel oil on the waters of coastal marshes in amounts of 20 gallons or more an acre. The oil damaged aquatic and plant life, but it killed mosquitoes and brought the Terror under control. Encouraged by these results, other states, including Florida, adopted similar programs. Today, there are some 350 organized mosquito control districts active in the U.S. Altogether, they spend some $50 million a year to kill mosquitoes.

11   But the mosquito has continued to fight back. In 1922 two million people caught dengue fever in Gulf Coast states. In 1933 mosquitoes killed 200 Missourians by infecting them with St. Louis encephalitis.

12   Then, in the 1940s, the world was handed a new weapon so miraculously effective against mosquitoes that some authorities boldly predicted victory in man's battle with the bug. The wonder-weapon was DDT. Dusted, sprayed, or fogged, DDT meant death to both adult and larval mosquitoes. Used throughout the world during the following decades, the chemical saved millions of people from disease and prevented countless deaths. Unfortunately, man has learned that his wonder-weapon has disadvantages. It isn't selective; it kills or contaminates creatures other than mosquitoes. It isn't readily biodegradable,[2] and can be passed along the food chain in increasingly concentrated quantity from tiny organisms that ingest it to larger species that ingest them and eventually to man. And, finally, a few mosquitoes strong enough to survive the nerve-paralyzing effects of DDT have produced offspring capable of resisting the poison. Today, DDT is largely ineffective as a mosquito control agent in most of the United States.

13   As these problems came to be recognized in the mosquito control districts of the country, entomologists[3] turned to new organophosphate pesticides

"They surpass in population and total weight all the other animals of the earth combined."

as an alternative to DDT. Introduced during the 1950s, these poisons proved effective for a time. Before long, however, mosquitoes in some areas developed immunity to organophosphates as well as DDT. The formidable combination of vast numbers and rapid life cycle is capable of producing pesticide-resistant generations faster than science can concoct new poisons. And man seems to be running out of poisons to try.

14   Two ominous news reports recently highlighted the problem. A story in *The New York Times* reported, "Two species of mosquitoes native to California have acquired complete immunity to all man-made pesticides." A month later the first paragraph of a widely published Associated Press dispatch read, "A type of mosquito which can infect humans with deadly sleeping sickness is reported out of control in California because it has developed immunity to all known pesticides."

15   A biologist specializing in mosquito control, whose experience includes both the Central Valley and the Rio Grande Valley in Texas, looks at the problem this way: "I don't want to be identified as a doomsday man," he says, "but the situation could get out of hand." With jet travel now commonplace, he suggests the possibility that poison-resistant mosquitoes could carry a fatal disease from one country to another without warning. "I live in fear that some Asian virus might mutate to a fatal disease—as the dengue fever virus did—and come sweeping out of there so fast that we couldn't stop it," he says.

Starting Time	
Finishing Time	
Reading Time	
Reading Rate	

---

[2]*biodegradable:* able to be broken down by bacteria or other organisms
[3]*entomologists:* scientists who study insects

COMPREHENSION

Read the following questions and statements. For each one, put an X in the box before the option that contains the most complete or accurate answer.

1. DDT does not
   n a. affect large animals.
   n b. pose any danger to man.
   n c. disintegrate quickly.
   n d. spare any mosquitoes.

2. The mosquito is
   n a. surprisingly vulnerable.
   n b. obviously predictable.
   n c. extraordinarily adaptable.
   n d. unfortunately misunderstood

3. Ways were found to rid large areas of mosquitoes, but not without
   n a. unnecessary loss of life.
   n b. unreasonable public opposition.
   n c. damage to the environment.
   n d. serious loss of jobs.

4. Science is faced with the problem of developing poisons that will destroy mosquitoes
   n a. without costing too much.
   n b. in heavily populated areas.
   n c. which infect domesticated animals.
   n d. without destroying people.

5. Experience with DDT and other pesticides illustrates the
   n a. helplessness of science.
   n b. incompetence of scientists.
   n c. vulnerability of mosquitoes.
   n d. hardiness of the mosquito.

6. The concern expressed by the biologist specializing in mosquito control is
   n a. realistic.
   n b. exaggerated.
   n c. groundless.
   n d. amusing.

7. The dreaded mosquito has
   n a. halted the advance of civilization.
   n b. influenced the course of history.
   n c. united the nations of the world.
   n d. proven no match for modern technology.

8. The selection sounds a note of
   n a. terror.
   n b. optimism.
   n c. alarm.
   n d. indignation.

9. The mosquito's resilience has left mosquito-control experts
   n a. relieved.
   n b. disoriented.
   n c. exasperated.
   n d. outraged.

10. The selection could be classified as
   n a. a debate.
   n b. a report.
   n c. an essay.
   n d. a short story.

Comprehension Skills Key

1. recalling specific facts
2. retaining concepts
3. organizing facts
4. understanding the main idea
5. drawing a conclusion
6. making a judgment
7. making an inference
8. recognizing tone
9. understanding characters
10. appreciating literary forms

VOCABULARY—PART TWO

Write the word that makes the most sense in each sentence.

contained
undiluted
immunity

pestilence
formidable

1. The tiny but deadly mosquito can be a(n) _____ enemy for disease controllers.

2. Mosquitoes love damp places, so sprays used to control them should be _____ with water.

3. They are hard to control anyway because they develop _____ to most pesticides.

4. Billions of dollars have been spent to control mosquitoes, but they are still not completely _____ .

5. A disease like yellow fever, if not controlled, can develop into a real _____ .

ominous
ingest
rancid

confrontation
coagulating

6. Mosquitoes like to _____ human blood; it is one of their favorite foods.

7. A chemical in their saliva keeps the blood from _____ , so it is not too thick for them to suck out.

8. The mosquito is a(n) _____ enemy because it spreads so many diseases.

9. If you are about to have a(n) _____ with a mosquito, attack it before it attacks you.

10. _____ grease and other foul-smelling treatments have little effect on mosquitoes.

Comprehension [ ]

Vocabulary [ ]

UNDERSTANDING THROUGH WRITING

People have a lot of theories about how to avoid mosquitoes. Write a short explanation of some of the ones you know. Explain which ones you think work.

_____

_____

_____

_____

_____

_____

_____

_____

_____

BUILDING STUDY SKILLS

Read the following passage and answer the questions that follow it.

Listening Effectively

A wise man once said that listening is the hardest thing in the world to do. Today, listening is a lost art for most people. Understanding listening faults is a prerequisite to overcoming them. Suggestions for improving listening help you to correct poor habits and cultivate good ones. Faulty listening leads to misunderstanding, and that can be the cause of many problems.

In industry, millions of dollars are lost annually as a result of poor listening. Consequently, it has become standard practice at most major companies to "write it down."

In school, many students fail to listen properly to instructions. After many exams we hear about students who lose credit because they did not follow directions.

Listening Faults

One of the causes of faulty listening is daydreaming. This listening fault affects almost everyone. Frequently a speaker will mention some person or thing that triggers an association in our minds and we begin to daydream. When we return to reality and begin listening again, we discover that point three is now being presented and we have no recollection of points one and two.

Opportunities for daydreaming are abundant because people speak at a much slower rate than we can think. Thus, when a speaker is talking at a rate of 125 words a minute, the listener's mind may wander off.

1. Misunderstanding is caused by

   _____ listening.

2. In _____ , poor listening causes a loss of millions of dollars annually.

3. In school, students often lose

   _____ in exams as a result of poor listening.

4. A speaker will often mention something that will trigger an association in our minds and cause us to

   _____ .

5. For example, a person who has been

   _____ by a bee might daydream about that experience as he or she begins to read paragraph 1 of the mosquito article.

A Day's Wait

Ernest Hemingway

READING PURPOSE—
A flue epidemic might not seem a terrible thing, but it could be if you didn't understand your own symptoms. Read to find out how a young boy deals with an attack of the flu.

VOCABULARY—PART ONE

All of these words are in the selection you are about to read. Study each word and its meaning. Then answer the questions below. As you read the selection, notice how each vocabulary word is used.

purgative: laxative

detached: cut off; indifferent to

lightheaded: dizzy; giddy

slithered: slid unsteadily along a surface

covey: small group or family

quail: game birds similar to pheasants

poised: balanced

commenced: began

kilometers: metric units of length equal to about .6 miles

slack: loose; not under control

---

1. Which word might describe your feelings if it seemed you were about to faint?

2. Which word names a medicine you might take if your stomach was upset?

3. Which word is an antonym for *ended*?

4. Which word could tell how a snake moved?

5. Which word might describe how you felt if you were in a meeting but not paying any attention to the proceedings?

1   He came into the room to shut the windows while we were still in bed and I saw he looked ill. He was shivering, his face was white, and he walked slowly as though it ached to move.

2   "What's the matter, Schatz?"

3   "I've got a headache."

4   "You better go back to bed."

5   "No. I'm all right."

6   "You go to bed. I'll see you when I'm dressed."

7   But when I came downstairs he was dressed, sitting by the fire, looking a very sick and miserable boy of nine years. When I put my hand on his forehead I knew he had a fever.

8   "You go up to bed," I said, "you're sick."

9   "I'm all right," he said.

10   When the doctor came he took the boy's temperature.

11   "What is it?" I asked him.

12   "One hundred and two."

13   Downstairs, the doctor left three different medicines in different colored capsules with instructions for giving them. One was to bring down the fever, another a purgative, the third to overcome an acid condition. The germs of influenza can only exist in an acid condition, he explained. He seemed to know all about influenza and said there was nothing to worry about if the fever did not go above one hundred and four degrees. This was a light epidemic of flu and there was no danger if you avoided pneumonia.

14   Back in the room I wrote the boy's temperature down and made a note of the time to give the various capsules.

15   "Do you want me to read to you?"

16   "All right. If you want to," said the boy. His face was very white and there were dark areas under his eyes. He lay still in the bed and seemed very detached from what was going on.

17   I read aloud from Howard Pyle's *Book of Pirates;* but I could see he was not following what I was reading.

18   "How do you feel, Schatz?" I asked him.

19   "Just the same, so far," he said.

20   I sat at the foot of the bed and read to myself while I waited for it to be time to give another capsule. It would have been natural for him to go to sleep, but when I looked up he was looking at the foot of the bed, looking very strangely.

21   "Why don't you try to go to sleep? I'll wake you up for the medicine."

22   "I'd rather stay awake."

23   After a while he said to me, "You don't have to stay in here with me, Papa, if it bothers you."

24   "It doesn't bother me."

25   "No, I mean you don't have to stay if it's going to bother you."

26   I thought perhaps he was a little lightheaded and after giving him the prescribed capsules at eleven o'clock I went out for a while. It was a bright, cold day, the ground covered with a sleet that had frozen so that it seemed as if all the bare trees, the bushes, the cut brush and all the grass and the bare ground had been varnished with ice. I took the young Irish setter for a little walk up the road and along a frozen creek, but it was difficult to stand or walk on the glassy surface and the red dog slipped and slithered and I fell twice, hard, once dropping my gun and having it slide away over the ice.

27   We flushed a covey of quail under a high clay bank with overhanging brush and I killed two as they went out of sight over the top of the bank. Some of the covey lit in trees, but most of them scattered into brush piles and it was necessary to jump on the ice-coated mounds of brush several times before they would flush. Coming out while you were poised unsteadily on the icy, springy brush they made difficult shooting and I killed two, missed five, and started back pleased to have found a covey close to the house and happy there were so many left to find on another day.

28   At the house they said the boy had refused to let any one come into the room.

29   "You can't come in," he said. "You mustn't get what I have."

30   I went up to him and found him in exactly the position I had left him, white-faced, but with the tops of his cheeks flushed by the fever, staring still, as he had stared, at the foot of the bed.

31   I took his temperature.

32   "What is it?"

33   "Something like a hundred," I said. It was one hundred and two and four tenths.

34   "It was a hundred and two," he said.

35   "Who said so?"

36   "The doctor."

37 "Your temperature is all right," I said. "It's nothing to worry about."

38 "I don't worry," he said, "but I can't keep from thinking."

39 "Don't think," I said. "Just take it easy."

40 "I'm taking it easy," he said and looked straight ahead. He was evidently holding tight onto himself about something.

41 "Take this with water."

42 "Do you think it will do any good?"

43 "Of course it will."

44 I sat down and opened the *Pirate* book and commenced to read, but I could see he was not following, so I stopped.

45 "About what time do you think I'm going to die?" he asked.

46 "What?"

47 "About how long will it be before I die?"

48 "You aren't going to die. What's the matter with you?"

49 "Oh, yes, I am. I heard him say a hundred and two."

50 "People don't die with a fever of one hundred and two. That's a silly way to talk."

51 "I know they do. At school in France the boys told me you can't live with forty-four degrees. I've got a hundred and two."

52 He had been waiting to die all day, ever since nine o'clock in the morning.

53 "You poor Schatz," I said. "Poor old Schatz. It's like miles and kilometers. You aren't going to die. That's a different thermometer. On that thermometer thirty-seven is normal. On this kind it's ninety-eight."

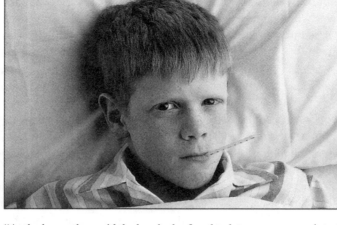

"At the house they said the boy had refused to let any one come into the room."

54 "Are you sure?"

55 "Absolutely," I said. "It's like miles and kilometers. You know, like how many kilometers we make when we do seventy miles in the car?"

56 "Oh," he said.

57 But his gaze at the foot of the bed relaxed slowly. The hold over himself relaxed too, finally, and the next day it was very slack and he cried very easily at little things that were of no importance.

Starting Time	
Finishing Time	
Reading Time	
Reading Rate	

COMPREHENSION

Read the following questions and statements. For each one, put an X in the box before the option that contains the most complete or accurate answer.

1. This story takes place in
   ☐ a. fall.
   ☐ b. winter.
   ☐ c. spring.
   ☐ d. summer.

2. It is clear that the boy has the flu because
   ☐ a. he has just gotten over a cold.
   ☐ b. there is a lot of flu in the community.
   ☐ c. he has many flu symptoms.
   ☐ d. he is not the type who would pretend to be ill.

3. The doctor comes
  ☐ a. around nine o'clock.
  ☐ b. at noon.
  ☐ c. in the early afternoon.
  ☐ d. at the end of the day.

4. The basis of this story is
  ☐ a. a father's love for his son.
  ☐ b. a son's loneliness.
  ☐ c. a misunderstanding.
  ☐ d. a doctor's visit.

5. In paragraphs 53–55 the father's explanation of a "different thermometer" means that
  ☐ a. some thermometers are more accurate than others.
  ☐ b. degrees are like kilometers.
  ☐ c. thermometers used for measuring body temperatures do not necessarily work when registering outdoor temperatures.
  ☐ d. the boy's temperature was measured by a Fahrenheit thermometer, which was not what his classmates used.

6. The father goes out to hunt because
  ☐ a. he thinks maybe the boy will sleep if he's left alone.
  ☐ b. they need some fresh meat for dinner.
  ☐ c. he wants his son to think about dying.
  ☐ d. it's a good way to give his dog an outing.

7. The boy more or less falls apart at the end of the story because he
  ☐ a. has been so upset thinking he was facing death.
  ☐ b. realizes that he won't get over the flu that quickly.
  ☐ c. thinks his father has lied to him.
  ☐ d. blames the doctor for misleading him.

8. The tone used in this story makes the incident sound like
  ☐ a. a joke.
  ☐ b. a sad confusion.
  ☐ c. a bitter lesson.
  ☐ d. a loving incident between father and son.

9. The narrator of this story
  ☐ a. shows little concern for his son.
  ☐ b. thinks hunting is the most important thing he can do.
  ☐ c. is fond of his son but doesn't understand him very well.
  ☐ d. wishes the boy's mother was around to help him.

10. This story is told from the point of view of
  ☐ a. the doctor.
  ☐ b. an omniscient narrator.
  ☐ c. the boy.
  ☐ d. the father.

Comprehension Skills Key

1. recalling specific facts
2. retaining concepts
3. organizing facts
4. understanding the main idea
5. drawing a conclusion
6. making a judgment
7. making an inference
8. recognizing tone
9. understanding characters
10. appreciating literary forms

VOCABULARY—PART TWO

Write the word that makes the most sense in each sentence.

lightheaded	covey
quail	poised
kilometers	

1. The difference between the two thermometers is like the difference between miles and

   _____ .

2. Before the boy understood that, he felt

   _____ on the edge of death.

3. He was not only _____ and dizzy, but badly frightened.

4. His father did not understand his fear and went out hunting for _____ .

5. He found a whole _____ of the birds in a nearby woods.

purgative   **detached**

slithered   **slack**

commenced

6. The doctor had recommended a

    _____ to relieve his stomach

    cramps.

7. Once he took it, he slowly _____

    to feel better physically.

8. His mind, however, went _____

    as a result of his fears.

9. Certain he was about to die, the boy seemed

    _____ from his surroundings.

10. The dog _____ in along the

     waxed floor and lay at his bedside.

Comprehension   ☐

Vocabulary   ☐

UNDERSTANDING THROUGH WRITING

Has a confusion like the one described in this story ever happened to you or someone you know? Write a short description of what happened.

_____

_____

_____

_____

_____

_____

_____

_____

_____

_____

_____

BUILDING STUDY SKILLS

Read the following passage and answer the questions that follow it.

Listening Faults

Here are some faults that will make your listening less effective than it should be.

1. Closed Mindedness. We often refuse to listen to ideas and viewpoints that are contrary to our preconceived notions about a subject. We say, in effect, "I know all I want to know, so there's no use listening."

Actually, this is an intellectual fault that leads to a listening problem. Closed mindedness interferes with learning by causing you to shut out facts you need to know—whether you agree with them or not.

2. False Attention. This is a protective device that everyone resorts to from time to time. When we're not really interested in what a person has to say, we just pretend to listen. We nod and make occasional meaningless comments to give the impression that we are paying attention, when actually our minds are elsewhere.

3. Intellectual Despair. Listening can be difficult at times. Often you must sit through lectures on subjects that are hard to understand.

Obviously, you'll never understand if you give up. The thing to do is to listen more carefully than ever; ask questions when practical and, most important, discuss the material with a classmate. Attack the problem as soon as it appears. Catch up right away and you'll feel less inclined to adopt an attitude of futility.

4. Personality Listening. It is only natural for listeners to appraise and evaluate a speaker. Our impressions should not interfere with our listening, however. The content must be judged on its own merits.

1. _____ interferes with learning by causing you to shut out facts that you don't agree with.

2. False _____ is a protective device that we all use at one time or another.

3. If you do not understand something from a lecture, it is a good idea to _____ the material with a classmate.

4. For instance, if Schatz had discussed his high _____ with his father right after the doctor told them, he would not have misunderstood what it meant.

5. The speaker is less important than the _____ of the speech.

Conquering Polio

Victoria Sherrow

READING PURPOSE—
The polio epidemic that plagued the world 50 years ago was brought under control because of the dedication of many scientific researchers. Read to find out about how they tested a possible polio vaccine.

VOCABULARY—PART ONE

All of these words are in the selection you are about to read. Study each word and its meaning. Then answer the questions below. As you read the selection, notice how each vocabulary word is used.

placebo: pill or shot with no active ingredients
vials: small glass or plastic bottles
incidences: ranges of occurrence

vital: extremely important; essential
disregarding: paying no attention to
cultures: growths of viruses prepared in special ways for medicinal use
strains: types; groups
colleagues: fellow members of a profession; associates
intensively: thoroughly and deeply
potent: powerful; very effective

---

1. Which word might you use in describing information that you absolutely must have to complete a project?

   _____

2. Which word would describe an antibiotic that immediately clears up even very serious infections?

   _____

3. Which word is a synonym for *ignoring*?

   _____

4. Which word might you use in identifying the people who work with you?

   _____

5. Which word would you use in identifying the sugar pill you gave your daughter when she pretended to be sick?

   _____

1   In November of 1953, Basil O'Connor made the announcement he had hoped to make for years: Tests of Salk's polio vaccine would be conducted in 1954. Plans called for more than 500,000 schoolchildren to take part in the first field tests.

2   Salk's former teacher and research associate, Dr. Thomas Francis Jr., had agreed to head the field trials. He was highly regarded by other scientists. They trusted him to conduct the tests and evaluate the results with care. Francis planned to use double blind studies, as he had for testing flu vaccine. Some children would get vaccine, others a placebo. Nobody involved in giving or taking the vaccine would know who had gotten what until the studies were done. Code numbers on the vials of liquid would tell the scientists what was inside. There would also be a control group that received nothing. When polio season arrived, the rates of disease in the groups could be measured.

3   A group of scientists decided where the tests would be held. They chose places that had experienced high incidences of polio in previous years, expecting that these places would experience similar rates of disease again. It was vital that local health departments be able to handle the problems and work involved in the trials. Finally, they wanted a broad range of people, from different racial and ethnic groups.

4   Eventually, about 1,839,000 children took part in the Salk vaccine field trials. They lived in 217 health districts in 44 states. The program cost about $27 million. Jane Smith described how she took part in the tests at age six:

5   *Some time in the early months of 1954, when I was midway through first grade at P.S. 61 in New York City, my parents signed a form in which they requested that I be allowed to participate in the testing of a new vaccine that might prove effective against poliomyelitis.... To the parents of the 1950s, there was nothing routine about polio. Everyone knew someone whose child had been stricken... The worst polio epidemic in history had been in the summer of 1952, only eighteen months before... It's no surprise that my parents, like millions of others, gratefully volunteered their child as a test subject for Jonas Salk's polio vaccine, disregarding any possible dangers in their desperate eagerness for protection.*

6   During that spring and summer, about one million children lined up and held out their arms to receive either a shot of vaccine or a clear, pink liquid that looked just like it but was a placebo. Another one million children got no injections. They made up the control group. Francis and his staff in Ann Arbor, Michigan, assembled a full health history of each child in all three groups.

7   The large amounts of poliovirus for the vaccine had been grown in tissue cultures at Connaught Laboratories in Canada. Three different strains of polio had been killed, filtered, then put together. Safety was the foremost concern, so after the manufacturer tested the vaccine samples, they were checked again at the National Institutes of Health in Bethesda, Maryland, and in Salk's Pittsburgh lab....

8   The first field trial began on April 26, 1954. It included 422,743 children, ages six to nine, who would get three doses of vaccine, spaced weeks apart. A similar size group got placebo. A six-year-old boy named Randy Kerr in McLean, Virginia, was the first official Polio Pioneer to be vaccinated. Private and public health doctors gave the shots. Afterward, the children got a lollipop and a button that read, "I was a Polio Pioneer."

9   Dr. Leona Baumgartner, the New York City commissioner of public health, visited public schools where children were being vaccinated. She found that they had learned a great deal about the science involved. She said, "I was very excited, because it seemed to me that if you could teach a generation of kids about what a controlled experiment was, and about what science really was, this was a plus value regardless of whether the vaccine was any good or not."

10   Volunteers were kept busy running the trials and completing the large amount of paperwork. They watched training films and read books that had been prepared by the NFIP [National Foundation for Infantile Paralysis]. Children in grades above third grade were not being vaccinated, but they helped, too. Some made name tags for the test children and volunteers. Others helped to clean their schools, set up equipment in the clinic rooms, or run errands during the tests.

11   Meanwhile, Thomas Francis had the immense job of analyzing these hundreds of thousands of tests. He had set up a Vaccine Evaluation Center in a small, empty hospital in Ann Arbor. A staff of people he selected had to organize and interpret the information that came in from local health departments conducting Salk trials. They worked with rising piles of cards, papers, letters, telegrams,

laboratory reports, and health records. That summer, while the evaluation was going on, the center got phone calls and letters from people asking if they had gotten "real vaccine." Some wanted gamma globulin injections, too, but Francis warned them that would confuse the test results. Reporters called often for news.

12 In Pittsburgh, Jonas Salk was working as he waited. He had found better ways to grow polioviruses and increase the vaccine's potency. His lab was doing blood tests for the trials. Salk was so busy with the ongoing work of the field trials, he had little time to write the scientific articles his <u>colleagues</u> were asking for. He was criticized for not publishing his latest findings promptly. Throughout America, people waited to find out if the foundation and scientists they believed in had brought them a vaccine that would end 40 years of fear.

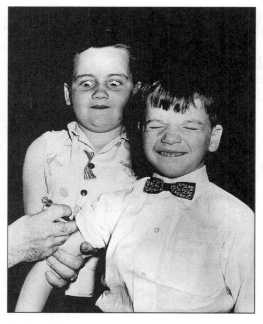

"About one million children lined up and held out their arms to receive either a shot of vaccine or a clear, pink liquid that looked just like it."

13 The long-awaited results of the Salk vaccine trials came in the spring of 1955. Francis and his team had finished the evaluation report and were ready to share their findings. At the University of Michigan, an attractive building with a large auditorium was chosen as the setting for the announcement. More than 500 people—government and public health officials, administrators of the NFIP, scientists, physicians, and journalists—had been invited to Ann Arbor to hear the Francis Report.

14 Jonas and Donna Salk arrived with their three sons. Salk had been eager to share this moment with his family, who had made many sacrifices during the years he was working <u>intensively</u> on the polio vaccine....

15 The report would be read at 10:20 A.M. Radio and television stations stood ready to broadcast the news all over America. Just after nine o'clock, reporters in the pressroom got a written copy of the announcement. There was shouting and excitement in the room as they read the key words in the report: "The vaccine works. It is safe, effective, and <u>potent</u>."

16 Francis used those same words to summarize the test results. He told the assembled guests that the vaccine had proven to be 90 to 100 percent effective against both type II and type III polio. It was less effective—60–70 percent—against the most dangerous variety of polio, the paralyzing type I. It was about 94 percent effective against the rare type of polio that disrupted breathing muscles. There were 50 percent fewer polio victims among vaccinated children than among unvaccinated children living in epidemic areas. None of the inoculated children had gotten polio from taking the vaccine....

17 Jonas Salk and the field-trial results were front page news. Headlines that Tuesday, April 12, claimed: THE SALK VACCINE IS SAFE, EFFECTIVE, AND POTENT. POLIO IS CONQUERED. Author Allan Chase writes that

to the millions of people who, in the darkest years of the great depression, had contributed dimes, then dollars, and had given years of their lives to help the March of Dimes...the announcement that those dimes and dollars had yielded a safe vaccine which would protect their children and grandchildren against polio was possibly the greatest moment in American life since the end of World War I. Now, as in November 1918, church bells and, in many cities, trolley bells and factory sirens hailed the development, the testing, and the licensing of the Salk vaccine as the great step forward for humankind that it was.

Starting Time	
Finishing Time	
Reading Time	
Reading Rate	

COMPREHENSION

Read the following questions and statements. For each one, put an X in the box before the option that contains the most complete or accurate answer.

1. Testing of the polio vaccine took place in the early
   - ☐ a. 1940s.
   - ☐ b. 1950s.
   - ☐ c. 1960s.
   - ☐ d. 1970s.

2. The testing took place
   - ☐ a. in six specific areas where polio had hit hard the year before.
   - ☐ b. in every elementary school in the country.
   - ☐ c. in specifically chosen school districts in just about every state.
   - ☐ d. in cities with 100,000 or more people.

3. The information in this story is presented
   - ☐ a. in spatial order.
   - ☐ b. from most to least important.
   - ☐ c. from least to most important.
   - ☐ d. in chronological order.

4. The main idea of this selection can be stated as follows:
   - ☐ a. Salk's testing confirmed that he had developed a successful polio vaccine.
   - ☐ b. Up until the time the vaccine was given, there was a polio epidemic in the United States.
   - ☐ c. Salk was highly honored for his groundbreaking work.
   - ☐ d. Most parents were anxious for their children to be part of the test.

5. The placebo was used
   - ☐ a. to make sure the real vaccine was actually working.
   - ☐ b. on children whose parents were nervous about the test.
   - ☐ c. only in the initial stages of the testing.
   - ☐ d. on a randomly selected 25 percent of the children.

6. The main concern with using an untested vaccine was that
   - ☐ a. it would not work.
   - ☐ b. the test wouldn't conclusively prove anything.
   - ☐ c. it should be tested on adults rather than children.
   - ☐ d. someone could get polio from it.

7. You can conclude from this selection that
   - ☐ a. the federal government was not in favor of the testing.
   - ☐ b. widespread testing of this type had never been done before.
   - ☐ c. the scientists were out to make a lot of money.
   - ☐ d. children got really excited about being part of the experiment.

8. The tone of this selection is
   - ☐ a. excited.
   - ☐ b. serious.
   - ☐ c. fearful.
   - ☐ d. sad.

9. The parents of most of the children who were tested
   - ☐ a. were expecting miracles.
   - ☐ b. already had one polio victim in their families.
   - ☐ c. were nervous but hopeful.
   - ☐ d. wanted to participate in the test themselves.

10. This selection is
   - ☐ a. a biography of Jonas Salk.
   - ☐ b. Salk's autobiography.
   - ☐ c. a piece of fiction.
   - ☐ d. a piece of informative nonfiction.

Comprehension Skills Key

1. recalling specific facts
2. retaining concepts
3. organizing facts
4. understanding the main idea
5. drawing a conclusion
6. making a judgment
7. making an inference
8. recognizing tone
9. understanding characters
10. appreciating literary forms

VOCABULARY—PART TWO

Write the word that makes the most sense in each sentence.

vials　　　　**incidences**
vital　　　　**cultures**
intensively

1. There was a dangerous polio epidemic occurring, so developing a vaccine against it was _____ .

2. To make sure a vaccine would work, it was necessary to work and plan _____ .

3. One way to choose who to test was to locate areas where _____ of the disease were highest.

4. Doses of the vaccine were stored in marked glass _____ .

5. These doses had been specially prepared in laboratory _____ .

strains　　　　**colleagues**
placebo　　　　**potent**
disregarding

6. Dr. Salk worked with his _____ to develop the vaccine.

7. There were several different _____ of polio around, and the vaccine had to work on all of them.

8. They hoped the vaccine would be _____ enough to get rid of polio in all its forms.

9. To tell whether the vaccine really worked, they tested it against a _____ .

10. _____ people who criticized them, they were confident enough to continue their research.

Comprehension [　　　]

Vocabulary [　　　]

UNDERSTANDING THROUGH WRITING

Suppose you were a school administrator trying to persuade a frightened parent to let her child have the vaccine. Write a persuasive letter convincing the parent. Use information from the story to make your case.

_____

_____

_____

_____

_____

_____

_____

_____

_____

BUILDING STUDY SKILLS

Read the following passage and answer the questions that follow it.

Good Listening, I

To help improve your listening habits, here are some positive steps you can take.

Prepare to Listen. Your attitude while attending class is important. If you feel that a particular class is a waste of time, you will obviously not be in the mood to listen. It is difficult and almost impossible to get anything out of a lecture that you are not prepared for. To prepare, resolve before class to make the lecture period a learning experience.

Another good way to prepare for a lecture is to keep ahead in your textbook and other required reading. The more you know about a subject in advance, the more interested you will be in hearing what the instructor has to say about it. The lecture will then become an exchange of ideas rather than a deluge of unfamiliar and seemingly unrelated facts.

Watch the Speaker. Don't take your eyes off the speaker. When you look away, you invite visual distractions that may compete for your attention. Listen with your eyes as well as with your ears.

Develop an awareness of the speaker's mannerisms. The gestures a speaker makes supplement his remarks. What a writer does with punctuation, bold print, headlines, and italics, a speaker does with vocal inflection and body gestures. All speakers communicate physically as well as orally. Watch as you listen.

1. It is important to attend class with a good

   _____ .

2. You will be more interested in the subject of the lecture if you read about it in

   _____ .

3. For example, if you read the polio vaccine article before your instructor lectured about it, you would know that the _____ proved to be safe and potent.

4. In class, you must listen with your

   _____ as well as with your ears.

5. The speaker's _____ supplement his remarks.

Needles and Nerves

Catherine Dold

READING PURPOSE—
Acupuncture is used in some parts of the world to relieve pain and suffering, although many Western doctors ridicule its effectiveness. Read to find out how one man's opinion of acupuncture changes.

VOCABULARY—PART ONE

All of these words are in the selection you are about to read. Study each word and its meaning. Then answer the questions below. As you read the selection, notice how each vocabulary word is used.

scoffed: ridiculed or made fun of

prototype: first model of something

attributed: associated with or belonging to a specific person

deficiency: shortage

stagnation: not flowing or moving freely

malfunction: failure to operate normally

manipulated: operated skillfully with the hands

endorphins: proteins that occur naturally in the brain and block pain

analgesia: absense of the sense of pain

pervasive: spread throughout

1. Which word would describe a new invention?

_____

2. Which word is the antonym of *plenty*?

_____

3. Which word describes what a broken-down vacuum cleaner does?

_____

4. Which word describes what you get from a shot of novocain at the dentist's office?

_____

5. Which word describes what a card dealer did with a deck of cards?

_____

1   Five years ago, while visiting his native Korea, physicist Zang-Hee Cho took a tumble down a hiking trail. "We were in the mountains for a picnic, and my shoes were not quite correct," recalls the 62-year-old professor from the University of California at Irvine. "I was thinking, as usual, and I fell down. It was like a flight, like a big jump down the mountain. The next day I returned to California and tried to stand up after 12 hours on the plane. I couldn't stand up. I said, 'Uh-oh, big trouble.'"

2   Eventually, Cho hobbled off the plane and made his way home, and later he began to look for some relief from the pain in his back. Relatives suggested he try acupuncture. Though he initially scoffed at the idea—as an educated person, he says, he didn't believe in acupuncture—he tried it. And much to his surprise, it worked. "After about ten minutes I felt the pain melting away."

3   Cho's unexpected relief prodded his professional curiosity. As a physicist working in radiology, Cho develops ways to image the complex inner workings of the body; one of his inventions was a prototype PET scanner around 1975. How, he wondered, could inserting needles into seemingly random points on the body possibly affect human health? So he decided to take a closer look, and what he found astounded him. While sticking needles into a few student volunteers, he took pictures of their brains and discovered that by stimulating an acupuncture point said to be associated with vision—but that is nowhere near anything known to be connected to the eyes—he could indeed trigger activity in the very part of the brain that controls vision. There just might be something to this acupuncture thing, he figured.

4   Acupuncture and other forms of traditional Chinese medicine have been around for more than 4,000 years. Yet the explanation for how acupuncture—and Chinese medicine as a whole—works has long been a mystery, if not an object of mockery, for most Western doctors. The basic theory is outlined in a text from 200 B.C., attributed to the Yellow Emperor (a mythical ruler). In brief, it recognizes in people and in nature a vital energy or life force known as qi (pronounced CHEE). Qi is the source of movements ranging from voluntary muscle action to blood flow; it protects the body from external influences, and it generates warmth. Qi flows through the body and to the organs by way of an extensive system of channels known as meridians. If the flow of the force is disturbed, the theory goes, the resulting deficiency, excess, or stagnation of qi causes bodily malfunction and thus illness. Acupuncture, in which needles are inserted into specific points along the meridians and manipulated, is said to restore the proper flow of qi and thereby return the body to health....

5   Doctors and licensed practitioners administer between 9 and 12 million acupuncture treatments each year in this country, most commonly for pain control and addictions to nicotine, heroin, and cocaine. As acupuncture has gained favor among Westerners, researchers have sought to unveil its mysteries. They want to understand just how this ancient medical practice could possibly work, especially when no Western researchers have ever been able to dissect a meridian or detect the flow of qi.

6   What those researchers *have* been able to measure is a flow of acupuncture-induced endorphins. According to neuroscientist Bruce Poneranz, of the University of Toronto, numerous studies over the past 20 years have shown that inserting needles into acupoints stimulates nerves in the underlying muscles. That stimulation, researchers believe, sends impulses up the spinal cord to a relatively primitive part of the brain known as the limbic system, as well as to the midbrain and the pituitary gland. Somehow that signaling leads to the release of endorphins and monoamines, chemicals that block pain signals in the spinal cord and the brain. The result: A well-documented generalized "acupuncture analgesia."

7   "The endorphin story is really nailed down." says Pomeranz. "It looks like it's nerves to the brain. The acupoints that have been mapped over thousands of years are likely the spots where nerves are concentrated." But the endorphin story "doesn't explain many of the other claims of acupuncture," he continues. "There have been a number of clinical trials showing that acupuncture is extremely useful for the nausea and vomiting caused by chemotherapy and early pregnancy. That's not the endorphin system. Nobody knows how that works."

8   Nor does the endorphin story explain what Cho found when exploring acupoints that are traditionally used to treat vision problems. Designated by Cho as VA1, VA2, VA3, and VA8, they are not found near the eyes but on the outside of the foot, running from the little toe to the ankle. The "VA"

in Cho's designation is for "vision-related acupoint." Acupuncturists say that these points are on the urinary bladder meridian and refer to them as BL67, BL66, BL65, and BL60, respectively. And they hold that stimulation of these points with needles will affect the eyes via the system of meridians rather than through the central nervous system.

9 To test that premise, Cho strapped student volunteers into an fMRI (functional magnetic resonance imaging) machine. While standard MRI provides static cross-sectional pictures of structures in the body, functional MRI goes further to reveal how those structures are working. It measures minute changes in the amount of oxygen carried in the blood, which is presumably a rough measure of glucose uptake by various tissues and thus a good indicator of which tissues are active; the results can be viewed as colorful fMRI brain activation maps.

10 Cho first stimulated the eyes of the volunteers through traditional means: he flashed a light in front of them. The resulting images, as expected, showed a concentration of color—an increase in activity—in the visual cortex, the portion of the brain that is known to be involved in eye function. Then Cho had an acupuncturist stimulate the acupoint VA1. In one person after another, the very same region of the brain—the visual cortex—lit up on the fMRI image.

11 As odd as it seemed, sticking a needle into someone's foot had the very same effect as shining a light in someone's eyes. And this was not the generalized analgesic effect, produced by the primitive limbic system, that was seen in the pain studies; this was a function-specific response occurring in the brain's cortex, the area responsible for such sophisticated functions as speech and hearing, memory and intellect. Moreover, the magnitude of brain activity seen on acupuncture stimulation was nearly as strong as that elicited by the flash of light.

"Acupuncture, in which needles are inserted into specific points along the meridians and manipulated, is said to…return the body to health."

12 "It was very exciting." recalls Cho. "I never thought anything would happen, but it's very clear that stimulating the acupuncture point triggers activity in the visual cortex." To eliminate the possibility of a placebo effect, Cho also stimulated a nonacupoint, in the big toe. There was no response in the visual cortex.…

13 Despite the absence of clear-cut explanations, acupuncture's clinical results are attracting interest from mainstream medicine. A panel of independent experts convened last year by the National Institutes of Health concluded that acupuncture is indeed effective in treating nausea due to anesthesia and chemotherapy drugs. It is also helpful in treating post-surgical and other forms of pain. Moreover, the panel noted, despite the pervasive belief in the superior clinical effects of Western medicine, plenty of conventional treatments for chronic pain show the same success rate as acupuncture—and often with harmful side effects.…

Starting Time

Finishing Time

Reading Time

Reading Rate

COMPREHENSION

Read the following questions and statements. For each one, put an X in the box before the option that contains the most complete or accurate answer.

1. Acupuncture originated in
   - ☐ a. China.
   - ☐ b. Korea.
   - ☐ c. Japan.
   - ☐ d. New York.

2. Acupuncture has been used effectively in the Western world
   - ☐ a. to stimulate the intellect.
   - ☐ b. as treatment for pain and nausea.
   - ☐ c. to completely replace Western medicine.
   - ☐ d. to improve vision.

3. Zang-Hee Cho ran his tests on acupuncture
   - ☐ a. before he perfected the functional MRI machine.
   - ☐ b. when he needed to write a new research report.
   - ☐ c. after his own pain had been relieved by acupuncture.
   - ☐ d. before his accident while on vacation in Korea.

4. Which of the following is the main idea of this selection?
   - ☐ a. Cho should use acupuncture for every illness he has.
   - ☐ b. Acupuncture is being proven an effective form of medicine.
   - ☐ c. Western medicine should be eliminated so people would use acupuncture instead.
   - ☐ d. The fMRI machine is an incredible invention.

5. Western doctors generally do not prescribe acupuncture treatments because
   - ☐ a. they are prejudiced against the Chinese.
   - ☐ b. they don't have the needles.
   - ☐ c. it's more expensive than pills.
   - ☐ d. they are skeptical about a treatment they do not understand.

6. Westerners should consider using acupuncture because
   - ☐ a. it does not have the harmful side effects that many medications have.
   - ☐ b. it costs less than Western medicine.
   - ☐ c. it's an older form of medicine.
   - ☐ d. it works through the brain and nervous system.

7. The studies done by Cho and other researchers show that
   - ☐ a. we know everything we need to know about acupuncture.
   - ☐ b. acupuncture is not a simple or easily understood medicine.
   - ☐ c. Chinese medicine is better than Western medicine.
   - ☐ d. acupuncture only works sometimes.

8. The tone of paragraph 12 in this selection is
   - ☐ a. amazed.
   - ☐ b. confused.
   - ☐ c. happy.
   - ☐ d. frightened.

9. How does Cho feel about using acupuncture?
   - ☐ a. He knows it works, but he is puzzled about how it works.
   - ☐ b. He will never use it again.
   - ☐ c. He thinks it should replace conventional Western medicine.
   - ☐ d. He thinks it should not be used until we understand it completely.

10. This selection is
   - ☐ a. a biography of Zang-Hee Cho.
   - ☐ b. a short story.
   - ☐ c. a piece of informative nonfiction.
   - ☐ d. a report.

Comprehension Skills Key

1. recalling specific facts
2. retaining concepts
3. organizing facts
4. understanding the main idea
5. drawing a conclusion
6. making a judgment
7. making an inference
8. recognizing tone
9. understanding characters
10. appreciating literary forms

VOCABULARY—PART TWO

Write the word that makes the most sense in each sentence.

deficiency   **malfunction**
endorphins   **pervasive**
scoffed

1. Acupuncture can be used when the body has a

    _____ that causes pain or illness.

2. We have a _____ belief in the

    superiority of Western medicine.

3. Many doctors and patients have

    _____ at the idea of using

    acupuncture.

4. Acupuncturists believe a _____

    of qi causes illness.

5. Acupuncture stimulates the brain's release of

    _____ to block pain signals.

prototype   **attributed**
stagnation   **manipulated**
analgesia

6. The theory of acupuncture is

    _____ to the Yellow Emperor

    around 200 B.C.

7. Illness may be caused by the

    _____ of qi in the body.

8. Needles are inserted in acupoints and

    _____ so that qi flows properly

    and restores health.

9. Zang-Hee Cho invented a _____

    scanner to image the inner workings of the body.

10. Cho was searching for _____

    when he first decided to try acupuncture.

Comprehension [ ]

Vocabulary [ ]

UNDERSTANDING THROUGH WRITING

Pretend you are having intense pain that is not lessened by any medication your doctor has given you. Write down several points you could use to persuade your doctor to prescribe acupuncture treatments for your pain.

_____

_____

_____

_____

_____

_____

_____

_____

_____

_____

_____

_____

_____

BUILDING STUDY SKILLS

Read the following passage and answer the questions that follow it.

Good Listening, II

Note Questions. Listen closely to questions asked in class. When an instructor asks a question, he or she is probably about to discuss something important and is calling for your attention. This is an important signal between a speaker and the listeners.

Speakers' questions are designed to help you listen and learn. You should also notice questions asked by others in the class. Student questions signal the instructor; they indicate how the message is coming across. The instructor will elaborate and illustrate, repeat and paraphrase, to help the listeners understand the matter.

Listen Creatively. Don't think about other things while listening to a speaker; give your entire attention to the speaker's words.

Ask Questions. If questions are not permitted during a class session, write yours in your notebook and get the answers later.

Bring Questions to Class. Your attention is sharpened when you are listening for answers. If your instructor calls for class participation, don't be afraid or shy about speaking up. Your attention is focused most sharply when you are on the firing line; and if you are mistaken and are corrected in class, you won't be likely to forget the correct response at exam time.

1. Instructors use questions as a way to call for

   _____ .

2. When you listen, do not _____ about other things.

3. Your attention is sharpened when you are
   _____ for answers.

4. If you are mistaken and corrected in class, you will
   not _____ the correct response
   later.

5. For example, if you mistakenly answered that the
   vital energy or life _____ is called
   endorphins, the right answer would probably stick
   in your mind at exam time.

TOPIC REVIEW
React to Topic 4

Respond to one or more of these questions as your instructor directs.

1. Both selections 16 and 17 end in a negative tone. Review the selections and compare the authors' opinions about the future of the Ebola virus and mosquito-carried diseases.

_____

_____

_____

_____

_____

2. Scientists in selections 19 and 20 spend a lot of time testing their theories and medicines. Make a list of three or four similar steps these scientists used in their testing and write a brief paper comparing their methods.

_____

_____

_____

_____

_____

3. In Building Study Skills 16 you learned about how words are changed by the addition of prefixes and suffixes. Look at selection 17 and write down words with these prefixes and suffixes: *-ation, -ly, -able, un-, in-*. (Be sure each word you write has a recognizable root word.) Then explain how each affix has changed the meaning of the root word.

_____

_____

_____

_____

4. Daytime talk shows are well known for featuring people with unusual problems. Use your imagination to come up with three unique diseases or infections that people might have and want to talk about. Make your diseases far-fetched and amusing rather than serious; for example, a man might develop a swollen tongue from talking on the phone too long. Outline what each person would want to say to the audience, including things like causes, symptoms, time span of the infection or outbreak, and treatments or cures.

_____

_____

_____

_____

_____

5. Do you think humanity's fight against epidemics will ever succeed? Or will a new epidemic arise for every one that is conquered? In writing a short response, consider the selections you have read in this unit as well as what you know about things like AIDS and even the common cold. Use specifics such as these to back up your opinion.

_____

_____

_____

_____

_____

6. Over the years, many films have been made about plagues attacking the world. *Outbreak*, for example, was inspired by Richard Preston's account of Ebola. In other films, plagues come in the form of reptiles or insects. Think of one or two films about plagues that you're familiar with. Write an explanation of what caused the plague, where it began and what it did, and how it was finally conquered.

_____

_____

_____

_____

_____

Words-per-Minute Table

Selection # words	1	2	3	4	5	6	7	8	9	10	11	12	13	14	15	16	17	18	19	20
	1483	1864	2008	1302	1475	866	1134	1054	1770	1148	1667	1248	1441	1650	1444	1450	1306	1063	1384	1275
1:20	1112	1398	1506	977	1106	650	851	791	1328	861	1250	936	1081	1238	1083	1088	980	797	1038	956
1:40	890	1118	1205	781	885	520	680	632	1062	689	1000	749	865	990	866	870	784	638	830	765
2:00	742	932	1004	651	738	433	567	527	885	574	834	624	721	825	722	725	653	532	692	638
2:20	636	799	861	558	632	371	486	452	759	492	714	535	618	707	619	621	560	456	593	546
2:40	556	699	753	488	553	325	425	395	664	431	625	468	540	619	542	544	490	399	519	478
3:00	494	621	669	434	492	289	378	351	590	383	556	416	480	550	481	483	435	354	461	425
3:20	445	559	602	391	443	260	340	316	531	344	500	374	432	495	433	435	392	319	415	383
3:40	404	508	548	355	402	236	309	287	483	313	455	340	393	450	394	395	356	290	377	348
4:00	371	466	502	326	369	217	284	264	443	287	417	312	360	413	361	363	327	266	346	319
4:20	342	430	463	300	340	200	262	243	408	265	385	288	333	381	333	335	301	245	319	294
4:40	318	399	430	279	316	186	243	226	379	246	357	267	309	354	309	311	280	228	297	273
5:00	297	373	402	260	295	173	227	211	354	230	333	250	288	330	289	290	261	213	277	255
5:20	278	350	377	244	277	162	213	198	332	215	313	234	270	309	271	272	245	199	260	239
5:40	262	329	354	230	260	153	200	186	312	203	294	220	254	291	255	256	230	188	244	225
6:00	247	311	335	217	246	144	189	176	295	191	278	208	240	275	241	242	218	177	231	213
6:20	234	294	317	206	233	137	179	166	279	181	263	197	228	261	228	229	206	168	219	201
6:40	222	280	301	195	221	130	170	158	266	172	250	187	216	248	217	218	196	159	208	191
7:00	212	266	287	186	211	124	162	151	253	164	238	178	206	236	206	207	187	152	198	182
7:20	202	254	274	178	201	118	155	144	241	157	227	170	197	225	197	198	178	145	189	174
7:40	193	243	262	170	192	113	148	137	231	150	217	163	188	215	188	189	170	139	181	166
8:00	185	233	251	163	184	108	142	132	221	144	208	156	180	206	181	181	163	133	173	159
8:20	178	224	241	156	177	104	136	126	212	138	200	150	173	198	173	174	157	128	166	153
8:40	171	215	232	150	170	100	131	122	204	132	192	144	166	190	167	167	151	123	160	147
9:00	165	207	223	145	164	96	126	117	197	128	185	139	160	183	160	161	145	118	154	142
9:20	159	200	215	140	158	93	122	113	190	123	179	134	154	177	155	155	140	114	148	137
9:40	153	193	208	135	153	90	117	109	183	119	172	129	149	171	149	150	135	110	143	132
10:00	148	186	201	130	148	87	113	105	177	115	167	125	144	165	144	145	131	106	138	128
10:20	144	180	194	126	143	84	110	102	171	111	161	121	139	160	140	140	126	103	134	123
10:40	139	175	188	122	138	81	106	99	166	108	156	117	135	155	135	136	122	100	130	120
11:00	135	169	183	118	134	79	103	96	161	104	152	113	131	150	131	132	119	97	126	116
11:20	131	164	177	115	130	76	100	93	156	101	147	110	127	146	127	128	115	94	122	113
11:40	127	160	172	112	126	74	97	90	152	98	143	107	124	141	124	124	112	91	119	109
12:00	124	155	167	109	123	72	95	88	148	96	139	104	120	138	120	121	109	89	115	106
12:20	120	151	163	106	120	70	92	85	144	93	135	101	117	134	117	118	106	86	112	103
12:40	117	147	159	103	116	68	90	83	140	91	132	99	114	130	114	114	103	84	109	101
13:00	114	143	154	100	113	67	87	81	136	88	128	96	111	127	111	112	100	82	106	98
13:20	111	140	151	98	111	65	85	79	133	86	125	94	108	124	108	109	98	80	104	96
13:40	109	136	147	95	108	63	83	77	130	84	122	91	105	121	106	106	96	78	101	93
14:00	106	133	143	93	105	62	81	75	126	82	119	89	103	118	103	104	93	76	99	91
14:20	103	130	140	91	103	60	79	74	123	80	116	87	101	115	101	101	91	74	97	89
14:40	101	127	137	89	101	59	77	72	121	78	114	85	98	113	98	99	89	72	94	87
15:00	99	124	134	87	98	58	76	70	118	77	111	83	96	110	96	97	87	71	92	85

Minutes and Seconds Elapsed

136

Progress Graph

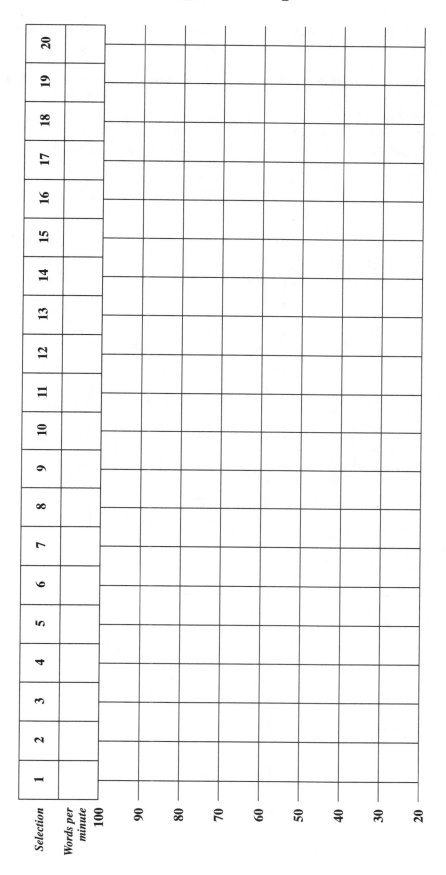

Comprehension Skills Profile

The graph below is designed to help you see your areas of comprehension weakness. Because all the comprehension questions in this text are coded, it is possible for you to determine which kinds of questions give you the most trouble.

On the graph below, keep a record of the questions you have answered incorrectly. Following each selection, darken a square on the graph next to the number of the question missed. The columns are labeled with the selection numbers.

By looking at the chart and noting the number of shaded squares, you should be able to tell which areas of comprehension you are weak in. A large number of shaded squares across from a particular skill signifies an area of reading comprehension weakness. When you discover a particular weakness, give greater attention and time to answering questions of that type.

Further, you might wish to check with your instructor for recommendations of appropriate practice materials.

Selection

Categories of Comprehension Skills	1	2	3	4	5	6	7	8	9	10	11	12	13	14	15	16	17	18	19	20
1. recalling specific facts																				
2. retaining concepts																				
3. organizing facts																				
4. understanding the main idea																				
5. drawing a conclusion																				
6. making a judgment																				
7. making an inference																				
8. recognizing tone																				
9. understanding characters																				
10. appreciating literary forms																				

Blast Off!

Malachy Doyle

Illustrated by
Gill McLean

QEB Publishing

The toys have found an empty spaceship.

"Hey!" yelled Rocco Rabbit. "I could be
the first bunny in space!"

"But there's only room for one of us inside,"
said Emily Elephant. "Who's it going to be?"

"Oh dear!" sighed Jim Giraffe.
"I think I'm a bit too tall!
I'd better stay down here."

"I'm not! And I'm not too
small, either!" shouted Rocco.

10...

"Is there anyone else who might not want to go?"
asked Lenny Lion. "It's best to decide now."

"It looks a bit of a squeeze!" said Emily Elephant.
"I think I'll stay with Jim."

9...

As Emily turned away, her trunk caught on the light switch.

"BAAAAAAAA!"

"Scared of the dark, Sally Sheep?"
asked Patricia Pig. "I think you'd be
happier at home with Emily and Jim."

"Rabbits live in holes.
We're used to the dark!"
said Rocco.

8...

"Maybe you'd better stay here too, Chickadoodle," said Henry Horse.
"You're a bit little to be flying off on your own."

"OK!" replied the shy little chick.

"Hey!" called Rocco. "I'm not the smallest after all!
Maybe I've got a chance!"

7...

There were only six animals left.
They climbed up on top of the wardrobe.

"Does everyone like being up so high?"
asked Martha Monkey.

"Not me!" groaned Lenny Lion. "I just like prowling through the grass!"

6...

"Don't forget
to open your
parachutes
everyone!"
cried Rocco.

"I think you'd be happier on the ground, Patricia," said Henry Horse.

"I think you're right," grunted Patricia.

5...

"OK, there's only four of us now," said Barney Bulldog. "Let's see who's fit enough to fly!"

"Fit as a flea!"

"This is fun!"

"I'm a good hopper!"

"Count me out!
I've had enough!"
moaned Henry.

4...

"So – it's just us three now," said Barney.
"Who can get through the Mystery Maze?
We don't want anyone getting lost in space!"

"I love digging!"
exclaimed Rocco.

"Help!" squealed Martha. "I'm lost already!"

3...

"So now there's only you and me!" said Rocco. "Do you like aliens?"

"Not at all!" yapped Barney.

"They don't scare me!" said Rocco.

2...

"Well done, Rocco!" cried Barney.
"You're going to be an astro-bunny!"

"Woo-hay!" yelled Rocco.

1...

Blast off!

Notes for Parents and Teachers

- Look at the cover and pictures in the book before reading it to the children. Can they guess what the story is about?

- Ask the children to find out as much as they can about spaceships and space travel. Have any real animals ever flown into space? When did the first person land on the Moon?

- If the children were the ones who had to choose who could go up in a spaceship, how would they decide? What do they think people need to know, if they're going to fly in space? What would people need to be like?

- Can the children find a word to describe each of the main characters in the story? For example, they might say Rocco Rabbit is brave.

- Can the children count down from ten to one backward? They can finish their countdown with the words "Blast off!" Can they count down from twenty to one?

- Encourage them to think of an animal beginning with the letter A, and then try to think of an animal for as many letters of the alphabet as they can. Then ask them to give each of the creatures a name that starts with the same letter—e.g., Adam Ant, Rocco Rabbit. They could draw a picture of each one, with the name below.

- What do they think happened after the book ended? Ask them to tell the story of Rocco's journey into space. Where did he go? What did he see? Who did he meet? How did he get home again?

Editor: Alexandra Koken
Designer: Chris Fraser

Copyright © QEB Publishing, Inc. 2011

Published in the United States by
QEB Publishing, Inc.
3 Wrigley, Suite A
Irvine, CA 92618

www.qed-publishing.co.uk

Library of Congress Cataloging-in-Publication Data

Doyle, Malachy.
  Blast off! / Malachy Doyle ; [illustrated by Gill McLean].
    p. cm. -- (Storytime)
  Summary: Rocco the rabbit vies with the other animals to see which of them is most suited for space travel.
  ISBN 978-1-60992-031-9 (library bound)
  [1. Animals--Fiction. 2. Space flight--Fiction.] I. Title. II. Series.

PZ7.D775Bl 2012
[E]--dc22

2010053310

ISBN 978 1 84835 548 4

Printed in China